INTEGRATED ELECTRICAL AND ELECTRONIC EN
FOR MECHANICAL

C000150236

Charles Fraser and John Milne
Dundee Institute of Technology

McGRAW-HILL BOOK COMPANY

London · New York · St Louis · San Francisco · Auckland · Bogotá · Caracas
Lisbon · Madrid · Mexico · Milan · Montreal · New Delhi · Panama · Paris
San Juan · São Paulo · Singapore · Sydney · Tokyo · Toronto

Published by
McGRAW-HILL Book Company Europe
Shoppenhangers Road, Maidenhead, Berkshire, SL6 2QL, England
Telephone 01628 23432
Fax 01628 770224

British Library Cataloguing in Publication Data
Fraser, C. J.
 Integrated Electrical and Electronic
 Engineering for Mechanical Engineers
 I. Title II. Milne, J. S.
 621.3

ISBN 0–07–707973–6

Library of Congress Cataloging-in-Publication Data
Fraser, Charles,
    Integrated electrical and electronic engineering for mechanical engineers
Charles Fraser and John Milne.
     p. cm.
 Includes bibliographical references and index.
 ISBN 0–07–707973–6
 1. Mechatronics.   I. Milne, John.   II. Title.
 TJ163. 12.F73 1994
 621.3—dc20   93–46574
                                                                           CIP

2345 CUP 97654

Typeset by Keyword Publishing Services Ltd
and printed and bound in Great Britain at the University Press, Cambridge

Printed on permanent paper in compliance with the ISO Standard 9706

CONTENTS

PREFACE

Manufacturing industry has continuously stated a case for a supply of so-called electro-mechanical engineers with the ideal candidate for recruitment being the person with a sound background knowledge both in mechanical and electrical engineering. The underlying reason for industry's traditional requirement is self-evident in the predominantly electro-mechanical nature of many, if not most, of the everyday manufactured products.

During the era of the last decade, however, the advances made in microelectronics, and in particular the development of the microprocessor, has engendered a huge expansion in the application of microprocessor devices as an integral component in many common manufactured goods. The software aspects, which are inherently associated with computer technology, have also figured prominently in these latest developments, and the electro-mechanical engineer now also requires to have skills in software concepts and computer programming. This is particularly the case for those involved in the manufacture of consumer products, which would include, for example, such articles as cameras, hi-fi sound equipment and washing machines. The automotive industry constitutes another good example in which computer technology has resulted in tangible benefits such as engine management systems, intelligent suspensions, anti-lock braking systems and controlled power steering. The electro-mechanical engineer therefore, already a well-established and highly sought-after commodity within the engineering community, must now also be able to cope with the computer-based technology that has become an inseparable element of manufacturing engineering. In recent times the fusion of electrical engineering, mechanical engineering and computer-based technology has popularly come to be known as 'mechatronics'.

The term 'mechatronics' is of Japanese origin and was first introduced in the late 1970s. It implies a synergetic integration of mechanical and electronic principles in conjunction with computer technology to the intelligent control of machines, processes and mechanisms. Unfortunately for many Western economies their industries have not been as quick as the Japanese to implement the new technology into their product design philosophy. The need for change, however, is at least now recognized and is at last being addressed.

It is apparent therefore that the electro-mechanical engineers for the 1990s, and into the next millenium, will require additional skills and expertise if they are to respond to the rapid changes that are taking place and to successfully compete on international world markets. The mechatronics engineer, with broad multi-disciplinary expertise and a systems approach to design, represents something of an ideal solution to industry's immediate and future requirements. The purpose of this book is to provide a basic text to cover the multi-disciplinary principles required of a mechatronics engineer.

Since mechatronics is not a discipline in its own right, there is a breadth of knowledge required which cannot also be covered to the depth that would be expected in a specialist textbook. This does not mean, however, that the essential material must be presented in diluted form. Neither does it mean that the scope is limited. Mechatronics engineers require a sound grasp of many fundamental principles across a wide spectrum of subject areas. They do not, in general, require to have the detailed in-depth knowledge associated with that of an expert in any one particular discipline. The essential attribute for the mechatronics engineer is embodied in the level of integration required across all of the relevant subject areas. These essential subject areas include basic electrical technology, analogue and digital electronics, instrumentation and measurement, pneumatic and hydraulic systems, microprocessor technology, high- and low-level computer programming, and the principles of continuous and discrete control. The relevant subject areas obviously cover a vast range of material and we have no intention of attempting to match this in depth. It is intended, however, that as much material as necessary is included to instil the level of competence required of an engineer to practice a mechatronics philosophy.

It is quite likely that the practising electro-mechanical engineer will eventually develop a particular specialism within the general subject area in which he or she operates. It is our intention therefore that this book will lay a sound foundation from which the selected specialism can be built. An adequate number of references are included at the end of each chapter as an aid to this development.

The book is primarily intended for a B.Eng. course in mechanical engineering. It is assumed that students following the text will also be studying foundation courses in the main sub-topics of mechanical engineering, mathematics and computing. No previous knowledge is assumed with respect to electrical technology, fluid power, control engineering, or microprocessor technology and these sub-topics are all introduced at a basic level. The book should also prove useful to students who are studying in the earlier years of a degree course in electrical engineering, or the B.Tech. and SCOTVEC, National Certificate and Diploma courses in mechanical engineering with particular specialism in mechatronics.

Since mechatronics is closely allied to real applications, this fact is given great precedence within the text. In consequence many of the illustrative examples, particularly in the later chapters, represent complete solutions to the applications they describe. These complete solutions embody the hardware requirements, the component specifications, wiring details, the control strategy and its implementation in software. Readers should therefore be able to reproduce these systems, or to adapt the systems for their own particular needs, with a minimum of effort. Whenever possible, the semi-conductor devices and various other integrated circuits are referred to in the text by their generic type numbers. For the added benefit of UK readers, the RS Components stock reference numbers are also quoted. The computer programs which are presented should run without problems on an IBM-PC, or any other true compatible machine.

Charles Fraser
John Milne

ACKNOWLEDGEMENTS

In writing this book we have been fortunate to have had the support and encouragement of many of our academic and technical colleagues in the Department of Mechanical Engineering. Our appreciation also extends to our students, past and present, who have contributed to the contents herein through their commendable efforts in project and research investigations. We acknowledge NCR (Manufacturing) Ltd, Dundee, for allowing us to include the case study involving their product, the automatic teller machine. Lastly, our wives and families deserve a vote of thanks for their patience and understanding during a somewhat prolonged period of neglect.

Charles Fraser
John Milne
Dundee

a	area (m^2, or mm^2); transformation ratio
d	distance (m, mm, etc.)
e	electromotive force (V)
f	frequency (Hz); friction factor; forcing function
f_s	sampling frequency (Hz)
h	current gain; heat transfer coefficient (kW/m^2 K); head (m)
i	current (A, mA, etc.); integer number
k	system gain, or sensitivity; roughness height (mm); integer number
k/D	relative roughness parameter in pipe flow
l	length (m, mm, etc.)
n	integer number
p	instantaneous power (W); pressure (kN m^{-2}, N m^{-2}, etc.); number of pole pairs
q	flow rate (l s^{-1}, cm^3 s^{-1}, etc.)
r	resistance (Ω)
s	Laplacian operator (d/dt); slip
t	time (s)
u	forcing function
v	instantaneous voltage (V); velocity (m s^{-1})
x	linear displacement (mm)
z	z-transform
A	cross-sectional area (m^2); open circuit gain
B	magnetic flux density (Wb m^{-2}); binary number; bit number
C	capacitance (F); volumetric capacity (l/rev, cm^3/rev, etc.); thermal capacity (kJ/kg); viscous damping factor; controller transfer function
C_p	specific heat capacity (kJ/kg K)
D	diode; diameter (mm)

E	electromotive force (V); error signal
F	magnetic potential difference (A); force (N); damping resistance (Nm s/rad)
G	conductance (S); gauge factor; Gray number; plant, or process transfer function
H	magnetic intensity (A m^{-1}); head (m)
I	current (A, mA, etc.)
J	moment of inertia (kg m^2)
K	calibration constant; gain
K_e	e.m.f. constant (V s/rad)
K_G	gear ratio
K_T	torque constant (Nm/A)
L	inductance (H); length (m)
L^{-1}	inverse Laplace transform
M	mutual inductance (H); mass (kg); amplitude ratio modulus
N	number of turns; rotational speed (rev/s, rev/min); amplitude ratio in decibels
P	power (W, kW, etc.)
PV	process variable
Q	charge (coulombs); flow rate (m^3 s^{-1}, l/s, etc.)
R	resistance (ohms); damping factor
Re	Reynolds number
S	reluctance (A/weber); spring stiffness (N m^{-1}); slope
SP	set point
T	time constant (s); torque (N m); time delay (s)
T_d	derivative time constant
T_i	integral time constant
U	control effort
V	voltage, or potential difference (V)
W	work, or energy (J); load (N)
X	reactance (Ω); input; state variable
Y	output
Z	impedance (Ω); number of conductors

Greek

α	ratio, or proportionality
β	resistivity (Ω cm^{-1}); feedback fraction
δ	load angle
Δ	denoting a discrete change in a quantity
ε	permittivity (F/m); strain
ρ	resistivity (Ω m); density (kg m^{-3})
ν	Poisson's ratio; viscosity (Nm s^{-2})
Φ	magnetic flux (webers)
ϕ	phase angle; magnetic flux (webers)
σ	conductivity (S/m)
τ	time constant (s)
μ	permeability (H/m); viscosity (kg/m s)
θ	angular position; temperature (°C)
Ω	resistance (ohms); angular velocity (rad/s)
ω	circular frequency (rad/s)

ζ	damping ratio
η	efficiency
λ	leakage coefficient

Subscripts

a	axial
av	average
c	closed loop
crit	critical value
d	damped
e	equivalent
f	with feedback; fixed quantity
i, or in	input
m	maximum; motor
max	maximum
mech	mechanical
n	natural
o	reference quantity; cut-off value; output; overall
out	output
p	pump
r	relative
ref	reference quantity
s	source, or supply; synchronous
ss	steady state
t	transverse
v	voltage; volumetric; variable
x	referred to a linear displacement
AC	alternating quantity
D	differential
DC	average
L	load
T	total

Prefixes

M	mega (10^6)
k	kilo (10^3)
m	milli (10^{-3})
μ	micro (10^{-6})
n	nano (10^{-9})
p	pico (10^{-12})

INTRODUCTION

1.1 HISTORICAL PERSPECTIVE

Mechanical engineering degree courses have always incorporated some element of electrical technology within the core syllabus material. In the 1950s and early 1960s the emphasis in electrical technology for mechanical engineers was generally restricted to power applications involving the generation, transmission and utilization of electrical power. The predominant interest in electrical technology for mechanical engineers was thus centred round the design, application and performance of electrical power machines. Although the main thrust of modern development has been in microelectronics, the power applications of electrical engineering are still as vitally important now as they were when they were first introduced into mechanical engineering courses.

The basic transistor was invented in 1948, but it was not until the development of the integrated circuit, and subsequently the microprocessor, that mechanical engineers have taken recourse to a much more active involvement in the applications and utilization of microprocessor and integrated circuit devices. The mechanical engineer is not concerned with the internal structure, or the design of an integrated circuit, but rather with a familiarity with the operating characteristics, performance and practical applications of these devices. Consider for example an application where a certain machine performs a variety of functions based on the state of a limited number of control switches. These switches may be ON or OFF in any desired sequence and the machine performs the appropriate functions depending on the pattern set on the switches. The control electronics for such a machine might be based on a particular family of special integrated circuits called logic gates. Logic gates are mass-produced and very cheaply available in integrated circuit form. To construct a logic circuit, the engineer requires to understand the basic logic functions, the power supply requirements and the limitations of the devices used. Additional knowledge required would include an understanding of the techniques employed to minimize the circuit, how the circuit can be realized using only one kind of logic gate, how the logic circuit is to be interfaced to the control switches and other external functions, and some other practicalities related to the handling of unused input lines. The engineer would also need to be aware that there are various types of logic gate devices available and that each type has particular advantages and also some disadvantages. Other than this no specialist knowledge is required on the internal operation, or the circuit details of the logic devices themselves. Perfectly functional logic circuits can therefore be constructed knowing only the input/output characteristics, the interface requirements and the operational performance of the devices used. This might be thought of as a black box type of approach. It is nonetheless a perfectly viable approach and is extensively used in current practice.

The microprocessor can be considered as an extended and highly developed integrated circuit which operates through a complex and interrelated range of other logic circuits. While mechanical engineers would not be expected to design basic circuits involving microprocessor chips, they can certainly expect to use such ready-made boards and to integrate them, as perhaps a controller, in some novel prototype mechanical artifact. The essential knowledge base required of the mechanical engineer again relates to the specification, performance and potential applications for the available electronics hardware. The detailed internal design of the circuitry still justifiably remains within the domain of the electronics specialist.

In the 1980s there was a veritable explosion in microprocessor-based products. This is self-evident in the ever increasing power and reducing costs of the desktop microcomputer. It is little wonder then that the microcomputer has encroached into every aspect of traditional mechanical engineering. Initially extolled for its number crunching capabilities, the utility of the microcomputer, and other similar microprocessor-based devices, have been employed in countless applications to system monitoring, data handling, data presentation and control. The modern mechanical engineer must therefore be competent in the application of microprocessor devices if he or she is to be able to respond to the industrial developments which are currently taking place and which will continue to evolve. This means essentially that mechanical engineers can no longer afford to restrict their interest to the purely mechanical aspects of design. That is not to say that the materials selection, dynamics, kinematics, strength considerations, manufacturing routes, thermofluids and other mechanical aspects are not still important. They most certainly are and they must still be given due consideration. What is more important, however, is the overall design concept. This includes the control functions, the power systems, the implementation of the control through microprocessor devices and the software development. This is the so-called systems approach to design which has been actively practiced by the Japanese since the early 1970s; see Buur (1990a), Hunt (1988) and McLean (1983).

The integration between mechanical, electrical and computer technology has since become known as mechatronics and it is now becoming recognized as a curriculum topic in its own right. Mechatronics combines electronics engineering and computer technology within multi-disciplinary applications pertaining to the control of mechanical systems and processes. These systems might include complex mechanisms, dynamical elements, thermal and chemical processes, flexible manufacturing operations or any combination of these. This invariably means that mechatronics is very diverse in its applications. However, diverse as the applications may be, mechatronics is founded on well-established basic principles and concepts which will continue to stand the test of time. A firm grasp of the basic underlying principles is the key to success for the practising engineer.

1.2 8-BIT, 16-BIT AND 32-BIT TECHNOLOGIES

The first emergence of the microcomputer can be traced back to the latter end of the 1970s when the arrival of the Commodore 'PET' heralded the era of low-cost personal computing power. Until that time the computer systems which were in routine use were the so-called mainframe machines. Mainframes were physically large in that they usually occupied a considerable area of floorspace and required substantial air-conditioning facilities. By current standards the early mainframe computers were not particularly large either in terms of memory capacity or computing power.

The computing power of a microprocessor is a measure of its capability to process binary data. Part of this capability is the speed of operation of the central processing unit, CPU, and this relates to the technology by which the chip was manufactured. Modern microprocessor devices can now achieve instruction times down to nanosecond levels. Computing power is also related to the number of binary digits, or bits, which can be processed at any one time. This is referred to as the word length and initially the commonly used microprocessors were restricted to word lengths of 8-bits. The inherent accuracy of data represented in 8-bit words is 1 part in 256 and a simple expedient to improve on this accuracy was to handle the data as two consecutive 8-bit words, i.e. double precision. This effectively gives 16-bit accuracy but greatly reduces the processing speed. From the early 1980s, however, 16-bit microprocessors were being incorporated into many commercial microcomputers and more recent times have seen a move towards 32-bit technology. This has vastly improved the processing power of the modern microcomputer and these desktop machines have now generally exceeded the power of that associated with many of the mainframe machines of 1970s vintage.

1.3 THE MECHATRONICS PHILOSOPHY

While mechatronics encompasses many of the traditional disciplines, it can essentially be regarded as a philosophy. The subject embodies mechanical engineering, microelectronics and computer technology, but the whole forms more than the sum of the constituent parts. Mechatronics is often referred to in the literature as a synergistic integration of technologies. Because of the diversity of applications, however, mechatronics means different things to people of different backgrounds. To some, mechatronics is allied to computer-aided design and manufacture with the industrial robot epitomizing the general concept of integrated engineering. Others regard mechatronics as an interface technology associated with the automatic control of a paper making process, a power generating complex or a similar hierarchically controlled entity. A production engineer might view mechatronics as the implementation of a flexible manufacturing system, while the designer of a video recorder may think of mechatronics essentially as electronics with a minor bias towards a mechanical application. All of these perceptions of mechatronics are, in fact, correct. The thread of commonality lies in the application of computer-based digital control techniques, through various electrical and electronic interfaces, to the efficient operation of a multiplicity of mechanical functions.

The mechatronics philosophy then is that which gives equal rating to the component parts and identifies the interrelation between each of the subsystems and the composite whole. The essence of mechatronics is therefore encompassed in the pervasive integration between the contributing technologies. Buur (1990b) gives a detailed discussion on the perception of mechatronics as a philosophy. In retrospect there is nothing particularly new in this philosophical concept, except perhaps the inclusion of computer-based technology. The so-called electro-mechanical engineer is already a highly valued commodity within the engineering community. What mechatronics now provides, however, is a new opportunity for a focus through which the often diverging interests of electrical and mechanical engineers can effectively coalesce. This can only be to the benefit of the many industries which have for years stated their requirement for engineers with broad-based multi-disciplinary skills.

Engineering education is traditionally based on single-discipline activities and founded on a 'bottom up' approach. The bottom up method builds on fundamental principles and concepts pertaining to a particular discipline, and develops these essentially in isolation from other subjects. With the arrival of the new technology, engineers now need to adopt a systems approach to design. The systems approach gives consideration to the overall objectives rather than the individual elements and more emphasis is placed on what the subsystems and components can do, rather than on what they comprise. This systems attitude, in combining unlike technologies, constitutes a 'top down' approach to form an optimal solution to a product development enterprise. The mechatronics philosophy is synonymous with a top down systems approach.

1.4 INTELLIGENT MACHINES AND EXPERT SYSTEMS

The biggest single advantage to be gained through incorporating computer-based technology into a controlled system is the level of inbuilt intelligence which results. The level of machine intelligence may be quite low but it will almost certainly represent a more flexible improvement to the non-intelligent counterpart it replaces. As an example consider a thermal process in which a constant temperature is to be maintained by some means or another. It may be possible to use a simple bimetallic-strip-like device to control the temperature. Initially the process would be supplied with heat from a suitable source and the temperature would subsequently increase. The bimetallic device, which is exposed to the increasing process temperature, would tend to bend due to the disproportionate coefficients of thermal expansion in the two dissimilar metals used to make the strip. The bending of the strip could be employed to operate a switch which would disconnect the supply of heat to the process. As the process temperature then falls, the bimetallic strip straightens out, de-activates the control switch and the supply of heat is again re-established to the process. Such a control system could be finely adjusted to switch the heat source on, or off, at the desired process temperatures. In practice it would be found that the device switches on and off over a considerable range of temperature and that the response of the controller to the temperature variation would be quite slow. For many applications, of course, this may be perfectly adequate.

An alterative controller might be based on a microcomputer system in which the process temperature is measured by means of a thermocouple through a suitable interface circuit. The computer could then operate a simple solenoid, again through a suitable interface, to switch in the heat supply as and when required. The control action in this second method is relatively fast and can also be very precise, holding the required process temperature within very close tolerance limits. Additionally, the control function is based on machine intelligence principles, in which a parameter is first of all measured, is then compared with the desired value, and finally the control action is implemented depending on the outcome of the comparison. All of these functions are generated in lines of computer coding which are referred to as the control algorithm.

In this particular instance the bimetallic controller is certainly the cheaper alternative of the two. However, if the desired process temperature requires to be altered on a regular basis then the 'local' analogue controller, which has to be manually adjusted, could prove to be inconvenient. The computer-based controller, which can be either local or remote, is easily altered and requires only the numerical value of the desired temperature to be changed in the control program. This is fairly representative of the inherent flexibility associated with intelligent systems.

The relative merits of analogue and computer-based controllers do not provide a very good basis for comparison when considered for the control of a single variable. If, however, several temperatures and perhaps also interrelated pressures and flow rates are to be controlled, then the advantages offered by the computer-based system are manifest. Complex nonlinear relationships between the controlled parameters can be accommodated relatively easily in the software and the intelligence of the system thereby raised to quite sophisticated levels.

Inbuilt machine inteligence is a rapidly developing technology and is constantly finding numerous applications in many new commercial products. A recently introduced cooling fan, for example, utilizes a microprocessor in conjunction with a small temperature sensor to vary the fan speed in relation to the local ambient temperature. This simple level of intelligence has reputedly reduced the normal running costs and the noise levels of the fan by considerable margins.

If the level of machine intelligence is considerably greater than that used in the temperature controlled cooling fan, then the controller functions might be categorized as an expert system. Like the word mechatronics, expert system conjures up different interpretations for people with different backgrounds and experience. In general, however, an expert system can be properly classified as a computer-based system which makes use of the knowledge base associated with that of a human expert in some field of endeavour. The subject expertise is often pre-programmed into the system as a set of rules, or guidelines. The system then refers to these rules in an IF–THEN–ELSE decision type of strategy before any external functions are executed. A good example of a growing range of control devices based on expert system fundamentals are the so-called self-tuning controllers which are now marketed by a number of commercial vendors. Many self-tuning controllers make use of a well known set of empirical rules to adjust the controller variables to their optimum values. This involves the measurement, storage and analysis of the system's response to an input disturbance. The controller settings are then adjusted, according to the rules, in order to optimize the system's response to the same, or a similar input disturbance. This process is carried out continuously as the controller carries out its normal functions. Eventually the controller settings stabilize to their best overall values and little further adjustment takes place. The self-tuning controller, however, is still continuously monitoring itself and responding to the external environment and making minor adjustments to maintain optimum tuning. The Foxboro 'EXACT' controller (Kraus and Myron, 1984), is typical of this type of self-tuning industrial controller. The temperature controlled fan and the self-tuning controller are two examples of essentially self-contained expert systems. They may easily form part of a much wider network constituting an expert system on a much larger scale. Waterman (1986) provides a good introduction and overview on expert systems.

In the widest sense, machine intelligence includes any computer simulation of what are basically human attributes. These include vision systems, speech recognition and synthesis, general problem solving, simulated expertise and learning. Each of these subtopics are currently the subject of extensive research and all are already available in various levels of sophistication. There can be little doubt that artificial intelligence will continue to be improved and that the applications for such enhanced devices will become much more advanced. If the practising engineer is to keep abreast of the developing technology, then he/she must have a sound grasp of the basic underlying principles. The engineer can, however, take some solace from the fact that although the technology will continue to advance, the fundamental principles will remain as solid prerequisite building blocks.

1.5 MECHATRONIC APPLICATIONS

Perhaps the most readily noticeable applications of mechatronics are to be found in the familiar mass-produced consumer products. Microprocessor-based controllers are particularly prevalent as an integral component in modern hi-fi and video recorder systems, in automatic washing machines, in automatic cameras, photocopiers and sewing machines. The level of the technology incorporated into these kind of devices continues to increase, and voice input systems, for example, have already been developed for video recorders and sewing machines; see Yoshimura and Yashida (1985).

Other examples of product development involving microprocessor-based controllers include, from the authors' experience, the design of a road speed limiter for heavy goods vehicles, the design of an automatic assembly machine for the handles of woven polymer sacks and a pilot study on the integration of expert system technology within the control system of automated banking machines. These are all rather specific examples from typical consultancy projects. They serve to show, however, the characteristic diversity of mechatronic applications involving microprocessor-based controllers.

Mechatronic systems may be characterized by the fact that the transfer of information takes place either to, from, or within the system. If this characteristic is used to define a mechatronic device then mechatronics is evident in a hierarchy of increasingly complex subsystems. At the lowest level there are the components. Components would include sensors, transducers, actuators and control devices such as logic gates. All of these components invoke the transfer of information in some manner or another.

At the next higher level there are modules, which might be considered as sub-assemblies of components which perform specific independent functions in their own right. Modules might include such examples as composite electronic boards, self-contained controlled mechanisms such as stepper motors, an optical communications interface, or a programmable logic controller. Items defined as modules are identified as being separately testable and are capable of being interfaced with other modules in a variety of different ways.

At the next higher echelon are the mechatronic products, which can be categorized as assemblies of modules and components which together are capable of performing a closed function. The consumer goods already mentioned, computer-controlled machine tools and the industrial robot are good general examples of mechatronic products.

At the highest levels there are generalized systems which may be thought of as conglomerations of products which can interact to perform a variety of functions. The flexible manufacturing system (FMS), involving computer-controlled machines, robots, materials conveying and overall supervisory coordination, is the prime example of a mechatronics system. At all levels throughout the generalized system, however, the influence of mechatronics is apparent right down to the humble, or the not so humble, transducer.

1.6 CONCLUDING REMARKS

The expansion of microprocessor technology has sometimes been referred to as the third industrial revolution. The first and second industrial revolutions being, respectively, the advent of steam power and the production line concepts as advocated by Henry Ford as the beginning of the twentieth century. As the twentieth century draws to a close, the ubiquitous microprocessor is rapidly becoming a part of everyday life. The mechanical engineers for the twenty-first century will therefore require a firm grasp of the basic engineering principles, in conjunction with the potential applications for microprocessor technology, if they are to keep abreast of the technological developments which are currently taking place.

The purpose of this book is to present these principles in a way that will lay a sound foundation for subsequent development. Mechatronics is a hands-on technology and many practical examples are included in the text to help foster the applied nature of the subject. The case studies given in the last chapter represent complete and working solutions to the problems they address. These case studies include many aspects of mechanical engineering, electronics, control and software development. It is hoped that this active integration of the associated technologies will be carried forward and adopted by the reader when he or she comes to apply the techniques to their own particular problems. If this is the case then we will feel satisfied that we have achieved our purpose in engendering a modern systematic approach to the design and development of products and systems.

REFERENCES

Buur, J. (1990a) *Mechatronics Design in Japan*, Institute for Engineering Design, Technical University of Denmark, IK 89.58.

Buur, J. (1990b) *A Theoretical Approach to Mechatronics Design*, Institute for Engineering Design, Technical University of Denmark, IK 90.74.

Hunt, V. D. (1988) *Mechatronics: Japan's Newest Threat*, Chapman & Hall, London.

Kraus, T. W. and T. J. Myron (1984) 'Self-tuning PID controller uses pattern recognition approach', *Control Eng.*, June.

McLean, M. (1983) *Mechatronics: Developments in Japan and Europe*, Technova, Frances Pinter (Pub), London.

Waterman, D. A. (1986) *A Guide to Expert Systems*, Addison-Wesley, Reading, Massachusetts.

Yoshimura, M. and N. Yashida (1985) 'Application of voice I/O to a home sewing machine', *Proceedings of Speech Technology Conference*, New York, April 1985, Media Dimensions, New York.

FURTHER READING

Fraser, C. J. and J. S. Milne (1992) 'An educational perspective on applied mechantronics', *Mechatronic Systems Engng*, **3**(1), 49–57.

Milne, J. S. and C. J. Fraser (1990) 'Development of a mechatronics learning facility', *Mechatronic Systems Engng*, **1**(1), 31–40.

Milne, J. S. and C. J. Fraser (1992) 'Mechatronics in engineering courses', *Int. J. Mech. Engng Educ.*, **20**(2), 129–135.

TWO

BASIC ELECTRICAL TECHNOLOGY

2.1 INTRODUCTION

The level and range of electrical and electronic circuitry found in modern mechanical systems means that the practising mechanical engineer must have a good working knowledge of the principles of basic electrical technology. The basic principles are presented in this chapter and are supplemented with illustrative examples.

A thorough depth of understanding can only come through numerous applications of the basic principles to the solution of practical problems. Exercises, with answers, are included at the end of the chapter as an aid to the development of a proficiency in dealing with problems in electrical technology.

The graphical symbols used in the text are in accordance with BS 3939 (1986). Other symbols and abbreviations are consistent with the SI system of units as defined in PD 5686 (1970).

2.2 FLUX AND POTENTIAL DIFFERENCE

The concept of flux and potential difference enables a unified approach to be adopted for virtually all of the 'field' type of problems. Generally the flowing quantity is termed the flux and the quantity which drives the flow is called the potential difference. This consistency of method is equally applicable to problems in fluid flow, heat transfer, electrical conduction, electrostatics and electromagnetism, to name but a few. It is not particularly surprising therefore that thermodynamicists use an electrical analogy to describe many heat conduction phenomena, while electrical engineers often use heat and fluid flow analogies to enhance an understanding of electrical and electronics principles.

In general terms the flux may be written as

$$\text{flux} = \frac{(\text{field characteristic}) \times (\text{cross-sectional area}) \times (\text{potential difference})}{(\text{length})} \tag{2.1}$$

Equation (2.1) is an empirical relationship which means that it is based on numerous observations of experimental results. Many of the basic physical laws are empirical in nature and subsequent experiments generally reinforce the original validity of these laws. An empirical law can only cease to have validity when someone can devise an experiment which proves that the law does not hold under a given set of circumstances. Until such time, the known physical laws can be taken to be irrefutable axioms.

In specific terms for the flow of an electric current through a conducting medium, Eq. (2.1) takes the form:

$$I = \frac{\sigma a V}{l} \qquad (2.2)$$

where I = current, A

σ = conductivity of the medium, S/m i.e. the field characteristic
a = cross-sectional area of the medium, m^2
l = length of the medium, m
V = applied potential difference, or voltage, V.

The group $(\sigma a/l)$ is termed the conductance, denoted by G and measured in siemens, thus:

$$I = GV \qquad (2.3)$$

The reciprocal of conductance is referred to as the resistance, R, and is measured in units of ohms. Hence

$$I = V/R \qquad (2.4)$$

Equation (2.4) is the familiar 'Ohm's Law' which defines a linear relationship between voltage and current in a conducting medium. If the resistance, R, varies with the magnitude of the voltage, or the current, then the resistance is nonlinear. Rectifiers constitute one particular class of nonlinear resistors.

Comparing Eqs (2.4) and (2.2) gives

$$R = l/(\sigma a) \qquad (2.5)$$

It is more usual however to quote the 'resistivity' as opposed to the conductivity, and resistance is generally written as

$$R = \rho l/a \qquad (2.6)$$

where ρ is the resistivity of the conductor in ohm-metres ($\Omega\,$m).

The resistance of all pure metals is temperature dependent, increasing linearly for moderate increases in temperature. Other materials, including carbon and many insulators, exhibit a decreasing resistance characteristic for an increase in temperature.

Example Given that the resistivity of copper at 20°C is $1.76 \times 10^{-8}\,\Omega\,$m, determine the resistance of a circular copper wire of length 20 m and diameter 0.5 mm.
From Eq. (2.6)

$$R = \rho l/a = 1.76 \times 10^{-8} \times 20 \times 4/[\pi \times (0.0005)^2]$$

Hence $\qquad\qquad\qquad\qquad R = 1.79\,\Omega$

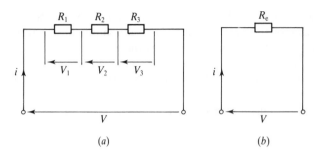

Figure 2.1 (*a*) Resistors in series; (*b*) equivalent circuit.

2.3 SIMPLE RESISTIVE CIRCUITS

Figure 2.1 shows three resistors connected in a series arrangement. Also shown in the figure is a circuit containing a single resistor which would be equivalent to the three resistors in series, i.e. circuit (*b*). The current flowing in circuit (*a*) is common to all three resistors. Therefore

$$V_1 = R_1 i \qquad V_2 = R_2 i \qquad V_3 = R_3 i$$

The total voltage drop in the circuit is equal to the sum of the voltage drops across the three resistors. Thus

$$V = V_1 + V_2 + V_3$$
$$= (R_1 + R_2 + R_3)i$$

If these three resistances were to be replaced by a single resistance, as in a circuit (*b*), then the total voltage drop is given by

$$V = R_e i$$

On equating the two expressions derived for the total voltage drop across the circuits it transpires that

$$R_e = R_1 + R_2 + R_3 \tag{2.7}$$

The analysis shows that for resistances connected in series, an equivalent single resistance is equal to the algebraic sum of the resistors in series. Although the analysis was applied to three resistors in series, Eq. (2.7) holds for any number of resistances so connected.

In Fig. 2.2(*a*) three resistors are connected in a parallel arrangement. Also shown, in Fig. 2.2(*b*), is an equivalent circuit containing a single resistor.

In the parallel arrangement, the voltage drop across the three resistors is common to each. Therefore

$$V = R_1 i_1 = R_2 i_2 = R_3 i_3$$

The current flowing in the parallel circuit may be written as

$$i_t = i_1 + i_2 + i_3$$

Note that i_t is the total current flowing round the circuit and i_1, i_2 and i_3 are the components of the current which split into the branches of the parallel circuit. On leaving the parallel circuit, the component currents regroup and sum to the original current.

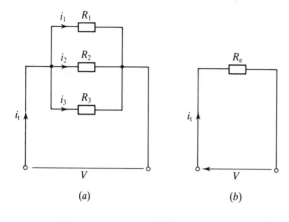

(a)   (b)

Figure 2.2 (*a*) Resistors in parallel; (*b*) equivalent circuit.

The equation for the current may be rewritten as

$$i_t = \left[\frac{V}{R_1} + \frac{V}{R_2} + \frac{V}{R_3}\right]$$

$$= \left[\frac{1}{R_1} + \frac{1}{R_2} + \frac{1}{R_3}\right] V$$

If these resistors could be replaced with an equivalent single resistor, as shown in circuit (*b*), then the current flowing in the circuit would be given by

$$i_t = \frac{V}{R_e}$$

On equating the two expressions obtained for the current, we obtain

$$\frac{1}{R_e} = \frac{1}{R_1} + \frac{1}{R_2} + \frac{1}{R_3} \qquad (2.8)$$

Equation (2.8) shows that for resistors connected in parallel, the inverse of the equivalent resistance is equal to the sum of the inverses of the parallel resistances.

Using Eqs (2.7) and (2.8), many series and parallel resistive circuits can be reduced to a single effective resistance. Back calculation can then yield the current and potential differences across all of the resistive elements which make up the circuit.

Example In the circuit shown in Fig. 2.3, calculate the voltage drop across each resistor and the current flowing through each.

Starting at the right hand end, R_7 and R_8 are connected in series. These can be replaced by a single $10\,\Omega$ resistor, R_9. Also R_5 and R_6 are connected in parallel. These may be replaced

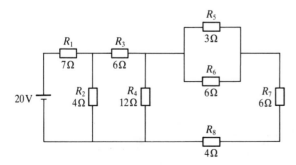

Figure 2.3 Series/parallel resistive circuit.

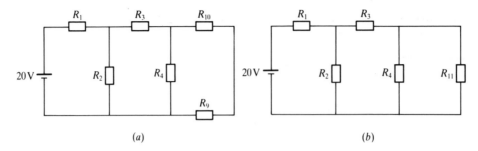

Figure 2.4 Reduced equivalent circuits.

with an equivalent $2\,\Omega$ resistor, R_{10}. At this point it may be convenient to redraw the equivalent circuit as shown in Fig. 2.4(a). The equivalent resistors, R_9 and R_{10}, can be seen to be in series. These can obviously be replaced with another equivalent $12\,\Omega$ resistor, R_{11}, as shown in Fig. 2.4(b).

We now have R_{11} and R_4 in parallel and these can be replaced with an equivalent resistor, $R_{12} = 6\,\Omega$, as shown in Fig. 2.5(a).

Combining the series resistors, R_{12} and R_3 to give $R_{13} = 12\,\Omega$, further reduces the circuit as shown in Fig. 2.5(b). Following the same consistent procedure allows R_{13} and R_2 to be replaced with an equivalent $3\,\Omega$ resistor, R_{14} (Fig. 2.5(c)). Finally combining R_{14} with the remaining R_1 gives the single equivalent resistance of the complete circuit, $R_{15} = 10\,\Omega$. Application of Ohm's law, Eq. (2.4), tells us that the current drawn by the circuit will be $20/10 = 2$ A.

The voltage drop across R_1 is $7 \times 2 = 14$ V. This leaves 6 V which is dropped over R_{14}, i.e. R_2 and R_{13} in parallel. Working back through the circuit, the current flowing in R_2 will be $6/4 = 1.5$ A, and the remaining 0.5 A will be fed to the rest of the circuit. Thus the current flowing in R_3 is 0.5 A. Following through this procedure yields the results shown in Table 2.1.

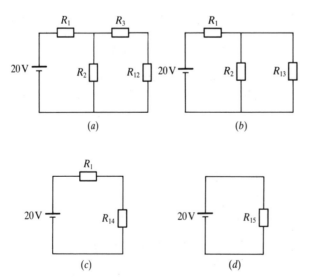

Figure 2.5 Further reduced circuits.

Table 2.1 Voltage and current for each resistor of circuit Fig. 2.3.

Resistor	Voltage drop, V	Current drawn, A
R_1	14	2
R_2	6	1.5
R_3	3	0.5
R_4	3	0.25
R_5	0.5	0.166 667
R_6	0.5	0.083 3
R_7	1.5	0.25
R_8	1	0.25

Any series/parallel resistive circuit, with one source of e.m.f., can be analysed in a similar manner by breaking the circuit down to a single equivalent resistance and working back to evaluate the current and voltage drops in each section of the circuit.

2.4 ELECTROMOTIVE FORCE AND POTENTIAL DIFFERENCE

In a metallic conductor which has a potential difference applied across opposite ends, free electrons are attracted to the more positive end of the conductor. It is this drift of electrons which constitutes the electric current and the effect is simply natures attempt to redress an energy imbalance. Although the negatively charged electrons actually drift towards the positive end of the conductor, traditional convention gives the direction of the current flow from positive to negative. There is nothing really at issue here since it is only a simple sign convention which was adopted long before the true nature of the atom and its associated electrons were postulated.

A current of 1 A is associated with the passage of 6.24×10^{18} electrons across any cross-section of the conductor per second. The quantity of charge is the coulomb, Q, and

$$Q = It \tag{2.9}$$

where 1 coulomb of charge is passed when a current of 1 ampere flows for a period of 1 second.

The electromotive force, e.m.f., is that which tends to produce an electric current in a circuit. Since e.m.f. is also measured in volts, the distinction between electromotive force and potential difference might at first appear to be rather subtle. Electromotive force, however, is associated with the energy source. Potential difference is simply the product of current and resistance across any resistive element in a circuit, irrespective of the energy source. Note that for circuit elements other than purely resistive, the potential difference across the element becomes a time-dependent function.

2.5 POWER AND ENERGY

Power is the rate at which energy is expended, or supplied. The potential difference across any two points in a circuit is defined as the work done in moving unit charge from a lower to a higher potential. Thus the work done in moving Q coulombs of charge across a constant potential difference of V volts is

$$W = QV \tag{2.10}$$

Power, which is the rate at which the work is done, is given by differentiating Eq. (2.10) with respect to time. Therefore

$$\text{power} = \frac{dW}{dt} = \frac{dQ}{dt} \times V$$

From Eq. (2.9), $(dQ/dt) = I$; thus

$$\text{power} = IV \tag{2.11}$$

Using Ohm's law, the power dissipated across a simple resistive circuit element is given by

$$\text{power} = IV = I(IR) = I^2 R \tag{2.12}$$

Example An electrical load is supplied with a current of 100 A through copper and aluminium cables which are connected in parallel. The total length of each cable is 500 m and each conductor has a cross-sectional area of 60 mm^2. Calculate the current carried by each cable and the power dissipated in each. The resistivity of copper and aluminium may be taken as 1.8×10^{-8} and $2.8 \times 10^{-8}\,\Omega$ m, respectively.

Resistance of the copper cable is given by

$$1.8 \times 10^{-8} \times 500/(60 \times 10^{-6}) = 0.15\,\Omega$$

Resistance of the aluminium cable is given by

$$2.8 \times 10^{-8} \times 500/(60 \times 10^{-6}) = 0.233\,\Omega$$

Since the cables are connected in parallel, then the equivalent resistance is given by

$$1/[(1/0.15) + (1/0.233)] = 0.0913\,\Omega$$

The voltage drop over the cables is given by

$$IR = 100 \times 0.0913 = 9.13\,\text{V}$$

The current carried by the copper cable is

$$9.13/0.15 = 60.867\,\text{A}$$

The current carried by the aluminium cable is

$$9.13/0.233 = 39.18\,\text{V}$$

Power dissipated in the copper cable is

$$I^2 R = (60.867)^2 \times 0.15 = 555.7\,\text{W}$$

Power dissipated in the aluminium cable is

$$(39.18)^2 = 0.233 = 357.67\,\text{W}$$

2.6 NETWORK THEOREMS

A network consists of a number of electrical elements connected in a circuit. If there is no source of electromotive force in the circuit, it is said to be passive. When the network contains one, or more, sources of electromotive force, it is said to be active.

Many practical resistive networks, including all those with more than one source of e.m.f., cannot be simplified to equivalent series and parallel arrangements. The unbalanced

Wheatstone bridge provides one classic and frequently encountered example. For this reason a number of well-established theorems have been developed for the analysis of such complex networks. The theorems are listed below:

Kirchhoff's first law The algebraic sum of the currents entering, +ve, and leaving, −ve, a junction is zero.

Kirchhoff's second law The algebraic sum of potential differences and e.m.f.s around any closed circuit is zero.

Superposition theorem In a linear resistive network containing more than one source of e.m.f., the resultant current in any branch is the algebraic sum of the currents that would be produced by each e.m.f. acting on its own while the other e.m.f.s are replaced with their respective internal resistances.

Thévenin's theorem The current through a resistor R, connected across any two points in an active network is obtained by dividing the potential difference between the two points, with R disconnected, by $(R + r)$, where r is the resistance of the network between the two connection points with R disconnected and each e.m.f. replaced with its equivalent internal resistance.

Although perhaps longwinded in definition, Thévenin's theorem has great practical application to complex resistive networks. An alternative statement of Thévenin's theorem is

Any active network can be replaced at any pair of terminals by an equivalent e.m.f. in series with an equivalent resistance.

The more concise version of Thévenin's theorem is perhaps a little more indicative of its power in application.

Norton's theorem Any active network can be replaced at any pair of terminals by an equivalent current source in parallel with an equivalent resistance. It might be apparent that Norton's theorem is complementary to Thévenin's theorem and both can be equally well used in the analysis of resistive networks.

Other useful network analysis techniques include 'mesh analysis', which incorporates Kirchhoff's second law, and 'nodal analysis' which is based on Kirchhoff's first law. Mesh and nodal analysis are also essentially complementary techniques.

The network theorems are best illustrated by means of an example. Figure 2.6 shows an active resistive network in which two sources of e.m.f. are present. For simplicity, the internal

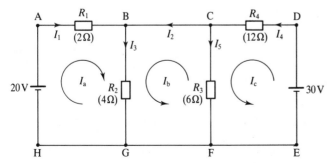

Figure 2.6 Active resistive network.

resistance of each source is assumed to be negligible. The problem resolves to one of determining the magnitude and direction of the currents flowing in each branch of the network.

Also shown in Fig. 2.6 are the 'assumed' directions of the currents flowing round each branch of the circuit. These directions are chosen quite arbitrarily; the analysis which follows will confirm, or otherwise, if the initial choices were correct. The mesh, or loop, currents I_a, I_b and I_c are not the same as the branch currents and these shall be considered later.

Using Kirchhoff's first and second laws Applying Kirchhoff's first law at junction B gives

$$I_3 = I_1 + I_2$$

Applying Kirchhoff's second law around the closed loop ABGH gives

$$20 = 2I_1 + 4I_3$$

Substituting for I_3 gives

$$20 = 2I_1 + 4(I_1 + I_2) = 6I_1 + 4I_2 \qquad \text{(i)}$$

Similarly at junction C we may write

$$I_5 = I_4 - I_2$$

Applying Kirchhoff's second law round the closed loop CDEF gives

$$30 = 12I_4 + 6I_5$$

Substituting for I_5 gives

$$30 = 12I_4 + 6(I_4 - I_2) = 6I_2 + 18I_4 \qquad \text{(ii)}$$

Equations (i) and (ii) contain three unknowns, I_1, I_2 and I_4. A third equation is therefore required, involving some or all of these three variables, to form a closed solution. The third equation can be derived from consideration of the inner loop, BCFG.

Applying Kirchhoff's second law around BCFG, we obtain

$$0 = 6I_5 - 4I_3 = 6(I_4 - I_2) - 4(I_1 + I_2) = -4I_1 - 10I_2 + 6I_4 \qquad \text{(iii)}$$

These three equations may now be solved simultaneously to yield

$$I_1 = 3.75\,\text{A} \qquad I_2 = -0.625\,\text{A} \qquad I_3 = 3.125\,\text{A} \qquad I_4 = 1.458\,\text{A} \qquad I_5 = 2.083\,\text{A}$$

The significance of the negative sign attached to I_2 indicates that the original assumed direction for I_2 was wrong. The correct direction for the current I_2 is therefore from B to C and not from C to B as shown in Fig. 2.6. The assumed directions for all the other currents were found to be correct since the numerical answers are all positive.

Using the superposition theorem The superposition theorem can be illustrated by solving for the current I_3 in the network shown in Fig. 2.6.

With the 20 V source acting alone, resistors R_2, R_3 and R_4 are effectively in parallel. The equivalent resistance is therefore $2\,\Omega$. Since this equivalent resistance is in series with R_1, then the equivalent resistance of the complete circuit is $2 + R_1 = 4\,\Omega$. Hence

$$I_1 = V/R_e = 20/4 = 5\,\text{A}$$

The potential difference across R_1 is $5 \times 2 = 10$ V and this leaves 10 V potential difference remaining across the rest of the circuit. Thus

$$I_3 = 10/4 = 2.5\,\text{A} \text{ (from B to G)}$$

Now considering the 30 V source acting alone. Resistors R_1, R_2 and R_3 are in parallel with an equivalent resistance of 1.0909 Ω. This is in series with R_4 and the equivalent resistance of the complete circuit is 13.0909 Ω. Therefore

$$I_4 = 30/13.0909 = 2.292\,\text{A}$$

The potential difference across R_4 is $12 \times 2.292 = 27.5\,\text{V}$. This then leaves a remaining 2.5 V potential difference across the rest of the circuit. Hence

$$I_3 = 2.5/4 = 0.625\,\text{A} \;(\text{from B to G})$$

Superimposing these two component values of I_3 gives the actual value of the current, i.e.

$$I_3 = 2.5 + 0.625 = 3.125\,\text{A}$$

This as expected, complies with the answer obtained for I_3 when using Kirchhoff's first and second laws.

Using Thévenin's theorem Thévenin's theorem may be applied to calculate (say) the current through the R_1 resistor. To apply the theorem, R_1 is 'replaced' by a pair of open terminals and the equivalent resistance as seen at the open terminals is evaluated.

With R_1 removed, R_2, R_3 and R_4 are effectively in parallel. The equivalent Thévenin resistance is then given by

$$\text{Thévenin resistance} = r = 1/[(1/4 + (1/6) + (1/12)] = 2\,\Omega$$

In addition, with R_1 replaced by a pair of open terminals there can be no current flow between A and B. The 30 V source, however, will still be able to supply current to the rest of the circuit. The equivalent resistance of this circuit is

$$R_2 \times R_3/[R_2 + R_3] + R_4 = 4 \times 6/(4+6) + 12 = 14.4\,\Omega$$

The current drawn from the 30 V source is $30/14.4 = 2.083\,\text{A}$. This results in a potential difference across R_4 of $2.083 \times 12 = 25\,\text{V}$. The remaining 5 V is the potential difference across BG. It is apparent therefore that a 5 V potential exists at B and there is an opposing 20 V potential at A. The effective potential from A to B is therefore $20 - 5 = 15\,\text{V}$ and this would tend to drive a current from A to B if they were connected through a resistor. This is in fact the equivalent Thévenin potential difference, v, and the current I_1 may finally be calculated as

$$I_1 = v/(R_1 + r) = 15/(2+2) = 3.75\,\text{A} \;(\text{from A to B})$$

Figure 2.7 illustrates the above application of Thévenin's theorem in terms of the appropriate equivalent circuits.

Using Norton's theorem As an alternative to Thévenin's theorem, the current R_1 might have been evaluated using Norton's theorem. The procedure employed is very similar in that the open-circuit equivalent resistance and the potential difference across AB both have to be calculated as before.

Using the previously calculated values, the Norton equivalent current source is

$$I = v/r = 15/4 = 7.5\,\text{A}$$

The equivalent Norton circuit is depicted in Fig. 2.8. The equivalent resistance of the circuit shown in Fig. 2.8 is

$$1/[(1/2 + (1/2)] = 1\,\Omega$$

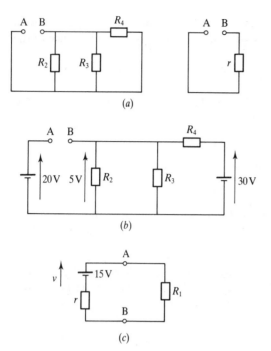

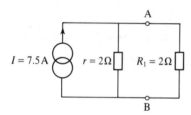

(a)

(b)

(c)

Figure 2.7 Illustration of the application of Thévenin's theorem: (a) equivalent Thévenin resistance; (b) equivalent Thévenin potential difference; (c) equivalent Thévenin circuit.

Figure 2.8 Illustration of Norton's theorem.

This gives a potential difference across the parallel resistors as $7.5 \times 1 = 7.5\,\mathrm{V}$. The current through R_1 is therefore

$$I_1 = 7.5/2 = 3.75\,\mathrm{A}$$

Using mesh analysis Mesh, or loop, analysis uses Kirchhoff's second law and voltage equations for each closed loop in the network can be written down by inspection. Referring to the resistive network and the assumed mesh currents shown in Fig. 2.6, the voltage equations can be written as

$$20 = 2I_a + 4I_a + 4I_b$$
$$0 = -4I_a - 4I_b - 6I_b + 6I_c$$
$$-30 = 6I_b - 12I_c - 6I_c$$

Rewriting the set of equations as

$$20 = 6I_a + 4I_b$$
$$0 = -4I_a - 10I_b - 6I_c$$
$$-30 = +6I_b - 18I_c$$

and solving the three equations simultaneously gives

$$I_a = 3.75\,\text{A} \qquad I_b = -0.625\,\text{A} \qquad I_c = 1.4583\,\text{A}$$

Note that the negative sign attached to I_b simply denotes that the assumed direction for I_b was wrong.

The branch currents are then

$$I_1 = I_a = 3.75\,\text{A}$$
$$I_2 = I_b = 0.625\,\text{A (from B to C)}$$
$$I_3 = I_1 - I_2 = 3.125\,\text{A}$$
$$I_4 = I_c = 1.4583\,\text{A}$$
$$I_5 = I_2 + I_4 = 2.0833\,\text{A}$$

Once again the results, as expected, are consistent with those obtained using the previous methods of analysis.

Nodal analysis uses Kirchhoff's first law and consists essentially of writing a set of simultaneous equations to describe the current relationships at the salient nodes of a resistive network. Nodal analysis is less commonly used, however, since it invokes the use of equivalent current sources and the network is usually handled in terms of conductances rather than resistances.

The choice of method used to solve a particular active resistive network might depend on the practical requirements of the problem. If say the current, or the power loss, in only one particular branch of a network is required then the superposition, Thévenin, or Norton theorems might render the most expeditious solution. If, on the other hand, the currents in the entire network are required then mesh analysis or the application of Kirchhoff's laws may be more easily applied. In any event, all of the methods considered are equally applicable and personal preference, or confidence, may be the deciding factor in choosing which theorem to use.

2.7 DOUBLE SUBSCRIPT NOTATION

To avoid ambiguity in the direction of current, e.m.f. of potential difference, a double subscript notation may be adopted. Figure 2.9 shows a source of e.m.f. which is acting from D to A. The e.m.f. is therefore E_{da}. The current flows from A to B, by traditional convention, and is designated I_{ab}. From this simple circuit it is apparent that $I_{ab} = I_{bc} = I_{cd} = I_{da}$. The potential difference across the load R is denoted V_{bc} to indicate that the potential at B is more positive than that at C. If arrow heads are used to indicate the potential difference, then they should point towards the more positive potential.

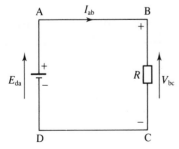

Figure 2.9 Double subscript notation.

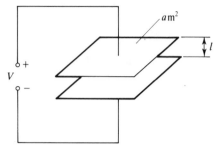

Figure 2.10 Electrostatic system.

2.8 ELECTROSTATIC SYSTEMS

Electrostatic systems are quantified by the physical behaviour of the somewhat intangible concept of 'charge'. Fortunately the unified field approach lends itself well to the quantification of electrostatic systems.

Figure 2.10 shows two parallel, conducting metal plates separated by an evacuated space. A potential difference is applied across the plates such that they become charged at equal magnitude, but opposite sign. For the electrostatic system, Eq. (2.1) is written

$$Q = \frac{\varepsilon_0 a V}{l} \tag{2.13}$$

where Q = total charge, C (coulombs)
ε_0 = permittivity of free space, F/m (Farads/m), i.e. the field characteristic
a = cross-sectional area of the plates, m^2
l = distance separating the plates, m
V = applied potential difference, V

The group $(\varepsilon_0 a/l)$ is termed the capacitance of the system. It is usually denoted by C, and is measured in units of Farads (F). Thus

$$Q = CV \tag{2.14}$$

Since the Farad (F) is an unwieldy, large number, it is more common to use the microfarad, μF, or the picofarad, pF, as the unit of measurement:

$$1\,\mu F = 10^{-6}\,F \qquad 1\,pf = 10^{-12}\,F$$

If the plates are separated by an insulating medium other than free space, then these so-called dielectric media have a different value of permittivity. The actual permittivity is related to the permittivity of free space by the relative permittivity of the dielectric, i.e.

$$\varepsilon = \varepsilon_0\,\varepsilon_r \tag{2.15}$$

where ε_r is the relative permittivity of the dielectric.

The permittivity of free space, ε_0 is numerically equal to $(1/36\pi) \times 10^{-9}$. The relative permittivity of some of the more common dielectric materials are listed in Table 2.2.

Simple Capacitive Circuits

Figure 2.11 shows three capacitors connected in a simple parallel arrangement. The total charge flowing in the circuit is

$$Q = Q_1 + Q_2 + Q_3$$

Table 2.2 Relative permittivities of some typical dielectric materials.

Material	Relative permittivity
Air	1
Paper	2–2.5
Porcelain	6–7
Mica	3–7

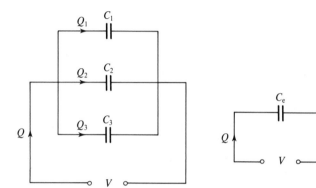

Figure 2.11 Capacitors in parallel.

From Eq. (2.14), this may be written as

$$Q = (C_1 V + C_2 V + C_3 V) = (C_1 + C_2 + C_3)V$$

Comparing this with the circuit containing one equivalent capacitor, i.e. $Q = C_e V$, then

$$C_e = C_1 + C_2 + C_3 \tag{2.16}$$

where C_e is the total equivalent capacitance.

Equation (2.16) shows that capacitances connected in parallel have an equivalent capacitance which is equal to the algebraic sum of the capacitances in parallel.

It may similarly be shown that for the series capacitance arrangement in Fig. 2.12, the total equivalent capacitance is related through the inverse summation.

In Fig. 2.12, the charge is common to all three capacitors, i.e.

$$Q = C_1 V_1 = C_2 V_2 = C_3 V_3$$

and

$$V = V_1 + V_2 + V_3$$

i.e.

$$V = \frac{Q}{C_1} + \frac{Q}{C_2} + \frac{Q}{C_3} = \left[\frac{1}{C_1} + \frac{1}{C_2} + \frac{1}{C_3}\right]Q$$

For the single equivalent capacitor:

$$V = \frac{Q}{C_e}$$

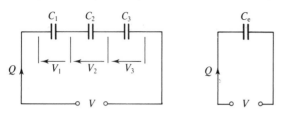

Figure 2.12 Capacitors in series.

Comparing the two expressions derived for the total voltage drop gives

$$\frac{1}{C_e} = \frac{1}{C_1} + \frac{1}{C_2} + \frac{1}{C_3} \tag{2.17}$$

Equations (2.16) and (2.17) can be used to reduce series and parallel capacitor circuits to a single equivalent capacitor.

Example In the circuit shown in Fig. 2.13 parallel plate capacitors having identical dimensions are used. The plates have an area of $1000\,\mathrm{cm}^2$ and are placed 5 mm apart. The relative permittivity of the dielectric medium used for C_1, C_2 and C_3 is 2 and for C_4, C_5 and C_6, the relative permittivity is 4. Determine the electric stress, in kV/mm, across C_3 when the applied DC voltage is 10 kV.
The capacitance is given as

$$C = \varepsilon_0\, \varepsilon_r\, a/l$$

If we denote the capacitance of C_1, C_2 and C_3 as C, then the capacitance of C_4, C_5 and C_6 is $2C$. Now capacitors C_5 and C_6 are in series and they can be replaced with a single capacitor:

$$C_7 = 1/[(1/2C) + (1/2C)] = C$$

Capacitor C_7 is in parallel with C_4 and these can be replaced with an equivalent capacitor:

$$C_8 = (2C + C) = 3C$$

Capacitor C_8 is in series with C_3. Therefore the equivalent capacitor to replace these is given by

$$C_9 = 1/[(1/3C) + (1/C)] = 3C/4$$

C_9 in parallel with C_2 gives

$$C_{10} = (3C/4 + C) = 7C/4$$

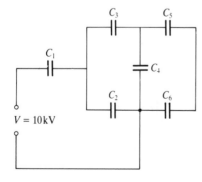

Figure 2.13 Series/parallel capacitive circuit.

Finally, C_{10} in series with C_1 gives the equivalent capacitance of the complete circuit as

$$C_{11} = 1/[(4/7C) + (1/C)] = 7C/11$$

From Eq. (2.14), the charge is given by

$$Q = CV = (7C/11) \times 10^4$$

Working back through the equivalent circuits, the potential difference across C_{10} is given by

$$Q/C_{10} = [(7C/11) \times 10^4] \times 4/7C = 40/11 \, \text{kV}$$

The charge on C_9 is given by

$$(3C/4) \times (40 \times 10^3)/11 = 3C \times 10^4/11$$

This is also the charge on C_3, since C_3 and C_8 are in series. The potential difference across C_3 is given by

$$(3C \times 10^4/11)/C = 2.727 \, \text{kV}$$

Therefore the electric stress on C_3 is given by

$$2.727/5 = 0.545 \, \text{kV/mm}$$

The process of reducing the circuit to a single equivalent capacitor is illustrated in Fig. 2.14(a)–(e).

Composite capacitors, involving different dielectric media, may also be treated in the same manner as a series capacitor arrangement.

Charging a Capacitor

Figure 2.15 shows a parallel plate capacitor which is connected in series with a resistor to a source of e.m.f., say a battery, through a switch.

Initially the capacitor is uncharged before the switch is closed. When the switch is closed a charging current will flow until such time that the potential difference across the capacitor is

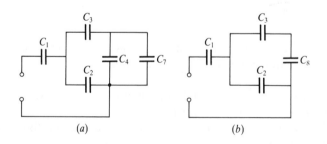

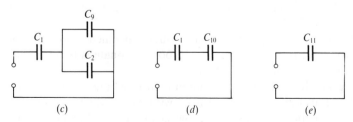

Figure 2.14 Equivalent capacitor circuits.

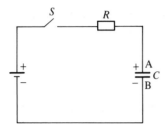

Figure 2.15 Charging a capacitor.

equal to the e.m.f. available from the source. The charging process consists of taking electrons from A and transferring them through the external wiring to plate B. The energy required to do this is derived from the battery. The build up of electrons from the negative terminal of the battery to plate B of the capacitor induces a dielectric flux between the plates and a balancing positive charge is developed on plate A. As long as the dielectric flux is changing, a current will flow externally. Eventually a state of equilibrium will be reached. Note that no electrons can pass through the dielectric since it is an insulator. The instantaneous current during charging is given by

$$i = dQ/dt$$

From Eq. (2.14), this may be written for a capacitor as

$$i = dQ/dt = C(dv/dt) \tag{2.18}$$

where v is the instantaneous voltage. The instantaneous power is therefore

$$p = iv = Cv(dv/dt)$$

The energy supplied over the time period, dt, is

$$Cv(dv/dt)\, dt = Cv\, dv$$

Hence the total energy supplied is

$$\int_0^V Cv\, dv = \frac{1}{2}\, CV^2 \tag{2.19}$$

Types of Capacitor

1. *Air capacitors*. These usually consists of one set of fixed plates and another set of moveable plates. The area between the capacitor plates is therefore variable and so also, from Eq. (2.13), is the capacitance.
2. *Paper dielectric capacitors*. These consist of metal foil interleaved with wax, or oil impregnated paper and rolled into a compact cylinder form.
3. *Mica dielectric capacitors*. These consists of alternate layers of mica and metal foil, tightly clamped together. They are used mainly for high-frequency applications.
4. *Ceramic capacitors*. The electrodes are formed by a metallic coating, usually silver, deposited on the opposite faces of a thin ceramic disc.
5. *Polycarbonate capacitors*. Polycarbonate is a plastic insulating material which is produced in a range of thicknesses, down to about two micrometres. The polycarbonate is bonded with aluminium foil and rolled to form the capacitor element.
6. *Electrolytic capacitors*. These generally consist of two aluminium foils, one with an oxide film and the other without. The foils are usually interleaved with paper which is saturated with a suitable electrolyte. Electrolytic capacitors have the advantage of having a large capacitance for a relatively small physical volume. They are used extensively for smoothing

out the ripple voltage from rectified alternating current power supplies. They are only suitable, however, in circuits where the applied voltage across the capacitor can never reverse its direction.

Dielectric Strength

If the potential difference across opposite faces of a dielectric material is increased above a particular value, then the material breaks down. The failure of the material takes the form of a small puncture, which renders the material useless as an insulator. The potential gradient necessary to cause breakdown is normally expressed in kilovolts/millimetre and is termed the 'dielectric strength'. The dielectric strength of a given material decreases with increases in the thickness. Table 2.3 gives approximate values for some of the more common dielectric materials.

2.9 ELECTROMAGNETIC SYSTEMS

The magnetic field can be defined as the space in which a magnetic effect can be detected, or observed. A standard school physics experiment involves the sprinkling of iron filings on a sheet of paper under which a barmagnet is placed. On tapping the paper lightly, the filings arrange themselves along closed loops of equi-potential and are clearly visible. An obvious magnetic field is also observable around a straight length of conductor carrying a current. In particular, the exact same magnetic field as that produced by the bar magnet is observed when the current carrying conductor is formed into a helical type coil. The equi-potential loops, describe the path of the magnetic flux, ϕ, and although the flux lines have no physical meaning, they provide a convenient vehicle to quantify various magnetic effects.

The direction of the magnetic flux is governed by the so-called 'right-hand screw rule'. This states that the direction of the magnetic field produced by a current corresponds with the direction given by turning a right-hand screw thread. The direction of the current corresponds with the translational movement of the screw.

Magnetic Field of a Toroid

Figure 2.16 shows a toroidal coil, of N turns, which is wound round an annular former. A resultant magnetic flux, shown as broken lines, is generated when the coil carries a current. For the magnetic field, Eq. (2.1) takes the general form:

$$\phi = \frac{\mu a F}{l} \tag{2.20}$$

Table 2.3 Dielectric strength of some common insulators.

Material	Thickness, mm	Dielectric strength, kV/mm
Air	0.2	5.75
	0.6	4.92
	1.0	4.36
	10.0	2.98
Mica	0.01	200
	0.1	115
	1.00	61
Waxed paper	0.10	40–60

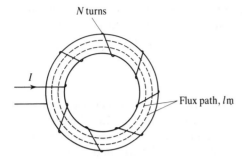

Figure 2.16 Toroid.

where ϕ = magnetic flux (webers, Wb)
μ = permeability of the medium (H/m)
a = cross-sectional area of the flux path in the toroid (m^2)
l = length of the flux path (m)
F = magnetic potential difference, or magnetomotive force (A)

The magnetomotive force, m.m.f., is equal to the product of the number of turns on the coil and the current carried, i.e.

$$F = IN \qquad (2.21)$$

Note that the m.m.f. is descriptively expressed in 'ampere-turns'. Since the number of turns is already a dimensionless quantity, the accepted unit of magnetomotive force is the ampere, A.

The group $(\mu a/l)$ is termed the permeance and the inverse of permeance is the reluctance, S. Thus Eq. (2.20) may be rewritten as

$$\phi = F/S \qquad (2.22)$$

Equation (2.22) represents an electromagnetic version of Ohm's law.

Alternatively, Eq. (2.20) can be expressed as:

$$\frac{\phi}{a} = \frac{\mu F}{l}$$

or

$$B = \mu H \qquad (2.23)$$

where $B = \phi/a$ is the magnetic flux density (Wb/m^2, or tesla)
$H = F/l$ is the magnetic intensity (A/m)

Permeability

The permeability of free space, μ_0, is numerically equal to $4\pi \times 10^{-7}$. The absolute permeability of other materials is related to the permeability of free space by the relative permeability, i.e.

$$\mu = \mu_0 \mu_r \qquad (2.24)$$

For air and other non-magnetic materials, the absolute permeability is the same constant. For magnetic materials, absolute permeability is not a fixed constant but varies nonlinearly with the flux density. The nonlinear variation of permeability is conveniently displayed as a functional plot of magnetic flux density, B, against magnetic intensity, H. Figure 2.17 illustrates a number of B–H curves for some common materials.

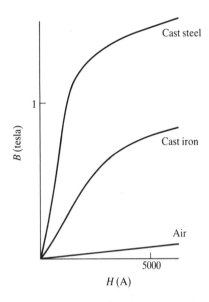

Figure 2.17 B–H curves for some common materials.

From Eq. (2.23) it is apparent that the absolute permeability is given by the slope of a tangent to the *B–H* curve at any particular value.

Also shown in Fig. 2.17 is the B–H curve for air, the only straight-line relationship in the diagram. It is apparent that for an applied magnetic intensity, the magnetic flux developed in a coil with a ferrous core is many times greater than that through a similar coil with an air core. In most practical systems therefore, a ferrous core is normally used since it greatly facilitates the establishment of a magnetic flux.

Faraday's Law

Perhaps the most fundamental law of electromagnetic systems, Faraday's law states that the e.m.f. induced in a magnetic circuit is equal to the rate of change of flux linkages in the circuit. In mathematical terms, Faraday's law is given as

$$e = N(\mathrm{d}\phi/\mathrm{d}t) \tag{2.25}$$

where *e* is the instantaneous induced e.m.f.

Equation (2.25) forms the basis of all electrical power generation machines and is a statement of the fact that an electric current can be produced by the movement of a magnetic flux relative to a coil. In most rotating electrical generators, it is actually the coil which is moved relative to the magnetic field. The net result, however, is exactly the same.

The direction of the induced e.m.f. is always such that it tends to set up a current to oppose the motion, or the change of magnetic flux, which was responsible for inducing the e.m.f. This is essentially a statement of Lenz's law. In many texts therefore the right-hand side of Eq. (2.25) is often shown as a negative quantity.

The motion, or change of flux is associated with the application of a mechanical force which ultimately provides the torque required to drive the electric generator. Figure 2.18 shows a single conductor of length *l* m, carrying an induced current *I* and lying perpendicular to a magnetic field of flux density *B* tesla. The force applied causes the conductor to move through a distance d*x* m. The mechanical work done is therefore *F* d*x*. The electrical energy produced is given as the

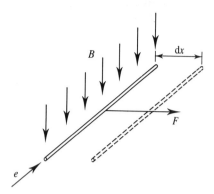

Figure 2.18 Generation of e.m.f.

product of the power developed and the time duration, i.e. $eI\mathrm{d}t$. For no external losses, the mechanical work done is converted into electrical energy. Thus

$$eI\mathrm{d}t = F\mathrm{d}x \qquad (2.26)$$

Using Faraday's law, Eq. (2.25), the induced e.m.f. is equal to the rate of change of flux linkage. For a single conductor, $N = 1$ and in consequence:

$$e = (Bl\mathrm{d}x)/\mathrm{d}t$$

Therefore $(Bl\,\mathrm{d}x/\mathrm{d}t)I\,\mathrm{d}t = F\mathrm{d}x$; i.e.

$$F = BlI \qquad (2.27)$$

Equation (2.27) relates the applied force to the corresponding current generated in a current carrying conductor moving through a magnetic field. The equation applies equally to an electric generator, or conversely to a motor in which case the electrical power supplied is converted into a mechanical torque via the electromagnetic effect.

Self-induced E.M.F.

If a current flows through a coil a magnetic flux links with that coil. If in addition, the current is a time varying quantity, then there will be a rate of change of flux linkages associated with the circuit. The e.m.f. generated will oppose the change in flux linkages.

When dealing with electric circuits it is convenient if the voltage across individual elements can be related to the current flowing through them. Figure 2.19 shows a simple circuit comprising a coil having N turns and resistance R, connected effectively in series with a time varying voltage. The voltage drop across the terminals A and B can be split into two

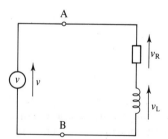

Figure 2.19 Self-induced e.m.f.

components. First, there is the voltage drop purely due to the resistance of the coiled element. Second, there is a voltage drop which is a consequence of the self-induced e.m.f. generated through the electromagnetic effect of the coil. Thus

$$v = v_R + v_L$$
$$= iR + N \frac{d\phi}{dt}$$

(2.28)

From Eqs (2.20) and (2.21)

$$\phi = \frac{\mu a F}{l} = \frac{\mu a i N}{l}$$

Therefore

$$v = iR + N \frac{d}{dt}\left[\frac{\mu a i N}{l}\right]$$

(2.29)

$$= iR + N^2\left[\frac{\mu a}{l}\right]\frac{di}{dt}$$

The group $N^2(\mu a/l)$ is called the self-inductance of the coil and is denoted by L. The unit of self inductance is the henry (H). Therefore

$$v = iR + L \frac{di}{dt}$$

(2.30)

By comparing Eqs (2.28) and (2.30) it is apparent that

$$L \frac{di}{dt} = N \frac{d\phi}{dt}$$

Integration then gives

$$L = N\phi/i$$

(2.31)

Example A coil of 1500 turns generates a flux of 2.5 mWb when carrying a certain current. If the current is reversed in a total time of 0.2 s, determine the average value of the e.m.f. induced in the coil
The induced e.m.f. is given by either $L(di/dt)$ or by $N(d\phi/dt)$.
If the current is reversed, then the flux is also reversed. The flux then changes from $+2.5$ mWb to -2.5 mWb over 0.2 s. The induced e.m.f. is given by

$$N(d\phi/dt) = 1500 \times [2.5 - (-2.5)] \times (10^{-3})/0.2 = 37.5\,\text{V}$$

The nature of the self-induced e.m.f., i.e. (Ldi/dt), is such that it will oppose the flow of current when the current is increasing. When the current is decreasing the self-induced e.m.f. will reverse direction and attempt to prevent the current from decreasing.

Energy Stored in an Inductor

Instantaneous power $= vi$

  Energy stored

$$W = \int_0^t vi \, \mathrm{d}t$$

$$= \int_0^t L \frac{\mathrm{d}i}{\mathrm{d}t} i \, \mathrm{d}t \qquad\qquad (2.32)$$

$$= L \int_0^t i \, \mathrm{d}i = \frac{1}{2} LI^2$$

Hysteresis in Magnetic Circuits

Hysteresis can be described with reference to a toroidal coil wound on an iron core, see Fig. 2.16. The current supplied to the coil can be imagined to be taken through a cyclic process where it is increased from 0 to $+I$A, back through 0 to $-I$A and again back through 0 to $+I$A. Measurement of the flux density in the core, as the current varies, results in a B–H curve as depicted in Fig. 2.20.

The behaviour of the B–H relationship is a 'hysteresis loop'. This behaviour is typical for ferrous cores and is an illustration of the fact that all of the electrical energy supplied to magnetize an iron core is not returned when the coil current is reduced to zero. The loss of energy is called 'hysteresis loss' and it is manifested as heat in the iron core. It can be shown that the hysteresis loss is directly proportional to the area enclosed by the hysteresis loop. It is to obvious advantage therefore that any magnetic system which is subject to a cyclic variation of flux density should incorporate a magnetic core in which the hysteresis loop is minimally small. In practical applications a low-loss core of silicon iron, or the nickel–iron alloys such as Mumetal and Permalloy are normally used. Some strain-relieving heat treatment process is also usually involved, after cold-working, to restore the original magnetic condition of the material.

Hysteresis is characterized by two parameters which are the 'remanent flux density', or 'remanence' and the 'coercive force'. The remanent flux density is the flux density which remains in the core when the magnetic intensity, i.e. the coil current, has been reduced to zero. The remanent flux density is represented by line OA in Fig. 2.20. The coercive force is the magnetic intensity required to reduce the remanent flux density to zero and is represented by line OC in Fig. 2.20.

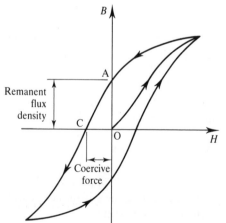

Figure 2.20 Hysteresis loop for an iron-cored toroid.

Eddy Current Loss

Faraday's law, Eq. (2.25), shows that a time varying magnetic flux will induce an e.m.f. in a coil. If the ends of the coil are connected and form a closed circuit, then the induced voltage will circulate a current round the closed loop. Consider now an iron core, in which a time varying magnetic flux exists. Since iron is a conductor then there will be a multitude of arbitrary closed paths within the iron matrix. These closed paths constitute effective conduction routes and the varying magnetic flux will generate a flow of current round them. The currents are called 'eddy currents' and because of the ohmic resistance of the core, the end result is an energy loss as the eddy currents are dissipated as heat.

Eddy current losses can be greatly reduced by building the iron core in the form of laminations which are insulated from one another. The laminated assembly confines the path lengths for the eddy currents to each respective lamination. The cross-sectional area of the eddy current path is also reduced and the eddy current loss is approximately proportional to the square of the thickness of the laminations. A practical minimum thickness for any lamination is about 0.4 mm. Increasing manufacturing costs could not justify the use of much thinner laminations.

The eddy current phenomenon, while basically a detrimental effect, can be utilized to good purpose in the form of 'induction heating'. In this type of heater, a metallic workpiece is enclosed within a coil which is powered with an alternating current supply. The induced eddy currents are dissipated as heat in the workpiece. Induction heating is basically a surface heating technique where the 'depth' of heating is dependent on the depth of eddy current activity. This in turn, is dependent on the frequency of the alternating current supplied to the coil. A high-frequency supply produces a relatively low depth of heat penetration and this is used extensively in surface, or case hardening heat treatment processes.

Kirchhoff's Laws and the Magnetic Circuit

Figure 2.21 shows a magnetic circuit in which a magnetizing coil is wound on one of the limbs and another limb incorporates the usual feature of an 'air gap'.

Using the analogy between magnetic and conduction circuits, the magnetic circuit can be represented in terms of an energy source, or m.m.f., and each limb of the magnetic circuit is written in terms of the appropriate reluctance S. This is illustrated in Fig. 2.22.

Given all of the relevant dimensions and material properties, the problem resolves to one of calculating the current required to establish a prescribed magnetic flux density in the air gap. The solution invokes the use of Kirchhoff's laws as they apply to magnetic circuits. These are:

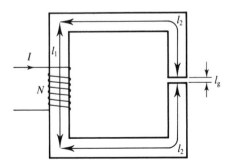

Figure 2.21 Magnetic circuit.

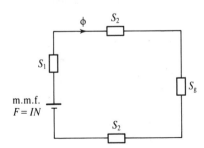

Figure 2.22 Representation of the magnetic circuit of Fig. 2.21.

First law: At any instant in time, the sum of the fluxes flowing into a node is equal to the sum of the fluxes flowing out.

Second law: Around any closed magnetic circuit the total magnetomotive force is equal to the sum of all the m.m.f.s round the circuit.

Manipulation of Eqs (2.20) to (2.24) then yields the required solution. The self-inductance of the coil, if required, may be calculated from Eq. (2.31), or from the definition:

$$L = N^2(\mu a/l) = N^2/S \tag{2.33}$$

Example Figure 2.23(a) shows a cast steel magnetic core and the approximate dimensions of the flux paths within the core. The centre limb has a cross-sectional area of $13\,\mathrm{cm}^2$ and the other limbs have a cross-sectional area of $10\,\mathrm{cm}^2$. The centre limb carries a coil of 200 turns and the right-hand limb features an air gap of length 1 mm. Figure 2.23(b) shows the schematic representation of the magnetic circuit, and Fig. 2.23(c) the approximate magnetic characteristics of cast steel. Calculate:

(i) The current required to set up a flux density of 0.2 tesla in the air gap.

(ii) The self-inductance of the coil at this flux density.

Considering first of all, the air gap. Flux density in the air gap $= 0.2$ tesla $= B_\mathrm{a}$.

From Eq. (2.23)

$$H_\mathrm{a} = B_\mathrm{a}/\mu_0 = 0.2/(4\pi \times 10^{-7}) = 10^6/2\pi \ \mathrm{A/m}$$

The m.m.f. in the air gap is given by

$$F_\mathrm{a} = H_\mathrm{a}l_\mathrm{a} = [10^6/(2\pi)] \times 0.001 = 159.2 \ \mathrm{A}$$

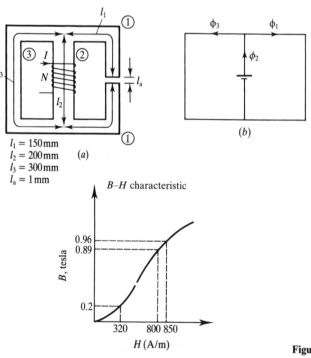

$l_1 = 150\,\mathrm{mm}$
$l_2 = 200\,\mathrm{mm}$ (a)
$l_3 = 300\,\mathrm{mm}$
$l_\mathrm{a} = 1\,\mathrm{mm}$

Figure 2.23 Electromagnetic circuit: (a) physical; (b) electrical; (c) B–H characteristic.

At the right-hand side of the circuit, the flux density in limb 1 of the core is equal to that in the air gap. Thus $B_1 = B_a = 0.2$ tesla. From the B–H characteristic for cast steel, $H_1 = 320$ A/m. Thus

$$F_1 = H_1 l_1 = 320 \times 0.30 = 96 \text{ A}$$

Note that the total length, l_1, includes both parts of the limb on either side of the air gap. Applying Kirchhoff's second law around the outer closed loop of the magnetic circuit gives

$$F_3 = F_1 + F_a = 96 + 159.2 = 255.2 \text{ A}$$

Therefore

$$H_3 = F_3/l_3 = 255.2/0.3 = 850.5 \text{ A/m}$$

From the B–H characteristic, $B_3 = 0.96$ tesla. Hence

$$\phi_1 = B_1 a_1 = 0.2 \times 10 \times 10^{-4} = 0.2 \times 10^{-3} \text{ Wb}$$

and

$$\phi_3 = B_3 a_3 = 0.96 \times 10 \times 10^{-4} = 0.96 \times 10^{-3} \text{ Wb}$$

From Kirchhoff's first law, $\phi_2 = \phi_1 + \phi_3$; therefore

$$\phi_2 = (0.2 + 0.96) \times 10^{-3} = 1.16 \times 10^{-3} \text{ Wb}$$

Thus

$$B_2 = \phi_2/a_2 = (1.16 \times 10^{-3})/0.0013 = 0.892 \text{ tesla}$$

From the B–H characteristic, $H_2 = 800$ A/m, therefore

$$F_2 = H_2 l_2 = 800 \times 0.02 = 160 \text{ A}$$

From Eq. (2.21)

$$I = F_2/N = 160/200 = 0.8 \text{ A}$$

This then is the required current to create a magnetic flux density of 0.2 tesla in the air gap. From Eq. (2.31), the self-inductance of the coil is $L = N\phi/i$, therefore

$$L = 300 \times (1.16 \times 10^{-3})/0.8 = 0.435 \text{ H}$$

It has already been shown that the lowest permeability is that of air and that the m.m.f. required to produce a flux density in air is many times greater than that required to produce the same flux density in a ferrous material. It may reasonably be questioned therefore why air gaps are used at all in iron cored magnetic circuits. The only function of the air gap is to provide a measure of linearity to the magnetic system such that the inductance remains reasonably constant over a range of operating currents.

2.10 ALTERNATING QUANTITIES

If an electrical quantity varies with time, but does not change its polarity, it is said to be a direct current, DC, quantity. If the quantity alternates between a positive and a negative polarity, then it is classified as an alternating, AC, quantity.

The period, T, is the time interval over which one complete cycle of the alternating quantity varies. The inverse of the period is the frequency, f, in cycles per second (cycle/s), or Hertz (Hz).

Circular frequency, ω, in radians per second (rad/s) is also commonly used. (NB One cycle/s corresponds to 2π rad/s.)

Instantaneous values of the quantities encountered in electrical systems are usually denoted by lower case letters. Since the instantaneous values are difficult to measure and quantify, AC quantities are usually expressed as 'root mean square', r.m.s., values. For a periodically varying AC quantity, the r.m.s. value is given by

$$\text{r.m.s.} = \sqrt{\left[1/t \int_0^t (\text{quantity})^2 \, dt\right]} \tag{2.34}$$

If in a periodically varying AC quantity, the positive and negative half-cycles are identical in all but sign, then the average value of the quantity is zero. The average value of the half-cycle is sometimes useful, however, particularly when dealing with rectified signals.

Many electrical quantities vary in a sinusoidal manner and it can easily be shown that the r.m.s. value is simply related to the maximum value by

$$\text{r.m.s.} = \text{max}/(\sqrt{2}) = 0.707 \text{ max} \tag{2.35}$$

Relationship Between Voltage and Current in *R*, *L* and *C* Elements

For a simple resistive element, current is directly proportional to voltage. The current waveform will therefore be essentially the same shape as the voltage waveform.

For an inductive coil with negligible resistance, i.e. $R = 0$, the relation between voltage and current is given by Eq. (2.30), i.e.

$$v_L = L \frac{di}{dt}$$

Thus

$$i = \frac{1}{L} \int_0^t v_L \, dt \tag{2.36}$$

If, for example, the voltage is an AC square wave, then the current will take the shape of a 'sawtooth' waveform, Fig. 2.24.

The relation between voltage and current for a capacitive element is given by Eq. (2.18), i.e.

$$i = C \frac{dv_c}{dt}$$

For the capacitive element it can be seen that a current will flow only when the voltage is changing. No current can flow if the voltage is constant since (dv_c/dt) will then be equal to zero. The capacitor then, will block any steady DC input and indeed is sometimes used for this express purpose.

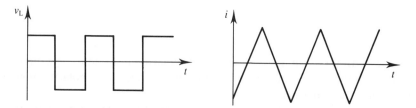

Figure 2.24 Voltage and current relationship for an inductive element.

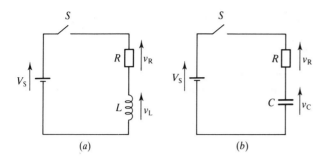

Figure 2.25 Simple *RL* (*a*) and *RC* (*b*) circuits under transient switching conditions.

RL and *RC* Circuits under Transient Switching Conditions

Circuits involving a single resistor, capacitor or inductance are rare. It is more usual to find circuits involving some or other combination of these elements in both DC and AC applications. Figure 2.25 illustrates two simple *RL* and *RC* circuits.

RL **circuit** With the switch open there is no flow of current in the circuit (Fig. 2.25 (*a*)). At the instant of switching, the current will rise and eventually reach a steady-state value of V_s/R. The transient period is governed by Eq. (2.30) which represents a first-order, ordinary differential equation in *i*. The solution of Eq. (2.30) involves the technique of separating the variables to allow integration. The general solution is

$$i = I[1 - \exp(-Rt/L)] \tag{2.37}$$

where *I* is the final steady-state current in the circuit (see Fig. 2.26).

Equation (2.37) shows that the current growth in the circuit will rise exponentially to reach a steady-state value as time *t* increases. It may also be shown that

$$v_L = L \frac{di}{dt} = V_s \exp(-Rt/L) \tag{2.38}$$

If the initial rate of increase in current were to be maintained, then the steady-state current would be achieved in a time of *T*s. From Fig. 2.26

$$\left[\frac{di}{dt}\right]_{t=0} = \frac{I}{T}$$

At the instant of switching the current is zero, v_R is zero and $v_L = V_s$. Hence at $t = 0$, $v_L = V_s = LI/T$. Therefore

$$T = LI/V_s = L/R \tag{2.39}$$

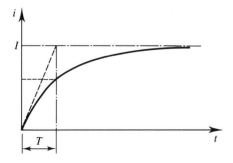

Figure 2.26 Transient current growth in an inductive element.

Equation (2.39) defines the 'time constant' for the *RL* circuit. The actual value of the current in the circuit when $t = T$ is $0.632\,I$.

RC circuit In Fig. 2.25(*b*) with the switch open there is zero potential difference across the capacitor. On closing the switch the voltage across the capacitor will rise in an asymptotic manner, reaching a steady-state value of V_s. From Kirchhoff's second law:

$$V_s = iR + v_c \tag{2.40}$$

where v_c is the instantaneous voltage across the capacitor.

From Eq. (2.18) we can write

$$V_s = RC \frac{dv_c}{dt} + v_c \tag{2.41}$$

Equation (2.41) shows that the instantaneous voltage across the capacitor also conforms to a first-order system. The solution of Eq. (2.41) gives

$$v_c = V_s[1 - \exp(-t/RC)] \tag{2.42}$$

Considering the initial rate of increase of voltage, it can be shown that the appropriate time constant for the simple *RC* circuit is

$$T = RC \tag{2.43}$$

Both the simple *RL* and *RC* circuits are first-order systems with a generalized form of transient behaviour.

In circuits containing both inductive and capacitive elements, the transient behaviour is governed by a second-order ordinary differential equation. The transient behaviour of these circuits, however, is less important than their response to sinusoidally varying inputs.

An interesting additional feature of the *RC* circuit is its ability to function as an integrating or differentiating circuit. Figure 2.27 depicts an *RC* integrator. The components of the circuit are selected such that $v_R \gg v_c$. To a reasonable approximation then, $v_s = v_R$, therefore $i = v_s/R$. Since $v_c = (1/C) \int i \, dt$, then

$$v_c = (1/RC) \int v_s \, dt \tag{2.44}$$

Equation (2.44) shows that the output voltage is proportional to the integral of the input voltage, with $(1/RC)$ the constant of proportionality.

The *RC* differentiator is shown in Fig. 2.28. For the *RC* differentiator the components are selected such that the voltage drop across the capacitor, v_c, is very much greater than that over the resistor, v_R, i.e. $v_s = v_c$. Therefore $v_s = (1/C) \int i \, dt$, and thus

$$i = C \frac{dv_s}{dt}$$

Taking the output across the resistor gives

$$v_R = iR = RC \frac{dv_s}{dt} \tag{2.45}$$

It is apparent from Eq. (2.45) that the output is in proportion to the first derivative of the input.

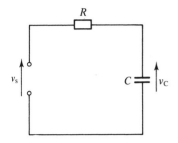
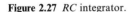

Figure 2.27 *RC* integrator.

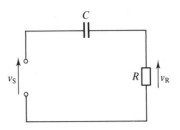

Figure 2.28 *RC* differentiator.

Steady-state Alternating Currents

In most practical applications in electrical engineering the voltages and currents are sinusoidal. A simple series *RLC* circuit is depicted in Fig. 2.29.

Since the current is common to each of the circuit elements, it is used for reference purposes. The instantaneous current is defined as

$$i = I_m \sin(\omega t) \tag{2.46}$$

where I_m is the maximum, or peak, value of the current and ω is the angular, or circular frequency in rad/s.

The voltage drop across the resistor is given by

$$v_R = iR = I_m R \sin(\omega t) \tag{2.47}$$

Equation (2.47) indicates that the voltage drop across the resistor is in phase with the current. In other words, v_R reaches a positive maximum at the same instant as the current, *i*.

The voltage drop across the inductor is:

$$\begin{aligned} v_L = L\frac{di}{dt} &= L\frac{d}{dt}[I_m \sin(\omega t)] \\ &= LI_m \omega \cos(\omega t) \\ &= \omega L I_m \sin(\omega t + 90) \end{aligned} \tag{2.48}$$

The relationship between current and voltage drop across the inductor is shown in Fig. 2.30. It can be seen that there is a phase difference between the voltage drop and the current through the

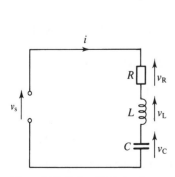

Figure 2.29 Series *RLC* circuit.

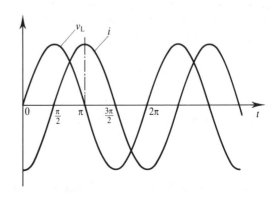

Figure 2.30 Current and voltage drop across an inductor.

inductor. In fact, v_L reaches a positive maximum 'before' i, and v_L is said to 'lead' the current by 90°.

For the capacitor, the voltage drop is given by

$$v_c = (1/C) \int i \, dt = (1/C) \int I_m \sin(\omega t) \, dt$$

$$= \frac{-I_m}{\omega C} \cos(\omega t) \tag{2.49}$$

$$= +\frac{I_m}{\omega C} \sin(\omega t - 90)$$

The voltage drop across the capacitor therefore reaches its positive maximum after that of i. In general terminology, v_c 'lags' i by 90°.

Equations (2.47), (2.48) and (2.49) are all of similar form in that they can be expressed as

$$\text{voltage drop} = \text{constant} \times \text{current}$$

In Eq. (2.48), the constant ωL is termed the 'inductive reactance' and is denoted by X_L. In Eq. (2.49), the constant $(1/\omega C)$ is the 'capacitive reactance', which is denoted as X_C. Both of these reactances have the units of ohms.

The total voltage drop across the three circuit elements is:

$$v = v_R = v_L + v_c$$

$$= iR + L\frac{di}{dt} + \frac{1}{C}\int i \, dt$$

Therefore

$$v = I_m R \sin(\omega t) + \omega L I_m \sin(\omega t + 90) + \frac{I_m}{\omega C} \sin(\omega t - 90) \tag{2.50}$$

While Eq. (2.50) defines the total instantaneous voltage drop in mathematical terms, it is a little cumbersome to deal with. To simplify the analysis, the addition of AC voltages is conveniently performed using a graphical technique involving 'phasors'.

Phasor Diagrams

Any sinusoidally varying quantity can be represented as a phasor, which is a vector quantity. The length of the phasor is proportional to the magnitude of the product of the reactance and the maximum current. The direction of the phasor is determined by the phase angle and its relation to some common reference.

For the RLC circuit of Fig. 2.29, the voltage drop across the inductance may be arbitrarily assumed greater than that across the capacitor. The total voltage drop in the circuit is then given as the phasor addition of the three individual potential difference components. This is illustrated in Fig. 2.31.

The vector addition of the three phasors shows that the source voltage leads the current by an angle of ϕ degrees, i.e.

$$\overline{V} = V_m \sin(\omega t + \phi) \tag{2.51}$$

The circuit therefore is essentially inductive and using the standard notation the total phasor voltage is designated by a capital letter with an overscore.

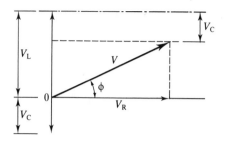

Figure 2.31 Phasor diagram for *RLC* circuit.

Complex Notation

Since inductive and capacitive elements in AC circuits involve a phase shift of $+90°$ and $-90°$, respectively, the complex number notation is used extensively to manipulate phasor quantities.

The complex operator j, defined as $\sqrt{-1}$, is a unit operator which, when multiplying a phasor, shifts it by $90°$ in an anti-clockwise direction. Thus for the series *RLC* circuit:

$$\overline{V}_R = \overline{I}R \qquad \overline{V}_L = j\overline{I}X_L \qquad \text{and} \quad \overline{V}_C = -j\overline{I}X_C$$

where $\overline{I}$ can be taken as the r.m.s. value of the current.

The voltage drop across the complete circuit can then be written as

$$\begin{aligned} \overline{V} &= \overline{I}R + j\overline{I}X_L - j\overline{I}X_C \\ &= \overline{I}[R + j(X_L - X_C)] \end{aligned} \qquad (2.52)$$

The term within the square brackets is called the 'impedance' of the circuit and is denoted by Z. Thus

$$\overline{V} = \overline{I}Z \qquad (2.53)$$

Equation (2.53) represents Ohm's law for AC circuits.

The phase angle between the source voltage and the current is given by

$$\phi = \tan^{-1}[(X_L - X_C)/R] \qquad (2.54)$$

The Parallel *RLC* Circuit

A parallel *RLC* circuit is shown in Fig. 2.32. The applied voltage is common to all of the circuit elements and is therefore chosen as the reference. Using Ohm's law, the currents through each of the circuit elements are

$$\overline{I}_R = \overline{V}/R \qquad \overline{I}_L = \overline{V}/X_L \qquad \overline{I}_C = \overline{V}/X_C$$

Applying Kirchhoff's first law, the total current is the vector sum of the three currents $\overline{I}_R$, $\overline{I}_L$ and $\overline{I}_C$.

The magnitude and phase of the total current may subsequently be determined from a phasor diagram, or calculated using the complex number notation. Using the latter, and noting that the current through an inductor lags the voltage while the current through a capacitor leads the voltage, it may be shown that

$$\begin{aligned} \overline{I} &= \overline{I}_R + \overline{I}_L + \overline{I}_C \\ &= \overline{V}\left[\frac{1}{R} + j\left[\frac{1}{X_L} - \frac{1}{X_C}\right]\right] \end{aligned} \qquad (2.55)$$

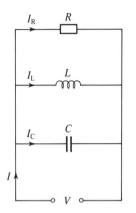

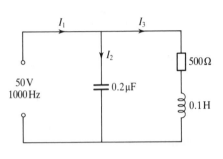

Figure 2.32 Parallel *RLC* circuit.   Figure 2.33 Circuit with AC supply.

and the phase angle is given by

$$\phi = \tan^{-1}\left[\frac{R(X_\mathrm{L} - X_\mathrm{C})}{X_\mathrm{L}X_\mathrm{C}}\right] \tag{2.56}$$

Example In the circuit shown in Fig. 2.33, the supply voltage is 50 V at 1000 Hz. Determine the magnitude and phase of the current drawn from the supply.

$$X_\mathrm{L} = \omega L = 2\pi fL = 2\pi 1000 \times 0.1 = 628.3 \ \Omega$$

$$X_\mathrm{C} = 1/\omega C = 1/2\pi fC = 10^6/((2\pi 1000 \times 0.2) = 795.8 \ \Omega$$

Using the complex conjugate gives

$$\bar{I}_2 = \frac{50}{-\mathrm{j}795.8} \times \frac{\mathrm{j}795.8}{\mathrm{j}795.8} = \frac{\mathrm{j}(50 \times 795.8)}{(795.8)^2} = \mathrm{j}0.0628$$

$$\bar{I}_3 = \frac{50}{500 + \mathrm{j}628.3} \times \frac{500 - \mathrm{j}628.3}{500 - \mathrm{j}628.3} = \frac{25000 - \mathrm{j}(50 \times 628.3)}{[500^2 + 628.3^2]} = 0.0388 - \mathrm{j}0.0487$$

From Kirchhoff's first law

$$\bar{I}_1 = \bar{I}_2 + \bar{I}_3 = \mathrm{j}0.0628 + 0.0388 - \mathrm{j}0.0487$$
$$= 0.0388 + \mathrm{j}0.0141$$

Hence

$$\bar{I}_1 = \sqrt{(0.0388)^2 + (0.0141)^2} = 0.0413 \text{ A}$$

and

$$\phi = \tan^{-1}(0.0141/0.0388) = 19.97°$$

i.e. the source voltage leads the current by 19.97°.

Example In the circuit shown in Fig. 2.34, calculate the minimum and maximum current in the 2000 Ω resistor.

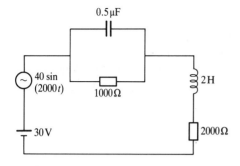

Figure 2.34 Circuit with AC and DC supply.

The AC and DC circuits can be treated individually and the results combined using the superposition principle.

$$X_L = \omega L = 2000 \times 2 = 4000 \ \Omega$$

$$X_C = 1/\omega C = 10^6/(2000 \times 0.5) = 1000 \ \Omega$$

DC circuit
The capacitor will block the DC component such that the DC circuit consists of two resistors connected in series. This gives a DC current of $30/(1000 + 2000) = 0.01$ A $= 10$ mA.

AC circuit
Combining the $2000 \ \Omega$ resistor and the inductor in series gives an impedance of

$$Z_1 = (2 + j4) \times 10^3 \ \Omega = (2 + j4) \ k\Omega$$

Combining the $1000 \ \Omega$ resistor and the capacitor in parallel gives an impedance of

$$1/Z_2 = 1/1000 + 1/-j1000 = (-j1000 + 1000)/(-j10^6)$$

Thus

$$Z_2 = \frac{-j10^6}{1000 - j1000} \times \frac{1000 + j1000}{1000 + j1000} = \frac{10^9 - j10^9}{2 \times 10^6} = 0.5 - j0.5 \ k\Omega$$

Z_1 and Z_2 are in series with an equivalent impedance of $Z_3 = Z_1 + Z_2$, i.e.

$$Z_3 = (2 + j4) + (0.5 - j0.5) = 2.5 + j3.5 \ k\Omega$$

$$I_{max} = V_{max}/Z_3 = \frac{40}{2.5 + j3.5} \times \frac{2.5 - j3.5}{2.5 - j3.5} = \frac{100 - j140}{6.25 + 12.25} = 5.4 - j7.57$$

Thus

$$I_{max} = \sqrt{(5.4)^2 + (7.57)^2} = 9.29 \text{ mA}$$

Note that the current is in mA because the impedances are quoted in $k\Omega$.
Therefore by superimposing the results for the DC and the AC circuits we obtain

$$\text{minimum current} = 10 - 9.29 = 0.71 \text{ mA}$$
$$\text{maximum current} = 10 + 9.29 = 19.29 \text{ mA}$$

In addition, the source voltage leads the current by $\tan^{-1}(7.57/5.4) = 54.5°$

Power and Power Factor in AC Circuits

Generally, for any AC circuit there will exist a phase difference between the voltage and the current. If the circuit elements are purely resistive, the phase difference will be zero. In all other cases the phase difference will be a finite positive or negative value. Denoting the phase angle between the voltage and the current as ϕ, it may be shown that the average power is given by

$$P_{av} = \frac{V_m}{\sqrt{2}} \frac{I_m}{\sqrt{2}} \cos(\phi)$$

In terms of r.m.s. values:

$$P_{av} = VI \cos(\phi) \tag{2.57}$$

The term $\cos(\phi)$ is called the 'power factor'.

Power factor is an important parameter when dealing with electrical transformers and generators. All such machines are rated in terms of kVA (kilovolt amperes), which is a measure of the current carrying capacity for a given applied voltage. The power that can be drawn depends both on the kVA rating and the power factor of the load. Figure 2.35 shows the relationship between kW, kVA and power factor, sometimes referred to as the power triangle.

It can readily be seen that

$$kW = kVA \cos(\phi) \tag{2.58}$$

and

$$kVA_r = kVA \sin(\phi) \tag{2.59}$$

where kVA_r is the reactive power.

Thus knowing the kVA rating and the power factor of a number of various loads, the power requirements from a common supply may be determined.

When quoting power factor in practical applications it is usual to state the phase of the current with respect to the voltage. For an inductive load the current lags the voltage and the power factor is said to be lagging. For a predominantly capacitive load the current leads the voltage and the power factor is leading.

If the power is supplied from say an alternator rated at 400 V and 1000 A, then these are the highest voltage and current that the machine can tolerate without overheating. The phase difference between the voltage and current is entirely dependent upon the load. Thus if the power factor of the load is unity then the 400 kVA alternator can supply 400 kW of power to the load. Neglecting losses, the prime mover which drives the alternator must also be capable of supplying 400 kW. If on the other hand the power factor of the load is 0.5, then the power supplied will only be 200 kW. This means that although the generator will be operating at its rated kVA, the prime mover which drives the generator will be operating at only half of its capacity.

An alternative way of looking at this phenomenon is to consider a load of say 100 kW, with a lagging power factor of 0.75. If the supply voltage is 50 V, then the required current, from Eq. (2.57), is 2.67 A. If, however, the power factor of the load were to be increased to unity, then the required current would be reduced to 2 A. This means that the conducting cables, in supplying a

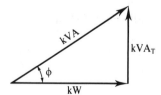

Figure 2.35 Power triangle.

reduced current, may have a correspondingly reduced cross-sectional area. In general, the size of an electrical system including transmission lines, switchgear and transformers is dependent upon the size of the current. It is economically viable therefore to ensure that the current is minimized. As a further incentive to industrial consumers, the electricity supply authorities normally operate a two-part tariff system. The two-part system consists of a fixed rate depending on the kVA rating of the maximum demand and a running charge per unit kilowatts consumed per hour.

For these reasons it is advantageous to try to increase the power factor such that it is close to, but not quite unity. A unity power factor is in fact avoided because it gives rise to a condition of resonance. In practice, capacitors, connected in parallel, are often used to improve the power factor of predominantly inductive loads such as electric motors. For large-scale power systems, a separate phase advance plant is used.

Example A factory has a load of 200 kVA at a power factor of 0.7 lagging. The supply voltage is 440 V at 50 Hz. Calculate the value of a capacitance which, when connected in parallel with this load, will improve the power factor to 0.9 lagging.
Considering first the original system without the additional capacitor:
Original current taken by the load is

$$I_1 = 200 \times 10^3 / 440 = 454.5 \text{ A}$$

Active component of this current is

$$454.5 \cos(\phi_1) = 454.5 \times 0.7 = 318.2 \text{ A}$$

Phase angle

$$\phi_1 = \cos^{-1}(0.7) = 45.6°$$

Reactive component of original current is

$$454.5 \sin(\phi_1) = 454.5 \sin(45.6) = 324.6 \text{ A}$$

Now consider the new circuit with the additional capacitor connected in parallel with the load:
The active component of the new current remains unchanged, but the power factor is increased, i.e. the active component is given by

$$318.2 = I_2 \cos(\phi_2) = I_2 \times 0.9$$

Thus

$$I_2 = 318.2 / 0.9 = 360.7 \text{ A}$$

The improved power factor gives a lower phase angle:

$$\phi_2 = \cos^{-1}(0.9) = 25.84°$$

The new reactive current is then

$$I_2 \sin(\phi_2) = 360.7 \times \sin(25.84) = 157.2 \text{ A}$$

By adding the capacitor in parallel with the load, the active component of the supply current does not change but the reactive current is reduced and the power factor improved. The current taken by the capacitor is the difference between the original and the new reactive currents, i.e. current taken by capacitor

$$I_C = 324.61 - 157.2 = 167.4 \text{ A}$$

also $I_C = 2\pi fCV$, hence

$$C = I_C(2\pi fV) = 167.4/(2\pi 50 \times 440) = 1211 \text{ μF}$$

Frequency Response of Circuits

Since both inductive and capacitive reactance are frequency dependent, it is clear that the output from circuits involving capacitive and inductive elements will also depend upon the frequency of the input signal.

The 'frequency response' of a circuit is usually presented as a plot of the ratio of output over input against the frequency as base. The ratio plotted could be one of voltages, currents or powers. Since the range of frequencies involved may be quite large, a logarithmic scale is normally employed. A logarithmic scale is also usually adopted for the vertical axis and the output/input ratio quoted in decibels, dB, i.e.

$$\text{voltage ratio in dB} = 20 \log_{10} \left[\frac{V_{\text{out}}}{V_{\text{in}}} \right] \tag{2.60}$$

Considering the series RLC circuit shown in Fig. 2.29 and taking the voltage across the resistor as an output:

$$V_{\text{out}} = IR$$
$$V_{\text{in}} = I[R + j(\omega L - 1/\omega C)]$$

Therefore

$$\frac{V_{\text{out}}}{V_{\text{in}}} = \frac{R}{R + j(\omega L - 1/\omega C)}$$

Using the complex conjugate and calculating the modulus of the voltage ratio gives

$$\left| \frac{V_{\text{out}}}{V_{\text{in}}} \right| = \frac{R}{[R^2 + (\omega L - 1/\omega C)^2]^{0.5}} \tag{2.61}$$

The phase angle is given by

$$\phi = -\tan^{-1} \left[\frac{(\omega L - 1/\omega C)}{R} \right] \tag{2.62}$$

From Eq. (2.61) it can be seen that the voltage ratio will have a maximum value of unity when the frequency is such that $(\omega L - 1/\omega C) = 0$. Equating this expression gives:

$$\omega = \frac{1}{\sqrt{LC}} \tag{2.63}$$

Equation (2.63) defines the so-called 'resonance' condition at which the inductive and capacitive reactances are equal and self cancelling. The resonant frequency is usually denoted ω_0 and it is the frequency at which the power transferred through the circuit is maximum. At any other frequency, above or below ω_0, the power transferred is reduced.

The impedance of the circuit is given by:

$$Z = R + j(X_L - X_C) \tag{2.64}$$

At the resonant frequency the total reactance is zero and the circuit behaves as if only the resistive element were present.

The general variation of the voltage ratio, or amplitude ratio, and phase angle with frequency is illustrated in Fig. 2.36.

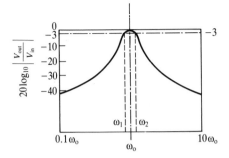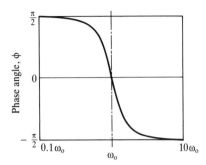

Figure 2.36 Voltage ratio and phase angle versus frequency (series *RLC*).

Also shown on Fig. 2.36 are the two frequencies, ω_1 and ω_2, at which the amplitude ratio is -3 dB. The -3 dB amplitude ratio is arbitrary but it is traditionally chosen because it corresponds to a halving in the power transmitted when the voltage ratio, $V_{\text{out}}/V_{\text{in}} = 1/\sqrt{2}$.

The 'bandwidth' is defined as the frequency range between ω_1 and ω_2.

2.11 THREE-PHASE CIRCUITS

Most electrical energy is generated in large power stations and then transmitted through the National Grid to the domestic and industrial consumers. The generation and transmission of electrical energy is based on a three-phase (3-ph), alternating current system and almost every device, apart from battery operated ones and general domestic appliances, rely on a three-phase system for their source of power.

Originally, DC machines were used to generate commercial power. However, DC machines are limited in the voltage they can generate. Because of their efficiency and performance, three-phase machines have emerged as the dominant type of electrical generator and motor and on a world-wide basis three-phase electrical distribution networks are the norm.

Generation of Three-phase E.M.F.s

Figure 2.37 shows three similar coils displaced at 120° relative to each other. Each loop terminates in a pair of 'slip-rings' and if the coils are to be isolated from one another, then six slip-rings are required in total. If the three coils are rotated in the anti-clockwise direction at constant speed, then each coil will generate a sinusoidally varying e.m.f. with a phase shift of 120° between them.

Star and Delta Connections

The three coils shown in Fig. 2.37 can be connected together in either of two symmetrical patterns. These are the 'star', or 'wye' connection, and the 'delta', or 'mesh' connection. The two types of connection are shown in Fig. 2.38.

The star pattern is made by joining R_0, Y_0 and B_0 together. This connection point is referred to as the 'neutral point'. The delta pattern is formed by connecting R_0 to Y_1, Y_0 to B_1 and B_0 to R_1.

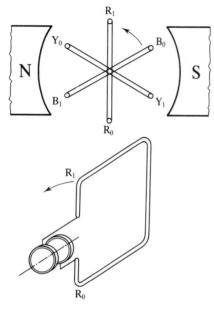

Figure 2.37 Generation of three-phase e.m.f.s.

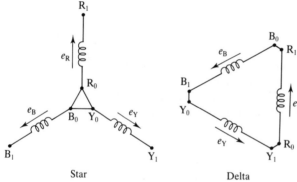

Star   Delta

Figure 2.38 Star and delta connections for three-phase systems.

Three-phase Voltage and Current Relations

Figure 2.39(*a*) shows a three-phase star-connected alternator supplying currents I_R, I_Y and I_B to a balanced, or equal, resistive load. The circuit is also shown redrawn (Fig. 2.39(*b*)) to highlight the use of four lines in the transmission cable. Since there are only four transmission cables involved, then the alternator connected in a star pattern will only require four slip-rings.

For a balanced system the phase voltages V_{RN}, V_{YN} and V_{BN} are all equal in magnitude and equally displaced by a phase angle of 120°. The currents I_R, I_Y and I_B are also equal in magnitude and equally displaced in phase angle but they all lag their respective phase voltages by some angle ϕ. Phasor addition of the currents show that the neutral current, I_N, is zero.

The voltages between the transmission cables are called the 'line' voltages. If the phase voltages are all equal then the phasor addition shows that the line voltages are given by

$$V_{\text{line}} = 2V_{\text{phase}} \cos(30)$$

or

$$V_L = \sqrt{3}\, V_P \tag{2.65}$$

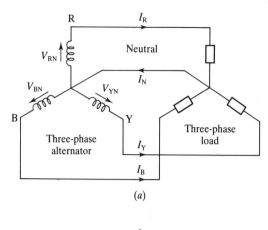

(a)

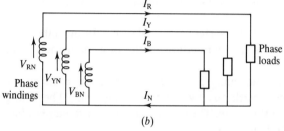

(b)

Figure 2.39 Three-phase supply connections.

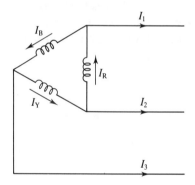

Figure 2.40 Alternator windings in delta connection.

For the star connection, the line currents, I_L, are equal to the phase currents, I_P.

Figure 2.40 shows the alternator windings connected in the delta pattern. In the delta pattern the line voltages are equal to the phase voltages. Phasor addition of the currents shows that if the phase currents are equal then the line currents are given by

$$I_L = \sqrt{3}\, I_P \tag{2.66}$$

Power in Three-phase Circuits

The power per phase is given by

$$P_{\text{phase}} = V_P I_P \cos(\phi) \tag{2.67}$$

where V_P = phase voltage, V
$\quad I_P$ = phase current, A
$\quad \phi$ = phase angle between V_P and I_P, degrees

The total power for a three-phase circuit is simply three times the power for one of the phases, i.e. three times Eq. (2.67).

For a star connection:

$$P = 3\,\frac{V_L}{\sqrt{3}}\,I_L\,\cos(\phi) = \sqrt{3}\,V_L I_L\,\cos(\phi) \qquad (2.68)$$

For the delta connection:

$$P = 3\,V_L\,\frac{I_L}{\sqrt{3}}\,\cos(\phi) = \sqrt{3}\,V_L I_L\,\cos(\phi)$$

The exact same relation is obtained. In terms of line voltages and currents therefore, the power in a three-phase circuit is independent of the winding connection and is given by Eq. (2.68).

Equation (2.68) does not apply, however, if the system is unbalanced. In an unbalanced system the total power can only be obtained as the summation of the powers in each of the individual phases.

The measurement of three-phase power is normally performed by connecting the current coils of two dynamometer wattmeters in series with any two of the supply lines. The voltage circuits of the wattmeters are connected to the third line. The sum of the two wattmeter readings then gives the average power supplied to the load.

In practice most sources of three-phase supply are connected in star whereas the loads may be either star-connected or delta-connected. The star-connected generator gives a neutral point which is advantageous when supplying an unbalanced star-connected load. The neutral point also ensures that each phase of the load receives the same applied voltage.

Example A 200 kVA, 3300 V alternator is delta-connected and supplies a balanced three-phase load at a power factor of 0.9 lagging. Determine the magnitude of the line currents.

Power supplied $=$ kVA $\cos(\phi) = 200 \times 0.9 = 180$ kW. From Eq. (2.68) the power may also be written as $\sqrt{3}V_L I_L\,\cos(\phi)$, thus

$$I_L = 180 \times 10^3/(\sqrt{3} \times 3300 \times 0.9) = 35\ \text{A}$$

Example A delta-connected load is arranged as shown in Fig. 2.41 and is supplied by a three-phase voltage of 415 V at 50 Hz. Calculate the phase currents, the line currents and the power consumed by the circuit.

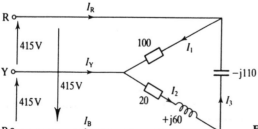

Figure 2.41 Delta-connected load.

Phase currents

$I_1 = 415/100 = 4.15$A, in phase with V_{RY}, i.e. $\phi_1 = 0$

$I_2 = 415/(\sqrt{20^2 + 60^2}) = 6.526$ A, lagging V_{YB} by $\phi_2 = \tan^{-1}(60/20) = 71.56°$

$I_3 = 415/110 = 3.773$ A, leading V_{BR} by $\phi_3 = 90°$

Power

Red phase $= V_{RY}I_1 \cos(\phi_1) = 415 \times 4.15 \times \cos(0) = 415 \times 4.15 = 1722.25$ W

Yellow phase $= V_{YB}I_2 \cos(\phi_2) = 415 \times 6.526 \times \cos(-71.56) = 856.7$ W

Blue phase $= V_{BR}I_3 \cos(\phi_3) = 415 \times 3.773 \times \cos(90) = 0$ W

The total power consumed is then $= (1722.25 + 856.7 + 0) = 2579$ W $= 2.58$ kW

Line currents

From Kirchhoff's first law, the line current I_R is given as the phasor subtraction of $I_1 - I_3$. The phasor relation between the phase voltages and currents are shown in Fig. 2.42. To obtain the phasor subtraction $I_1 - I_3$, the direction of I_3 is reversed and this is added vectorially to I_1 as shown. Consideration of the geometry gives

$$dl = 3.773 \sin(30) = 1.8865$$
$$dh = 1.8865/\tan(30) = 3.2675$$

Thus

$$I_R = \sqrt{(1.8865)^2 + (4.15 + 3.2675)^2} = 7.654 \,\text{A}$$

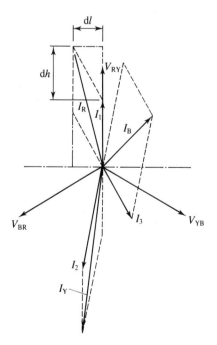

Figure 2.42 Phasor relationship between voltages and currents for circuit of Fig. 2.41.

Similarly the line current I_Y is given as the phasor substraction of $I_2 - I_1$. Consideration of the geometry results in

$$I_Y = 10.66\,\text{A}$$

Lastly, I_B is obtained from the phasor subtraction of $I_3 - I_2$. Consideration of the geometry gives

$$I_B = 4.5\,\text{A}$$

2.12 TRANSFORMERS

Transformers utilize the phenomenon of mutual inductance to increase or decrease an alternating voltage. Transformers incorporate a laminated iron core and have no dynamically moving parts. Since they involve a magnetic circuit, AC voltages, and form the basic element in most DC power supplies, it is appropriate that they are considered in this section as an integrated practical application of some fundamental principles of electrical technology.

In the United Kingdom, common practice for power distribution systems is to generate voltages at 11–22 kV. Transformation up to 33 kV, or 132 kV, precedes transmission on the National Grid to the consumer centres. At these centres, the voltages are then transformed back down to 415 V, or 240 V, and finally distributed to the industrial and domestic users.

Basic Transformer Action

Figure 2.43 illustrates a simple single-phase transformer in which two separate coils are wound onto a ferrous core.

The coil which is connected to the supply is called the 'primary winding' and that which is connected to the load is called the 'secondary winding'. The ferrous core is made in laminations, which are insulated from one another, to reduce eddy current losses.

If a sinusoidal voltage V_1 is applied across the primary winding, a current I_1 in the coil will induce a magnetic flux ϕ in the core. From Faraday's law, Eq. (2.25), the induced e.m.f. in the primary coil is given by

$$E_1 = N_1(\mathrm{d}\phi/\mathrm{d}t) \tag{2.69}$$

Since the magnetic flux is common to both coils then the e.m.f. induced in the secondary winding is given by

$$E_2 = N_2(\mathrm{d}\phi/\mathrm{d}t) \tag{2.70}$$

Hence

$$\frac{E_1}{E_2} = \frac{N_1}{N_2} \tag{2.71}$$

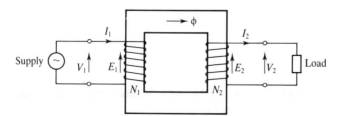

Figure 2.43 Single-phase transformer.

The ratio of primary coil turns to secondary coil turns, N_1/N_2, is called the 'transformation ratio'.

The primary and secondary winding impedances, Z_1 and Z_2, respectively, are both very small such that when the secondary winding is on open circuit, then $V_1 = E_1$ and $V_2 = E_2$. Therefore

$$\frac{V_1}{V_2} = \frac{N_1}{N_2} \qquad (2.72)$$

In Eqs (2.71) and (2.72) there is an implicit assumption that there is no loss of magnetic flux round the core. In practice there are some losses but these are fairly minor. Equation (2.72) then describes the basic function of a transformer whereby the load voltage, V_2, can be either stepped up or stepped down depending on the ratio of turns on the primary and second coils.

When a load is connected across the secondary winding a current, I_2, will flow in the secondary winding. From Lenz's law, this will set up a flux which will tend to oppose the main flux, ϕ. If the main flux is reduced then E_1 would be correspondingly reduced and the primary current, I_1 would then increase. The increased primary current would tend to produce a flux to oppose that induced by the secondary current. In this manner the main flux is generally maintained. In steady state, the ampere-turns in the primary and secondary windings are balanced, i.e.

$$I_1 N_1 = I_2 N_2$$

or

$$\frac{I_1}{I_2} = \frac{N_2}{N_1} \qquad (2.73)$$

Transformer Voltage Equation

In normal operation, the flux may be considered to be a sinusoidally varying quantity, i.e.

$$\phi = \Phi_m \sin(\omega t) \qquad (2.74)$$

where Φ_m is the maximum flux and ω is the circular frequency in rad/s.

The induced e.m.f., from Faraday's law, is given by, for the primary side

$$e = N_1(\mathrm{d}\phi/\mathrm{d}t) = N_1 \omega \Phi_m \cos(\omega t) = N_1 2\pi f \Phi_m \cos(\omega t)$$

where f is the frequency in Hz. The r.m.s. value of the induced e.m.f. is

$$E_1 = \frac{2}{\sqrt{2}} \pi f N_1 \Phi_m = 4.44 f N_1 \Phi_m \qquad (2.75)$$

Similarly for the secondary side,

$$E_2 = 4.44 f N_2 \Phi_m$$

In the design of a transformer, the number of coils used in each winding is chosen such that the maximum flux density does not approach values close to the saturation value. For this reason, Eq. (2.75) is often expressed generally as

$$E = 4.44 f N B_m A \qquad (2.76)$$

where B_m is the maximum allowable magnetic flux and A is the chosen cross-sectional area for the iron core.

Example A single-phase transformer, 415/22 000 V at 50 Hz, has a core area of 100 000 mm^2 and a maximum operating flux of 1.2 tesla. Determine the number of turns required in each winding.

$E_1 = 4.44fN_1B_mA$, thus

$$N_1 = E_1/(4.44fB_mA) = 415/(4.44 \times 50 \times 1.2 \times 0.01) = 155.8 = 156$$

Note that the number of turns is always rounded up to the nearest whole number. Also

$$N_2 = N_1(V_2/V_1) = 156(415/22000) = 8270$$

Transformer Losses

Equations (2.72) and (2.73) define the ideal transformer in which there are no resistive, or inductive losses. An actual transformer does, of course, involve some losses which are defined as:

1. *I^2R losses.* The I^2R loss, formerly termed the 'copper loss', is associated with the power dissipated in the windings of the transformer. In large power transformers, the windings are usually immersed in oil in order to dissipate the heat generated through the I^2R loss.
2. *Core losses.* These are associated with magnetic hysteresis effects and eddy current losses in the core. The core losses are essentially constant for a particular value of supply voltage but they are highly dependent upon the supply frequency, increasing generally with the square of the frequency.
3. *Flux leakage.* The useful, or main flux, is that which effectively links both coils. In practice some of the flux will escape, or otherwise fail to link both coils. The e.m.f.s produced by the leakage fluxes are proportional to, and leading the fluxes by 90°. The effect of flux leakage may be likened to having an additional inductive coil in series with the primary and secondary coils. In practice, the flux leakage loss is usually lumped together with the core loss.

Determination of Transformer Losses

Open-circuit test The secondary coil is on open-circuit and the full rated voltage is applied to the primary winding. The transformer takes a small no-load current to supply the core loss and the copper losses are essentially zero. Since the normal voltage and frequency are applied, a wattmeter connected to the primary side will give a measure of the core loss. The core loss can then be taken as a constant irrespective of the load.

Closed-circuit test With the secondary winding short-circuited the transformer requires only a small input voltage to circulate the full load current. The wattmeter, on the primary side then gives an indication of the full load I^2R losses. If the load is expressed as a fraction of the full load, then the I^2R losses at reduced loads are proportional to the load squared. At half load, for example, the I^2R losses are one quarter of the full load value.

Referred Values

In dealing with transformers it is usual to base all calculations on one side of the transformer. Parameters on the negelcted side are accounted for by 'referring' them over to the side on which the calculation is to be based. The transformation ratio is used to scale the equivalent values.

For example, the I^2R loss on the secondary side can be referred to the primary side through the relation

$$I_2'^2 R_2' = I_2^2 R_2 \diagup \tag{2.77}$$

where the prime denotes the referred values. Using Eq. (2.73) the referred resistance becomes

$$R_2' = \{N_1/N_2\}^2 R_2 \tag{2.78}$$

Thus Eq. (2.78) gives an equivalent resistance, R_2', in the primary side which accounts for the actual resistance, R_2, of the secondary winding. Reactances may be similarly referred to one, or other side of the transformer for calculation purposes.

Example A 10/1 step-down transformer has a load resistance of $100\,\Omega$ connected to the secondary coil. Determine the equivalent resistance referred to the primary side.
Using Eq. (2.78)

$$R_e = (10/1)^2 R_L = (10/1)^2 \times 100 = 10^4\,\Omega = 10\,k\Omega$$

Example If the $100\,\Omega$ resistor in the previous example is replaced with a $4\,\mu F$ capacitor, determine the equivalent capacitance referred to the primary side.

$$Z_2 = 1/(2\pi fC) = 1/(2\pi f4 \times 10^{-6}) = 397\,88.7/f$$
$$Z_e = (10/1)^2 Z_2 = 397\,88.7 \times 100/f$$
$$C_2' = 1/(2\pi fZ_e) = f/(2\pi f397\,887\,0) = 0.04\,\mu F$$

Note that since it is the capacitive reactance which is scaled by the square of the transformation ratio, then the referred capacitance is 100 times smaller than the secondary side capacitance.

Transformer Efficiency

The transformer efficiency, as with any machine, is the ratio of the output power to the input power. The difference between the output and the input power is the sum of the losses, which for the case of a transformer are the I^2R and the core losses; i.e.

$$\eta = \frac{\text{output}}{\text{input}} = \frac{\text{output}}{\text{output} + I^2R\,\text{loss} + \text{core loss}}$$

Therefore

$$\eta = \frac{V_2 I_2 \cos(\phi_2)}{V_2 I_2 \cos(\phi_2) + I_2^2 R_e + C_e} \tag{2.79}$$

Note that R_e represents an equivalent resistance which consists of the resistance of the secondary winding and the resistance of the primary winding referred over to the secondary side, i.e.

$$R_e = R_2 + (N_2/N_1)^2 R_1 \tag{2.80}$$

The core loss, C_e, is assumed to be constant and $\cos(\phi_2)$ is the load power factor, also assumed constant.

By dividing the numerator and the denominator of Eq. (2.79) by I_2 and then differentiating the denominator with respect to I_2, and equating the result to zero, it can be shown that for maximum efficiency, $I_2^2 R_e = C_e$. Maximum transformer efficiency thus occurs when the I^2R

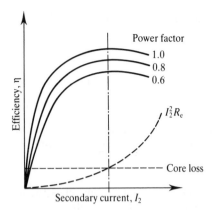

Figure 2.44 Transformer efficiency characteristics.

loss is equal to the core loss. The general efficiency characteristics for a transformer are shown in Fig. 2.44.

Because there are no mechanically moving parts, the efficiency of a transformer is generally very high except at the extremely low load conditions.

Equation (2.79) shows that the output will be influenced by the load power factor. At unity power factor the output, and hence also the efficiency, is maximized. As the power factor decreases, the transformer efficiency also decreases proportionally.

Example A 40 kVA single–phase transformer gave the following test results. With the secondary coil open-circuited the input power to the primary side was 2 kW. With the secondary winding close-circuited, the power supplied to the transformer with full load current flowing, was 4 kW. Calculate the efficiency of the transformer under the following conditions:

(i) full load unity power factor;
(ii) 50 per cent load, at a power factor of 0.8 lagging.

Determine also at which load the transformer will be operating at maximum efficiency.

The open circuit test gives the core loss, i.e.

$$\text{core loss} = 2\,\text{kW}$$

The close circuit test gives the full load I^2R loss, i.e.

$$I^2R \text{ loss} = 4\,\text{kW at full load}$$

At unity power factor, the full load output is $40 \times 1 = 40\,\text{kW}$, hence the efficiency is

$$40/(40 + 2 + 4) = 0.8695 = 87\%$$

At a power factor of 0.8 lagging, the 50 per cent load output is

$$40 \times 0.5 \times 0.8 = 16\,\text{kW}$$

The I^2R loss at 50 per cent load is $(0.5)^2 \times 4 = 1\,\text{kW}$, hence the efficiency is

$$16/(16 + 2 + 1) = 0.842 = 84.2\%$$

At maximum efficiency, the I^2R loss is equal to the core loss, thus

$$I^2R = 2\,\text{kW}$$

$$(x)^2 \times 4 = 2$$

$$x = \sqrt{(2/4)} = 0.707$$

The transformer then operates at maximum efficiency when the output is 70.7 per cent of full load.

Impedance Matching for Maximum Power Transfer

Figure 2.45 shows a DC source with an internal resistance R_i, connected in series to an external load of resistance R_L.

The current drawn by the circuit is

$$i = V/(R_i + R_L)$$

The power dissipated in the load resistor is

$$P = i^2 R_L = R_L V^2/(R_i + R_L)^2$$

or

$$P = R_L V^2 (R_i + R_L)^{-2}$$

Using the product rule and differentiating P with respect to R_L gives

$$\frac{\mathrm{d}P}{\mathrm{d}R_L} = V^2(R_i + R_L)^{-2} - 2R_L V^2 (R_i + R_L)^{-3}$$

Equating $\mathrm{d}P/\mathrm{d}R_L = 0$ gives

$$\frac{V^2}{(R_i + R_L)^2} = \frac{2R_L V^2}{(R_i + R_L)^3}$$

Hence $R_L = R_i$.

The reader may show, as an exercise, that the second derivative of P with respect to R_L is negative for the condition $R_L = R_i$. This is the necessary condition for a maximum and the power transferred to the load is therefore maximized when the load resistance is equal to the source resistance. This condition is also found to apply in AC circuits, where in addition to the load and source impedances being equal, they must also have the same phase relationship.

Since the impedance on one side of a transformer can be referred to the other side through the transformation ratio, then full advantage can be made of this fact to use a transformer as an

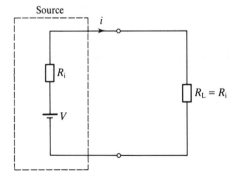

Figure 2.45 DC circuit for maximum power transfer.

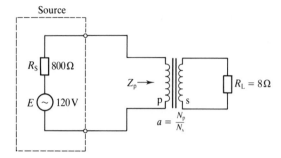

Figure 2.46 Use of a transformer for impedance matching.

impedance matching device. In this manner, the transformation ratio can be selected to ensure maximum power transfer to the load. The principle can be illustrated by consideration of the circuit depicted in Fig. 2.46.

For maximum power transfer, the load resistance should be 800 Ω. If the transformer were not included in the circuit, then the power transferred to the load would be

$$i^2 R_L = [E/(R_s + R_L)]^2 R_L = [120/(800 + 8)]^2 8 = 0.176\,\text{W} = 176\,\text{mW}$$

However, if a transformer is included in the circuit as shown, and the impedance referred to the primary side is $Z_p = 800\,\Omega$, then maximum power will be delivered, i.e.

$$Z_p = 800 = a^2 R_L$$

Therefore $a = \sqrt{(800/8)} = 10$, or $a = N_p/N_s = 10$. The primary current is

$$I_p = 120/(R_s + Z_p) = 120/(800 + 800) = 0.075\,\text{A}$$

The secondary current

$$I_s = a I_p = 10 \times 0.075 = 0.75\,\text{A}$$

Power transferred to the load resistance is

$$I_p^2 R_L = (0.75)^2 8 = 4.5\,\text{W}$$

The ratio of power transferred with the transformer in the circuit to that without the transformer is

$$4.5/0.176 = 25.6$$

Three-phase Transformers

Modern large three-phase transformers are usually constructed with three limbs as shown in Fig. 2.47. In the figure the primary windings are star-connected and the secondary windings are delta-connected. In actual fact, the primary and secondary windings can be connected in any pattern depending upon the condition under which the transformer is to operate. It is important, however, to know how the three-phase transformer is connected, particularly when two, or more, transformers are to be operated in parallel. It is essential, for instance, that parallel operation transformers belong in the same main group and that their voltage ratios are perfectly compatible.

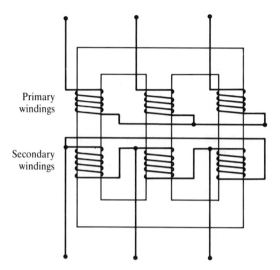

Figure 2.47 Three-phase transformer.

Auto-transformers

The auto-transformer is characterized by having part of its winding common to both the primary and secondary circuits, see Fig. 2.48. Neglecting losses and leakage, the transformation ratio is

$$a = V_2/V_1 = I_1/I_2 = N_2/N_1$$

The current in CB of the winding is the resultant of I_1 and I_2. These currents are essentially in phase opposition and since I_2 is greater than I_1, the resultant current is $(I_2 - I_1)$.

The main application of the auto-transformer is to provide a variable voltage and as such it is often called a 'variac'. These are used, for example, to limit the starting current drawn by an induction motor.

A major disadvantage of the auto-transformer is that the primary and secondary windings are not electrically isolated from one another. This presents a serious risk of electric shock and auto-transformers should not be used for interconnecting high-voltage and low-voltage systems.

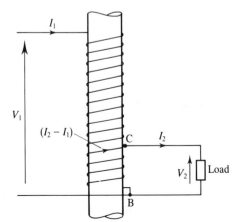

Figure 2.48 Auto-transformer.

REFERENCES

BS 3939 (1986) *Guide for Graphical Symbols for Electrical Power, Telecommunications and Electronics Diagrams*, Part 1 of 13 parts, British Standards Institution, London.
PD 5686 (1970) *The International System of Units*, British Standards Institution, London.

FURTHER READING

Bell, D. A. (1984) *Fundamentals of Electric Circuits*, 3rd edn, Reston Publishing Co. Ltd, Prentice-Hall, Reston, Virginia.
Hughes, W. (1987) *Electrical Technology*, 6th edn, revised by I. McKenzie Smith, Longman, London.
McKenzie Smith, I. (1978) *Electrical and Electronic Principles, Level 2*, Longman Technician Series, Electrical & Electronic Engineering, Longman, London.
McKenzie Smith, I. (1979) *Electrical and Electronic Principles, Level 3*, Longman Technician Series, Electrical & Electronic Engineering, Longman, London.

EXERCISES

2.1 Figure Q2.1 shows a resistive circuit powered by a 120 V battery. Determine:
  (*a*) the current drawn from the battery;
  (*b*) the potential difference across the 15 kΩ resistor;
  (*c*) the magnitude and direction of the current through PR.

[11.2 mA, 81.7 V, 3.27 mA from P to R]

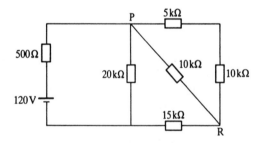

Figure Q2.1

2.2 A resistance of 5 Ω is connected in series with two resistors of 10 Ω and 20 Ω connected in parallel. A potential difference of 100 V is applied across the whole circuit. Determine the power dissipated in each resistor and the voltage across the 5 Ω resistor.

[368 W, 164 W, 328 W, 42.8 V]

2.3 Figure Q2.3 shows a resistive circuit. Calculate the power supplied to the circuit and the power dissipated in the 12 Ω resistor.

[6.72 W, 7.85 mW]

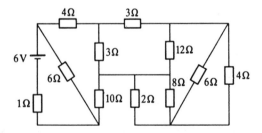

Figure Q2.3

2.4 For the circuit shown in Fig. Q2.4, determine the magnitude and direction of the current in the 1000 Ω resistor.

[17.6 μA]

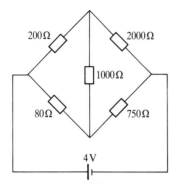

Figure Q2.4

2.5   In the circuit shown in Fig. Q2.5, determine:
   (*a*) the capacitance of capacitor A;
   (*b*) the charge on capacitor B;
   (*c*) the total voltage required to sustain the configuration of voltages and charges.

[0.2 F, 0.75 coulombs, 198.8 V]

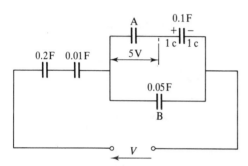

Figure Q2.5

2.6   Calculate the energy stored in the circuit shown in Fig. Q2.6.

[2.9 J]**2.7**

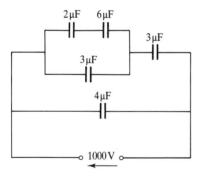

Figure Q2.6

Two parallel metal plates are placed 6 mm apart. Between the plates is a glass sheet 2.5 mm thick and of relative permittivity 7. The remainder of the dielectric consists of an air gap. If there is a uniform charge of 15 microcoulombs per square metre between the metal plates, determine the potential difference which is applied between the plates.

[6543 V]

2.8   In the network shown in Fig. Q2.8, determine the current flowing in each branch and hence determine the value of V_{AB}.

[$V_{AB} = -25.4$ V]

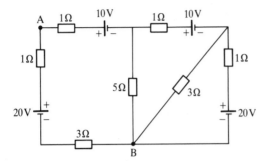

Figure Q2.8

2.9 A conductor of active length 300 mm carries a current of 100 A and lies at right angles to a magnetic field of flux density 0.4 tesla. Calculate the force exerted on the conductor. If the force causes the conductor to move at a velocity of 10 m/s, calculate:

(a) the e.m.f. induced in the conductor;
(b) the power developed.

[12 N, 1.2 V, 120 W]

2.10 A coil of 1500 turns gives rise to a magnetic flux of 2.5 mWb when carrying a certain current. If this current is reversed in 0.2 s, determine the average value of the e.m.f. induced in the coil.

[37.5 V]

2.11 A cast steel ring of cross-sectional area 650 mm² is closely wound with 200 turns of insulated wire and includes an air gap of length 1.6 mm. The mean length of the magnetic flux path is 250 mm and the *B–H* characteristic of the material is given as

$$H = 2430(B) - 3760(B)^2 + 2100(B)^3$$

Calculate the current required to produce a flux of 0.1 mWb and the self-inductance of the coil.

[1.345 A, 14.9 mH]

2.12 A magnetic circuit made of cast steel is arranged as shown in Fig. Q2.12. The centre limb has a cross-sectional area 800 mm² and each of the side limbs have a cross-sectional area of 500 mm². The centre limb carries a coil of 100 turns and incorporates an air gap of length 1 mm. The *B–H* characteristic for the material is the same as that given in question 2.11. Calculate the current required to produce a magnetic flux of 0.1 mWb in the centre limb.

[2.07 A]

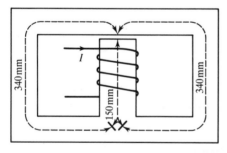

Figure Q2.12

2.13 A circuit consists of a single coil of resistance 0.05 Ω and inductance 0.5 H. If a DC supply of 10 V is suddenly switched on, determine:

(a) the time constant of the circuit;
(b) the final steady-state current;
(c) the induced e.m.f. in the coil after 5 s;
(d) the potential difference across the coil after 5 s;
(e) the time taken for the current to reach 50 per cent and 98 per cent of the final steady-state value.

[10 s, 200 A, 6.06 V, 10 V, 6.93 s, 40 s]

2.14 A coil of resistance $10\,\Omega$ and inductance $0.1\,H$ is connected in series with a $50\,\mu F$ capacitor to an AC supply of frequency $50\,Hz$. The potential difference across the capacitor measures $180\,V$. Calculate:

    (*a*) the supply voltage;

    (*b*) the voltage across the coil;

    (*c*) the power factor of the circuit;

    (*d*) the power factor of the coil;

    (*e*) the power dissipated in the circuit.

                           [99.5 V, 93.2 V, 0.295 leading, 0.303 lagging, 80 W]

2.15 An alternating voltage, $(80 + j60)\,V$ is applied to a circuit and the current which flows is $(-4 + j10)\,A$. Determine the impedance of the circuit, the power dissipated and the phase angle.

                          [$9.28\,\Omega$, 280 W, 75° leading]

2.16 A circuit consists of a $500\,\Omega$ resistor connected in series with a $0.2\,\mu F$ capacitor. A $0.25\,H$ inductor is then connected in parallel with these two elements and the supply voltage is $20\,V$ at $1000\,Hz$. Determine the magnitude and phase of the current drawn from the supply and the power dissipated in the circuit.

                          [12.5 mA, 25° lagging, 226.5 mW]

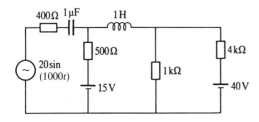

Figure Q2.17

2.17 For the circuit shown in Fig. Q2.17, determine the maximum and minimum values of the current in the inductor.

                                      [10.52 mA, 0.22 mA]

2.18 A single-phase, $10\,kW$ motor operates off a $415\,V$, $50\,Hz$ supply. The power factor is 0.75 lagging. Determine the capacitance required to be connected in parallel with the motor to improve the power factor to 0.9 lagging.

                                          [73.5 μF]

2.19 An induction motor load of $1500\,W$ at a power factor of 0.75 lagging is combined with a load of $500\,VA$ at a power factor of 0.65 leading. Determine the overall power factor and the value of kVA_r required to make the overall power factor equal to 0.95 lagging.

                                    [0.89 lagging, 0.35 kVA_r]

2.20 A series resonant circuit consists of a $25\,mH$ inductor, a $0.1\,\mu F$ capacitor and a $15\,\Omega$ resistor. Determine:

    (*a*) the resonant frequency;

    (*b*) the current drawn at resonance when the supply voltage is $10\,V$;

    (*c*) the potential difference across the inductor and capacitor at resonance.

                                    [3183 Hz, 0.667 A, 333.5 V]

2.21 A resistor and capacitor are connected in series with a variable inductor. When the circuit is connected to a $200\,V$, $50\,Hz$ supply the maximum current obtainable by varying the inductance is $0.314\,A$. The potential difference across the capacitor is then equal to $300\,V$. Determine the values of the circuit parameters.

                                 [3.3 μF, 3.04 H, 637 ohms]

2.22 Three $18\,\Omega$ resistors are connected in delta to a balanced $415\,V$, three-phase supply. Determine the phase currents, the line currents and the power consumed.

                                  [23.05 A, 39.86 A, 28.64 kW]

2.23 Three $20\,\Omega$ resistors are connected in delta to a $415\,V$, three-phase supply. Calculate:

    (*a*) the total power dissipated in the circuit;

    (*b*) the total power dissipated if the resistors were connected in star to the same supply.

                                    [25.8 kW, 8.61 kW]

2.24 Figure Q2.24 shows a four-wire cable supplying a star-connected unbalanced load. The phase voltages are balanced at $240\,V$. Determine the power consumed and the magnitude and phase of the line and neutral currents, quoting phase angles relative to V_R.

      [$13.54kW$, $I_R = 44.57\underline{/+68.2°}$, $I_Y = 42.43\underline{/-165°}$, $I_B = 28.09\underline{/50.55°}$, $I_N = 52.5\underline{/97.2°}$]

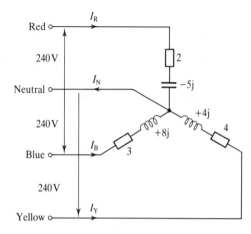

Figure Q2.24

2.25 A step-up transformer contains a load resistor of $500\,\Omega$ and a load coil of $2\,H$, both connected in series with the secondary winding of the transformer. If the transformation ratio is $1/5$, and the supply frequency is $50\,Hz$, determine the equivalent resistance and inductance referred to the primary side of the transformer.

[$20\,\Omega$, $80\,mH$]

2.26 A $50\,kVA$, $5000/500\,V$, $50\,Hz$ transformer gave the following results under test conditions. With the low voltage winding open-circuited, the input power to the high voltage side was $800\,W$. With the low voltage winding close-circuited, the power supplied to the transformer, with full load current flowing, was $1200\,W$. Determine the efficiency of the transformer at $1/4$, $1/2$, $3/4$, 1, and $5/4$ load when

(a) the load power factor is unity;

(b) the load power factor is 0.8 lagging.

Determine also the percentage load at which the transformer is operating at maximum efficiency.

[93.45, 95.8, 96.2, 96.15, 93.2; 92, 94.8, 95.3, 95.2, 91.7; 81.65%]

2.27 A $400\,kVA$ transformer has a core loss of $2\,kW$ and the maximum efficiency at 0.8 power factor lagging occurs when the load is $240\,kW$. Calculate:

(a) the maximum efficiency at unity power factor;

(b) the efficiency on full load at 0.7 power factor.

[98.8%, 98.05%]

2.28 An AC source of $100\,V$, and internal resistance $576\,\Omega$ is to power a load resistance of $9\,\Omega$. Determine the transformation ratio of a transformer connected between the source and the load to give maximum power transfer. Determine also the power transferred to the load resistor with and without the transformer in the circuit.

[8, $263\,mW$, $4.34\,W$]

2.29 A three-phase transformer has 500 turns on the primary winding and 43 turns on the secondary winding. The supply voltage is $3300\,V$. Determine the secondary line voltage on no load when:

(a) the windings are connected star/delta;

(b) the windings are connected delta/star.

[$164\,V$, $491\,V$]

THREE

ANALOGUE ELECTRONICS

3.1 SEMICONDUCTORS

Semiconductors can be described as those materials which have a resistivity in the mid-range between that of a good conductor and that of a good insulator. In this respect, a semiconductor possesses none of the qualities which would make it particularly suitable as either an insulator, or a conductor. Semiconductors do however exhibit a resistive sensitivity to the polarity of an applied voltage and it is this characteristic which has promoted their extensive use in the electronics industries.

The common materials used for semiconductors are germanium and silicon. In recent times silicon has all but replaced germanium as a semiconductor material. The semiconductor materials have a crystalline structure such that each atom is surrounded by equally spaced neighbours. The basic structure can be visualized as a two-dimensional grid where the node points represent the central nucleus and the inner shell electrons, while the connecting lines of the grid represent the four valence electrons associated with each nucleus. For a tightly packed atomic structure, such as silicon, each valence electron is shared between two nuclei. It follows therefore that each positive nucleus has four electron pairs surrounding it. These electron pairs are referred to as covalent bonds, and they serve to keep the nuclei together in the crystalline structure. This grid concept adequately describes an intrinsic, or 'pure' semiconductor.

At absolute zero temperature the crystalline structure is perfect and the electrons are all strongly held in covalent bonds. Since there are no current carriers available, the crystal behaves as a perfect insulator. As the temperature rises above absolute zero an increasing number of valence bonds are broken, releasing pairs of free electrons and their associated 'holes'. In the absence of an applied field the free electrons move randomly in all directions. When an electric field is applied the electrons drift in a preferential direction to oppose the field and a net flow of current is established. The resistivity of the semiconductor therefore decreases with increasing temperature.

The covalent bond, with a missing electron, has a large affinity for electrons such that an electron from a neighbouring bond may easily be captured. This will leave the neighbouring atom depleted of electrons and the flow of electrons is generally associated with a counterflow of so-called holes. The mobile hole, to all intents and purposes, is essentially a simple positive charge.

Doped Semiconductors

Doped semiconductors are those in which an impurity has been introduced into a very pure intrinsic silicon. The nature of the impurity depends on the type of semiconductor required.

n-type. Impurities with five valence electrons, such as arsenic, phosphorous or antimony, can be added to produce a negative type of semiconductor. These impurities are referred to as 'donors' since the additional electron is very easily freed within the matrix. The conductivity of the semiconductor is considerably increased and, in the n-type semiconductor, the free electrons are the dominant current carriers.

p-type. The p-type semiconductor is one in which the added impurities have only three valence electrons. Materials such as indium, boron, gallium and aluminium are all used to form the impurity within the matrix. Such impurities are called 'acceptors' and they produce a positive type of semiconductor within which hole conduction is the dominant current carrier.

pn Junction Diode

A pn junction is formed by doping a crystal in such a way that the semiconductor changes from p-type to n-type over a very short length, typically 10^{-6} m. The transition zone from p-type to n-type is called the 'carrier depletion layer', and due to the high concentrations of holes on one side and electrons on the other, a potential difference exists across this layer. The diffusion of holes from p to n and electrons from n to p is the majority carrier movement, called the 'diffusion current'. The drift of electrons from p to n and holes from n to p is the minority carrier movement referred to as the 'drift current'. When there is no externally applied potential difference, the diffusion current and the drift current are balanced in equilibrium. If an electric field is applied across the device then two situations can exist as illustrated in Fig. 3.1.

Figure 3.1(*a*) shows the reverse bias mode in which the potential barrier is increased. The diffusion current is reduced while the drift current is barely altered. Overall the current is negative and very small. When forward bias is applied, as in Fig. 3.1(*b*), the potential barrier is reduced and a large diffusion current flows. The rapid rise in current, in the forward bias mode, only occurs when the potential difference exceeds a threshold value. For silicon-based semiconductors, the threshold voltage is about 0.7 V. For applied voltages above the threshold value, the current is positive and large. These general characteristics are the basis of a semiconductor diode which displays the typical current/voltage relationships depicted in Fig. 3.2.

Figure 3.2 shows clearly that a very high impedance is presented by the diode to an applied voltage of reverse polarity. A low impedance is presented to a forward polarity voltage. In

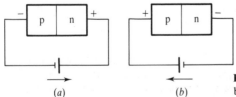

(*a*) (*b*)

Figure 3.1 pn junction with applied potential difference: (*a*) reverse biased; (*b*) forward biased.

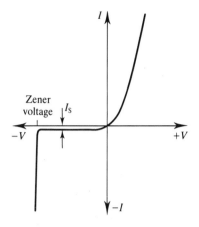

Figure 3.2 Current/voltage relationship for a pn semiconductor diode.

simple terms, the diode accommodates a forward flow of current but greatly inhibits a reverse flow. The diode may be likened therefore to a switch which is activated 'on' for forward voltages and 'off' for reverse voltages. The reverse saturation current, I_s, is typically of the order of a few nano-amperes and can sensibly be regarded as zero.

The general characteristic also shows that the reverse voltage has a critical limiting value at which a 'breakdown' occurs. Depending upon the diode construction, the breakdown, or 'Zener' voltage may range from as low as one volt to as much as several thousand volts. Up to the breakdown voltage, the reverse saturation current is independent of the reverse voltage.

Since the current/voltage relationship for a diode is a nonlinear exponential function, the analysis of circuits involving diodes can become complicated. A simple awareness of the diode's practical function as a rectifier is perhaps more important than a proficiency in the analysis of circuits involving diode elements.

AC rectification Figure 3.3 shows an AC circuit with a diode in series with a load resistor. When the diode is forward biased a current flows in the direction indicated by the arrowhead. No current can flow when the diode is reverse biased, provided, of course, that the applied voltage does not exceed the breakdown value. The resultant current waveform through the resistor, for a sinusoidal voltage input, will therefore consist of positive only half-sine-waves. Since the output waveform is positive only, then it is by definition a DC voltage. The r.m.s. voltage across the resistor is given by

$$V^2 = \frac{1}{2\pi} \int_0^\pi \frac{R_L^2}{(R_F + R_L)^2} \, V_m^2 \sin^2(\omega t) \, \mathrm{d}(\omega t)$$

Note that over the period from π to 2π, the voltage across the load resistor is zero. As a result, the integration is carried out over the period from zero to π only, where the load resistor voltage is finite and positive.

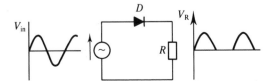

Figure 3.3 Half-wave rectification circuit.

Replacing $\sin^2(\omega t)$ with $0.5[1 - \cos(2\omega t)]$ and integrating gives

$$V = \frac{V_m}{2} \times \frac{R_L}{R_L + R_F} \tag{3.1}$$

where R_L = load resistance
R_F = diode forward resistance
V_m = peak input voltage
The average, or DC voltage is given by

$$
\begin{aligned}
V_{DC} &= \frac{1}{2\pi} \int_0^\pi \frac{R_L}{(R_F + R_L)} V_m \sin(\omega t) \, d(\omega t) \\
&= \frac{V_m}{2\pi} \times \frac{R_L}{R_F + R_L} [- \cos(\omega t)]_0^\pi \\
&= \frac{V_m}{2\pi} \times \frac{R_L}{R_F + R_L} [-(-1) + (1)] \\
V_{DC} &= \frac{V_m}{\pi} \times \frac{R_L}{R_F + R_L}
\end{aligned}
\tag{3.2}
$$

Determination of R_F is problematic, however, and models of varying complexity are used to simulate the diode in the circuit.

The single-diode circuit results in half-wave rectification. To obtain full-wave rectification, a diode bridge circuit can be used. The diode bridge is shown in Fig. 3.4. When A is positive with respect to B then diodes D_1 and D_3 are conducting. When B is positive with respect to A then diode D_2 and D_4 are conducting. The circuit arrangement ensures that the current, which consists of a continuous series of positive half-sine-waves, is always in the same direction through the load R_L.

With full-wave rectification there are twice as many half-sine-pulses through the load as there are with half-wave rectification. In addition, there are always two diodes effectively in series with the load. The resultant r.m.s. voltage across the load resistor for the full-wave diode bridge rectification circuit is given by

$$V^2 = \frac{1}{\pi} \int_0^\pi \frac{R_L^2}{(R_L + 2R_F)^2} V_m^2 \sin^2(\omega t) \, d(\omega t)$$

Integration then gives

$$V = \frac{V_m}{\sqrt{2}} \times \frac{R_L}{(R_L + 2R_F)} \tag{3.3}$$

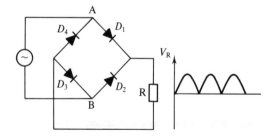

Figure 3.4 Full-wave rectification using a diode bridge.

The average voltage is given by

$$V_{DC} = \frac{1}{\pi} \int_0^{\pi} \frac{R_L}{(R_L + 2R_F)} V_m \sin(\omega t) \, d(\omega t)$$

$$V_{DC} = \frac{2V_m}{\pi} \times \frac{R_L}{(R_L + 2R_F)}$$

(3.4)

The 'peak inverse voltage' (PIV) is defined as the maximum reverse bias voltage appearing across a diode. When used as a rectifier then, the diodes must have a significantly high reverse voltage rating in excess to the peak inverse voltage that the circuit can generate. For both the half- and the full-wave rectification circuits considered, the peak inverse voltage is equivalent to the negative peak supply voltage, V_m. Additional manufacturer's diode specifications would normally include the maximum power rating and the maximum allowable forward current. The maximum forward current will largely determine the value of load resistance, R_L, which must be at least equal to V/I to avoid burnout of the diode.

The Zener Diode

The diode breakdown effect is also used in a variety of circuits to provide a stabilized reference voltage. Special diodes which are designed to operate continuously in the reverse bias mode are called 'Zener diodes'. These diodes are manufactured with a range of breakdown voltages from three to seventy volts. Figure 3.5 shows a Zener diode being used in a circuit to give a stable voltage which is essentially independent of the current flowing through the device. The series resistor in the circuit is included to limit the reverse current through the diode to a safe value.

3.2 THE TRANSISTOR

The Bipolar, or Junction Transistor

Originally developed in 1948, the transistor has revolutionized electronics and has influenced almost every aspect of life in the industrialized world. The term transistor, derived from 'transfer resistor', describes a device which can transfer a current from a low resistance circuit to a high resistance circuit with little change in current during the process. The junction transistor consists of two pn diodes formed together with one common section, making it a three-layer device, see Fig. 3.6.

Current flow in the transistor is due to both electron and hole conduction. The common central section is referred to as the 'base' and is typically of the order of 25 µm in length. Since the base can be made either in n-type, or a p-type semiconductor, then two basic configurations

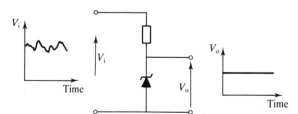

Figure 3.5 Zener diode as a reference voltage source.

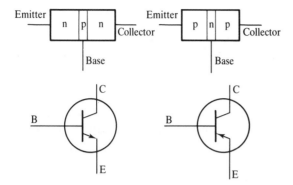

Figure 3.6 npn and pnp junction transistors.

are possible. These are the npn and the pnp types as illustrated in Fig. 3.6. The two other terminals are called the 'emitter' and the 'collector'. An arrowhead is traditionally shown between the emitter and the base to indicate the conventional direction of the current flow in that part of the circuit.

A brief description of the physical operation of the junction transistor can be made with respect to the npn type. The mode of operation of the pnp type is the same as that of the npn type, except that the polarities of all applied voltages, currents and charge carriers are reversed. In normal use, as a linear amplifier, the transistor is operated with the emitter-to-base junction forward biased and the collector-to-base junction reversed biased. For the npn transistor, the emitter is therefore negative with respect to the base while the collector is positive with respect to the base, see Fig. 3.7.

The currents I_E, I_B and I_C are shown in their conventional directions. These currents are mainly a result of the internal flow of electrons within the device as depicted in Fig. 3.7. Note, however, that hole conduction also contributes to the generation of the three transistor currents.

The junction n_1p is forward biased such that the free electrons drift from n_1 to p. On the other hand, junction n_2p is reverse biased and it will collect most of the electrons from n_1. The electrons which fail to reach n_1 are responsible for the current at the base terminal, I_B. By ensuring that the thickness of the base is very small and that the concentration of impurities in the base is much lower than either that of the emitter or the collector, the resultant base current will be limited to some 2 per cent of the emitter current. The basic transistor characteristic is therefore:

$$I_C = h_{FB}I_E \tag{3.5}$$

where I_C = collector current
I_E = emitter current
h_{FB} = current gain between the collector and the emitter
Normally, h_{FB} would range between 0.95 and 0.995 for a good-quality transistor.

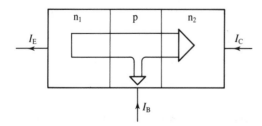

Figure 3.7 npn transistor in normal operation.

Common-base Characteristics

Figure 3.8 shows an npn transistor connected in a circuit to determine its static common base characteristics. The emitter current I_E is kept constant by varying R_1 and a range of values for I_C are imposed by varying R_2. The value of V_{CB}, the collector-base voltage, is noted. The test is repeated for another fixed value of I_E and the results are as depicted in Fig. 3.9.

It is found that over a wide range of collector-base voltages, the collector current is essentially independent of the collector-base voltage. This is because most of the electrons entering the npn junction are attracted to the collector. In effect the collector circuit has a very high impedance and acts as a constant current source. The actual value of the collector current is determined by the emitter current and the two are related through Eq. (3.3) which is the common-base characteristic. The general characteristics also show that the collector-base voltage must be reversed, i.e. collector negative with respect to base, in order to reduce the collector current to zero. With the emitter current equal to zero, the collector current is very small but not zero. This non-zero collector current is the reverse current of the collector-base junction, I_{CBO} and is referred to as the 'collector–base leakage current'. Finally at a high collector–base voltage, the collector current increases rapidly in consequence of the Zener effect. The same characteristics are observed with the pnp transistor except that the signs are in the reverse direction to that shown in Fig. 3.8.

Common-emitter Characteristics

Figure 3.10 shows the npn transistor with its emitter terminal connected both to the base current circuit and to the collector current circuit.

Using the same test procedure as before, the resulting characteristics are as shown in Fig. 3.11.

The first significant observation is that the collector–emitter voltage, V_{CE}, must be positive to produce a positive collector current. At low values of V_{CE}, the collector current I_C is also low, but when V_{CE} exceeds the so-called 'knee' voltage the characteristic assumes a linear relationship. The gradient of the linear region is generally much higher than that for the common-base configuration and the collector impedance is therefore lower than that for the common-base circuit. When the base current is zero, the collector current still has a positive finite value, I_{CEO}. This leakage current is larger than the equivalent leakage current in the common-base mode.

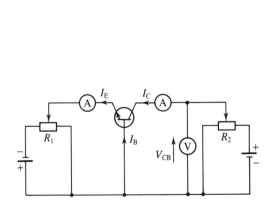

Figure 3.8 npn transistor in common-base circuit.

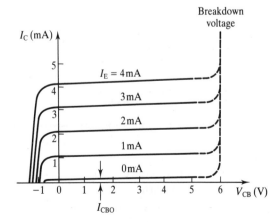

Figure 3.9 Common-base characteristics.

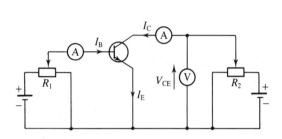

Figure 3.10 npn transistor in common-emitter circuit.

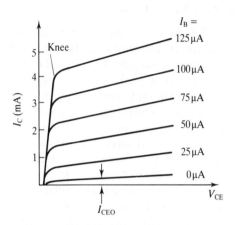

Figure 3.11 Common-emitter characteristics.

The common-emitter characteristic is generally written as

$$I_C = h_{FE} I_B \tag{3.6}$$

where h_{FE} is the current gain between the collector and base.

Application of Kirchhoff's first law to the common emitter circuit gives

$$I_E = I_C + I_B$$

Using Eq. (3.3) and eliminating I_E, it can be shown that

$$\frac{I_C}{I_B} = \frac{h_{FB}}{1 - h_{FB}} = h_{FE} \tag{3.7}$$

For a transistor with a steady-state current gain in common-base of 0.95, the common-emitter gain is given by

$$h_{FE} = \frac{0.95}{1 - 0.95} = 19$$

If, owing to some temperature effect, h_{FE} undergoes a minor change to say 0.96, then the new value of h_{FE} becomes 24. It is clear therefore that the common emitter gain h_{FE} is much more sensitive to small-order effects than the common-base gain, h_{FB}.

For a pnp transistor the characteristics of the common-emitter circuit are the same, except that the polarity of all voltages and currents are again in reverse order to that shown in Fig. 3.10.

The Transistor in a Circuit

In most practical applications, transistors are operated in the common-emitter mode where the emitter terminal forms the common connection between the input and output sections of the circuit, see Fig. 3.12.

The transistor collector characteristics are shown again in Fig. 3.13. The load line for the resistor, R_C, is superimposed and the operating point is given by the intersection of the load line with the collector characteristic. The operating point will therefore be dependent on the base current since this controls the collector characteristic. Also shown in Fig. 3.13 is the maximum power dissipation curve (broken line), which represents the locus of the product of collector

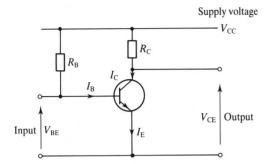

Figure 3.12 npn transistor in a practical common-emitter circuit.

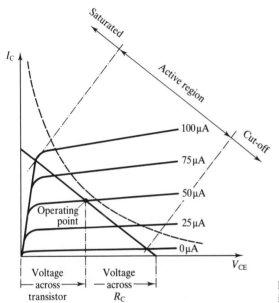

Figure 3.13 Common-emitter characteristics with super-imposed load line.

current and collector-emitter voltage. The maximum power dissipation curve represents a physical limitation and the operating point must be constrained to lie below the curve at all times.

The base current is limited by the value of the base resistance, R_B. As the base current is reduced the operating point moves down the load line. When I_B reaches zero the collector current will be minimized and the transistor is said to be 'cut off'. Alternatively, as the base current is increased the operating point moves up the load line and eventually reaches a maximum value at which the transistor is said to be 'bottomed', or 'saturated'. When saturated, the collector–emitter voltage is at a minimum of about 0.1 to 0.2 V and the collector current is a maximum. The two extremes between cut-off and saturation represent a very high and very low impedance state of the transistor, respectively. These extremes have great practical application to rapid, low-power switching and transistors operating between cut-off and saturation are frequently used in digital electronics circuitry. The low-impedance state represents a switch closed, or on, and the high-impedance state represents the switch open, or off. When operating as a linear current amplifier, the operating point is ideally located in the centre of the active region of the characteristic.

The analysis of circuits involving transistors is conveniently dealt with by representing the transistor in terms of an equivalent circuit and using the conventional current flow direction from positive to negative. Consideration of the charge carriers, i.e. holes or electrons, is only necessary to describe the internal physical operation of the transistor.

Example For the transistor shown in Fig. 3.12, calculate the collector voltage given that $R_B = 100\,k\Omega$, $R_C = 1.5\,k\Omega$, $V_{CC} = 12\,V$, $V_{BE} = 0.7\,V$, $h_{FB} = 0.98$. The collector–base leakage current may be taken as $I_{CBO} = 1\mu A$.

The equivalent transistor circuit is as shown in Fig. 3.14. Note that in the equivalent circuit the emitter–base voltage is simulated as a battery in series with the emitter connection. The collector–base leakage current, I_{CBO}, is represented as a constant current generator across the collector–base junction.

The base current is given by

$$I_B = (V_{CC} - V_{BE})/R_B = -(12 - 0.7)/(100 \times 10^3) = 0.113\,mA = 113\,\mu A$$

The total base current is

$$(I_B + I_{CBO}) = (113 + 1) = 114\,\mu A$$

From Eq. (3.5)

$$h_{FE} = h_{FB}/(1 - h_{FB}) = 0.98/(1 - 0.98) = 49$$

The total collector current $I_C = I_{CT} + I_{CBO} = h_{FE}I_{BT} + I_{CBO}$. Note that I_{BT} and I_{CT} are the ideal transistor base and collector currents, respectively. Thus

$$I_C = (49 \times 114) + 1 = 5586 + 1 = 5587\,\mu A = 5.587\,mA$$

The collector voltage is given by

$$V_{CE} = V_{CC} - (I_C R_C) = 12 - (5.587 \times 10^{-3} \times 1500) = 3.621\ V$$

In the previous circuit the collector current, and ultimately the collector voltage V_{CE} are hightly dependent on the value of the common emitter gain h_{FE}. Since h_{FE} is highly sensitive to external parameters, then so also is V_{CE}. A better common emitter circuit is shown in Fig. 3.15.

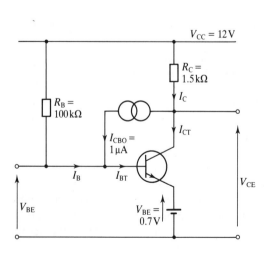

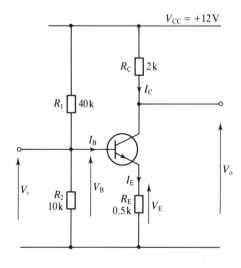

Figure 3.14 Equivalent circuit for the transistor circuit shown in Fig. 3.12.

Figure 3.15 Improved common-emitter circuit.

The input circuit includes an additional resistor, R_2, connected between the input line and ground. The value of this resistor is chosen such that it is much less than the input resistance of the transistor. This means that the loading effect of the input resistance of the transistor can be neglected and the value of V_B is determined by the relative values of R_1 and R_2, i.e.

$$V_B = R_2 V_{CC}/[R_1 + R_2] = (10 \times 12)/(40 + 10) = 2.4\,V$$

The voltage V_E will be equal to V_B less one forward biased diode voltage, i.e.

$$V_E = V_B - 0.7 = 2.4 - 0.7 = 1.7\,V$$

Thus

$$I_E = V_E/R_E = 1.7/500 = 0.0034\,A = 3.4\,mA$$

If we neglect the base current, then to a reasonable approximation, $I_C = I_E$. Hence

$$V_{CE} = V_{CC} - I_C R_C = 12 - 0.0034 \times 2000 = 6.8\,V$$

The circuit is biased therefore to operate with $I_C = 3.4$ mA and $V_{CE} = 6.8$ V. Note also that the common-emitter gain has not featured in the analysis and does not therefore have any significant influence on the operation of the circuit.

The Emitter-follower Circuit

Figure 3.16 shows the circuit diagram for an emitter-follower. The output voltage, V_E, is equal to the input voltage, V_B, less one forward biased diode voltage drop, i.e.

$$V_E = V_B - 0.7$$

Note that there is no resistor in the collector circuit and that the emitter resistor, R, may be the actual load, or may be coupled in parallel with an external load.

If the base voltage is changed by an amount, ΔV_B, then the corresponding change in emitter voltage will be ΔV_E, the two voltage changes being equal. Thus

$$\Delta I_E = \Delta V_E/R = \Delta V_B/R$$

using $I_E = I_C + I_B$, and $I_C = h_{FE} I_B$, then

$$I_E = I_B(h_{FE} + 1)$$

The corresponding change in I_B for a change in emitter current, ΔI_E is given by

$$\Delta I_B = \Delta I_E/(h_{FE} + 1) = \Delta V_B/R[h_{FE} + 1]$$

The input resistance, R_i, is $\Delta V_B/\Delta I_B$, i.e.

$$R_i = R(h_{FE} + 1) \tag{3.8}$$

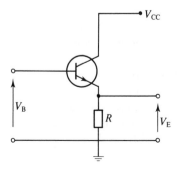

Figure 3.16 Emitter-follower circuit.

Since h_{FE} is typically of the order of 100, then the input resistance is effectively 100 times greater than the output, or load resistance. This means that the input signal requires much less power to drive a load than would be the case if the load was driven directly by the input circuit. The emitter–follower circuit therefore functions as a power amplifier. Although there is no voltage gain, the current supplied to the load, and hence also the power, is much greater than that supplied at the input.

The emitter–follower circuit is often encountered as a power amplification stage in many DC circuits, including DC motor drives. To further increase the amplification ratio, the emitter of a first-stage transistor can be connected to the base of a second-stage transistor where the emitter of the second transistor is used to drive the load. This is the basis of the 'Darlington' connection which uses such a pair of transistors in a series arrangement to form a high power gain emitter–follower circuit. The overall current gain is given as the product of the two individual transistor gains, h_{FE}. Typically the overall current gain is of the order of 10 000.

Emitter–follower circuits are also used as reference voltage sources, for impedance matching purposes, and generally for isolating signal sources from the loading effects of subsequent circuit stages.

The Field Effect Transistor (FET)

Field effect transistors, or FETs, are a much more recent development than bipolar transistors and they operate on a substantially different mechanism in achieving signal amplification. Operationally, FETs are voltage-controlled devices as opposed to the bipolar transistor which is a current-operated device. FETs are often described as unipolar since conduction in the FET is the result of only one predominant charge carrier.

The junction field effect transistor (JFET) consists of a thin bar of semiconductor which forms a channel between its two end connections which are referred to as the 'source' and the 'drain'. If the semiconductor used in the construction of the FET is n-type, then the device is called an 'n-channel' device. Conversely, a FET made from a p-type semiconductor is called a 'p-channel' device.

If the channel consists of a uniformly doped semiconductor, then the conductivity will be constant and the FET will function as a linear resistor. By introducing two opposite type semiconductor layers on either side of the channel, the effective thickness of the channel and hence the current flow, can be controlled. The opposite type layers are denoted as 'gates' and in normal operation they are reverse biased by a DC potential, V_{GS}, referred to as the 'gate source voltage'. The reverse bias ensures that no current can flow between the two gates and the gate inputs have an extremely high impedance. By using a lightly doped semiconductor for the channel, the gate depletion layer, which is determined by V_{GS}, can be made to extend well into the channel width. This controls the resistance of the path between the source and the drain. The general characteristics of such a field effect transistor are shown in Fig. 3.17.

For a given value of V_{GS}, an increase in drain-source voltage from zero initially gives a linear rise in drain current. Further increases in drain–source voltage results in a so-called 'pinch-off' in the drain current which then becomes independent of the drain–source voltage. Finally at a particular limiting value of drain–source voltage, a breakdown is initiated. The similarity between Figs 3.17 and 3.11, or 3.13, are clear and it is evident therefore that the bipolar junction transistor and the unipolar FET can perform essentially a similar function in any given application. Many other types of transistor, for example the metal oxide semiconductor field effect transistor, or MOSFET, use alternative means to control the resistance of the source to drain channel. The general characteristics of these devices, however, are all very similar to that shown in Fig. 3.17.

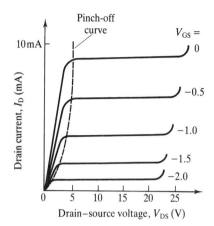

Figure 3.17 Characteristics of a field-effect transistor.

Integrated Circuits

While transistor-based amplifiers are still found as individual elements in many working circuits, the modern trend is towards the development of integrated circuits where all of the circuit elements are housed within a single silicon wafer. MOSFET technology is predominant in this area since the number of components on a single silicon chip can be packed up to twenty times more densely than with bipolar technology.

The integrated circuit components include diodes and transistors which may be either bipolar junction type, or FETs. Resistors can be deposited on top of the wafer in the form of tantalum, which is a poor conductor, or built into the wafer as 'pinch' resistors, which are partially turned-off FETs. Capacitors can also be produced within the silicon wafer. Capacitive elements may be formed when a pn junction diode is reverse biased. The p-type and n-type layers form the plates of the capacitor and the carrier depletion layer acts as a dielectric. The capacitance is, however, limited to a few picofarads. There is no microelectronic equivalent for an inductor, but most circuit designs can generally avoid the requirement for coiled inductive elements.

When the integrated circuit is complete it is usually encapsulated as a 'dual-in-line' (DIL) package. This is the normal form in which the integrated circuit is sold. An 8-pin DIL package may contain a relatively simple circuit, but a 40-pin DIL could easily contain all of the electronics associated with a central processing unit (CPU) for a computer system. These latter devices contain an enormous number of transistors and diodes, approaching 10 000 on a chip less than 10 mm square. The technology to produce this density of integration is commonly called 'very large scale integration', or VLSI.

3.3 THE THYRISTOR

Both the bipolar transistor and the FET can be utilized for switching operations. These devices, however, are usually associated with low power switching. For switching very large currents and voltages a special device called a 'thyristor', formerly known as a silicon controlled rectifier (SCR), is normally used.

The thyristor is a four-layer, unidirectional semiconductor device with three connections, referred to as the anode, cathode and the control gate, see Fig. 3.18.

The current flow is from the anode to the cathode only and with the cathode positive with respect to the anode, the device has a very high impedance. Under normal circumstances, the

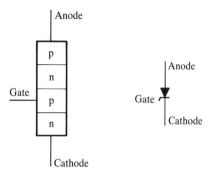

Figure 3.18 Thyristor device and circuit symbol.

thyristor will fail to conduct current in any direction. If a voltage is applied such that if the thyristor were a diode it would conduct in the forward biased direction, then application of a very small current between the gate and the cathode will cause the thyristor to abruptly change from non-conducting to conducting mode. The turn-on is rapid, within a few microseconds, and once turned on the thyristor will remain on, even if the gate current is removed.

Once triggered into conduction, the thyristor will turn off again only when the current flowing through it is reduced below a critical value. This minimum conducting current is called the 'holding current' and may range from a few microamps to a few tens of milliamps. Thyristors are additionally connected in series with a resistor which serves to limit the current to a safe value. The basic thyristor function is that of a power control device and they are used extensively for switching mains electricity and as a speed controller for DC motors.

3.4 THE TRIAC

The triac, or bidirectional thyristor, is similar in operation to the thyristor but differs in that it can be switched into conduction in either direction. In essence the triac is equivalent to two thyristors mounted back to back. Triacs find application to switching in full-wave alternating power supplies.

3.5 AMPLIFIERS

In dealing with amplifiers in practical applications, a 'systems' approach is normally adopted. The systems approach limits the considerations to the relationship between the input and output of the amplifier and the effect of feedback on the system. An amplifier may consist of a single transistor in a circuit, or as a complex arrangement of many transistors within an integrated circuit. In using the systems approach, the internal physical workings of the device are of no particular concern.

In general, electronic amplifiers are supplied with energy from a DC source. An input signal to the circuit controls the transfer of energy to the output and the output signal should be a higher power version of that supplied to the input. The increased power across the amplifier is invariably drawn from the supply.

The term 'amplifier' is actually a shortened form for the complete specification, 'voltage amplifier'. This has transpired because most amplifiers are intended to magnify voltage levels. Any other type of amplifier is normally prefixed with the name of the quantity which is amplified, e.g. current amplifier, charge amplifier, or power amplifier.

Amplifiers may be broadly classified with reference to the frequency range over which they are designed to operate. In this respect there are two general categories, these being 'wideband' and 'narrowband' amplifiers. The names are self-explanatory in that the wideband amplifier exhibits a constant power gain over a large range of input signal frequencies. The narrowband, or 'tuned' amplifier, on the other hand, provides a power gain over a very small frequency range. The power gain is usually expressed in decibels and is defined by Eq. (2.60).

The bandwidth of an amplifier is used in the same context as in Sec. 2.10, i.e. to define the operating frequency range. In this respect the -3 db amplitude ratio is used consistently to define the upper and lower input signal frequencies at which the power transferred across the amplifier is halved.

Using the system model, the amplifier can be represented as shown in Fig. 3.19. The amplifier is shown enclosed within the broken lines. There is a single input, a single output and one common connection. The amplifier also features an internal input impedance, shown as resistance R_i, and an internal output impedance, shown as resistance R_o. In reality the input and output impedances could have both inductive and capacitive components as well as the simple resistances shown in the figure.

Connected to the input stage of the amplifier is a voltage source, V_s, and its associated internal resistance, R_s. This could be taken to represent some form of transducer having a low voltage output in the millivolt range. At the output stage, the amplifier acts as a voltage source where A_v is the voltage gain. The output is shown connected to an external load, R_L, which might be considered to be some sort of recording instrument such as a digital voltmeter.

Considering the input stage, it may be shown, from Ohm's law, that

$$V_i = \frac{V_s}{(1 + R_s/R_i)} \tag{3.9}$$

Equation (3.9) indicates that the voltage applied to the amplifier input stage, V_i, will approach the source voltage, V_s, only when R_i tends to infinity. The amplifier should ideally therefore have a very large input impedance to prevent serious voltage attenuation at the input stage. By a similar argument, the output impedance, R_o, should be very small in comparison with the load resistance, R_L, for maximum voltage gain.

Example For the amplifier shown in Fig. 3.19, the open-circuit voltage gain is 100. Given that $R_i = 10\,k\Omega$, $R_o = 100\,\Omega$ and $R_s = 300\,\Omega$, determine the overall voltage gain and the power gain when the amplifier is driving a load resistance of $50\,\Omega$ from a source voltage of $10\,mV$.

Input stage

$$V_i = R_i V_s/(R_i + R_s) = 10^4 \times 10 \times 10^{-3}/(10^4 + 300) = 0.009\,708 \text{ V}$$

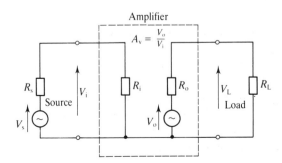

Figure 3.19 System representation of an amplifier.

The open circuit output voltage is given by

$$V_o = A_v V_i = 100 \times 0.009708 = 0.9708 \, \text{V}$$

Output stage

$$V_L = R_L V_o / (R_L + R_o) = 50 \times 0.9708 / (100 + 50) = 0.3236 \, \text{V}$$

The overall voltage gain is

$$0.3236 / 0.009708 = 33.33$$

Output power is given by

$$V_o^2 / R_L = (0.3236)^2 / 50 = 2.09 \, \text{mW} = 2090 \, \mu\text{W}$$

Input power is given by

$$V_i^2 / R_i = (0.009708)^2 / 10000 = 0.009 \, 425 \, \mu\text{W}$$

Power gain is

$$2090 / 0.00945 = 221 \, 762$$

The example shows that the overall voltage and power gains are influenced by the input and output impedances of the amplifier and by the load and source resistances in the output and input sides, respectively. If R_i and R_L are both very large however, then the overall voltage gain approaches the open circuit voltage gain A_v.

Normally the gains are expressed in decibels. From Eq. (2.60):

$$\text{voltage gain} = 20 \, \log_{10}(33.33) = 30.5 \, \text{dB}$$
$$\text{power gain} = 10 \, \log_{10}(221762) = 53.45 \, \text{dB}$$

Note that the voltage gain is also a measure of the power transfer since it is the ratio of the voltages squared which is actually expressed in decibels; i.e.

$$\text{voltage gain} = 10 \log_{10}(V_o^2 / V_i^2) = 20 \log_{10}(V_o / V_i)$$

If in the above example, R_i had been equal to R_L, then the voltage gain and the power gain would have had the same numerical value.

Effect of Feedback on Amplifiers

The amplifier illustrated in Fig. 3.19 is specified by its input and output impedances and its open-circuit gain A_v, the open-circuit gain being that gain obtained when the load resistance is infinite. These parameters are not fixed, but vary with ambient temperature, power supply voltage variation and age. The adverse effects of these variabilities can be minimized through the application of 'negative feedback'.

One particular method of obtaining negative feedback is the so-called 'series voltage' method, see Fig. 3.20. The feedback system in Fig. 3.20 is applied by connecting a potentiometer across the output terminals and tapping off a fraction, β, of the output signal. This fraction is connected in series with the input and with a polarity which will always oppose the input signal. Assuming both that the input impedance of the amplifier is very large in comparison with the internal resistance of the voltage source and the resistance of the potentiometer is very large in comparison with the output impedance of the amplifier, then

$$V_i = V_s - \beta V_o \tag{3.10}$$

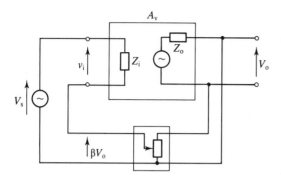

Figure 3.20 Series voltage method of negative feedback.

Since $V_o = A_v V_i$, then

$$V_o = A_v V_s - \beta A_v V_o$$

The overall gain of the system with feedback, A_f, is given by

$$A_f = \frac{V_o}{V_s} = \frac{A_v}{1 + \beta A_v} \tag{3.11}$$

Equation (3.11) shows that the feedback loop has reduced the original gain by the factor $(1 + \beta A_v)$. If in addition, the original gain A_v was in itself very large such that $A_v \gg 1$, then

$$A_f = A_v/(\beta A_v) = 1/\beta \tag{3.12}$$

Under the above circumstances, the overall gain of the system with feedback is essentially dependent only on the feedback fraction, β. Therefore any changes which alter the original gain, A_v, of the amplifier will not significantly affect the gain of the overall system with feedback.

Example An amplifier of open-circuit gain 500 employs a series voltage negative feedback system in which one-tenth of the output voltage is fed back to the input. If the open-circuit gain is reduced to 300, determine the percentage change in the overall gain with feedback. Initially

$$A_f = A_v/(1 + \beta A_v) = 500/(1 + 0.1 \times 500) = 9.804$$

Finally

$$A_f = 300/(1 + 0.1 \times 300) = 9.68$$

Percentage change is

$$(9.804 - 9.68)/9.804 = 0.0129 = 1.29\%$$

The example shows that a change of some 40 per cent in the open-circuit gain results in a nominal change of 1.3 per cent in the overall gain with feedback.

Consideration of the system with and without the feedback loop shows that the effect of series voltage negative feedback is to increase the input resistance by the factor $(1 + \beta A_v)$, and to reduce the output resistance by the same factor. Both of these effects are of benefit to the operation of the system. These comments, however, refer only to a negative feedback system using the series voltage method. Other methods of obtaining negative feedback can be used, including series current feedback, shunt current and shunt voltage feedback. These alternative methods have different effects on the overall gain and on the input and output impedances of the amplifier.

Noise and Distortion in Amplifiers

Noise is inherently present in all electronic amplifier systems. Noise arises from a number of effects, which include random charge movements within solid-state devices, thermoelectric potentials, electrostatic and electromagnetic pick-up and interference from the standard 50 Hz, or 60 Hz, mains power supply. The noise is fairly evenly distributed across the whole frequency spectrum and appears superimposed upon the output signal. Since noise is simply a random fluctuating voltage level, then negative feedback will have the same effect on noise that it has on the output voltage. If the noise is generated at the input stage of the amplifier then the 'signal to noise' ratio will not be improved by feedback. The signal to noise ratio can be improved, however, if an intermediate amplifying stage, free from noise effects, can be included in the system.

Distortion is another undesirable feature which arises when the amplifier input/output characteristic, or transfer characteristic, deviates from an ideal linear relationship. If the transfer characteristic is linear then the output signal will be a faithful amplified replica of the input. A nonlinear characteristic will give a distorted output and a non-sinusoidal output will be generated from a sinusoidal input. Distortion is usually associated with a high level of input signal which overextends the linear operating range of the amplifier.

Amplifier Frequency Response

The frequency response of an amplifier is usually illustrated as a plot of the gain in decibels against the input signal frequency. The graph is called a 'Bode plot' and the phase relationship between the output and input is also shown for completeness.

High-frequency response The high-frequency response is limited by the charge transit time through the active device and by the effect of stray capacitance between the signal leads and earth. Stray capacitance can be represented as a capacitor connected in parallel across the output signal line and earth, see Fig. 3.21.

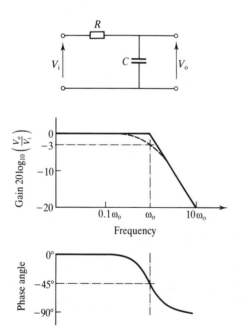

Figure 3.21 High frequency response with stray capacitance.

Using complex notation, the ratio of output voltage to input voltage is

$$\frac{V_o}{V_i} = \frac{1/(j\omega C)}{[R + 1/(j\omega C)]} = \frac{1}{(1 + j\omega CR)} = \frac{1}{[1 + j(\omega/\omega_0)]}$$

where $\omega_0 = 1/(CR)$.

Using the complex conjugate and evaluating the modulus of the voltage ratio gives

$$\frac{V_o}{V_i} = \frac{1}{1 + j(\omega/\omega_0)} \times \frac{1 - j(\omega/\omega_0)}{1 - j(\omega/\omega_0)} = \frac{1 - j(\omega/\omega_0)}{1 + j(\omega/\omega_0)^2}$$

$$\left|\frac{V_o}{V_i}\right| = \frac{\sqrt{1 + (\omega/\omega_0)^2}}{[1 + (\omega/\omega_0)^2]} = \frac{1}{\sqrt{1 + (\omega/\omega_0)^2}}$$

(3.13)

The phase angle between output and input is given by

$$\phi = \tan^{-1}(-\omega/\omega_0)$$

(3.14)

When $\omega \ll \omega_0$, the term $(\omega/\omega_0)^2$ is small and the voltage ratio $|V_o/V_i|$ is approximately equal to unity. The gain in decibels is $20\log_{10}(1) = 0$. In addition, the phase angle ϕ, is small.

When $\omega = \omega_0$, then the voltage ratio is equal to $1/\sqrt{2} = 0.707$ and the phase angle is $\tan^{-1}(-1) = -45°$. The gain in decibels is $20\log_{10}(1/\sqrt{2}) = -3\,\text{dB}$. This particular frequency represents the upper limiting frequency, or 'cut-off' frequency, at which the power transferred between the input and output is halved and the output lags the input by 45°.

When $\omega \gg \omega_0$, $(\omega/\omega_0)^2$ is large compared with unity and the voltage ratio decreases considerably. For example at $\omega = 10\omega_0$, the voltage ratio is reduced approximately to 1/10 and the corresponding attenuation in decibels is $20\log_{10}(0.10) = -20\,\text{dB}$.

At these higher frequencies, the gain is decreasing uniformly at the rate of $-20\,\text{dB}$ per decade and the phase angle is asymptotically approaching $-90°$ as the frequency approaches infinity.

The circuit shown in Fig. 3.21, with its resulting gain and phase characteristics, often forms the basis of a simple passive 'low-pass' filter. Such a filter will have little effect on a low frequency input signal. Higher frequency input signals, above the cut-off value, will be progressively attenuated at the rate of $-20\,\text{dB}$ per decade. In many practical circuits, background noise is often prevalent in the form of random high frequency components, superimposed upon the main signal. A circuit such as that shown in Fig. 3.21 will eliminate much of the high frequency noise with no significant adverse effect on the main signal. In designing such a low-pass filter, the values of resistance and capacitance are chosen such that the cut-off frequency $(\omega_0 = 1/CR)$ is suitably greater than the frequencies of interest in the main signal.

Low frequency response At the low end of the spectrum, the amplifier can theoretically respond to input frequencies right down to zero hertz. However because of the variabilities due to ageing effects, a lower cut-off frequency is often imposed by including series capacitors on one, or both, of the input connections. Figure 3.22 illustrates the equivalent circuit which includes a coupling capacitor connected in series in the signal input line.

The voltage ratio may be written as

$$\frac{V_o}{V_i} = \frac{R}{R + 1/(j\omega C)} = \frac{1}{1 + (1/j\omega CR)} = \frac{1}{1 + (\omega_0/j\omega)} = \frac{1}{1 - j(\omega_0/\omega)}$$

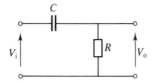

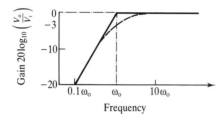

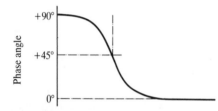

Figure 3.22 Low frequency response with a coupling capacitor.

Note that $\omega_0 = (1/CR)$ as before, but the values of R and C are selected, in this instance, such that ω_0 is a relatively low frequency. Thus

$$\frac{V_o}{V_i} = \frac{1}{1 - j(\omega_0/\omega)} \times \frac{1 + j(\omega_0/\omega)}{1 + j(\omega_0/\omega)} = \frac{1 + j(\omega_0/\omega)}{1 + (\omega_0/\omega)^2}$$

The modulus of the voltage ratio is given by

$$\left|\frac{V_o}{V_i}\right| = \frac{\sqrt{1 + (\omega_0/\omega)^2}}{1 + (\omega_0/\omega)^2} = \frac{1}{\sqrt{1 + (\omega_0/\omega)^2}} \tag{3.15}$$

The phase angle is given by

$$\phi = \tan^{-1}(+\omega_0/\omega) \tag{3.16}$$

When $\omega \gg \omega_0$, the term $(\omega_0/\omega)^2$ is negligible. The modulus, $| V_o/V_i |$ is approximately equal to unity and the gain, in decibels, is zero. The phase angle is very small, with the output leading the input.

When $\omega = \omega_0$, the voltage ratio is $1/(\sqrt{2})$, the gain $-3\,$dB and the phase angle $+45°$. The condition where $\omega = \omega_0$ therefore represents the lower cut-off frequency.

When $\omega \ll \omega_0$, the term $(\omega_0/\omega)^2$ is large and the voltage ratio is directly proportional to the input signal frequency. If, for example $\omega = \omega_0/10$, then the gain is $20 \log_{10}(0.1) = -20\,$dB. As the input signal frequency becomes very small then, the gain reduces at the rate of $-20\,$dB per decade and the phase angle approaches $+90°$.

The circuit shown in Fig. 3.22 functions as a 'high-pass' filter where high-frequency input signals are largely unaffected. Input signals with a frequency below the cut-off value are progressively attenuated at $-20\,$dB per decade as the frequency approaches zero hertz. Such a

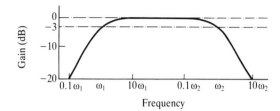

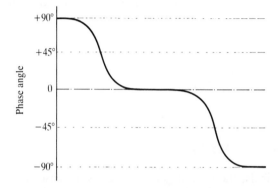

Figure 3.23 Amplifier characteristic with coupling capacitor and stray capacitance.

circuit could conceivably be used therefore to eliminate undesirable low frequency unsteadiness from an input signal.

The gain characteristics for an amplifier incorporating both a coupling capacitor and any stray capacitance have the general form outlined in Fig. 3.23. Note that the cut-off frequencies do not represent discontinuities in the amplifier response and the actual amplifier response takes the form of a smooth curve which asymptotes between the extremities of the gain behaviour. This is shown as the full line in the figure.

In Fig. 3.23 the maximum gain is shown as 0 dB. This, however, is only a reference quantity and the plot basically illustrates how the amplifier gain varies in relation to the mid-range gain which depends on the amplifier's open-circuit gain.

Example An amplifier (see Fig. 3.24) has an open-circuit gain of 100, an input resistance of 50 kΩ and an output resistance of 1 kΩ. The amplifier input is driven by a transducer having a source resistance of 2 kΩ and a coupling capacitor of 0.1 μF is connected in series with the input line. The amplifier output capacitance, including stray capacitance, is 200 pF. The amplifier is used to drive a load resistance of 10 kΩ.
Estimate the upper and lower cut-off frequencies and hence sketch the approximate system response in the form of a Bode plot.
In the mid-frequency range, the effects of the coupling and output capacitors are both negligible.
Input stage

$$\frac{V_i}{V_s} = \frac{R_i}{R_s + R_i} = \frac{50 \times 10^3}{(2 + 50) \times 10^3} = \frac{50}{52}$$

Voltage gain over the input stage is

$$20 \log_{10}(50/52) = -0.3407 \, \text{dB}$$

Amplifier stage The amplifier open circuit voltage ratio is 100, thus the amplifier open circuit voltage gain is $20 \log_{10}(100) = 40 \, \text{dB}$.

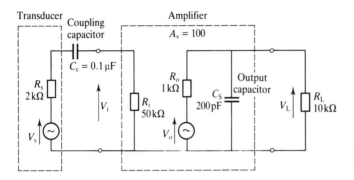

Figure 3.24 Transducer amplifier and load resistance.

Output stage

$$\frac{V_L}{V_o} = \frac{R_L}{R_L + R_o} = \frac{10}{(10+1)} = \frac{10}{11}$$

Voltage gain over the output stage is

$$20\log_{10}(10/11) = -0.828\,\text{dB}$$

With the individual gains expressed in decibels, the overall gain in a series, or cascaded, system is equal to the algebraic sum of all the gains in series. For the example considered, the overall gain of the system is

$$-0.3407 + 40 - 0.828 = +38.83\,\text{dB}$$

The lower cut-off frequency is given by

$$\omega_1 = 1/[C_c(R_s + R_i)] = 10^6/[0.1(2+50) \times 10^3] = 192.3\,\text{rad/s}$$

where C_c is the coupling capacitance in the input line; thus

$$f_1 = 192.3/(2\pi) = 30.6\,\text{Hz}$$

For the upper cut-off frequency

$$\omega_2 = 1/(C_s R_e)$$

where C_s is the stray capacitance and R_e is the effective resistance of R_o and R_L in parallel. Hence

$$R_e = 1 \times 10^3 \times 10 \times 10^3/(1+10) \times 10^3 = 0.9091 \times 10^3 = 909.1$$

thus

$$\omega_2 = 10^{12}/(200 \times 909.1) = 5.5 \times 10^6\,\text{rad/s}$$

or

$$f_2 = 5.5 \times 10^6/(2\pi) = 875.3\,\text{kHz}$$

The lower and upper cut-off frequencies define the amplifier bandwidth. The complete frequency response of the amplifier is shown in Fig. 3.25.

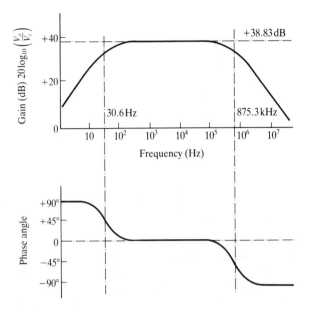

Figure 3.25 Amplifier frequency response characteristics.

Effect of Negative Feedback on Amplifier Frequency Response

In considering the effect of stray capacitance on the high frequency response of an amplifier, it was shown that the ratio of output voltage to the input voltage was modified by the relation

$$\frac{V_o}{V_i} = \frac{1}{1 + j(\omega/\omega_0)}$$

or

$$V_o = \frac{V_i}{1 + j(\omega/\omega_0)}$$

If a proportion of the output is used to form a negative feedback loop, then the system may be represented in block diagram form as shown in Fig. 3.26. Analysis of the system with feedback gives

$$V_o = E[1/\{1 + j(\omega/\omega_o)\}] = (V_i - \beta V_o)[1/\{1 + j(\omega/\omega_o)\}]$$

Rearranging gives

$$\frac{V_o}{V_i} = \frac{1/[1 + j(\omega/\omega_o)]}{1 + \beta/[1 + j(\omega/\omega_o)]} = \frac{1}{1 + j(\omega/\omega_o) + \beta}$$

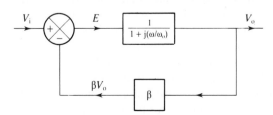

Figure 3.26 Effect of feedback on high frequency response.

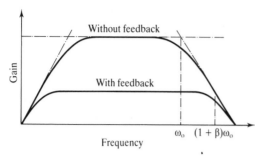

Figure 3.27 Effect of feedback on amplifier frequency response.

i.e.

$$\frac{V_0}{V_i} = \frac{1/(1+\beta)}{1 + j[\omega/(1+\beta)\omega_0]} = \frac{1/(1+\beta)}{1 + j(\omega/\omega_0')}$$

where $\omega_0' = (1+\beta)\omega_0$.

It is readily apparent that the frequency ω_0' is higher than ω_0 and that the effect of the feedback loop has been to increase the upper cut-off frequency. It is also apparent that the gain has been reduced by the factor $(1+\beta)$. An analysis of the low-frequency response shows a similar trend and the overall effect of feedback on the amplifier frequency response is as depicted in Fig. 3.27. In general terms, the feedback loop has increased the bandwidth of the amplifier, but at the expense of the overall gain.

Positive Feedback and Stability

In Fig. 3.20 a negative feedback signal is produced by using a series voltage. If the phase of the series voltage was changed such that the feedback signal augmented the input, then the nature of the feedback loop would become positive. With this positive feedback system, the overall gain would then become

$$A_f = A_v/(1 - \beta A_v) \tag{3.17}$$

Positive feedback therefore increases the overall system gain. If indeed the product (βA_v) is made equal to unity then the overall gain becomes infinite. Positive feedback, however, is inherently unstable since the output signal tends to increase indefinitely in an uncontrolled manner. Systems with positive feedback are found, nonetheless, in oscillator circuits where the amplifier produces its own input signal via a positive feedback loop.

3.6 THE OPERATIONAL AMPLIFIER

Modern amplifier systems rely less on discrete active devices such as transistors and much more on the vast range of 'linear integrated circuits' which are readily available. One of the most prevalent operational amplifiers based on integrated circuit technology is the generic type SN 72741, or as it is often abbreviated, the '741'. The 741 is available as an 8-pin DIL package and internally consists of 20 bipolar transistors, 11 resistors and 1 capacitor. The DIL package takes up less area than a small postage stamp and costs less than a cup of coffee. Figure 3.28 shows the usual representation of the 741 operational amplifier, or 'op-amp', and its DIL form.

The internal circuitry is quite complex but is conveniently reduced to the basic schematic form shown in the figure. The operational amplifier consists of an output, an inverting input and a non-inverting input. The IC, in addition requires a bipolar power supply which may range anywhere from $+/-3$ V to $+/-18$ V. There is also provision for an offset null on connection

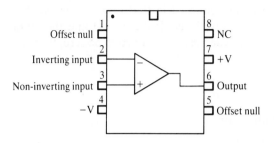

Figure 3.28 SN72741 operational amplifier.

pins 1 and 5. For the most part, the offset pins can be ignored. The operational amplifier has a high input impedance, a low output impedance and a very high open circuit gain A. Ideally the gain should be infinite. The bandwidth should also ideally be infinite but the 741 has an effective bandwidth limited between 0 Hz and about 1 MHz.

For operational amplifiers such as the 741, there are a number of standard circuits which are used routinely to perform specific functions. These are:

Inverting Amplifier

Figure 3.29 shows an op-amp wired up for an inverted output. The ouput impedance, R_o, is assumed to be zero. The input current i_1 is given as V_1/R_1 and because the amplifier input impedance, R_i, is very high, then the current flowing into the input terminal is approximately zero. This is equivalent to having the potential available at point E equal to zero. For this reason E is referred to as a 'virtual earth'.

From Kirchhoff's first law then, it is apparent that $i_1 = -i_2$. Thus $V_1/R_1 = -V_o/R_2$, and the gain can be written as

$$\frac{V_o}{V_1} = \frac{-R_2}{R_1} \tag{3.18}$$

Thus provided the open circuit gain of the amplifier is very high, then the overall gain with this negative feedback system is given by the ratio of the two external resistors and is independent of the open-circuit gain.

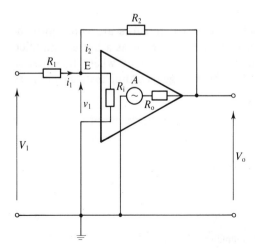

Figure 3.29 Inverting amplifier.

In the above analysis, two limiting conditions were imposed in that it was assumed that both the input impedance and the amplifier gain were very large. If the gain A and the input impedance R_i are taken into account and the output impedance still assumed to be zero, then the potential available at E is v_1. Summing the currents at E then gives

$$\frac{V_1 - v_1}{R_1} + \frac{V_o - v_1}{R_2} = \frac{v_1}{R_i}$$

In addition, $V_o = -Av_1$ or $v_1 = -V_o/A$. Substituting for v_1 gives

$$\frac{(V_1 + V_o/A)}{R_1} + \frac{(V_o + V_o/A)}{R_2} = -\frac{(V_o/A)}{R_i}$$

i.e.

$$V_1/R_1 = [(-1/A)(V_o/R_i + V_o/R_1 + V_o/R_2) - V_o/R_2]$$
$$V_1/R_1 = (-V_o/R_2)[1 + (1/A)(R_2/R_1 + R_2/R_i + 1)]$$
$$\frac{V_o}{V_1} = \frac{(-R_2/R_1)}{[1 + (1/A)(R_2/R_i + R_2/R_1 + 1)]}$$

The more detailed analysis shows that Eq. (3.18) can only be true when A is very large. Some typical values are $R_1 = 100 \, \text{k}\Omega$, $R_2 = 1 \, \text{M}\Omega$, $R_i = 500 \, \text{k}\Omega$ and $A = 10^3$. Equation (3.18) gives the gain as

$$V_o/V_1 = -10^6/(100 \times 10^3) = -10$$

The gain according to the more complete relation is -9.87 and an error of about 1.3 per cent is incurred in using the approximate relation. For many operational amplifiers, the open circuit gain is very much higher than 10^3 and Eq. (3.18) adequately defines the overall amplifier voltage gain.

Manual adjustment of the voltage gain could be implemented by making R_2 a variable resistance. This is not done in practice, however, because the negative input terminal to the amplifier is very sensitive to spurious inputs. Variable gain is normally actioned by supplying R_2 through a variable potentiometer connected across the output terminals of the amplifier. In this manner, it is the voltage across R_2 which is varied in order to alter the overall gain of the amplifier.

Unity Gain Amplifier

Figure 3.30 depicts a unity gain amplifier in which no external resistors are wired into the circuit. The unity gain amplifier is also known as a voltage follower, or as a buffer amplifier. This type of amplifier circuit is often used in instrumentation systems where the internal resistance of a voltage generating transducer and that of the voltage recording instrument are so

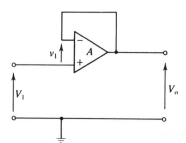

Figure 3.30 Unity gain amplifier.

poorly matched that the transducer voltage is seriously attenuated. This situation arises when the transducer internal resistance is large in comparison with that of the recording instrument. Since the buffer amplifier has a large input impedance and a low output impedance it can be interfaced between the transducer and the recording instrument to provide optimum impedance matching. This gives a low source impedance and high destination impedance between both the transducer and amplifier and also between the amplifier and the instrument. The output voltage is

$$V_o = Av_1 = A(-V_o + V_1)$$

i.e.

$$V_o(1 + A) = AV_1$$

or

$$V_o/V_1 = A/(1 + A)$$

When A is very large then

$$V_o/V_1 = 1 \tag{3.19}$$

Non-inverting Amplifier

Figure 3.31 shows the operational amplifier connected up for a non-inverting output. For the case where R_i tends to infinity and R_o tends to zero, the potential available at E is

$$v_1 = V_o R_1/(R_1 + R_2)$$

Also

$$V_o = A(V_1 - v_1) = A[V_1 - V_o R_1/(R_1 + R_2)]$$

Rearranging gives

$$\frac{V_o}{V_1} = \frac{1}{[(1/A) + R_1/(R_1 + R_2)]}$$

When A is very large

$$\frac{V_o}{V_1} = \frac{R_2 + R_1}{R_1} \tag{3.20}$$

If, in addition $R_2 \gg R_1$, then

$$\frac{V_o}{V_1} = \frac{R_2}{R_1} \tag{3.21}$$

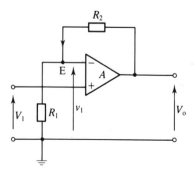

Figure 3.31 Non-inverting amplifier.

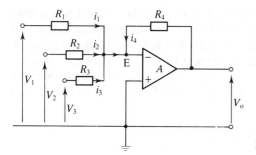

Figure 3.32 Summing amplifier.

Summing Amplifier

The summing amplifier is shown in Fig. 3.32. As point E is a virtual earth, then

$$-i_4 = i_1 + i_2 + i_3$$

Therefore

$$\frac{V_o}{R_4} = \frac{V_1}{R_1} + \frac{V_2}{R_2} + \frac{V_3}{R_3}$$

or

$$V_o = -R_4 \left[\frac{V_1}{R_1} + \frac{V_2}{R_2} + \frac{V_3}{R_3} \right] \tag{3.22}$$

If the resistances used in the circuit are all of equal value, then the output voltage will be equivalent to the summation of all the input voltages and with a reversed sign. Subtraction of any of the voltages can be performed by reversing its polarity, i.e. by first of all passing the voltage through a unity gain inverting amplifier, before it is passed on to the summing amplifier.

Integrating Amplifier

The integrating amplifier uses a capacitor, as opposed to a resistor, in the feedback loop (Fig. 3.33). The voltage across the capacitor is

$$(1/C) \int_0^t i_2 \, dt$$

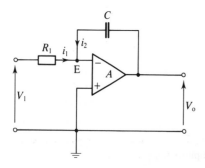

Figure 3.33 Integrating amplifier.

Since E is a virtual earth, then $i_1 = -i_2$. Therefore $i_2 = -(V_1/R_1)$. The voltage across the capacitor, which is in effect V_o, is given by

$$V_o = -(1/C) \int_0^t (V_1/R_1) \, dt = -(1/CR_1) \int_0^t V_1 \, dt \qquad (3.23)$$

Thus the output voltage is related to the integral of the input voltage.

Current-to-Voltage and Voltage-to-Current Converters

In some circuits it is necessary to change an input signal from a voltage level to a proportional current and vice versa. The I/V and V/I converters are shown in Fig. 3.34(a) and (b), respectively.

The current-to-voltage converter shown in Fig. 3.34(a), is basically a voltage follower with a resistor connected from the non-inverting input to ground. The input impedance of the amplifier is very large such that the input current passes to ground through the resistor R. Thus

$$v_2 = i_{in} \times R$$

As there is no resistor in the feedback loop, then $v_1 = V_o$, however

$$V_o = A(v_2 - v_1)$$

where A is the open-circuit gain of the amplifier. Thus

$$V_o(1 + A) = Ai_{in}R$$

or

$$V_o = Ai_{in}R/(1 + A)$$

When A is very large

$$V_o = i_{in}R$$

It can be seen therefore that the output voltage, V_o, is proportional to the input current, i_{in}, with the resistor R being the constant of proportionality. The circuit thus functions as a current-to-voltage converter.

The voltage-to-current converter is depicted in Fig. 3.34(b). This circuit is essentially a non-inverting amplifier where the current in the feedback loop forms the basis of the output signal. The output current i_{out} passes to ground through the load resistor R_L and the scaling resistor R. Thus

$$v_1 = i_{out}R \qquad \text{and} \qquad v_2 = V_{in}$$

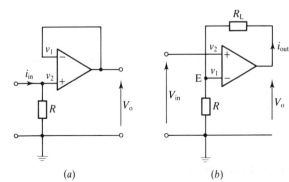

Figure 3.34 Current-to-voltage (a) and voltage-to-current (b) converters.

(a)   (b)

Note also that

$$V_o = i_{out} R_L = A(v_2 - v_1)$$

therefore

$$V_o = A(V_{in} - i_{out} R)$$

or

$$i_{out} R_L = A V_{in} - A i_{out} R$$

Hence

$$i_{out}(R_L + AR) = A V_{in}$$

For very large A

$$i_{out} AR = A V_{in}$$

i.e.

$$i_{out} = V_{in}/R$$

It is apparent that the output current, i_{out}, is proportional to the input voltage, V_{in}, and the circuit functions therefore as a current-to-voltage converter.

Apart from various mathematical processes, operational amplifiers are also used in active filtering circuits, waveform generation and shaping, and as a voltage comparator and in analogue-to-digital (A/D) and digital-to-analogue (D/A) integrated circuits.

3.7 THE DIFFERENTIAL AMPLIFIER

The differential amplifier, or subtractor, has two inputs and one output as shown in Fig. 3.35. Summing the currents at X gives

$$\frac{V_1 - v_1}{R_1} = \frac{v_1 - V_o}{R_2}$$

Rearranging to make v_1 the subject gives

$$v_1 = \frac{V_1 R_2 + V_o R_1}{(R_1 + R_2)}$$

Summing the currents at Y gives

$$\frac{V_2 - v_2}{R_3} = \frac{v_2}{R_4}$$

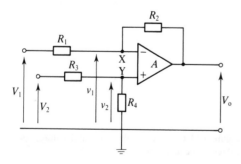

Figure 3.35 The differential amplifier.

i.e.

$$v_2 = \frac{R_4 V_2}{(R_3 + R_4)}$$

The amplifier output voltage, V_o, is proportional to the difference between the inverting and the non-inverting inputs. Thus

$$A(v_1 - v_2) = V_o$$

or

$$(v_1 - v_2) = \frac{V_o}{A} = \frac{V_1 R_2 + V_o R_1}{(R_1 + R_2)} - \frac{V_2 R_4}{(R_3 + R_4)}$$

$$V_o \left[\frac{R_1}{(R_1 + R_2)} - \frac{1}{A} \right] = \frac{V_2 R_4 (R_1 + R_2) - V_1 R_2 (R_3 + R_4)}{(R_3 + R_4)(R_1 + R_2)}$$

For large A

$$V_o = \frac{V_2 (R_4/R_3)[1 + (R_2/R_1)]}{[1 + (R_4/R_3)]} - V_1 (R_2/R_1)$$

The resistor ratios (R_4/R_3) and (R_2/R_1) can be made equal, in which case

$$V_o = (R_2/R_1)[V_2 - V_1] \qquad (3.24)$$

The input signals to a differential amplifier, in general, contain two components, these being the 'common-mode' and 'difference-mode' signals. The common-mode signal is the average of the two input signals and the difference-mode is the difference between the two input signals. Ideally the differential amplifier should affect the difference mode signal only. However, the common-mode signal is also amplified to some extent. The common-mode rejection ratio (CMRR) is defined as the ratio of the difference signal voltage gain to the common-mode signal voltage gain. For a good quality differential amplifier, the CMRR should be very large.

Although particularly important to the differential amplifier, the common-mode rejection ratio is a fairly general quality parameter used in most amplifier specifications. The 741 op-amp has a CMRR of 90 dB and the same signal applied to both inputs will give an output approximately 32 000 times smaller than that produced when the signal is applied to only one input line.

Example Figure 3.36 shows a strain gauge bridge (see Sec. 4.5), in which the bridge resistors are foil gauges of resistance 120 Ω. The active gauge is stressed in such a way that its resistance is increased by an amount ΔR. If the amplifier resistors R_2 are each 10 kΩ, determine the output voltage V_o when the ratio $\Delta R/R$ is equal to 0.001 and the bridge supply voltage, V_s, is 10 V.

The current in C is $(V_s - v_1)/R$. Similarly the current in D is v_1/R. Since X is a virtual earth then the summation of the currents at node X is

$$\frac{(V_s - v_1)}{R} - \frac{v_1}{R} + \frac{(V_o - v_1)}{R_2} = 0$$

Multiplying through by R and rearranging to solve for v_1 gives

$$v_1 = [V_s + (R/R_2)V_o]/[2 + (R/R_2)]$$

If $R \ll R_2$, then

$$v_1 = [V_s + (R/R_2)V_o]/2 \qquad (i)$$

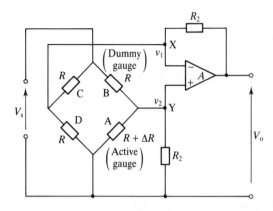

Figure 3.36 Strain gauge bridge circuit with amplified output.

The current through B is $(V_s - v_2)/R$. The current through A is $v_2/(R + \Delta R)$. Also since Y is a virtual earth then the summation of the currents at node Y gives

$$\frac{(V_s - v_2)}{R} - \frac{v_2}{(R + \Delta R)} - \frac{v_2}{R} = 0$$

Multiplying through by R and solving for v_2 gives

$$v_2 = V_s/[1 + (R/R_2) + 1/\{1 + (\Delta R/R)\}]$$

For $R \ll R_2$, then

$$v_2 = V_s/[1 + 1/\{1 + (\Delta R/R)\}]$$

or

$$v_2 = V_s[1 + (\Delta R/R)]/[2 + (\Delta R/R)] \tag{ii}$$

For the amplifier

$$[v_1 - v_2] = V_o/A \tag{iii}$$

Substituting equations (i) and (ii) into (iii) gives

$$\frac{V_s + (R/R_2)V_o}{2} - \frac{V_s[1 + (\Delta R/R)]}{[2 + (\Delta R/R)]} = \frac{V_o}{A}$$

$$V_o[(2/A) - (R/R_2)] = V_s\left[1 - \frac{2\{1 + (\Delta R/R)\}}{\{2 + (\Delta R/R)\}}\right]$$

For very large open loop gain A

$$V_o(R/R_2) = V_s\left[\frac{2\{1 + (\Delta R/R)\}}{\{2 + (\Delta R/R)\}} - 1\right]$$

i.e.

$$V_o = V_s\{R_2/R\}\{\Delta R/R\}/[2 + (\Delta R/R)]$$

$(\Delta R/R)$ is usually small such that to a reasonable approximation

$$V_o = V_s\{R_2/R\}\{\Delta R/R\}/2$$

Thus

$$V_o = 10\{10000/120\}\{0.001\}/2 = 0.417\,\text{V}$$

3.8 INSTRUMENTATION AMPLIFIER

Instrumentation amplifiers are precision devices having a high input impedance, a low output impedance, a high common-mode rejection ratio, a low level of self-generated noise and a low offset drift. The offset drift is attributable to temperature-dependent voltage outputs. Figure 3.37 shows the schematic representation of a precision instrumentation amplifier.

Considering first of all the input stage. The two amplifiers, A_1 and A_2 are input buffers with feedback resistors, R_2, providing a first stage gain. The input impedances of these amplifiers are very large such that the voltage at point A is essentially equal to v_1. Similarly, the voltage at B is equal to v_2. The voltage difference $(v_1 - v_2) = V_1$, is effectively applied across R_1. Thus from Ohm's law, the current $I = V_1/R_1$. Because of the large input impedances of A_1 and A_2, the current I flows through both R_2 resistors. Thus the input voltages from each buffer amplifier are

$$v_1' = v_1 + R_2 V_1/R_1 \qquad \text{and} \qquad v_2' = v_2 - R_2 V_1/R_1$$

The difference between these buffer amplifier outputs form the differential input to the second stage of the amplifier; i.e.

$$(v_1' - v_2') = v_1 + R_2 V_1/R_1 - v_2 + R_2 V_1/R_1 \tag{3.25}$$

or

$$\begin{aligned}(v_1' - v_2') &= (v_1 - v_2) + 2V_1(R_2/R_1) \\ &= V_1 + 2V_1(R_2/R_1) = V_1[1 + 2(R_2/R_1)]\end{aligned} \tag{3.26}$$

Since the point X is a virtual earth, then $i_1 = i_2$ and we can write

$$\frac{v_1' - v_X}{R_3} = \frac{v_X - V_o}{R_4} \tag{3.27}$$

The differential input to A_3 is virtually zero such that $v_Y = v_X$. Rearranging Eq. (3.27) gives

$$V_o = (1 + R_4/R_3)v_Y - v_1' R_4/R_3 \tag{3.28}$$

For the non-inverting input of the differential amplifier

$$(v_2' - v_Y)/R_5 = v_Y/R_6$$

or

$$v_Y = (R_6/R_5)v_2'/(1 + R_6/R_5) = v_2'/(1 + R_5/R_6)$$

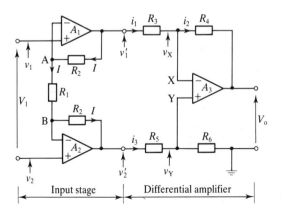

Figure 3.37 Precision instrumentation amplifier.

Substituting the expression for v_Y back into Eq. (3.28) gives

$$V_o = \frac{(1 + R_4/R_3)v_2'}{(1 + R_5/R_6)} - (R_4/R_3)v_1' \qquad (3.29)$$

The differential amplifier output voltage may also be written as

$$V_o = A_D(v_2' - v_1') = A_D v_2' - A_D v_1' \qquad (3.30)$$

where A_D is the gain associated with A_3 in differential mode.

Comparing Eqs (3.29) and (3.30) shows that a necessary condition for equality is $A_D = R_4/R_3$.

Also required for equality is the condition

$$A_D = \frac{(1 + R_4/R_3)}{1 + R_5/R_6} = \frac{(1 + A_D)}{(1 + R_5/R_6)}$$

Solving for A_D gives

$$A_D = R_6/R_5$$

The analysis shows that the resistance ratios (R_4/R_3) and (R_6/R_5) must both be equal to the differential gain of the amplifier, A_D. From Eqs (3.26) and (3.30) the relationship between the output and the input is

$$V_o = (R_4/R_3)[1 + 2(R_2/R_1)]V_1 \qquad (3.31)$$

A number of instrumentation amplifiers are packaged in IC form and these are suitable for the amplification of signals from strain gauges, thermocouples and other low-level differential signals from various bridge circuits.

3.9 POWER SUPPLIES

In Sec. 3.4 the use of pn junction diodes were illustrated as a means of AC voltage rectification. Both the half-wave and full-wave rectification circuits give outputs, which although varying with respect to time, are essentially DC in as much that there is no change in the output voltage polarity. These rectification circuits provide a second stage in the production of a steady DC voltage from an AC power supply. The first stage of a DC power supply circuit consists of a transformer which functions to isolate the AC mains from the DC output and to provide a suitably transformed voltage in the secondary winding.

The ripple factor is defined as

$$\text{ripple factor} = \frac{\text{effective value of all AC components}}{\text{average, or DC, component}}$$

For the circuits shown in Figs 3.3 and 3.4, the load current is

$$I_L = I_{DC} + I_{AC}$$

The power dissipated through the load is

$$(I_{rms})^2 R_L = (I_{DC})^2 R_L + (I_{AC})^2 R_L$$

Hence

$$I_{AC} = \sqrt{(I_{rms})^2 - (I_{DC})^2}$$

Thus, the ripple factor is

$$I_{AC}/I_{DC} = \sqrt{[(I_{rms})^2 - (I_{DC})^2]}/I_{DC}$$

or

$$\text{ripple factor} = \sqrt{[I_{rms}/I_{DC}]^2 - 1} \qquad (3.32)$$

Equation (3.32) may be written with the corresponding voltages in place of the r.m.s. and DC currents.

Assuming that the forward resistance of the diode is negligible, for half-wave rectification Eqs (3.1) and (3.2) result in a ripple factor given by

$$\text{half-wave ripple factor} = \sqrt{\left[\frac{V_m}{2}\frac{\pi}{V_m}\right]^2 - 1} = \sqrt{\pi^2/4 - 1} = 1.21$$

Similarly using Eqs (3.3) and (3.4) and assuming that the forward resistance of the diodes is negligible, then the full-wave ripple factor is given by

$$\text{full-wave ripple factor} = \sqrt{\left[\frac{V_m}{\sqrt{2}}\frac{\pi}{2V_m}\right]^2 - 1} = 0.483$$

Some further refinements are added to the circuits, however, to reduce the variation, or 'ripple', in the DC output voltage. The ripple factor can be greatly reduced by adding a 'reservoir', or smoothing, capacitor, as shown in Fig. 3.38(a), which is connected in parallel with the load.

While the supply voltage is positive and rising, the diode is forward biased and will conduct. The capacitor has a short charging time constant and the capacitor voltage follows the supply voltage initially. When the supply voltage reaches its peak value and starts to reduce, the capacitor voltage does not fall so rapidly. The diode therefore becomes reverse biased and no longer conducts. All of the load current is then supplied by the capacitor until such time that the supply voltage again becomes more positive than the capacitor voltage and the diode again conducts. The DC load voltage is thereby 'smoothed' as shown in Fig. 3.38(b) and the ripple is effectively reduced. A further reduction in ripple can be achieved by using a full-wave rectification circuit since there are then twice as many voltage pulses and the time during which the capacitor discharges is halved. The reservoir capacitor is of necessity quite large and

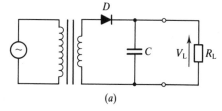

(a)

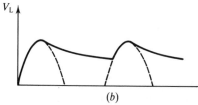

(b)

Figure 3.38 Half-wave rectification circuit with reservoir capacitor: (a) circuit; (b) waveform.

electrolytic capacitors are often used in this application. A leakage resistor is also frequently connected in parallel with the reservoir capacitor as a safety feature. In the event that the load is disconnected leaving the reservoir capacitor fully charged, the leakage resistor will dissipate the charge safely.

Example A diode bridge circuit is supplied with an AC voltage of 50 V rms, at 50 Hz frequency. The bridge supplies a load resistance of 1 kΩ. Determine the value of a capacitor connected in parallel with the load which will limit the peak to peak ripple to 5 V.

Since the capacitor voltage is sinusoidal for part of the cycle and exponential for the remainder of the cycle, the calculation of the ripple voltage is fairly complex. However, if the ripple voltage is small the output waveform can be assumed to be triangular as depicted in Fig. 3.39.

The average, or DC voltage is $V_{DC} = V_m - v_r/2$ where V_m is the peak voltage and v_r is the ripple voltage. For a capacitor $Q = CV = It$, thus, for the smoothing capacitor

$$v_r = I_{DC}t/C$$

The capacitor discharge time is

$$t = [\pi - (\theta_2 - \theta_1)]/\omega$$

The average current is $I_{DC} = V_{DC}/R$, where R is the load resistance. Hence

$$v_r = I_{DC}[\pi - (\theta_2 - \theta_1)]/(C\omega)$$

If the ripple is very small then $(\theta_2 - \theta_1) \ll \pi$ and

$$v_r = I_{DC}\pi/(C\omega) \tag{3.33}$$

For the example considered

$$V_m = 50\sqrt{2} = 70 \text{ V}$$
$$V_{DC} = 70 - 5/2 = 67.5 \text{ V}$$
$$I_{DC} = 67.5/1000 = 67.5 \text{ mA}$$
$$v_r = 5 \text{ V}$$

As the supply frequency is 50 Hz, the capacitor discharge time is approximately 10 ms. From Eq. (3.33)

$$C = I_{DC}\pi/(v_r\omega) = 0.0675 \times \pi/(5 \times 2 \times \pi \times 50) = 135 \times 10^{-6} \text{ F} = 135 \,\mu\text{F}$$

For a triangular waveform it can be shown that the r.m.s. value is given as $v_r/2\sqrt{3}$. The ripple factor for the smoothed output is then given by

$$\text{ripple factor} = (v_r/2\sqrt{3})/V_{DC} = (5/2\sqrt{3})/67.5 = 0.0214 = 2.14\%$$

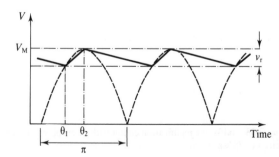

Figure 3.39 Approximate output waveform for smoothed full-wave rectification circuit.

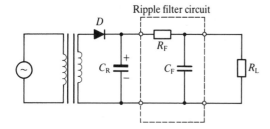

Figure 3.40 Half-wave rectification circuit with electrolytic reservoir capacitor and ripple filter circuit.

An important factor on the use of a smoothing capacitor is that the diode, or diodes, only conduct over a reduced part of the cycle, in the time increment $(\theta_2 - \theta_1)$. However, all of the energy drawn by the load must be supplied while the diodes are conducting and the capacitor is charging. The current supplied during charging is therefore much greater than that which would be supplied in the absence of a smoothing capacitor. A large smoothing capacitor will reduce the diode conduction period and correspondingly increase the diode current during conduction. Some care must therefore be exercised to ensure that the diode peak current rating is not exceeded by the use of an overly large smoothing capacitor.

The use of a smoothing capacitor also has an effect on the peak inverse voltage of a diode when used in a half-wave circuit. The peak inverse voltage for both the half-wave and full-wave circuits without a smoothing capacitor is equal to the negative peak supply voltage V_m. A smoothing capacitor, however, essentially holds the direct voltage at, or near, the positive peak supply voltage. During the non-conducting part of the cycle the resultant peak inverse voltage appearing across the diode is approximately equal to $2V_m$. This does not occur in the full-wave circuit where the peak inverse voltage remains equal to V_m.

For applications where the reservoir capacitor still cannot reduce the ripple to an acceptable level, an additional ripple filtering circuit may be added. This consists of an additional series ripple resistor and a ripple capacitor as shown in Fig. 3.40. The ripple filter is normally interfaced in the circuit between the reservoir capacitor and the load.

The circuit shown in Fig. 3.40 acts as a low-pass filter where the low-frequency content, or DC component, of the input is largely unaffected but the higher frequencies, i.e. the ripple components, are attenuated. This then provides further smoothing to the DC output voltage. Further enhancements might include a variable resistor either in series, or in parallel with the load. The function of the variable resistor is to allow regulation of the voltage supplied to the load. The Zener diode discussed in Sec. 3.1 is often used in this capacity to provide a stabilized voltage supply.

Example Design a stabilizing circuit to supply an output current of 10 mA at 6 V. The stabilizer is fed from a full-wave rectified and smoothed source giving a DC voltage of 10 V with a superimposed peak-to-peak ripple of 6 V. The stabilizing circuit is to use a Zener diode having a nominally constant dynamic resistance (dV/dI) of 10 Ω, a Zener voltage of 6 V and a minimum Zener current of 2 mA.

The basic circuit is illustrated in Fig. 3.41 where the Zener dynamic resistance, R_z, is shown in series with the Zener diode symbol. These represent an equivalent circuit for the Zener diode which, of course, is a single circuit element.

At maximum output current

$$V_o = (I_z R_z + V_z) = (0.002 \times 10 + 6) = 6.02\,\text{V}$$

The DC current flowing through resistor R is

$$I_s + I_z + I_o = 0.002 + 0.010 = 0.012\,\text{A}$$

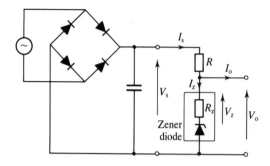

Figure 3.41 Zener diode in a voltage stabilizing circuit.

Therefore

$$R = (V_s - V_o)/I_s = (10 - 6.02)/0.012 = 332\,\Omega$$

At zero output current

$$V_o = V_z + (V_s - V_z)R_z/(R + R_z) = 6 + (10 - 6)10/(332 + 10) = 6.117\,\text{V}$$

Total voltage variation between no load and maximum load is

$$6.117 - 6.02 = 0.097\,\text{V}$$

Assuming that the output waveform is approximately triangular then

$$V_{DC} = 6.117 - 0.097/2 = 6.07\,\text{V}$$

$$\text{ripple factor} = (v_r/2\sqrt{3})/V_{DC} = (0.097/2\sqrt{3})/6.07 = 0.00461 = 0.461\%$$

The stabilizing circuit therefore produces a nominal 6 V DC output with a ripple factor of approximately 0.5 per cent. By comparison, the input signal to the stabilizing circuit has a ripple factor of some 13.3 per cent. With an output current of only 10 mA, the power supplied by the circuit is quite low at 60 mW. This may be perfectly adequate, however, to drive many integrated circuit devices. In addition, when the output current is low, the Zener diode must take the full supply current at the Zener voltage V_z. The product $(V_z I_s)$ must not therefore exceed the rated dissipation of the device. If the load requires a higher power rating then the output from the Zener can be used to supply a high input impedance, low output impedance power amplifier.

Generally for high power systems, thyristors are used in place of diodes as the rectification element. The controlled conduction properties of thyristors allow close control to be exercised on the power supplied to the load. Figure 3.42 shows a simple method of controlled triggering for a thyristor operating in a half-wave rectification circuit.

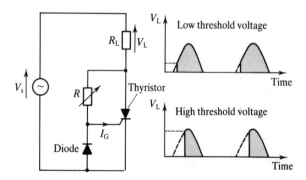

Figure 3.42 Half-wave rectification circuit using a thyristor.

The thyristor does not conduct until a critical anode–cathode voltage is reached. This critical threshold voltage is adjusted by altering the gate current through the variable resistor in the circuit. Increasing the variable resistance will increase the threshold voltage and the conduction point of the thyristor can be positioned to any location over the first quarter cycle of the AC input voltage. Once conduction is initiated, the thyristor continues to conduct until the anode–cathode voltage is reduced almost to zero at the end of the half-cycle. The polarity of the supply voltage then changes and no further conduction takes place until the polarity again changes and the threshold voltage is reached at the appropriate point in the next positive half-cycle. If the threshold voltage is increased up to the maximum voltage of the supply, then the thyristor no longer conducts. The diode is included in the circuit to prevent the supply voltage being applied in reverse direction between the cathode and the gate during the non-conducting part of the cycle. The power supplied to the load may thus be varied between 50 per cent and 100 per cent of that which would be supplied using a normal half-wave rectifier circuit.

An alternative method of producing a full-wave rectified output is to use a centre-tapped transformer as shown in Fig. 3.43.

In Fig. 3.43 when A is positive with respect to B then B is also positive with respect to C. Diode D_1 is then forward biased and conducts while D_2 is reverse biased and does not conduct. A flow of current is thereby established through D_1 and the load resistor R_L. During the negative half-cycle of the supply voltage, D_1 becomes reverse biased but D_2 will conduct and the flow of current to the load will be maintained through D_2. The load voltage therefore takes the form of a full-wave rectified signal. This method of full-wave rectification is less commonly used than the diode bridge circuit since the extra cost of the centre-tapped transformer is greater than the cost of the two additional diodes used in the bridge. The transformer is also inefficiently utilized since only half of the windings are conducting at any given time. As each half winding must be rated to take the full load current, then the transformer is generally larger than would otherwise be required. A further disadvantage is that the maximum reverse voltage across a diode in the non-conducting phase is $2V_m$, where V_m is the peak supply voltage in the secondary winding. The peak inverse voltage rating of the diodes must therefore be well in excess of $2V_m$.

The output ripple factor may, however, be improved by incorporating any of the additional circuitry previously considered for half-wave and full-wave rectification circuits.

Polyphase Rectifiers

The full-wave rectification obtained from the circuit using the centre-tapped transformer might be considered as a two-phase, half-wave rectifier circuit. Each phase supplies current to the load for one half of the AC supply cycle and the net result is a full-wave rectified supply to the load. If the number of phases were to be increased then the ripple factor would be reduced and the

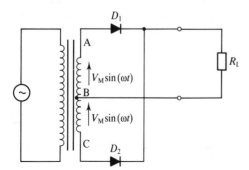

Figure 3.43 Full-wave rectification using a centre-tapped transformer.

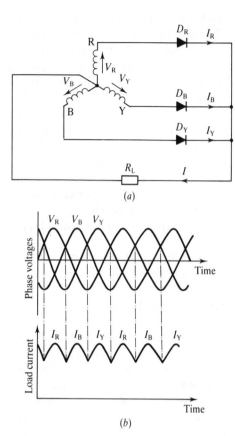

(a)

(b)

Figure 3.44 Three-phase, half-wave rectifier: (a) circuit; (b) waveforms.

average voltage supplied to the load increased. Fig. 3.44(a) shows a three-phase half-wave rectifier supplied from a star-connected source, say a three-phase transformer. The rectified voltage from each phase supplies current to a load and the return line is connected to the star point of the supply.

The phase voltages are all displaced 120° relative to one another and these are shown in Fig. 3.44(b). Considering, for example the instant when V_R is at its peak value. With R positive with respect to the star point the other phase voltages are negative with respect to the star point. Diode D_R will therefore conduct while D_Y and D_B are reversed biased and non-conducting. Conduction through D_R will continue until such time that V_B becomes more positive than V_R. With $V_B > V_R$, D_B will conduct while the other two diodes are reversed biased. In such a manner each diode conducts over one third of the supply cycle in sequence. The current/voltage to the load will then consist of a series of sinusoidal segments as illustrated in Fig. 3.44(b).

Power rectifier systems are not restricted to the three-phase configuration and multi-phase systems provide for improved ripple factors and increased DC voltages.

FURTHER READING

Ahmed, H. and P. J. Spreadbury (1973) *Electronics for Engineers, An Introduction*, Cambridge University Press, Cambridge.

Bell, E. C. and R. W. Whitehead (1987) *Basic Electrical Engineering & Instrumentation for Engineers*, 3rd edn, Granada Publishing, London.

Horowitz, P. and W. Hill (1989) *The Art of Electronics*, 2nd edn, Cambridge University Press, Cambridge.
Horrocks, D. H. (1990) *Feedback Circuits and Op. Amps*, 2nd edn, Chapman & Hall, London.
Watson, J. (1983) *Mastering Electronics*, Macmillan, London.

EXERCISES

3.1 The transistor circuit shown in Fig. Q3.1 has the base connected to the digital output port of a personal computer as shown. The transistor characteristics are $h_{FB} = 0.98$, the collector–base leakage current is $I_{CBO} = 1\,\mu A$ and the emitter–base diode voltage, $V_{BE} - 0.7\,V$. Determine the value of the output voltage, V_o, when
  (a) the port signal is set low, with $V_i = 0\,V$;
  (b) the port signal is set high, with $V_i = 5\,V$.

[5.95 V, 0.255 V]

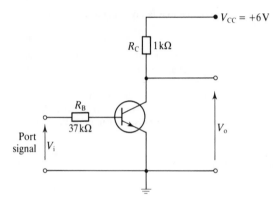

Figure Q3.1

3.2 For the circuit shown in Fig. Q3.1, determine the true base current, I_{BT}, and the output voltage, V_o, for input voltage values $V_i = 1, 2, 3$ and $4\,V$, respectively.

[9.1 μA, 36.1 μA, 63.3 μA, 90.2 μA, 5.55 V, 4.23 V, 2.95 V, 1.63 V]

3.3 A popular silicon npn transistor, BC107, has the following typical operating parameters:

$$V_{CE} = +10\,V, \quad I_{CT} = 25\,mA, \quad I_{BT} = 100\,\mu A, \quad V_{BE} = +0.7\,V$$

If the transistor is connected in the circuit shown in Fig. Q3.3, with a supply of $+20\,V$, determine the values of the load and base resistors which will achieve these operating conditions when $V_i = 0\,V$. Calculate the output voltage, V_o, when $V_i = 8\,V$.

[$R_B = 93\,k\Omega$, $R_L = 398\,\Omega$, 2.05 V]

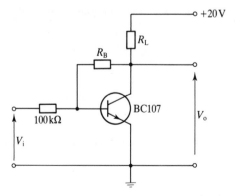

Figure Q3.3

3.4 An emitter-follower circuit uses a transistor with $h_{FE} = 100$. The supply voltage is $+15\,V$ and the base voltage is $+12\,V$. The emitter drives a load of $20\,\Omega$. Determine:
  (a) the input resistance of the amplifier;

(b) the input power supplied to the amplifier;

(c) the output power delivered to the load;

(d) the ratio of output voltage to input voltage.

[2.02 kΩ, 71.3 mW, 7.2 W, 0.94]

3.5   An amplifier has an internal input resistance of 20 kΩ, an output resistance of 80 Ω and an open circuit gain of 400. A voltage source of 20 mV and associated resistance 50 Ω supplies the amplifier which subsequently drives an external load of 200 Ω. Determine as a ratio and in decibels:

(a) the voltage gain between the load and the amplifier input;

(b) the overall power gain.

[285.7, 49.1 dB, 8163.3, 39.1 dB]

3.6   An amplifier of open circuit gain 1000, input resistance 2 kΩ and negligible output resistance employs negative voltage feedback, in which 1/20th of the output is coupled in series with the input. Calculate the voltage gain and the input resistance with feedback.

[19.6, 102 kΩ]

3.7   If the amplifier in question 3.6 has a reduced open circuit gain of 900, due to a faulty component, determine the resulting voltage gain with the same proportion of negative voltage feedback.

[19.56]

3.8   (a) An amplifier has an open circuit gain of 500, an input resistance of 40 kΩ and an output resistance of 500 Ω. The amplifier is driven by a voltage source having an internal resistance of 1 kΩ and a coupling capacitor of 0.2 μF is connected in series with the input line. The amplifier, which has a stray capacitance of 800 pF, is used to drive a load resistance of 5 kΩ. Estimate the upper and lower cut-off frequencies and the amplifier gain over the mid-frequency range.

[19.4 Hz, 437.7 kHz, 52.9 dB]

(b) If an additional capacitor of 0.01 μF is connected in parallel with the load resistor, determine the resulting upper cut-off frequency.

[32.4 kHz]

3.9   Determine the voltage gain of the operational amplifier shown in Fig. Q3.9.

[101]

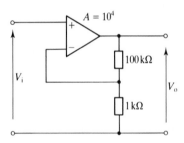

Figure Q3.9

3.10   For the operational amplifier circuit shown in Fig. Q3.10, determine from first principles the gain for each of the switch positions 'A' and 'B'.

[+1, −1]

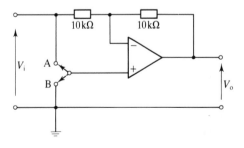

Figure Q3.10

3.11   Design a current-to-voltage converter, see Fig. 3.34(a), which will convert a 20 mA input signal to a 5 V output signal.

[R = 250 Ω]

3.12 Design a voltage-to-current converter, see Fig. 3.34(b), which will convert a 120 V DC input signal into a 20 mA output current signal.

$$[R = 6 \text{ k}\Omega]$$

3.13 An instrumentation amplifier is to provide an overall differential gain of 100. If the differential gain of the input and output stages are to be equal, select suitable values for the circuit resistors.

$$[R_1 = R_3 = R_5 = 10 \text{ k}\Omega, \ R_2 = 45 \text{ k}\Omega, \ R_4 = R_6 = 100 \text{ k}\Omega]$$

3.14 A transformer supplies 40 V r.m.s. at 50 Hz, via a single diode to a load of 2 kΩ. Calculate the value of a capacitor connected in parallel with the load such that the peak-to-peak ripple voltage is limited to 4 V. Calculate also the ripple factor for the circuit.

$$[136 \ \mu\text{F}, \ 2.1\%]$$

3.15 If the single diode in question 3.14 is replaced with a full diode bridge, determine the new value of smoothing capacitor required for the same peak-to-peak ripple voltage.

$$[68 \ \mu\text{F}]$$

3.16 A transformer supplies 70 V r.m.s. at 50 Hz, to a diode bridge circuit. The bridge output supplies a load of 5 kΩ and a smoothing capacitor of is connected in parallel with the load. If the ripple factor is to be 1 per cent, determine the value required for the smoothing capacitor.

$$[58 \ \mu\text{F}]$$

3.17 Using a mains transformer and full-wave rectification, it is required to supply an electronic circuit with 100 mA at 20 V DC. What is the value required of a smoothing capacitor which will ensure that the output ripple is no greater than 5 per cent of the DC voltage.

$$[1000 \ \mu\text{F}]$$

3.18 A stabilization circuit incorporates a Zener diode having a dynamic resistance of 12 Ω, a Zener voltage of 8 V and a Zener current of 1 mA. The stabilizer is fed from a full-wave rectified and smoothed source having a DC voltage of 12 V with a peak-to-peak ripple of 1 V. Select a suitable resistor, to be coupled in series with the Zener diode, such that the circuit will supply 20 mA at a nominal 8 V between full and zero load conditions. Calculate also the output ripple factor between the full and zero load conditions.

$$[190 \ \Omega, \ 1.6\%]$$

FOUR

INSTRUMENTATION, SENSORS AND MEASUREMENT

The implementation of any control action is based on the error which exists between the current value of the entity being controlled, or process variable, and the required value, or set point. Establishment of the error requires a measurement to be made of the process variable. In some cases, the set point is also a measured parameter. For an electronically based control system, either analogue or digital, the connection between the physical world and the control system is transmitted by some form or other of transducer, or sensor.

4.1 ANALOGUE AND DIGITAL TRANSDUCERS

The function of a tranducer is, in the broadest sense, one of energy conversion. To this end an electric motor could be considered as a transducer which converts electrical power into mechanical power. In the context of instrumentation and measurement, the transducer provides the means of conversion between the physical variable, which is representative of the process, to a proportional voltage or current. The proportional voltage, or current then forms the basic signal which represents the state of the process at any particular instant in time.

In manufacturing engineering, the most commonly measured parameters, for control purposes, are position and speed. These two parameters form the basic feedback variables associated with the control of machine tools, robots and automatic guided vehicles. Feedback control may also be based on a measurement of force, or on some visual criterion, particularly in the control of robotic arms and manipulators. In the general field of process control the measured variables might also include temperature, flow rate, torque, power, displacement, angle, strain, humidity, light intensity, acidity, sound or perhaps simply time. The list as given probably represents about 90 per cent of all the measurements made in the industrial environment. With the appropriate transducer and suitable output signal processing, all of the above physical parameters can be converted into a proportional voltage.

Most conventional transducers have an analogue output voltage which could be measured using fairly traditional instrumentation including, for example, an oscilloscope or a voltmeter. The output of many transducers, however, are in the millivolt range and more often than not the basic output must be further processed, or conditioned, to produce a useful signal. The processing required might only involve simple amplification, but if the controller is digitally based then additional signal processing is needed to convert the analogue voltage into a digital representation. This latter processing is performed using an analogue-to-digital convertor (see Sec. 10.2). An obvious advantage would be a transducer which can produce a direct digital output. Such a device could then dispense with the intricacies both of signal conditioning and analogue-to-digital conversion. There are, however, very few devices available which can easily produce a digital output in response to a physical variable. Figure 4.1 shows two possible arrangements for a liquid level sensor.

In Fig. 4.1(*a*) a separate flotation tube is connected to the tank as shown. The float is coupled to a variable potentiometer and the output voltage, *v*, forms the analogue representation of the liquid level in the tank. If the voltmeter used to measure the output voltage has a very large internal resistance, then the relation between the output voltage and the liquid level will be essentially linear. In the true analogue sense, the output voltage is directly proportional to the liquid level and infinitely variable over the range of the measurement. In practice the system might be subject to some friction effects which would make the movement, and subsequently the output, a little erratic and jerky.

The digital liquid level sensor, Fig. 4.1(*b*), consists of a group of float type switches arranged at equidistant heights in the side of the tank. As the liquid level rises, more of the switches are closed and these in turn connect more equal value resistors into the parallel circuit. There is also

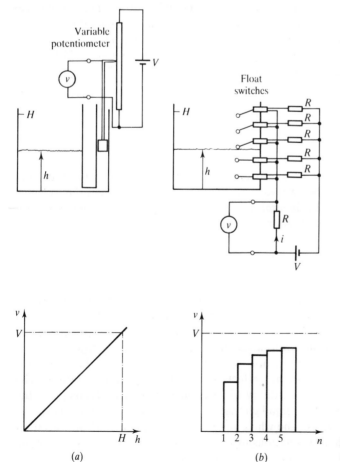

Figure 4.1 Liquid level sensors: (*a*) analogue; (*b*) digital.

one additional resistor, of equal value, connected in series with the battery and the parallel network. The equivalent resistance of the parallel network is given as R/n, where n is the number of float switches which are connected. It may easily be shown that the voltage across the series resistor is given by

$$v = nV/(n + 1) \tag{4.1}$$

It is apparent from Eq. (4.1) that the output voltage is nonlinearly related to the number of closed switches. The operation of the sensor is also discrete and there will be no change in output voltage while the liquid level rises between two consecutive switches. For the figure as shown, there are only five separately identifiable levels which can be distinguished. The accuracy of the digital sensor could be improved by including more switches with a reduced spacing between them. This, of course, will increase the cost and may not always be a viable proposition. Note also that the change in discrete voltage level decreases as the liquid level approaches the maximum value.

Although the sensor depicted in Fig. 4.1(*b*), is essentially digital in nature, the output still varies discretely in a nonlinear manner. A purer digital sensor could be actioned by removing the resistive network altogether and connecting all of the float switches in series with each other. A measure of the voltage between ground and the connection point between each consecutive switch would then indicate the presence, or otherwise, of the supply voltage. If the voltage is present then all switches below the measuring point must be on. If the measured voltage is zero then the switch immediately below the measuring point is in the off position. This would also suggest that all of the switches above the measuring position would then be in the off position. A survey of the voltage levels at each interconnection point between the switches would serve to indicate the state of the switches as being either on, or off. This is more consistent with a true digital system which operates between on and off states only.

4.2 STATIC CHARACTERISTICS

The general performance characteristics of a transducer can be subdivided into static and dynamic characteristics. If the variable being measured changes very slowly, then the dynamic response need not be of great concern. The dynamic characteristics, however, become important when the measured variable, or measurand, changes rapidly.

Static Calibration

The static calibration is the complete relation between the input measurand and the output signal from the transducer. Under calibration conditions the input variable is measured independently to an accuracy typically ten times better than that which is expected of the transducer being calibrated. The static calibration would include the effects of additional known influencing parameters such as the ambient temperature, or the age. Ideally these external influencing parameters should have a minimal effect on the transducer calibration. The calibration data yields the transducer static sensitivity which is the ratio of a small change in the output as a consequence of a correspondingly small change in the input. Under ideal conditions, this ratio should have a constant value over the whole range of measurements taken. Variation in the static sensitivity indicates a nonlinear relationship between the input and the output of the transducer.

Zero and Sensitivity Drift

If the input quantity is held at zero and the output then varies in response to changing external influences, then the transducer exhibits the adverse phenomenon of zero drift. Zero drift is usually expressed as the corresponding change in the output quantity for a known change in the influencing parameter, e.g. 0.5 mV/degree C. Similarly, sensitivity drift denotes the change in the calibration relationship over the range of measurement for a known change in the influencing parameter. The general effects of zero and sensitivity drift are shown in Fig. 4.2.

Linearity

In an ideal transducer the output is always equal to a constant times the basic input. Nonlinear characteristics tend to distort the output in the manner illustrated in Fig. 4.3.

Figure 4.3 shows that the variation of the input over a substantial nonlinear range of the transducer characteristic will result in a seriously distorted output signal. If the variation of the input occurs over a small range, which can be regarded as approximately linear, then the output will be only marginally distorted.

Ideally a transducer should have an input/output characteristic which is as close as possible to a straight line relationship. To account for small departures from perfect linearity, manufacturers often quote an accuracy, or an error band, which applies over the range of measurement of transducer,

$$\text{i.e. accuracy} = \pm A\% \text{ of reading}$$

$$\text{or accuracy} = \pm B\% \text{ of full scale reading}$$

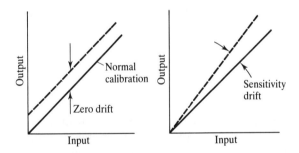

Figure 4.2 Effect of zero and sensitivity drift.

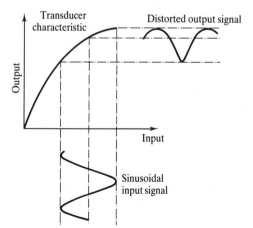

Figure 4.3 Distortion of output due to a nonlinear transducer characteristic.

The first type of accuracy specification recognizes the desirability of having a constant percentage nonlinearity. The second specification recognizes the impossibility of testing for small deviations near the zero measurement and is the more common type of accuracy, or nonlinearity, specification.

Hysteresis

Hysteresis is the difference between the input–output relationship for an increasing input, followed by a decreasing input. The causes of hysteresis are due to molecular friction, dry and viscous friction effects in mechanisms and magnetic effects as outlined in Sec. 2.9.

Threshold and Resolution

The threshold is the minimum value of input above the zero level which causes a measurable change in the output. On the other hand, the increment of input from some non-zero value, which causes a measurable change in the output, is referred to as the resolution. Background electrical noise, generated within the measuring system, usually determines the threshold and resolution of electro-mechanical measurement transducers. Hysteresis effects however may also influence the threshold and resolution.

Measuring Range, or Span

The span is the range between the lowest input value, set by the threshold, and the highest input value, set by the electrical or mechanical limitations of the transducer. The range is often referred to in the transducer specification as the 'dynamic range' and is quoted as the ratio of highest to lowest input signal value. The dynamic range is alternatively called the 'signal to noise ratio' and is frequently quoted in terms of decibels.

4.3 DYNAMIC CHARACTERISTICS

The dynamic characteristics of a measurement transducer determines how the instrument will respond to a time-varying input signal. An ideal instrument, with a perfect dynamic response, will be able to measure accurately any input irrespective of how quickly the input changes. In practice, all transducers have finite time responses, and there is a limit to the speed at which the transducer can change the output signal to reflect a corresponding change at the input. Although the input signal may vary in a completely random manner, the dynamic response of a transducer is usually defined by the behaviour it exhibits to particular standard input signals. The two most common test input signals are the discrete step change and the sinusoidal input.

The step input is applied to give a measure of the transducers transient response. The information gained from such a step input will show how rapidly the transducer output can follow a large and instantaneous change in the measured parameter. The nature and form of the transducer response will also reveal how the transducer can be mathematically modelled as a dynamic system.

The sinusoidal input is applied with constant amplitude, but varying frequency, to assess how the transducer is affected by the rate of change of the input signal. Many transducers exhibit a characteristic in which the output voltage decreases, or attenuates, as the input signal frequency increases. This decreasing output signal is also associated with a significant change in the phase relationship between the input and the output. The sinusoidal input therefore can reveal the transducers limitations with respect to a time-varying input signal. Normal practice is to quote an upper limiting input signal frequency, above which the transducer output is not an accurate replication of the input.

Although the standard test inputs may not be strict representations of the actual inputs to which the transducer will be subject, they cover a comprehensive enough range and a transducer system which performs satisfactorily under step and sinusoidal input signals will, in general, perform well under a more natural range of inputs. Other test signals include a linearly varying input, or ramp input, and a parabolically varying input. These, however, particularly the parabolic input, are less commonly used as a test signal.

Differential equations are used to model the relationship between the input and output of the transducer. The most widely used models are based on first-order, or second-order linear differential equations. A special ideal case is the zero-order equation, which is included for academic interest.

Zero-order Systems

The perfect measurement system is one in which the output is always directly proportional to the input and is additionally independent of the rate of change of the input. Such ideal characteristics are rarely encountered in the majority of industrial measurement systems.

First-order Systems

Many transducer systems, particularly those used in temperature measurements, can be adequately modelled as a first-order linear differential equation. The general form of the first-order equation is

$$\tau(\mathrm{d}Y/\mathrm{d}t) + Y = kX \tag{4.2}$$

where X and Y are the input and output, respectively. The parameter τ denotes the system time constant and k represents the general system gain, or for a measurement transducer, the static sensitivity. Equation (4.2) can be solved by rewriting it in a general form and introducing an integrating factor, i.e.

$$(\mathrm{d}Y/\mathrm{d}t) + (1/\tau)Y = kX/\tau$$

The integrating factor is

$$\exp\left[\int(1/\tau)\,\mathrm{d}t\right] = e^{(t/\tau)}$$

Multiplying through by the integrating factor gives

$$e^{(t/\tau)}(\mathrm{d}Y/\mathrm{d}t) + e^{(t/\tau)}(1/\tau)Y = e^{(t/\tau)}kX/\tau$$

or

$$\mathrm{d}/\mathrm{d}t(e^{(t/\tau)}Y) = e^{(t/\tau)}kX/\tau$$

Integrating both sides gives

$$e^{(t/\tau)}Y = \int(e^{(t/\tau)}kX/\tau)\,\mathrm{d}t = \tau e^{(t/\tau)}kX/\tau + C$$

$$Y = kX + Ce^{(-t/\tau)}$$

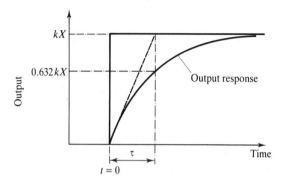

Figure 4.4 Response of a first-order system to a step input.

The constant C can be determined from the initial conditions at time $t = 0$: i.e. at time $t = 0$, $Y = 0$, thus

$$0 = kX + C \quad \text{or} \quad C = -kX$$

Hence

$$Y = kX[1 - e^{-t/\tau}] \tag{4.3}$$

The form of the solution is depicted in Fig. 4.4.

Equation (4.3) is an exponential function which approaches the value kX as time approaches infinity. Theoretically the output never reaches kX and the response is termed an exponential lag. The time constant τ represents the time which the output would take to reach the value kX if the initial rate of response were maintained. This is indicated by the broken line which is a tangent to the solution curve at time $t = 0$. The actual value of the output when $t = \tau$, is 63.2 per cent of the final steady-state value. For practical purposes the final steady-state output is taken to have been reached in a time of about five time constants.

Example A temperature measuring instrument has a dynamic response to a step input which is given by the relation

$$75(dV/dt) + 7.2\,V = 4 \times 10^{-4}T$$

where T is the measured temperature in degrees Centigrade and V is the output voltage from the transducer.
Determine:
(a) the time constant of the transducer;
(b) the static sensitivity;
(c) the time period which should be allowed before a measurement is taken following a step change in the temperature.
Rewriting the response equation to conform with the general form given in Eq. (4.2) gives

$$(75/7.2)(dV/dt) + V = (4 \times 10^{-4}/7.2)T$$

By comparison with Eq. 4.2, the time constant is

$$\tau = (75/7.2) = 10.4\,\text{s}$$

Similarly the static sensitivity is

$$k = (4 \times 10^{-4}/7.2) = 0.000\,055\,55\,\text{V/}^\circ\text{C} = 55.55\,\mu V/^\circ\text{C}$$

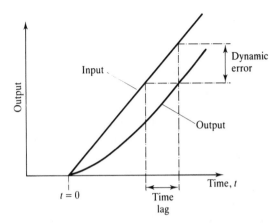

Figure 4.5 First-order system response to a ramp input.

Allowing five time constants to elapse before making a temperature measurement after a step change, gives a time period of

$$5 \times 10.4 = 52.1\,\text{s}$$

If the input is a ramp function then the response of a first-order system is shown in Fig. 4.5. The ramp input is simulated by making the right-hand side of Eq. (4.2) a linear function of time, i.e. kXt. The right-hand side of the equation may be solved using the method of integration by parts, with the result

$$Y = kX[t - \tau(1 - e^{-t/\tau})] \tag{4.4}$$

The solution equation shows that as time becomes large the output tends to $kX(t - \tau)$. The output response is therefore asymptotic to a steady-state lag $(kX\tau)$.

The response of a first order system to a sinusoidal input can be obtained by setting the right-hand side of Eq. (4.2) equal to $kX\sin(\omega t)$, where ω is the circular frequency in rad/s. The solution yields

$$Y = \frac{kX}{\sqrt{(1 + \tau^2\omega^2)}}\,[e^{-t/\tau}\,\sin\alpha + \sin(\omega t - \alpha)] \tag{4.5}$$

where $\alpha = \tan^{-1}(\tau\omega)$. The response is shown in Fig. 4.6.

The output response exhibits a decaying transient amplitude in combination with a steady-state sinusoidal behaviour of amplitude $kX/[\sqrt{(1 + \tau^2\omega^2)}]$ and lagging the input by the angle α.

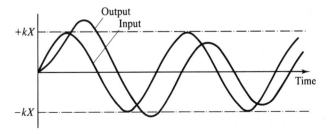

Figure 4.6 First-order system response to a sinusoidal input.

Second-order Systems

While some instrumentation transducers may be adequately modelled as a first-order linear differential equation, many more systems are more conformitively represented by a differential equation of the second order. The second-order differential equation has the general form

$$(\mathrm{d}^2 Y/\mathrm{d}t^2) + 2\zeta\omega_\mathrm{n}(\mathrm{d}Y/\mathrm{d}t) + \omega_\mathrm{n}^2(Y) = \omega_\mathrm{n}^2 K \tag{4.6}$$

ζ is termed the damping ratio and is defined as the ratio of the actual damping in the system to that which would produce critical damping, ω_n is the undamped natural frequency of the system, Y is the output and K is the input, or forcing function.

The solution of Eq. (4.6) is composed of two parts. The first part is called the complementary function and is the solution obtained when the right-hand side of the equation is set equal to zero. The complementary function describes the transient part of the solution. The second part is called the particular integral and this is a solution which satisfies the complete equation. The particular integral is obtained by assuming a solution for the case when the steady-state is reached. The form of the assumed solution is of the same order as the forcing function. Thus if the forcing function is a constant step input of amplitude K, then the assumed solution is also a constant, say A. Table 4.1 shows some typical input forcing functions and the corresponding assumed solutions for the particular integral.

The complete solution of Eq. (4.6) then consists of the sum of the complementary function and the particular integral.

Since both the first and second derivatives of Y are equal to zero when steady-state conditions are achieved, then the particular integral for Eq. (4.6) with a step input K, would have the general form $Y_\mathrm{PI} = A$.

The transient solution of Eq. (4.6), that is the complementary function, may be solved by the substitution $Y = D\,\mathrm{e}^{rt}$, where D is an arbitrary constant. Thus $\mathrm{d}Y/\mathrm{d}t = rD\,\mathrm{e}^{rt}$ and $\mathrm{d}^2 Y/\mathrm{d}t^2 = r^2 D\,\mathrm{e}^{rt}$. The general complementary function becomes

$$\begin{aligned} r^2 D\,\mathrm{e}^{rt} + 2\zeta\omega_\mathrm{n}rD\,\mathrm{e}^{rt} + \omega_\mathrm{n}^2 D\,\mathrm{e}^{rt} &= 0 \\ r^2 + (2\zeta\omega_\mathrm{n})r + \omega_\mathrm{n}^2 &= 0 \end{aligned} \tag{4.7}$$

Equation (4.7) is referred to as the auxiliary equation. The roots of the quadratic auxiliary equation are

$$r = (1/2)[-2\zeta\omega_\mathrm{n} \pm \sqrt{4\zeta^2\omega_\mathrm{n}^2 - 4\omega_\mathrm{n}^2}] = [-\zeta\omega_\mathrm{n} \pm (\sqrt{\zeta^2 - 1})\omega_\mathrm{n}]$$

$$r_1 = [-\zeta\omega_\mathrm{n} - (\sqrt{\zeta^2 - 1})\omega_\mathrm{n}] \quad \text{and} \quad r_2 = [-\zeta\omega_\mathrm{n} + (\sqrt{\zeta^2 - 1})\omega_\mathrm{n}]$$

Hence the complementary function becomes

$$Y = G \exp(r_1 t) + H \exp(r_2 t)$$

Table 4.1 Assumed solutions for obtaining the particular integral Y_PI.

Forcing function, $K = f(t)$	Assumed solution, Y_PI
K	A
Kt	$At + B$
Kt^2	$At^2 + Bt + C$
$K \sin(\omega t)$	$A \sin(\omega t) + B \cos(\omega t)$

where G and H are arbitrary constants. Substituting for r_1 and r_2 we obtain

$$Y = G \exp[-\zeta\omega_n t - (\sqrt{\zeta^2 - 1})\omega_n t] + H \exp[-\zeta\omega_n t + (\sqrt{\zeta^2 - 1})\omega_n t]$$

The complete solution, including the particular integral is

$$Y = G \exp[-\zeta\omega_n t - (\sqrt{\zeta^2 - 1})\omega_n t] + H \exp[-\zeta\omega_n t + (\sqrt{\zeta^2 - 1})\omega_n t] + A \qquad (4.8)$$

Equation (4.8) shows that the complete solution will be dependent on the magnitude of the damping ratio, which can be either greater than, equal to, or less than, unity.

Heavy damping, $\zeta > 1$ The solution is

$$Y = G \exp[-\zeta\omega_n t - (\omega_n \sqrt{\zeta^2 - 1})t] + H \exp[-\zeta\omega_n t + (\omega_n \sqrt{\zeta^2 - 1})t] + A \qquad (4.9)$$

Both roots of the auxiliary equation are real and the solution for heavy damping results in the sum of two exponentials, plus the additional particular integral.

Critical damping, $\zeta = 1$ Equation (4.8) reduces to

$$Y = G \exp(-\zeta\omega_n t) + H \exp(-\zeta\omega_n t) + A$$
$$Y = (G + H) \exp(-\zeta\omega_n t) + A = F \exp(-\zeta\omega_n t) + A$$

where $F = (G + H)$.

The above 'solution' is not strictly correct since there is only one arbitrary constant, F. For any second-order differential equation there must be two arbitrary constants in the solution. Critical damping represents a special case where the roots of the auxiliary equation are repeated. It may be shown that the correct solution is given by

$$Y = \exp(-\zeta\omega_n t)[Gt + H] + A = \exp(-\omega_n t)[Gt + H] + A \qquad (4.10)$$

Differentiation of Eq. (4.10) and substitution back into Eq. (4.6) will show that it does represent a correct solution of the original differential equation.

Light damping, $\zeta < 1$ With the damping ratio less than unity the roots of the auxiliary equation have both real and imaginary components, and, in fact, form a pair of complex conjugates. From Eq. (4.8) the solution may be written as

$$Y = \exp(-\zeta\omega_n t)\{G \exp[-(\sqrt{\zeta^2 - 1}\omega_n t)]\} + H \exp[+(\sqrt{\zeta^2 - 1}\omega_n t)] + A$$

Using the complex operator, $j = \sqrt{-1}$ gives

$$Y = \exp(-\zeta\omega_n t)\{G \exp[-j(\sqrt{1 - \zeta^2}\omega_n t)]\} + H \exp[+j(\sqrt{1 - \zeta^2}\omega_n t)] + A$$

The group of terms, $\sqrt{1 - \zeta^2}\omega_n$, is referred to as the damped natural frequency, ω_d. Substituting ω_d gives

$$Y = \exp(-\zeta\omega_n t)\{G \exp[-j\omega_d t]\} + H \exp[+j\omega_d t] + A$$

Now using the mathematical identity, $e^{jx} = \cos(x) + j\sin(x)$ gives

$$Y = \exp(-\zeta\omega_n t)[G\{\cos(\omega_d t) - j\sin(\omega_d t)\} + H\{\cos(\omega_d t) - j\sin(\omega_d t)\}] + A$$
$$Y = \exp(-\zeta\omega_n t)[(G + H)\cos(\omega_d t) + j(H - G)\sin(\omega_d t)] + A$$

This complex form of the solution may be modified to

$$Y = \exp(-\zeta\omega_n t)[G'\cos(\omega_d t) + H'\sin(\omega_d t)] + A \qquad (4.11)$$

The constants G' and H' may be real or complex but are normally real.

Equation (4.11) may also be expressed in the form:

$$Y = F' \exp(-\zeta\omega_n t) \sin(\omega_d t + \phi) + A \tag{4.12}$$

where $F' = \sqrt{G'^2 + H'^2}$ and $\phi = \tan^{-1}(H'/G')$.

Equation (4.12) indicates that the form of the response will consist of a sine wave of circular frequency ω_d, with a superimposed exponential decay.

With the system initially at rest, the constants G' and H' are determined by the conditions that $Y = 0$ and $dY/dt = 0$, at time $t = 0$. Note that in determining the values of these constants, the complete solution, including the particular integral must be considered (see example in Sec. 14.2).

The three possible solutions, for a step input, are shown in Fig. 4.7. The output Y is plotted as a percentage of the step input A against the parameter $\omega_n t$. This gives a dimensionless plot of the response which would be the same for all second-order systems subject to a step input.

For ζ equal to unity, the system is critically damped and the steady-state value is attained in the shortest possible time without any oscillatory response. With ζ greater than unity, the system is overdamped and the response curve is again exponential in form. Overdamped systems may have an undesirably sluggish response. Indeed since the effect of $\zeta > 1$ simply delays the response to the steady-state value then there is no real advantage to be gained in arbitrarily imposing high ζ values.

For cases where ζ is less than unity, the system is said to be underdamped and the response curve is oscillatory with an exponential decay. A number of performance measures are used to describe the response of an underdamped system to a step input. These are illustrated in Fig. 4.8.

It is worth noting at this juncture that the terms of periodic time, and circular frequency, only really apply to constant amplitude sine waves. In cases where the amplitude is decreasing, the periodic times only applies accurately across turning points and those points in the output response which cross the datum line when $Y = A$.

The speed of the response is reflected in the rise time τ_R and the peak time τ_P. For underdamped systems, the rise time is the time taken for the output to reach 100 per cent of the step input. The peak time is the time taken to the first maximum in the output response. For critically damped and overdamped systems, the time taken for the output to change between 10 and 90 per cent of the output is used alternatively as a measure of the speed of the response.

The degree to which the actual output response matches the input is measured by the percentage overshoot PO and the settling time. The percentage overshoot is defined as

$$PO = (M_{PT} - 100)/100 \tag{4.13}$$

where M_{PT} is the peak value of the output.

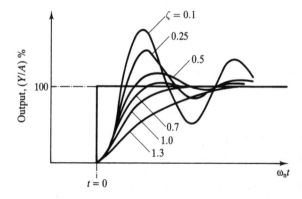

Figure 4.7 Response of a second-order system to a step input.

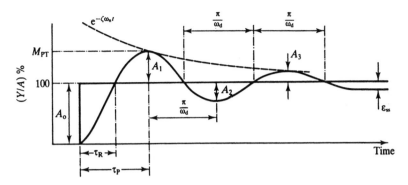

Figure 4.8 Response curve for an underdamped system to a step input.

Alternatively, using Eq. (4.12) we obtain

$$\frac{A_0}{A_1} = \frac{F' \exp(-\zeta\omega_n t_0) \sin(\omega_d t_0 + \phi)}{F' \exp(-\zeta\omega_n t_1) \sin(\omega_d t_1 + \phi)}$$

and

$$t_1 = t_0 + \pi/\omega_d$$

$$\frac{A_0}{A_1} = \frac{F' \exp(-\zeta\omega_n t_0) \sin(\omega_d t_0 + \phi)}{F' \exp(-\zeta\omega_n t_0) \exp(-\zeta\omega_n \pi/\omega_d) \sin(\omega_d t_0 + \pi/\omega_d + \phi)}$$

$$A_0/A_1 = \exp(\zeta\omega_n \pi/\omega_d)$$

or

$$A_0/A_1 = \exp(\zeta\pi/\sqrt{1-\zeta^2}) \tag{4.14}$$

Taking the natural logarithm of each side of the equation gives the numerical result

$$\ln[A_0/A_1] = \pi\zeta/\sqrt{1-\zeta^2} \tag{4.15}$$

Multiplying Eq. (4.14) by 100 will give the percentage overshoot. Equation (4.14) therefore represents a useful method of determining the damping factor from the response curve of a second-order system to a step input.

In general, after m half-cycles

$$\ln[A_0/A_m] = m\pi\zeta/\sqrt{1-\zeta^2} \tag{4.16}$$

and for the particular value of $m = 2$

$$\ln[A_0/A_2] = 2\pi\zeta/\sqrt{1-\zeta^2} \tag{4.17}$$

Equation (4.17) is referred to as the 'logarithmic decrement'. Note also that the logarithmic decrement can be evaluated from the ratio of any two consecutive peaks, or troughs, in the output response.

The settling time τ_s is the time taken for the oscillatory response to decay below a percentage of the input amplitude δ, often taken as 2 per cent.

Finally we have the steady-state error, ε_{ss}, which is the constant error which exists between the output and the input after the transient response has died away.

The response of the second-order system to a ramp input is shown in Fig. 4.9. The form of the response curves again depends on the value of the damping ratio but in each case the output

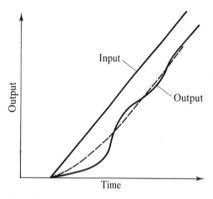

Figure 4.9 Response of a second-order system to a ramp input.

asymptotes to a steady-state lag. The lag is not the same in each case, however, since this is also dependent on the damping ratio.

The response of a second-order system to a sinusoidal input may also be considered. Generally the output response will lag behind the input with a transient decaying amplitude depending on the nature of the damping ratio.

The response of first- and second-order systems to sinusoidal input signals, however, is more appropriately handled in terms of Laplace transform methods which are considered in Chapter 11.

Example The dynamic performance of a piezo-electric accelerometer is described by the following differential equation:

$$\mathrm{d}^2v/\mathrm{d}t^2 + 2.4 \times 10^5(\mathrm{d}v/\mathrm{d}t) + 2.25 \times 10^{10}(v) = 10 \times 10^{10}$$

where v is the output voltage of the transducer. Determine:

(*a*) the undamped natural frequency;
(*b*) the damping factor;
(*c*) the damped natural frequency;
(*d*) the percentage overshoot expected for a step input signal.

Comparison with the general second-order differential equation, i.e. Eq. (4.6), gives

$$\omega_n^2 = 2.25 \times 10^{10}$$
$$\omega_n = \sqrt{2.25 \times 10^{10}} = 150\,000 \text{ rad/s}$$

or

$$f_n = 150\,000/2\pi = 23\,873 \text{ Hz} = 23.9 \text{ kHz}$$

Also

$$2\zeta\omega_n = 2.4 \times 10^5$$

therefore

$$\zeta = 2.4 \times 10^5/(2 \times 150\,000) = 0.8$$

Hence

$$PO = e^{-[\zeta\pi/\sqrt{1-\zeta^2}]} = e^{-[0.8\pi/\sqrt{1-0.8^2}]} = 0.0152 = 1.52\%$$

and

$$\omega_d = (\sqrt{1-\zeta^2})\omega_n = (\sqrt{1-0.8^2})150\,000 = 90\,000 \text{ rad/s}$$

or

$$f_d = 90\,000/2\pi = 143\,23.9 \text{ Hz} = 14.3 \text{ kHz}$$

Higher-order Systems

Generally, an nth-order differential equation will have an nth-degree characteristic equation and can be solved for the n roots. Making special provision for repeated roots and allowing the arbitrary constants to be real or complex numbers, the solution takes the form:

$$Y = C_1 e^{r_1 t} + C_2 e^{r_2 t} + C_3 e^{r_3 t} + \ldots + C_n e^{r_n t} \tag{4.18}$$

where C_1, C_2, C_3, . . . , C_n are arbitrary constants determined from n initial conditions.

Determination of the roots of the equation may be troublesome but the solution procedure is consistent and in principle can be applied to ordinary differential equations of any order. However, and fortuitously in most applications, the first- or second-order model will generally suffice to define the dynamic response of the system. In addition, although first- and second-order system models have been introduced at this point to describe the dynamic characteristics of transducers, the models have general applicability to dynamic systems. First- and second-order system models are often therefore used to quantify the behaviour of many of the elements which are encountered in industrial control systems.

4.4 TRANSDUCER PRINCIPLES

Many electrical transducers operate on the basis of one of the three quanities, resistance, capacitance or inductance.

Variable Resistance Transducers

The potential divider is one of the simplest of variable resistance transducers and for slowly varying systems, it is also the closest approximation to the ideal zero-order system (see also Sec. 4.5). Potential dividers are often used as a displacement transducer and they are commercially available in stroke lengths ranging from a few tenths of a millimetre to a few hundred millimetres.

Another form of variable resistance transducer is based on the nature of Eq. (2.6), which indicates that the resistance of a current-carrying conductor is directly proportional to the length of the conductor. This is the operating principle of the strain gauge, which is considered in more detail in Sec. 4.8. The physical quantities which might cause the conductor to alter its length are extensive and this makes the strain gauge a particularly versatile sensing element in a large variety of transducer designs.

The resistance of all metals are approximately linearly proportional to temperature. The resistance/temperature coefficients for metals, however, are usually very small and the change in resistance over a large temperature range is not very significant. On the other hand, many semiconductor materials, for example the so-called thermistor, exhibit a large decrease in resistance for a moderate increase in temperature. It would seem appropriate therefore that semiconductors would be able to function quite well as a temperature sensitive device. This is certainly true but the nonlinear resistance/temperature characteristics, coupled with undesirable self-heating and noise effects, have somewhat inhibited the popularity of semiconductor devices as temperature sensors.

Other forms of variable resistance transducer include the photodiode. Operating in reverse bias mode, the resistance of the photodiode is sensitive to incident light, the resistance decreasing as the light intensity increases. This makes the photodiode a useful light-sensitive transducer. The phototransistor is also light sensitive and it is often used to transmit signals across an opto-isolated interface.

Variable Capacitance Transducers

In Sec. 2.8 the term capacitance was introduced and it was shown that capacitance is directly proportional to both the plate area and the relative permittivity of the dielectric material and inversely proportional to the distance separating the plates. Capacitance can therefore be altered by changing either of the influencing parameters. Variable distance capacitive transducers are generally more sensitive then variable area devices. The variable area devices, however, are inherently more linear because of the direct proportionality relationship. Variable dielectric devices are not very common and are rarely encountered in practice.

Differential capacitive devices can be made using a three-plate device in which a central plate is free to move relative to two fixed outer plates. Such devices have improved linearity characteristics and are often used to monitor differential quantities such as pressure differences.

The external circuitry for capacitive tranducers usually involves a Wheatstone bridge supplied from an AC source. For complete balance of the bridge, both the magnitude and the phase relationship between each arm of the bridge must be equal. Another usual requirement is that the signal leads must be screened, or shielded, to counteract the effects of stray capacitance between the signal leads and ground.

Variable Inductance Transducers

Many other transducer systems operate under some means of variable inductance. Equation (2.29) shows that the inductance of a coil is given by

$$L = \mu A N^2 / l \tag{4.19}$$

For an iron cored coil with an air gap, Eq. (4.19) takes the composite form:

$$L = \frac{AN^2}{(l_{\text{iron}}/\mu_{\text{iron}}) + (l_{\text{air}}/\mu_{\text{air}})} \tag{4.20}$$

Even for small values of air gap, $(l_{\text{air}}/\mu_{\text{air}}) \gg (l_{\text{iron}}/\mu_{\text{iron}})$ the inductance L is very sensitive to changes in the length of the air gap. Many inductive transducers utilize this phenomenon as a basic principle of operation. The linear variable differential transformer, featured in Sec. 4.6, incorporates two further refinements. These are a differential output coil system and an additional winding in which a mutual inductance transformer action replaces the self-inductance of a single coil.

4.5 MEASUREMENT OF ANGULAR POSITION

The absolute shaft encoder is a suitable transducer for the measurement of angular position and has the added advantage of having a digital output which can be interfaced directly to a computer. Figure 4.10 illustrates the basic requirements of the device which incorporates a sectioned disc which is mounted onto the primary rotating element.

The disc is divided into a number of tracks, three in this case, and a number of sectors. If the number of tracks is denoted by m, then the number of sectors is numerically given by 2 raised to the power m. With $m = 3$, the number of sectors is eight and this also denotes the number of angular resolvable sections on the disc. For each resolvable section a unique pattern is generated. These patterns may be detected by optical, magnetic or direct contact methods. Resolution may be improved with the addition of more tracks. Twelve tracks for example give an angular resolution to within 0.09 degrees of rotation. The absolute shaft encoder may be used either to measure rotational speed, or angular displacement. In Fig. 4.10 a simple binary code has been used to illustrate the principle of the absolute shaft encoder. It can be seen that between sectors 3 and 4 and sectors 7 and 0 all of the tracks undergo a change in pattern. When all of the tracks change there must always be one which changes first before the others. Any misalignment of the track sensors therefore could generate a considerable error in rotational position measurement. For this reasons, practical shaft encoders use some 'unit distance code' in preference to a binary code. A unit distance code such as the 'Gray code' is one in which only one track changes pattern for each consecutive resolvable position.

A close relative, but one which operates on a rather different principle, is the incremental shaft encoder. The incremental shaft encoder consists of a disc in which a series of holes or marks, are arranged around the periphery. A light source, usually a light emitting diode, is positioned on one side of the disc and a photosensitive transistor on the other (Fig. 4.11).

Rotation of the disc will generate a series of light pulses which will be registered as a square pulse train output from the photosensitive transistor. By counting the number of pulses relative to a known datum, the angular position of the disc can be determined. By using two light sources and two photosensitive transistors, with a 90° phase difference between the two output signals, the direction of rotation may also be ascertained. The phase relationship between the two signals for clockwise and anticlockwise rotation is illustrated in Fig. 4.12. A similar system may equally well be used to measure linear position and direction.

In clockwise, or right-hand movement, the signal form S_2 comes on while the signal from S_1 is still on. For anticlockwise, or left-hand movement, S_2 comes on while the signal from S_1 is off. This relative switching of the two signals forms the basis of the direction sensing. In manufacturing applications, high-resolution incremental encoders are often used as position feedback sensors, either rotating with a leadscrew, or in linear motion with a machine slide.

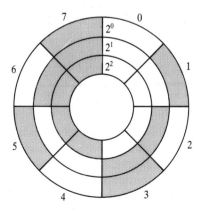

Figure 4.10 Absolute digital shaft encoder (3-bit binary code).

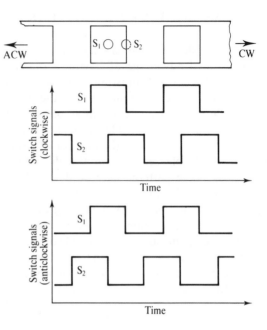

Figure 4.12 Direction sensing with an incremental shaft encoder.

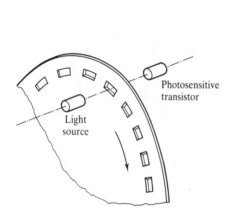

Figure 4.11 Incremental shaft encoder.

They are also used to measure the joint positions in robotic manipulators. In these applications, where high accuracy is essential the encoders consist of two glass gratings, one of which is fixed and the other which moves. Light which is transmitted through both gratings, varies in intensity with the relative displacement of the gratings. The light intensity is picked up by two phototransistors and the signals used to measure relative position and direction in much the same manner as described previously. The grating pitch is typically 100 per millimetre, but the resolution can be greatly increased by using the Moire fringe effect. Moire fringes are a diffraction effect which results when the gratings are inclined at a slight angle to each other. The important feature is that the spacing of the interference fringes are many times the spacing of the grid lines. A grid inclination angle of just less than half a degree, with 100 grid lines per millimetre, would produce a fringe pattern with a one millimetre spacing.

The main disadvantages of the incremental encoder are the possibility of missing a pulse during the count and the loss of the datum reference in the event of a power failure. Electrical noise and dirt between the light source and the phototransistor are also problematical. Nonetheless, incremental encoders are cheaper and generally more accurate than absolute encoders.

When accuracy is less important an angular position transducer based on the variable potential divider can be used (Fig. 4.13). By measuring the voltage between points A and B, a linear relationship between angular displacement, ϕ and voltage v is obtained

$$\phi = v(\Phi/V) \qquad (4.21)$$

where Φ is the maximum angular rotation and V is the supply voltage. The maximum voltage occurs when the sliding contact at B reaches the maximum rotation at J.

As an angular position transducer, however, the variable potential divider has a number of limitations. Equation (4.21) is strictly applicable only if the internal resistance of the voltmeter used to measure v can be considered to be infinite. Taking the internal resistance of the

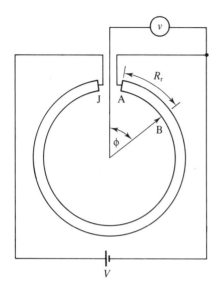

Figure 4.13 Variable potential angular position transducer.

voltmeter R_i into account, Ohms law for parallel resistors can be used to show that the total resistance between points A and B is

$$R_{total} = (R_i R_r)/(R_i + R_r) = R_r/(1 + (R_r/R_i)) \qquad (4.22)$$

where R_r is the resistance along the arc of resistor element enclosed by the angle ϕ.

Equation (4.22) shows that R_{total} will approach the value of R_r only when R_i tends to infinity. This is another manifestation of a loading error, which causes the net resistance between A and B to be reduced due to the additional circuit through the voltmeter.

Further limitations are associated with the sliding contact at B which is a source of friction and inevitable wear.

4.6 MEASUREMENT OF LINEAR DISPLACEMENT

The incremental encoder and the variable potential divider can each be easily adapted for the measurement of linear displacement. The most common transducer used to measure linear displacement however is the linear variable differential transformer (LVDT). LVDTs incorporate an iron core which can move freely within a primary, or power coil and two secondary coils (Fig. 4.14).

The secondary coils are connected in series opposition and are equally positioned with respect to the primary coil. When the core is centrally located the e.m.f.s generated in the secondary coils are equal and opposite and the net output voltage is zero. Displacement of the core relative to the central zero produces a proportional AC output which is converted to a DC output via rectification and smoothing circuits. LVDT transducers are essentially immune to friction and wear problems, they have infinite resolution and are highly linear and accurate. LVDTs are available with measurement ranges up to about one metre.

There are, in addition, a wide range of other displacement transducers which rely on inductive, or capacitive effects. These are mostly restricted to the measurement of relatively small displacements, of the order of 0.1 mm. Linear scales, also known as 'Inductosyns', are frequently used for the precision measurement of linear position (Fig. 4.15). They are especially prevalent as a position sensor in machine tool slides.

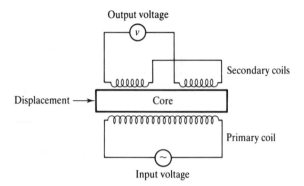

Figure 4.14 Linear variable differential transformer.

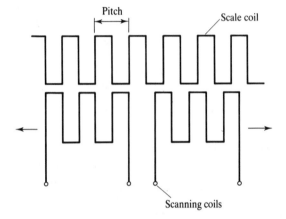

Figure 4.15 Linear scale, or 'Inductosyn'

The scale coil is in the form of a linear 'stator' and the scanning coils operate as movable 'rotors'. The pitch of the stator and rotor coils, typically 2 mm, is accurately formed and the two rotor coils are displaced relative to each other by 0.25 of the pitch. The unit operates in much the same way as a transformer, with the rotor coils representing the primary windings and the stator coil the secondary windings. An AC voltage is supplied to each of the rotor coils with a phase shift of 90° between the two signals. The voltage generated in the stator coil is the sum of the two rotor coil voltages. The scale coil output can be decoded through measurement of the phase changes induced by movement of the rotor coils. Accuracies of 0.001 mm are possible but it is necessary to count the number of cycles generated since the output signal is periodic. The inductosyn scale was developed from the synchro resolver which was the main shaft position transducer prior to the introduction of modern digital systems.

4.7 MEASUREMENT OF ROTATIONAL SPEED

Rotational speed is a commonly monitored parameter in general engineering measurement applications and there is considerable variety in the types of transducer used for the purpose. The absolute digital shaft encoder is suitable but the incremental shaft encoder is more easily adapted for the measurement of rotational speed. The output waveform from any one of the photosensitive transistors on the incremental encoder is either a square pulse train, or a sinusoidal-like signal. Measurement of the output signal frequency can then be simply converted to the rotational speed. The signal frequency can be determined in software using the timing facilities available on most microcomputers. Alternatively, the signal can be processed through a frequency to voltage convertor, to produce a DC output voltage which can be calibrated in direct proportion with the rotational speed. The latter method represents a more complete speed measuring sensor which facilitates easier interfacing to a computer. Frequency-to-voltage convertors are readily available in a range of integrated circuit forms.

The frequency-to-voltage converter also forms an integral part of many other types of speed measuring transducer. One fairly common speed measuring device is the magnetic pick-up. This passive transducer, requiring no external power supply, responds to the movement of ferrous parts past its pole piece by inducing an e.m.f. in a coil. Figure 4.16 shows the basic configuration which requires the transducer to be in close proximity to a toothed wheel. The output signal is approximately sinusoidal and a frequency-to-voltage convertor completes the signal processing for adaptation as a speed sensor.

Optical sensing devices are also fairly common and these include slotted opto-switches (Fig. 4.17). These usually incorporate a light emitting diode as a light source and a photosensitive transistor as a receiving device. A toothed wheel passing between the receiver and transmitter will generate the necesssary pulsed output signal. Frequency-to-voltage conversion again completes the system for speed measurement.

Optical devices containing both the receiver and the transmitter on the one unit are also available (Fig. 4.18). These units respond to the passage of a reflective surface as shown. This particular type of optical sensor is often used in hand-held tachometers.

Last, but not least in the list, is the well-established and fairly traditional tachogenerator. These are often found in older systems where they were once used as the standard transducer for speed measurement. The tachogenerator is a small permanent magnet alternator with an output voltage almost exactly proportional to speed. The voltage generated at full speed is typically of the order of 120 V. This voltage is much too high to be interfaced to a computer-based system and the output must be rectified and reduced through a voltage divider to be compatible with a digital system.

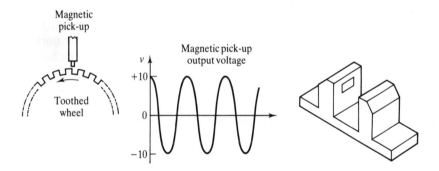

Figure 4.16 Magnetic pick-up speed sensor. Figure 4.17 Slotted opto-switch.

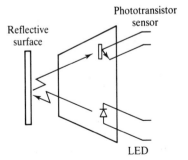

Figure 4.18 Opto-electrical sensor.

The frequency of the tachogenerator output is also proportional to speed, and alternative signal conditioning circuitry can be added to take advantage of the frequency characteristics. Conditioning circuits based on the frequency of the tachogenerator output either use a pulse counting system, or a frequency-to-voltage convertor. Due to high cost and the high driving power required, tachogenerators are now only used on fairly large rotating machine elements.

4.8 TRANSDUCERS BASED ON STRAIN MEASUREMENT

In transducer technology, 'strain bridge' circuits are featured predominantly. The underlying reason for this is simply that strain, which is essentially a displacement, can be measured as the resultant of a wide range of physical causes. The versatility of strain measurement is such that it finds applications in devices adapted for the measurement of force or load, torque, pressure, flow rate, acceleration, displacement and seismic activity amongst others. The common factor involved is that the physical variable to be measured ultimately causes, by design, a deflection in an elastic member. Direct measurement of the strain associated with the deflection can then be related back to the physical variable through a calibration. Strain sensitive sensors are invariably incorporated into a Wheatstone bridge circuit (Fig. 4.19).

The Wheatstone bridge consists of four resistors, a voltage source and usually a high impedance instrument to record the bridge output voltage. When the bridge is 'balanced', no current is drawn through the voltmeter. From Ohm's law it can be shown that for balanced conditions the resistance ratios A/C and B/D must be equal. Thus if C is a variable resistor, A may be determined if C, B and D are all known.

In most cases the sensing element constitutes one 'arm' of the bridge while the other three arms have constant resistances, usually equal to the sensing element resistance at particular reference conditions. These bridges normally operate in an unbalanced mode where the voltmeter reading is used to quantify the changing conditions at the sensing element, being the result of changes in the physical variable which is measured. Figure 4.20 shows the normal bridge configuration. Assuming that the bridge is initially in balance, with all elements having a resistance R. The sensing element is then subjected to a condition which causes its resistance to change to $(R + \Delta R)$. The bridge thus becomes unbalanced and a potential difference v is generated and registered on the voltmeter. Given that the voltmeter has nearly infinite resistance then there is zero current drawn through the voltmeter. The current drawn through

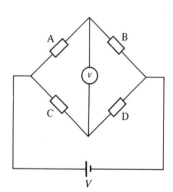

Figure 4.19 Resistive element Wheatstone bridge.

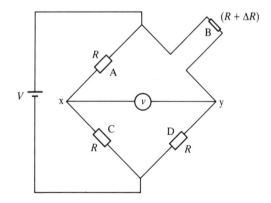

Figure 4.20 Unbalanced mode Wheatstone bridge.

A and C is $V/2R$, while that drawn through B and D is $V/(2R + \Delta R)$. The potential available at x is

$$(V - RV/2R) = V/2$$

The potential available at y is

$$(V - V\{R + \Delta R\}/\{2R + \Delta R\})$$

The resultant potential difference $(x - y)$ is

$$v = V/2 - V(1 - \{R + \Delta R\}/\{2R + \Delta R\})$$
$$= (V/2)(2\{R + \Delta R\}\{2R + \Delta R\} - 1)$$
$$v = \frac{V}{2} \frac{\Delta R}{R} (1/\{2 + \Delta R/R\})$$

If $R \gg \Delta R$ then the potential difference is given approximately as

$$v = \frac{V\Delta R}{4R} \tag{4.23}$$

Even if the voltage recording instrument has a low internal resistance, for example a centre-zero galvanometer, then application of Thevenin's theorem shows that a near-linear relationship still applies provided that ΔR remains small.

The simple resistive element Wheatstone bridge provides the basic circuit to be used with a variable resistance sensor to form a working transducer. The sensor could be a thermistor in a temperature sensitive system, or a strain gauge in a displacement sensitive system.

The principle embodied in a strain gauge is that a conductor, of initially uniform dimensions, will alter its proportions when subjected to an applied stress. Since the resistance of the conductor is also dependent on the physical proportions, then the stress will also influence the resistance of the conductor. The resistance of a conductor is given by Eq. (2.6), i.e.

$$R = \rho(L/A)$$

where ρ is the resistivity of the material, L is the length of the conductor, and A is the cross-sectional area of the conductor.

For a cylindrical conductor, the cross sectional area is $\pi D^2/4$, where D is the diameter of the cylinder. Differentiating Eq. (2.6) gives

$$(dR/R) = (d\rho/\rho) + (dL/L) - (dA/A)$$

Now $(dA/A) = 2(dD/D)$, thus $(dR/R) = (d\rho/\rho) + (dL/L) - 2(dD/D)$. Multiplying through by (L/dL) gives

$$(dR/R)(L/dL) = (d\rho/\rho)(L/dL) + 1 - 2(dD/D)(L/dL) \tag{4.24}$$

Now (dL/L) is the ratio of the change in length to the original length, which by definition is the axial strain, ε_a. Similarly (dD/D), by definition, is the transverse strain ε_t. Also $(dD/D)(L/dL) = (\varepsilon_t/\varepsilon_a) = -\nu$, where ν is Poisson's ratio for the material. Substitution of these parameters into Eq. (4.24) gives

$$(dR/R)(L/dL) = (d\rho/\rho)(1/\varepsilon_a) + 1 + 2\nu \tag{4.25}$$

The subject of Eq. (4.25) $((dR/R)(L/dL))$ is called the 'gauge factor' and is traditionally denoted by G. The constancy of the right-hand side of Eq. (4.25) determines the suitability of any material to function as a strain gauge. Since

$$G = (dR/R)(L/dL) = (dR/R)(1/\varepsilon_a)$$

then

$$dR = GR\varepsilon_a \qquad (4.26)$$

Values of G and R are specified by the manufacturer of the strain gauge and Eq. (4.26) shows that the change in resistance dR is directly proportional to the axial strain ε_a.

Evidently a high value of G would be advantageous in producing a high change in resistance for any input axial strain. Metallic strain gauge materials have gauge factors of about 2, although some semiconductor materials have gauge factors in excess of 100. The commonest form of strain gauge is the bonded foil type, Fig. 4.21.

Bonded foil strain gauges are rigidly fixed to the strained member and are electrically insulated from it. In typical applications, the change in resistance is very small, of the order of $0.25\,\text{m}\Omega$ per microstrain, and as a result of the measurement is very sensitive to temperature variations. Unless special temperature compensating gauges are available, it becomes necessary to provide some other means of compensation for temperature drift. The usual method is to incorporate a 'dummy' gauge into the bridge circuit (Fig. 4.22). The dummy gauge is at all times subject to the same ambient temperature as the active gauge, but it is attached to a separate, unstrained piece of the same material. In this manner resistance changes owing to temperature variation are cancelled out and the output voltage is a result only of applied strain on the active gauge. The extra 'compensation lead' shown in the diagram is used to negate the effect of temperature variations in the wiring to the active gauge. This is not an essential part of the circuit, but is advisable if the connecting cables to the active gauge are particularly long.

Example A strain bridge comprises two $120\,\Omega$ resistors, one active gauge and one unstrained gauge for temperature compensation. The two gauges have unstrained resistances of $120\,\Omega$ and a gauge factor of 2.1. Determine the bridge output for a bridge supply of 4 V when the active gauge is subjected to 800 microstrain.
Using Eq. (4.26)

$$dR = GR\varepsilon_a = 2.1 \times 120 \times 800 \times 10^{-6} = 0.2016\,\Omega$$

From Eq. (4.23)

$$v = V\Delta R/4R = (4 \times 0.2016)/(4 \times 120) = 0.001\,68\,\text{V} = 1.68\,\text{mV}$$

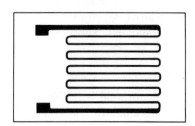

Figure 4.21 Bonded foil type strain gauge.

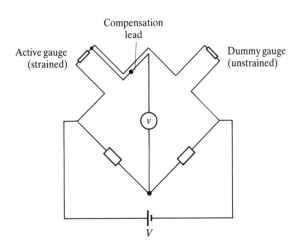

Figure 4.22 Strain bridge with temperature compensation.

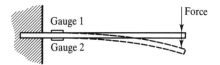

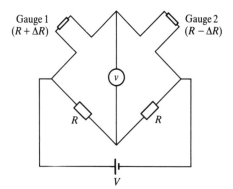

Figure 4.23 Cantilever-type load transducer.

The sensitivity of the circuit can be increased if it is known that the flexural member is subjected to equal and opposite strains on its opposite surfaces. Figure 4.23 illustrates an application to a load transducer in the form of a simple cantilever. The bridge output with two active gauges is

$$v = \frac{V\Delta R}{2R} \tag{4.27}$$

By using active gauges on all four arms of the bridge, the sensitivity can again be doubled. In either case, temperature compensation is automatic. The three forms of strain bridge described, using one, two and four active gauges are known, respectively, as quarter, half and full bridge circuits.

Even with four active elements in the bridge circuit the output is still measured in terms of millivolts and amplification of the output signal is essential (see Sec. 3.7). Additionally, since it is almost impossible to ensure equality of the resistances within the tolerance demanded by the sensitivity of the circuit, a zero-adjustment potentiometer is also virtually essential. Other problems are associated with noise, zero drift and nonlinearity but custom built precision amplifiers are readily available to condition output signals from resistive strain bridge circuits.

Strain bridges are often used as the sensing element in force transducers and commercial load cells. Propriety units are available in a large variety of types and sizes for the measurement of both tensile and compressive loads. Strain bridges are also attached to tubular elements to function in the capacity of a torque meter. Flexible diaphragms are also available with a strain bridge output and these are used extensively in pressure sensing applications.

The basic cantilevered structure depicted in Fig. 4.23 can be adapted for use as an accelerometer, or a seismic sensitive device. In these two cases it is the force due to an acceleration which is sensed through the measurement of strain. The acceleration is then determined via Newton's law relating force and acceleration. Impulsive and shock forces may also be monitored using a cantilevered element strain bridge system.

Volumetric and mass flow rate can equally well be measured. This is done using a strain bridge which is attached to a flexural member which deflects under the drag force exerted by the flowing fluid.

The examples cited are by no means exhaustive and indeed it may be the measurement of the strain itself which is the primary concern. This is certainly the case in experimental stress analysis.

The strain bridge circuit undoubtedly exhibits great flexibility in its applications as a commercial transducer. Furthermore it is probably the most extensively used sensor and circuit in many custom-built measurement applications.

4.9 GENERAL FORCE, PRESSURE AND ACCELERATION TRANSDUCERS

In the previous section the utility of the resistive strain bridge was highlighted in its varied applications as a transducer. In all of the examples considered it is the displacement of a flexural member which is actually measured. The measured displacement is then related back to the physical variable of interest through a calibration. Since the measured parameter is displacement, then there is no reason why any other displacement measuring system cannot be used as an alternative to the resistive strain bridge. Figure 4.24 shows five common types of commercial pressure transducer.

In all types, a change in pressure causes a deflection in a diaphragm which can be sensed using the various displacement transducers. Type (*a*) generates a change in capacitance between the flexible diaphragm and a central electrode. The conditioning circuitry required is quite complex and includes an AC sensitive capacitive bridge. The high sensitivity of the capacitance transducer, however, makes it a popular choice for many applications. The common capacitive microphone operates on these principles. Type (*b*), which is illustrated as a differential pressure transducer, relies on the induced currents generated in the coils for the sensing of the diaphragm deflection. Type (*c*) is a strain bridge and types (*d*) and (*e*), respectively, are miniaturized versions of the LVDT and the variable potential divider.

Many other mechanical configurations are possible and the basic sensing principles outlined above find general application in a wide range of force, pressure and acceleration transducers.

Force, pressure and acceleration transducers based on the piezoelectric effect belong in a totally separate class. A piezoelectric crystal, e.g. quartz, produces an electrostatic charge when subjected to a compressive strain. A difficulty exists, however, since the charge is generated as a

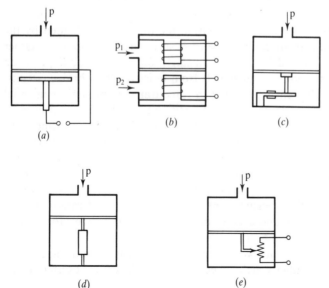

Figure 4.24 Commercial pressure transducers.

consequence of the application of the mechanical load. If the charge is subsequently dissipated, then no new charge would be generated until the loading state again changes. This feature makes piezoelectric devices unsuitable for static measurements. They are eminently suitable, however, for the measurement of dynamic loads. Piezoelectric transducers are used extensively therefore to monitor the time variation of pressure within the cylinders of internal combustion engines and as an accelerometer in vibration monitoring.

Measurement of the charge, however, without dissipating it, is problematic and piezoelectric transducers require sophisticated and expensive signal conditioning.

4.10 PROXIMITY SENSING

Proximity sensing has many applications in engineering, ranging from simple component counting functions to the ON/OFF switching of actuators and other devices in some overall control context. Spring-loaded microswitches are perhaps the simplest form of proximity sensor. These require mechanical contact to activiate the switch and can be used effectively in the sequence control of pneumatic and hydraulic cylinders. In typical operations, the movement of a ram is initiated and allowed to continue until a microswitch is tripped by a collar attached to the ram. The microswitch then perhaps activates a solenoid-operated control valve to reverse, or cut off the supply to the ram. Such systems can be extended as required to build up a fairly simple automated sequential processes.

As the name might suggest however, proximity switches are basically non-contacting devices. The magnetic pick-up and the slotted opto-switch, described for rotational speed measurement in Sec. 4.7, are both proximity devices and they can be used directly in this capacity. Many inductive and capacitive devices are also designed to function as a proximity switch. The most common type of proximity switch sensors nonetheless are the devices which operate on the 'Hall effect'. The Hall effect, named after its discoverer, is the phenomenon whereby an electron passing through a semiconductor material, and in the presence of a magnetic field, will experience a force which will defect the electron from its normal path. The effect is similar to that used to position the light spot on a cathode ray oscilloscope, but on a much smaller scale. Modern Hall effect sensors are supplied as complete integrated circuits with a convenient voltage output. A small permanent magnet is also usually supplied for attachment to the component to be sensed. Hall effect sensors have the advantages of high speed operation, no moving parts and are free from switch 'bouncing' effects (see Sec. 10.1).

All of the above devices essentially rely on close proximity for their actuation, a few millimetres or so. For longer range proximity sensing, light beam transmitting and receiving devices are used. A typical application is to be found in the batch counting of components moving along a conveyor belt. In these kind of applications a light beam is transmitted across a space, which may be up to about 15 m, and is continuously monitored by a receiving device. The passage of a non-transparent object interrupts the beam and triggers a voltage pulse which can be measured and recorded. Reflective-type proximity sensors, with the transmitter and receiver housed in the one unit, are also available.

4.11 MEASUREMENT OF FLOW RATE

The measurement of flow rate in process control covers a range of different transducers which can be subdivided as

1. pressure differential devices;
2. rotary devices;
3. vortex shedding devices;
4. non-intrusive devices.

Pressure differential devices include Venturi-meters, orifice plates, flow nozzles, or any similar device which presents a constriction in the flow path. For incompressible flows, the constriction causes the fluid to accelerate with an attendant drop in pressure. The operating principle of these devices is based on two fundamental laws of fluid dynamics. These are the equation of mass continuity and the steady flow energy equation, or Bernoulli equation. Application of these laws across any type of flow constriction results in an equation of the form:

$$\text{Flow rate} = B\sqrt{\Delta p} \tag{4.28}$$

where B is in general, an experimentally determined constant, and Δp is the measured pressure differential across the constriction.

The measurement of Δp is performed with a suitable differential pressure transducer and provided B is a well-behaved 'constant', the flow rate can be accurately calibrated against the square root of the output voltage from the pressure transducer.

If the fluid is a gas it is usually necessary to measure the local gas temperature and the absolute barometric pressure in addition to the meter differential pressure. The common differential pressure flow metering devices are shown in Fig. 4.25.

Rotary flowmeters may either be the positive displacement type, or the turbine type. In either case it is the speed of the rotational element which is measured and converted into an equivalent flow rate. In positive displacement meters, the total number of revolutions are also counted and used as a measure of the cumulative volume of flow. Figure 4.26 illustrates three contemporary rotary-type flowmeters.

The rotary-vane and lobed-rotor types are positive displacement meters in that for each revolution of the rotor, a fixed quantity of fluid is passed through from inlet to outlet. The turbine-type meter is not a positive displacement device.

In most rotary-type flowmeters, the rotational speed is detected with some form of proximity sensor which responds to the passage of a vane, lobe or blade as the case may be. A frequency-to-voltage converter is normally used in the signal conditioning process to produce a steady output voltage in proportion to the volumetric flow rate.

Vortex shedding flowmeters are comparative newcomers in the field of flow measurement but they have become well established as a general purpose flow monitoring device. The operating principle stems from the fact that when a 'blunt' body is exposed to an oncoming flow, the fluid particles cannot follow the severe surface contours of the body. The flow therefore breaks away from the body and periodic vortices, or eddies, are shed alternatively from the upper and lower extremities of the body (Fig. 4.27).

Over a reasonable range, the periodicity of the vortex shedding is in direct proportion to the fluid velocity. A measurement of the shedding frequency can therefore be related to the mean velocity and hence also to the flow rate. The vortex shedding frequency is sensed by a variety of methods. These include pressure variation with a piezoelectric pressure transducer, temperature variation with a heated thermistor and the interference of an ultrasonic beam transmitted across the wake behind the body. Vortex shedding flowmeters have no moving parts and can be used

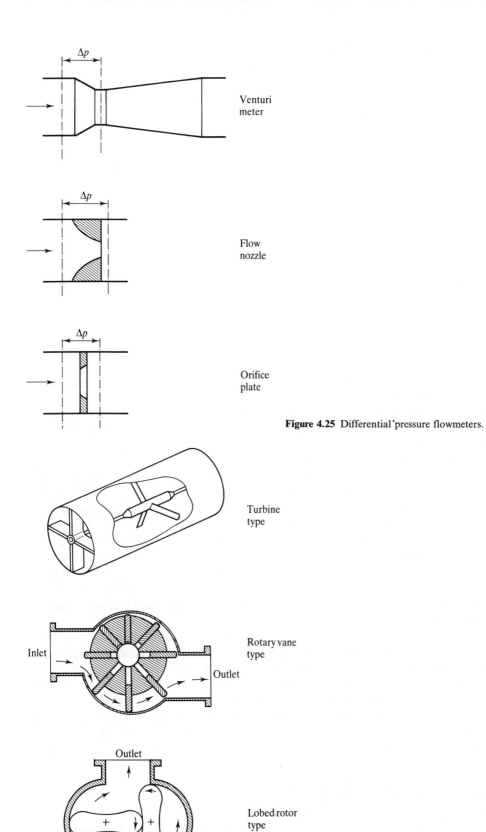

Venturi
meter

Flow
nozzle

Orifice
plate

Figure 4.25 Differential pressure flowmeters.

Turbine
type

Inlet

Outlet

Rotary vane
type

Outlet

+ +

Inlet

Lobed rotor
type

Figure 4.26 Rotary-type volumetric flowmeters.

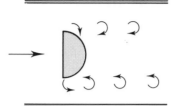

Figure 4.27 Vortex shedding from a blunt body

Transmitter/Receiver

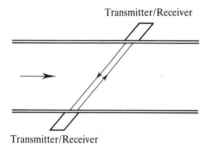

Transmitter/Receiver

Figure 4.28 Ultrasonic 'beat frequency' flowmeter.

with any fluid. The output signal is quite noisy, however, and the linear operating range might be too restrictive in some cases.

The last group of flow metering devices are the non-intrusive types. These are by far the most expensive flowmeters but they have the advantage of leaving the flow undisturbed with no attendant loss in pressure.

Laser–Doppler anemometry is a non-intrusive method which transmits a low-power Laser beam into the flow. The light scattered by minute particles flowing with the fluid transmits a signal back to a receiver and a measurement of the Doppler shift frequency can be used to determine the local fluid velocity. The Doppler shift frequency is also similarly utilized in some of the proprietry types of ultrasonic flowmeters.

Many other ultrasonic flowmeters operate on a beat frequency measurement. These meters incorporate two separate ultrasonic transmitter/receiver probes which pass signals in opposite directions across the flow path (Fig. 4.28) Due to the flow of fluid, the transit time of the two signals are unequal and by multiplying the signals together, a beat frequency can be measured. The beat frequency is proportionally related to the fluid mean velocity and its measurement can therefore be calibrated for volumetric flow rate.

The electromagnetic type of non-intrusive flowmeter is worthy of mention due to its wide usage in industrial applications. These flowmeters require the fluid to be conducting and their operating principle is based on Faraday's law of electromagnetic induction. A magnetic flux is generated in a direction perpendicular to the flow. As the flow constitutes a moving conductor, then a measurable voltage is generated between two electrodes positioned perpendicularly both to the magnetic field and the flow path. The magnetic field is energized with an alternating supply to prevent electrolysis and other problems associated with magneto-hydrodynamic action.

4.12 TEMPERATURE MEASUREMENT

The measurement of temperature is often required in system monitoring and general process control applications. For digital-based systems, thermoelectric devices are commonly utilized to generate the output signal in voltage form. The thermoelectric effect is a consequence of the fact

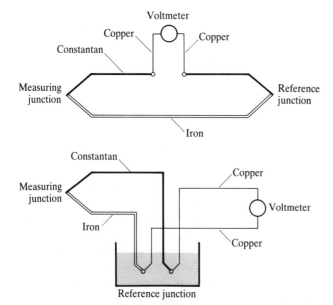

Figure 4.29 Basic thermocouple temperature transducer.

that the number of free electrons which can exist in a metal is a function both of the temperature and the composition of the metal. For practical purposes it is sufficient to know that when two dissimilar metals are joined together at their ends, a potential difference will exist if the two ends are held at different temperatures. This physical phenomenon provides the basis of a voltage output temperature transducer (Fig. 4.29). In wiring up to the voltmeter a third metal, usually copper, has been introduced into the circuit. This has no adverse effect provided that the temperature at the two copper connections are equal.

The thermocouple, however, is a differential, rather than an absolute temperature measuring device. To function as a temperature sensor therefore, the temperature at one of the junctions, the reference junction, must be known. The most convenient reproducible reference temperature available is that of melting ice at, or near, standard atmospheric pressure. This is zero degrees on the Centigrade scale and a range of specially selected materials have been rigorously calibrated against this reference, to be used as standard thermocouple combinations in industrial applications. A popular pair is nickel–chromium ('Chromel') and nickel–aluminium ('Alumel'). These two metals used in combination give the standardized 'K' calibration, approximately 4 mV per 100°C temperature difference.

The reference temperature need not be zero degrees Centigrade but can be any other known temperature, often room temperature at 15–20°C. In these cases the reduced potential due to the higher reference temperature can be compensated by the addition of the potential which would exist between 0°C and room temperature. This introduces a small error, however, since the calibrated relationship between temperature and voltage, although very near, is not quite linear. The output voltage, in addition, requires to be amplified to be compatible with a digital interface. Purpose-built amplifiers are readily available, however, particularly for K-type thermocouples, and these also usually incorporate a built-in ice point compensation circuit.

If high accuracy and long-term stability are required then a 'platinum-resistance thermometer' may be used as an alternative to the thermocouple. The temperature/resistance characteristics of the platinum-resistance thermometer are standardized in BS 1904. In practice the platinum sensor coil ultimately forms one arm of a Wheatstone bridge and matched compensating leads must be used in wiring up to the bridge (Fig. 4.30).

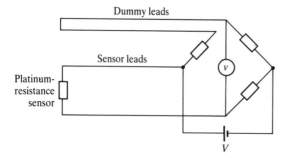

Figure 4.30 Platinum-resistance thermometer.

If absolute accuracy is not so important, then thermally sensitive resistors, or 'thermistors' as they are generally called, can be used. Thermistors are metal-oxide semiconductors with a large, usually negative, temperature coefficient of resistance. Thermistors are available in bead, rod, disc, washer and probe forms. They are extremely sensitive and have a very fast transient response. The resistance/temperature characteristic is however nonlinear and this has been a significant limitation on their general use in industry. The nonlinearity is much less of a problem in a microprocessor-based system, since the nonlinear effects can be easily accommodated in software, and thermistors are being increasingly used over much larger ranges than ever before. Thermistors with positive temperature coefficients of resistance are also available and these have particular application in over-temperature protection circuits.

All of the temperature sensing devices so far considered have an upper limiting temperature of about 1000°C. The 'S' type thermocouple can operate up to 1700°C, but for higher temperatures, radiation detection devices must be used. Radiation sensors incorporate a pyroelectric element which functions as a radiation sensitive capacitance. The voltage developed across the element decreases as the frequency of the incident radiation increases. Commercial temperature sensing devices are used in the steel making industries and in intruder alarm systems. The basic sensor principle can also be adapted to function as a gas detector and it is used as such to measure the presence and density of carbon monoxide, carbon dioxide and methane in gas flows.

4.13 LEVEL SENSING

The simplest form of level sensor is the float type switch. These are either ON or OFF depending on whether the liquid is above, or below the float. Ultrasonic and optical sensors are also used in level devices which measure the transit time of a beam reflected off the liquid free surface. A variable output, but nonlinear, level sensor is shown in Fig. 4.31.

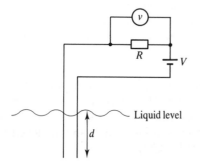

Figure 4.31 Variable output level sensor.

Provided the liquid is conducting, the resistance between the two unconnected wires depends on their depth of immersion, i.e. the liquid level. The voltage measured across the fixed resistor is inversely proportional to the depth of immersion of the two probe wires. Commercial sensors of this type, marketed as wave monitors, use an AC supply to circumvent the adverse effects of electrolysis.

4.14 ANALOGUE AND DIGITAL FILTERING

Noise is inherently present in all physical systems where measurements are made. In sampled data systems the effect of noise, illustrated in Fig. 4.32, can give rise to further misinterpretation in the form of 'aliases'.

Discrete sampling, shown in Fig. 4.32, results in an output signal which suggests that the measured variable is increasing linearly, but with a superimposed sinusoidal fluctuation. The apparent sinusoidal variation is entirely the effect of background noise and it is obviously good practice therefore to try to eliminate noise in the measurement system. It is perhaps fortuitous in mechanical systems that background noise is generally manifested at much higher frequencies than those associated with the primary variable of interest.

The sources of noise are varied and may originate from thermoelectric effects, electrochemical action, electrostatic and electromagnetic pick-up, self-generated component noise, offset voltages and common ground loops. If the frequency content of the signal to be measured is known beforehand, then positive steps can be taken to eliminate most of the unwanted effects of noise by the inclusion of suitable filters. Filters exists in three broad categories which are (i) low-pass, (ii) high-pass, and (iii) band-pass (see also Sec. 3.5). The gain characteristics for each type are shown in Fig. 4.33.

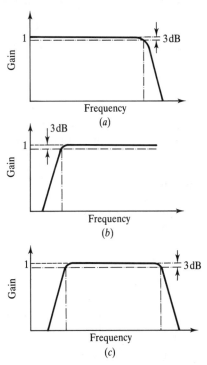

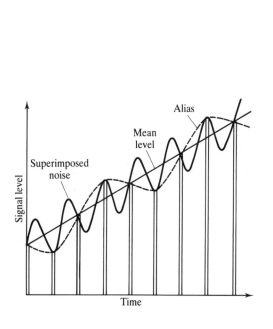

Figure 4.32 Noise generated 'aliases' in a sampled data signal.

Figure 4.33 Filter performance curves: (*a*) low-pass; (*b*) high-pass; (*c*) band-pass.

A low-pass filter is one which allows the transmission of signals below a particular cut-off frequency. Signals whose frequencies are above the selected cut-off are progessively attenuated. The high-pass filter, in contrast, transmits only that part of the signal whose frequencies are above the cut-off value. The band-pass filter transmits, without attenuation, the signal contained within an upper and a lower cut-off value. The cut-off frequency is defined as that at which the signal attenuation is $-3\,$dB. The simplest forms of analogue filter are those which incorporate only passive resistive, capacitive or inductive elements.

Low-pass Filter

Figure 4.34 shows the circuit diagram of a simple RC low-pass filter. Summing voltages round the circuit gives

$$V_i = V_R + V_o = iR + V_o$$

From Eq. (2.18) $i = C\,dV_o/dt$, thus

$$V_i = CR\,dV_o/dt + V_o$$

or

$$V_o + CR\,dV_o/dt = V_i \tag{4.29}$$

Writing this in Laplace (see Sec. 11.4) notation gives

$$V_o(1 + \tau s) = V_i$$

where τ is the system time constant ($\tau = CR$). Then

$$V_o/V_i = 1/(1 + \tau s) \tag{4.30}$$

Equation (4.30) represents the transfer function for a low-pass RC filter. The $-3\,$dB cut-off frequency is given by

$$f_c = 1/(2\pi RC) \tag{4.31}$$

A suitable choice of resistor and capacitor can therefore allow any desired cut-off frequency to be imposed in the signal conditioning train.

High-pass Filter

Figure 4.35 shows the circuit diagram of a simple RC high-pass filter. Summing voltages round the circuit gives

$$V_i = V_c + V_o$$

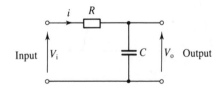

Figure 4.34 Low-pass filter.

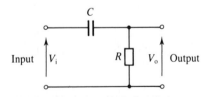

Figure 4.35 High-pass filter.

Using Eq. (2.18) gives

$$V_i = (1/C) \int i \, dt + V_o$$

$$= (1/C) \int (V_o/R) \, dt + V_o \qquad (4.32)$$

$$= (1/CR) \int V_o \, dt + V_o$$

In Laplace notation, Eq. (4.32) can be written as

$$V_i = (1/\tau)(1/s)(V_o) + V_o$$

The transfer function for the high-pass filter becomes

$$(V_o/V_i) = (\tau s)/(1 + \tau s) \qquad (4.33)$$

Expanding Eq. (4.33) gives

$$V_o(1 + \tau s) = V_i(\tau s)$$

or

$$V_o + \tau \, dV_o/dt = \tau \, dV_i/dt \qquad (4.34)$$

The cut-off frequency is similarly selected through a judicious choice of resistor and capacitor.

Bandpass filters might be thought of as a series arrangement of a low-pass and high-pass filter. With the appropriate combinations of resistors and capacitors, the low and high frequency noise components in the signal can be suitably attenuated as required.

Filters which include an amplifier in the circuit are referred to as active filters and the relationship between input and output is a much more complex function of time.

Figures 4.34 and 4.35 illustrate the simplest forms of passive analogue filter which are used to suppress background noise. The governing equations, Eqs. (4.29) and (4.34), may equally well be expressed in terms of finite differences. In finite difference form, the equations can be used to action the filtering process on a discretized version of the input signal. This is the basis of a digital filter which can be implemented in software and requires no external hardwired components.

The setting of the cut-off frequencies in the digital filter is achieved through adjustment of the constants appearing in the finite difference approximating function. These numerical constants are simply related to the physical time constant in the equivalent analogue filter and also the digital sampling rate.

The advantages that the digital filter has over its analogue counterpart are the ease with which the cut-off frequencies can be adjusted. The $-3 \, dB$ cut-off frequency can also be set exactly since no hardwired components, with physical tolerance bands, are used. The digital signal may also be filtered any number of times simply by processing the data repetitively through the filtering algorithm. The disadvantage incurred is that digital filtering takes longer in real time to perform. The end result of digital filtering on the signal are exactly the same as would be obtained using an analogue filter. That is, any time-varying signal whose frequency is outwith the cut-off value is subject to attenuation with a corresponding phase shift.

Example An analogue low-pass filter is to be constructed using a resistor and a capacitor. If the output voltage is to be attenuated by $3 \, dB$ at a frequency of $2 \, kHz$, determine time constant of the filter circuit and select suitable values of capacitor and resistor for the circuit.
From Eq. (4.31)

$$\tau = 1/(2\pi f_c) = 1/(2\pi 2000) = 0.0796\,\text{ms}$$

If the choose a capacitor of say $0.1\,\mu\text{F}$, then the required resistance is given by

$$R = 0.0796 \times 10^{-3}/(1 \times 10^{-7}) = 796\,\Omega$$

The nearest equivalent resistor would be $800\,\Omega$.

Example In a digital data acquisition system the data is sampled at approximately $10\,\text{kHz}$. The input signal varies at frequencies which are well below $1\,\text{kHz}$ and it is intended to filter the data digitally with an effective cut-off frequency of $1\,\text{kHz}$. Determine the form of the digital filtering algorithm required.

From Eq. (4.29), the finite difference approximation takes the form:

$$V_{o,k} + \tau(V_{o,k} - V_{o,k-1})/\Delta t = V_{i,k}$$

where k denotes the sampling intervals. Rearranging gives

$$V_{o,k}(1 + \tau/\Delta t) = V_{i,k} + (\tau\Delta t)V_{o,k-1}$$

$$V_{o,k} = \frac{V_{i,k}}{(1 + \tau/\Delta t)} + \frac{V_{o,k-1}}{(1 + \Delta t/\tau)}$$

Taking the cut-off frequency to be $1\,\text{kHz}$, then the filter time constant is $\tau = 1/(2\pi 1000)$, i.e.

$$\tau = 1.59 \times 10^{-4}\,\text{s}$$

$$\Delta t = 1/10^4 = 0.0001\text{s}$$

Substituting these values into the filtering algorithm gives

$$V_{o,k} = 0.386 V_{i,k} + 0.614 V_{o,k-1}$$

Note that the two constants always sum to unity in the low-pass filtering algorithm. The time constant, and hence the effective cut-off frequency, can be set to any value as required but it must never be greater than about half of the sampling interval. Normal practice would require a sampling interval of about five to ten times the time constant. This would essentially eradicate errors due to aliasing.

FURTHER READING

Barney, G. C. (1988) *Intelligent Instrumentation—Microprocessor applications in Measurement and Control*, 2nd edn, Prentice-Hall, New York.
Doebelin, E. O. (1983) *Measurement Systems—Application and Design*, 2nd edn, McGraw-Hill, New York.
Holman, J. (1984) *Experimental Methods for Engineers*, 4th edn, McGraw-Hill, New York.
Oliver, F. J. (1972) *Practical Instrumentation Transducers*, Pitman, London.
Williams, A. B. (1981) *Electronic Filter Design Handbook*, McGraw-Hill, New York.

EXERCISES

4.1 For the transducer shown in Fig. 4.1(*b*), show that the relationship between the liquid level h and the voltage output v is given by

$$h = \frac{H(v/V)}{5[1 - (v/V)]}$$

where V is the supply voltage and H the maximum level of liquid in the tank.

4.2   A displacement transducer has a dynamic response to a step input which is characterized by the relation $3.2(dV/dt) + 7.4V = 14.6X$ where X is the displacement in millimetres and V is the output voltage from the transducer in volts. Determine:
   (*a*) the time constant for the transducer;
   (*b*) the static sensitivity;
   (*c*) the minimum time interval between samples when measuring the dynamic response of a vibrating structure.

   [0.432 s, 1.973 V/mm, 2.16 s]

4.3   A vibration measuring system indicated an overshoot of 37 per cent when subjected to a step input. Calculate the damping ratio for the system.

   [0.3]

4.4   If the damping ratio of the system in question 4.3 is increased to 0.9, determine the percentage overshoot to be expected when a step input signal is applied.

   [0.15%]

4.5   A variable potential divider has a total resistance of 5 kΩ and is connected to a 10 V DC supply. The output voltage at the wiper arm is measured with a voltmeter having an internal resistance of 20 kΩ. Determine the loading error for wiper positions of $\frac{1}{4}$, $\frac{1}{2}$, and $\frac{3}{4}$ of the full stroke length.
   Note. The loading error is the difference between that which would be measured if the voltmeter had infinite resistance and the actual measured voltage with a finite internal resistance of 20 kΩ.

   [0.112 V, 0.291 V, 0.336 V]

4.6   Strain gauges are to be mounted onto a cantilevered structure to function as a simple force transducer. Show that by using four active gauges, two in compression and two in tension, that the bridge output voltage has the form $v = V(\Delta R/R)$ where V is the supply voltage, R is the unstrained gauge resistance and ΔR is the change in the gauge resistance under strain.

4.7   A strain bridge has two active gauges subject to equal and opposite strains. The unstrained resistance of the gauges is 130 Ω and two dummy gauges are used to complete the four arm circuit which is powered with 6 V from a DC supply. Determine the microstrain in the gauges when the gauge factor is 2.3 and the bridge output is measured as 2.7 mV.

   [391.3 microstrain]

4.8   A passive element band-pass filter is to be constructed using a series arrangement consisting of a high-pass and a low-pass filter. If the unity gain bandwidth is to range between 3 dB cut-off frequencies from 500 Hz to 20 kHz, determine the time constants for the low-pass and high-pass sections of the circuit. Select suitable values of capacitor and resistor for the two sections of the circuit.

   [7.96×10^{-6} s, 0.32×10^{-3} s, 0.01 μF, 800 Ω, 1.0 μF, 320 Ω]

4.9   The analogue output from a transducer is sampled and converted to digital form at a frequency of 5 kHz. Unsteadiness in the signal, due to extraneous time-dependent influences, occurs at frequencies of 10 Hz or less. In consequence, the data is to be digitally filtered through a high-pass filtering algorithm with a cut-off frequency of 20 Hz. Determine the form of the filtering algorithm required.
Hint: The finite difference approximation is based on Eq. (4.33).

   [$V_{o,k} = 0.8(V_{o,k-1} + V_{i,k} - V_{i,k-1})$]

FIVE

ELECTRICAL ACTUATORS

5.1 PHYSICAL PRINCIPLES

Electrical actuators operate on the principles of electromagnetic induction as quantified in Faraday's law, Eq. (2.25). The actuator can either produce a force, or torque, in response to an applied voltage, or operating as a generator, can produce an e.m.f. in response to an external driving force. Electrical actuators may be linear, or rotary and may be further subdivided into AC, or DC machines.

5.2 SOLENOID-TYPE DEVICES

The DC solenoid is perhaps the simplest of electrical actuators, consisting of a soft iron core enclosed within a current carrying coil. When the coil is energized a magnetic field, similar to that of the simple bar magnet, is set up within the coil. This field provides the magnetic force which drives the actuator. Many simple electro-mechanical devices are based on this principle of operation and these include lifting magnets, magnetic clutches, magnetic chucks, solenoid switches and a large variety of mechanical relays.

When a DC solenoid device is de-energized, the magnetic field collapses rapidly and a reversed e.m.f., or back e.m.f., is generated in the coil. These induced voltages can be very high and a diode is usually included in parallel with the coil to protect the circuit.

Solenoid-type devices based on AC excitation are also encountered. These devices incorporate laminated cores to reduce the eddy current losses.

5.3 DC MACHINES

The DC Generator

All conventional electrical machines consist of a stationary element and a rotating element which are separated by an air gap. In DC machines, generator or motor, the stationary element consists of salient 'poles' which are constructed as laminated assemblies with coils wound round them to produce a magnetic field. The rotating element is traditionally called the 'armature' and this consists of a series of coils located between slots around the periphery of the armature. The armature is also fabricated in laminations which are usually keyed onto a locating shaft. A very simple form of DC generator is illustrated in Fig. 5.1.

The single coil is rotated at constant speed between the opposite poles, north and south, of a simple magnet. From Eq. (2.25), the voltage generated in the coil is equal to the rate of change of flux linkages. When the coil lies in the horizontal plane, there is maximum flux linking the coil but a minimum rate of change of flux linkages. On the other hand when the coil lies in the vertical plane, there is zero flux linking the coil but the rate of change of flux linkages is a maximum. The resultant variation in generated voltage in the coil, as it moves through one revolution, is shown in Fig. 5.1(*b*). It is apparent that the generated voltage is alternating with positive and negative half-cycles. To change the AC output voltage into a DC voltage, a simple yet effective mechanical device called a 'commutator' is used. The commutator, Fig. 5.2, incorporates brass segments separated by insulating mica strips. External connection to the armature coil is made by stationary carbon 'brushes' which make sliding contact with the commutator. Referring to Figs 5.1(*a*) and 5.2(*a*), as the coil rotates from the horizontal plane through 180° the right-hand side of the coil is under the north pole and is connected via the commutator to the upper brush. Meanwhile the left-hand side of the coil is under the south pole and is connected to the lower brush. A further 180° of rotation effectively switches the coil sides to the opposite brushes. In this manner the coil side passing the north pole is always connected to the positive upper brush while the coil side passing the south pole is always connected to the negative lower brush. The resultant output voltage waveform is shown in Fig. 5.2(*b*).

If two coils, physically displaced by 90° are now used, the output brush voltage becomes virtually constant as shown in Fig. 5.3.

With the introduction of a second coil, the commutator requires to have four separate segments. In a typical DC machine there may be as many as 36 coils which would require a 72 segment commutator. The simple DC generator of Fig. 5.1 can be improved in perhaps three obvious ways. First, the number of coils can be increased, second, the number of turns on each coil can be increased, and third, there is no reason why another pair of poles cannot be introduced. A typical DC machine would therefore normally incorporate four poles, wired in such a way that each consecutive pole has the opposite magnetic polarity to each of its

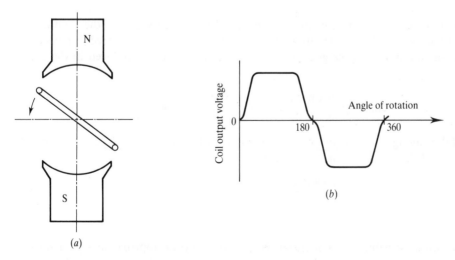

Figure 5.1 Single-coil, 2-pole DC generator: (*a*) physical arrangement; (*b*) output waveform.

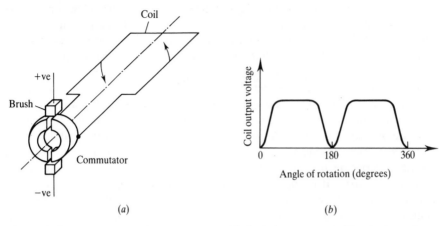

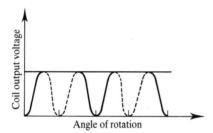

Figure 5.2 Commutator connections to armature: (*a*) physical arrangement; (*b*) output waveform.

Figure 5.3 Two-coil, 2-pole DC generator output voltage.

neighbouring poles. If the e.m.f.s generated in the armature coils are to assist each other then while one side of the coil is moving under a north pole, the other side of the coil must be moving under a south pole. With a two-pole machine the armature coils must be wound such that one side of the coil is diametrically opposite the other. With a four-pole machine the armature coils can be wound with one side of the coil physically displaced 90° from the other. The size of the machine will generally dictate how many coils, and the number of turns on each coil which can be used.

Armature e.m.f. If a conductor cuts flux then a voltage of 1 V will be induced in the conductor if the flux is cut at the rate of 1 Wb/s. Denoting the flux per pole as Φ and the speed in rev/s as N, for the single turn coil and two-pole generator of Fig. 5.1(*a*), the e.m.f. induced in the coil is given by

$$E_{\text{coil}} = \frac{\text{flux per pole}}{\text{time for half rev}} = \frac{\Phi}{1/(2N)} = 2N\Phi$$

For a machine having Z_s armature conductors connected in series, i.e. ($Z_s/2$ turns), and $2p$ magnetic poles, the total induced e.m.f. is given by

$$E = \frac{2N\Phi Z_s 2p}{2} = 2N\Phi Z_s p \quad \text{V} \tag{5.1}$$

Example The flux distribution in an idealized two-pole motor approximates to a square-wave function with 0.01 Wb per pole. The armature rotates at 2400 rev/min and carries a single coil having eight turns. Determine the coil voltage and the power consumed when the coil carries a current of 10 A.

The flux linking the coil changes from full value to zero during one quarter of a revolution. This occurs in a time of $\Delta t = 1/4N$, where N is the armature speed in rev/s; i.e.

$$\Delta t = 1 \times 60/(4 \times 2400) = 0.006\,25\,\text{s}$$

From Eq. (2.25), $E = n\,\mathrm{d}\phi/\mathrm{d}t$, where n is the number of turns on the coil; i.e.

$$E = 8 \times (0.01/0.00625) = 12.8\,\text{V}$$

Alternatively, using Eq. (5.1), $E = 2N\Phi Z_s p$, i.e.

$$E = 2 \times (2400/60) \times 0.01 \times (16) \times 1 = 12.8\,\text{V}$$

$$\text{power consumed} = E \times I = 12.8 \times 10 = 128\,\text{W}.$$

The number of armature conductors Z_s depends on the type of armature winding, and the two main types are 'lap-wound' and 'wave-wound'. The lap winding is characterized by the fact that the number of parallel paths through the winding is equal to the number of poles. In the alternative wave winding, the number of parallel paths through the winding is always equal to two. If Z denotes the total number of armature conductors then for the lap winding

$$Z_s = \frac{Z}{\text{number of parallel paths}} = \frac{Z}{\text{number of poles}} = \frac{Z}{2p}$$

For the wave winding

$$Z_s = \frac{Z}{\text{number of parallel paths}} = \frac{Z}{2}$$

Lap windings are generally used in low-voltage, heavy current machines and wave winding in all other cases.

Armature torque The force on a current carrying conductor is given by Eq. (2.27):

$$F = BLI$$

The torque on one armature conductor is therefore given by

$$T = Fr = B_{av}LI_a r \qquad (5.2)$$

where r = radius of the armature conductor about the centre of rotation
   I_a = current flowing in the armature conductor
   L = axial length of the conductor
   B_{av} = average flux density under a pole
Note that $B_{av} = \Phi/[(2\pi rL)/2p]$ so that the resultant torque per conductor is given by

$$T = \frac{\Phi 2pLI_a r}{2\pi rL} = \frac{\Phi p I_a}{\pi}$$

For Z_s armature conductors connected in series, the total torque on the armature is given by

$$T = \frac{\Phi p I_a Z_s}{\pi} \qquad \text{Nm} \qquad (5.3)$$

Example For the previous example, re-calculate the coil voltage from considerations of the power consumed and the generated torque.

The average flux is given by

$$B_{av} = \frac{\text{flux per pole}}{\text{area per pole}} = \frac{\Phi}{(2\pi rL)/2p} = \frac{\Phi p}{\pi rL} = \frac{0.01 \times 1}{\pi rL}$$

The linear velocity of conductors is

$$N2\pi r = \frac{2400}{60} \times 2 \times \pi \times r = 80\pi r$$

The power consumed is given by the force on conductors $\times$ distance moved per second, i.e.

$$16 \times B_{av} \times L \times I_{av} \times 80\pi r$$

$$= 16 \times \frac{0.01}{\pi rL} \times L \times I_{av} \times 80\pi r = 16 \times 0.01 \times 10 \times 80 = 128 \, \text{W}$$

For no losses, power $= E \times I_{av}$, thus

$$E = \text{power}/I_{av} = 128/10 = 12.8 \, \text{V}$$

From Eq. (5.3), the torque generated is

$$T = \frac{\Phi p I_a Z_s}{\pi} = \frac{0.01 \times 1 \times 10 \times 16}{\pi} = 0.509 \, \text{Nm}$$

Alternatively, the torque can be calculated from consideration of the power; i.e. power $= 2\pi NT$, thus the torque is given by

$$T = \text{power}/2\pi N = (128 \times 60)/(2 \times \pi \times 2400) = 0.509 \, \text{Nm}$$

An important point to realize is that although the example has been concerned with a DC motor, the same analysis could well have been applied to a DC generator having the same physical specifications. The difference is that if the generated voltage is of such polarity as to oppose the armature current, then electric power is being absorbed and the machine is functioning as a motor. If, on the other hand, the generated voltage aids the armature current, then the machine is functioning as a generator and the driving torque is being supplied from an external source.

Terminal voltage Denoting the terminal voltage by V, the armature current by I_a, the induced e.m.f. by E and the armature resistance by R_a, then

$$V = E - I_a R_a \quad \{\text{for a generator}\} \tag{5.4}$$

$$V = E + I_a R_a \quad \{\text{for a motor}\} \tag{5.5}$$

Methods of connection The methods of connecting the field and armature windings may be grouped as follows:

1. Separately excited—where the field winding is connected to a source of supply independently of the armature supply.
2. Self-excited—where the armature constitutes a DC source capable of supplying both the load and the field windings. Self-excited generators may be further subdivided into:
   (a) Shunt-wound—where the field winding is connected across the armature terminals.

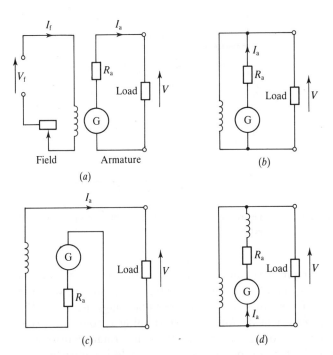

Figure 5.4 Methods of field connection: (*a*) separately excited; (*b*) shunt-wound; (*c*) series-wound; (*d*) compound-wound.

(b) Series-wound—where the field winding is connected in series with the armature winding.

(c) Compound-wound—which is a combination of shunt and series windings.

The four alternative methods of connection are illustrated in Fig. 5.4.

The separately excited generator Consider the separately excited generator, shown in Fig. 5.4(*a*), running at a constant rated speed with no load across the output. It is assumed that initially the poles were completely de-magnetized. If the field current, and hence the magnetic field, is gradually increased then a plot of terminal voltage against field current takes the form shown in Fig. 5.5.

As the field current increases the iron poles reach magnetic saturation and proportionality between the flux and field current no longer exists. If the field current is then reduced, the magnetic hysteresis causes the terminal voltage to have a slightly greater value than that obtained when the field current was being increased. When the field current is reduced to zero a 'residual voltage' remains. On increasing the field current once more, the curve follows the broken line to merge with the original lower curve. These curves are termed the 'open-circuit characteristics' of the machine. If the generator is now connected to a variable external load and driven at constant speed with a constant field current I_f, the terminal voltage variation with armature current is as shown in Fig. 5.6.

The decrease in terminal voltage with increase in load is due mainly to the voltage drop across the armature resistance R_a. Additionally, the decrease in terminal voltage is attributed to a decrease in flux caused both by the de-magnetizing ampere-turns of the armature and also the magnetic saturation in the armature teeth. These effects are collectively known as 'armature reaction'. Figure 5.6 is referred to as the 'load characteristic' of the generator. The separately excited generator has the disadvantage associated with a separate supply of direct current required for the field coils. They are used, however, in cases where a wide range of terminal voltage is required.

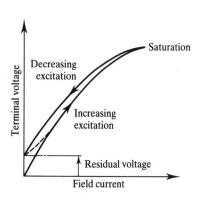

Figure 5.5 Open-circuit characteristics of a separately excited generator.

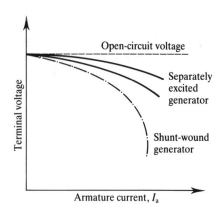

Figure 5.6 Load characteristics of a separately excited generator.

The shunt-wound generator The field winding in the shunt-wound generator is connected across the armature terminals as shown in Fig. 5.4(b) and is therefore in parallel, or 'shunt', with the load. A shunt generator will excite only if the poles have some residual magnetism and the resistance of the shunt circuit is less than some critical value. If when running at constant speed, the field is disconnected from the armature, the voltage generated across the armature brushes is very small and entirely due to residual magnetism in the iron. When the field is connected, the small residual voltage generates a flow of current in the field winding. The total flux in the field winding gradually builds up and the final terminal voltage depends on the resistance of the field winding and the magnetization curve of the machine. The general characteristic is shown in Fig. 5.7.

When connected to an external load the shunt-wound generator exhibits a drop in terminal voltage as the armature current is increased (Fig. 5.6). The drop in voltage in the shunt-wound generator is much greater than that in the separately excited generator. This stems from the fact that as the terminal voltage drops, the field current also drops which causes a further drop in terminal voltage.

The shunt-wound machine is the most common type of DC generator employed. The load current, however, must be limited to a value well below the maximum value to avoid excessive variation in terminal voltage.

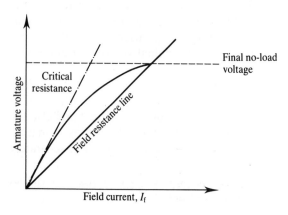

Figure 5.7 No-load characteristics for a shunt-wound generator.

The series-wound generator For the series-wound generator, the field winding is connected in series with the armature terminals as shown in Fig. 5.4(c). The armature current therefore determines the flux. The constant speed load characteristic, Fig. 5.8, exhibits an increase in terminal voltage as the armature, or load, current increases.

At large values of load current the armature resistance and reactance effects cause the terminal voltage to decrease. It is apparent from the figure that the series-wound generator is totally unsuitable if the terminal voltage is required to be reasonably constant over a wide range of load current.

The compound-wound generator The compound-wound generator, Fig. 5.4(d), is a hybrid between the shunt-wound and the series-wound generators. Normally a small series field is arranged to assist the main shunt field. This is termed 'cummulative compounding'. The shape of the load characteristic, Fig. 5.9, depends upon the number of turns on the series winding. A small series winding increases the terminal voltage above the shunt-only values at all load currents, giving an under-compounded characteristic. By increasing the number of turns in the series winding the terminal voltage can be held almost constant over the whole range of load currents. This results in a so-called level-compounded machine. A further increase in the number of turns in the series winding produces a characteristic which exhibits an increase in the terminal voltage for an increase in the load current. This is the over-compounded characteristic. If the series field is arranged to oppose the main shunt field, 'differentially compounded', a rapidly falling load characteristic, is obtained.

The DC Motor

There is no difference in basic construction between a DC generator and a DC motor. The only significant distinction between the two machines is quantified by Eqs. (5.4) and (5.5). These equations illustrate the fact that for a DC generator, the generated e.m.f. is greater than the terminal voltage. For the DC motor, the generated e.m.f. is less than the terminal voltage.

Equation (5.1), which gives the relationship between the induced e.m.f. and the speed of a DC generator, applies equally as well to the DC motor. Since the number of poles and number of armature conductors are fixed then a proportionality relationship can be derived to determine speed as a function of induced e.m.f. and flux:

$$N \propto E/\Phi \qquad (5.6)$$

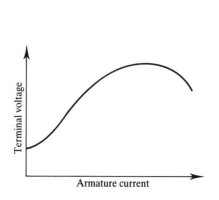

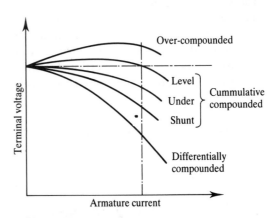

Figure 5.8 Constant speed load characteristic for the series-wound generator.

Figure 5.9 Load characteristic for the compound-wound generator.

or using Eq. (5.4),

$$N \propto (V - I_a R_a)/\Phi \qquad (5.7)$$

The value of $I_a R_a$ is usually less than about 5 per cent of the terminal voltage such that to a reasonable approximation,

$$N \propto V/\Phi \qquad (5.8)$$

In a similar manner, Eq. (5.3), which gives the armature torque on a DC generator, also applies to the DC motor. A proportionality relationship for the DC motor torque is therefore

$$T \propto I_a \Phi \qquad (5.9)$$

Equation (5.8) shows that the speed of a DC motor is approximately proportional to the voltage applied to the armature and inversely proportional to the flux. All methods of controlling the speed of DC motors are based on this proportionality relationship. Equation (5.9) indicates that the torque of a given DC motor is directly proportional to the product of the armature current and the flux per pole.

The shunt-wound motor The shunt wound motor is shown schematically in Fig. 5.10. Under normal operating conditions, the field current is constant and the flux is essentially independent of the armature current. As the armature current increases, however, the armature reaction effect weakens the field and the speed tends to increase. However, the induced voltage decreases due to the increasing armature voltage drop and this tends to decrease the speed. The two effects are not self-cancelling and overall the motor speed falls slightly as the armature current increases.

Since the flux is reasonably constant, the motor torque increases approximately linearly with the armature current until the armature reaction starts to weaken the field. These general characteristics are shown in Fig. 5.11(*a*) along with the derived torque–speed characteristic (5.11(*b*)).

Figure 5.11(*a*) shows that no torque is developed until the armature current is large enough to supply the constant losses in the machine. Since the torque increases dramatically for a slight decrease in speed, the shunt-wound motor is particularly suitable for driving equipment like pumps, compressors and machine tool elements where the speed must remain 'constant' over a wide range of load.

The series-wound motor The series-wound motor is shown in Fig. 5.12. As the load current increases, the induced voltage E decreases due to the armature and field resistance drops. Because the field winding is connected in series with the armature then the flux is directly proportional to the armature current. Equation (5.8) therefore suggests that the speed is approximately inversely proportional to the armature current. Similarly, Eq. (5.9) indicates that the torque/armature current characteristic will have a parabolic nature. These general

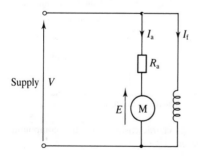

Figure 5.10 The shunt-wound motor.

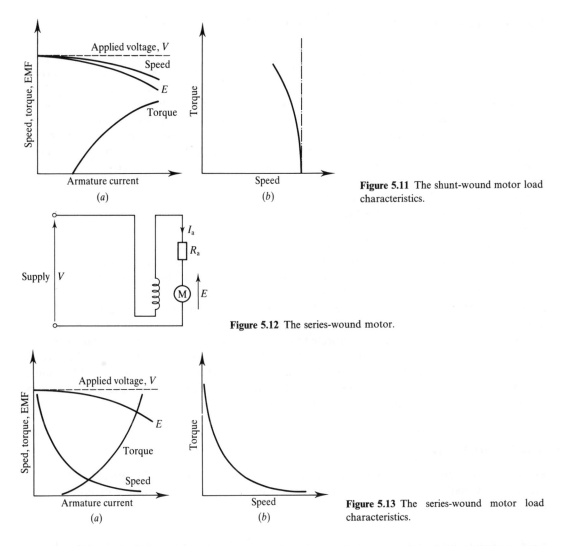

Figure 5.11 The shunt-wound motor load characteristics.

Figure 5.12 The series-wound motor.

Figure 5.13 The series-wound motor load characteristics.

characteristics are illustrated in Fig. 5.13(*a*) along with the derived torque/speed characteristic (Fig. 5.13(*b*)).

The general characteristics indicate that if the load falls to a particularly low value then the speed may become dangerously high. Dangerous speeds are those in excess of about 5000 rev/min, which may cause motor explosion due to the large centrifugal forces on the rotor. A series-wound motor must never be used therefore in situations where the load is likely to be suddenly relaxed.

The main advantage of the series motor is that it provides a large torque at low speeds. Series motors are eminently suitable therefore for applications where a large starting torque is required for a directly coupled load. This includes for example lifts, hoists, cranes, electric trains and other similarly high inertia loads.

The compound-wound motor Compound-wound motors, like compound generators, are produced by including both series and shunt fields. The resulting characteristics of the compound-wound motor fall somewhere in between those of the series and the shunt wound machines depending upon the relative strengths of the shunt and series fields.

5.4 STARTING AND SPEED CONTROL OF DC MOTORS

With the armature stationary, the induced e.m.f. is zero. If while at rest, the full voltage is applied across the armature winding then the current drawn would be massive. This current would undoubtedly blow the fuses and thereby cut off the supply to the machine. To limit the starting current a variable external resistance is connected in series with the armature. On start-up the full resistance is connected in series. As the machine builds up speed and increases the back e.m.f., the external resistance can be reduced until at rated speed the series resistance is disconnected. Variable resistance 'starters' are also usually equipped with a return spring and an electromagnetic 'catch plate'. The catch plate keeps the starter in the zero resistance position while the machine is running at its rated speed. The electromagnet is powered by the field current and in the event of a supply failure the electromagnetic is de-energized and the return spring pulls the starter back to the full resistance 'off' position. This ensures that the full starting resistance will always be in series with the armature winding when the machine is restarted.

An overload cut-out switch is another normal feature incorporated into the starter mechanism. The overload cut-out is another electromagnetic switch which is powered this time by the supply current. The overload switch is normally 'off' but if the supply current becomes excessive the switch is activated and it short circuits the supply to the electromagnetic catch plate. This in turn de-energizes the catch plate and the return spring takes the starter back to the 'off' position. Figure 5.14 illustrates the essential features of a starter device for a DC motor.

Note how the field winding is connected to the supply in front of the bank of resistors used to limit the starting current. This means that when the machine is running normally, the current limiting resistors are included in the field winding circuit. The resistance of the field winding however is of the order of 100 times that of the current limiting resistors and these resistors therefore have only a marginal effect on the flux generated.

Speed Control of DC Motors

Equation (5.8) shows that the speed of a DC motor is influenced both by the applied voltage and the flux. A variation in either one of these parameters will therefore effect a variation in the motor speed.

Field regulator For shunt and compound motors a variable resistor, called a 'field regulator', can be incorporated in series with the field winding to reduce the flux. For the series motor the

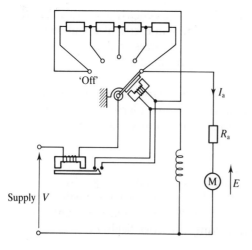

Figure 5.14 Starter device for DC motors.

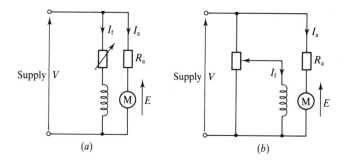

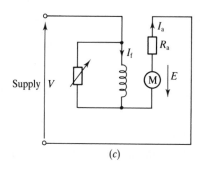

Figure 5.15 Speed control by flux reduction: (*a*) shunt-wound motor; (*b*) compound-wound motor; (*c*) series-wound motor.

variable resistor is connected in parallel with the field winding and is called a 'diverter'. Figure 5.15 shows the various methods of weakening the field flux for shunt, compound and series-wound motors. In all of these methods of speed control, the flux can only be reduced and from Eq. (5.8) this implies that the speed can only be increased above the rated speed. The speed may in fact be increased to about three or four times the rated speed. The increased speed, however, is at the expense of reduced torque since the torque is directly proportional to the flux which is reduced.

Example A DC series motor runs at 200 rev/min when the terminal voltage is 200 V and the current drawn is 25 A. The armature and field resistances are 0.4 Ω and 0.1 Ω, respectively. Determine the motor speed for a total current of 25 A at 2000 V when a 0.2 Ω resistor is connected in parallel with the field winding.

NB. Assume that the flux for a field current of 16.7 A is 85 per cent of that for a field current of 25 A.

Without diverter

$$E = 200 - 25(0.4 + 0.1) = 187.5 \, \text{V}$$

With diverter, total resistance of field circuit is

$$1/(1/0.1 + 1/0.2) = 0.0667 \, \Omega$$

Voltage across field circuit is

$$25 \times 0.0667 = 1.667 \, \text{V}$$

thus the field current is $1.667/0.1 = 16.67 \, \text{A}$.

$$E = 200 - 25(0.4 + 0.0667) = 188.33 \, \text{V}$$

Using Eq. (5.6), $N_1/N_2 = (E_1/E_2)(\Phi_2/\Phi_1)$, thus

$$N_2 = N_1(E_2/E_1)(\Phi_1/\Phi_2) = 2000(188.33/187.5)(1/0.85) = 2363 \, \text{rev/min}$$

Note also that from Eq. (5.9), the torque will be reduced to 85 per cent of the value that it had without the diverter in the field circuit.

Variable armature voltage Alternatively, the speed can be increased from standstill to rated speed by varying the armature voltage from zero to rated value. Figure 5.16 illustrates one method of achieving this. The potential divider, however, carries the same current as the motor and this limits this method of speed control to the smaller machines.

Example A shunt-wound DC motor has an armature resistance of $0.2\,\Omega$. The motor operates from a 240 V DC supply taking an armature current of 90 A and running at 100 rev/min. If an external resistance of $2\,\Omega$ is connected in series with the armature winding, while the field current remains unaltered, determine the effect on the speed of the machine and the output power.

Without the external resistance, armature input $= VI_a = 240 \times 90 = 21\,600$ W, therefore

$$E_1 = V - I_a R_a = 240 - (90 \times 0.2) = 222\,\text{V}$$

Including the external resistance, armature input $= VI_a = 240 \times 90 = 21\,600$ W. (NB the armature input is unaltered.) However

$$E_2 = 240 - (90 \times [2 + 0.2]) = 42\,\text{V}$$

Since the field current is unchanged then Φ also remains unaltered. From Eq. (5.6) $E_1/N_1 = E_2/N_2$ and hence

$$N_2 = (E_2/E_1) \times N_1 = (42/222) \times 1000 = 190\,\text{rev/min}$$

Power dissipated in the external resistor $= I_a^2 \times R_e = 90^2 \times 2 = 16\,200$ W, thus power delivered to load is

$$21\,600 - 16\,200 = 5400\,\text{W}$$

Note that although the power drawn by the motor remains unaltered, most of this power is inefficiently dissipated in the external resistor. The torque remains unaltered but the reduced speed means that less power is delivered to the driven load. This is a characteristic of speed control using variable armature resistance and can be a limiting constraint in higher power drives.

Ward Leonard drive In this case the variable DC voltage for the speed controlled motor is obtained from a separate DC generator which is itself driven by an induction motor (Fig. 5.17).

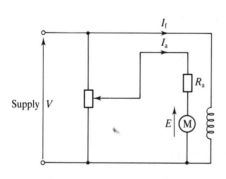

Figure 5.16 Speed control by varying the armature voltage.

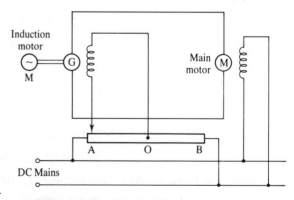

Figure 5.17 Ward Leonard drive.

The field coil for the DC generator is supplied from a centre-tapped potential divider. When the wiper arm is moved from O to A, the armature voltage of the DC motor is increased from zero and the motor speed increases. In moving the wiper from A to O and on through to B, the motor decelerates to a standstill and then increases in speed again, but in the opposite direction of rotation. The Ward Leonard drive is smooth and accurate in either direction and also provides for very responsive braking. The complexity, however, makes it a very expensive system and it is only used in high-quality applications.

Chopper control Figure 5.18 shows a thyristor circuit connected in series with the armature of a DC motor. The thyristor circuit is triggered such that it operates essentially as a high speed ON/ OFF switch and the resistance in the armature circuit then alternates between a very high value and a very low value. The resultant output waveform across the armature terminals is depicted in Fig. 5.19. The ratio of time on to time off, i.e. the 'mark/space ratio', can be varied with the result that the average voltage supplied to the armature is effectively varied between zero and fully on. The frequency of the signal may be up to about 3 kHz and the timing circuit is necessarily complex. Speed control of DC motors using thyristors, however, is effective, power efficient and relatively inexpensive. Thyristor control is used almost exclusively in battery-driven vehicles.

Efficiency of DC Machines

The losses in DC machines can be generally classified as

1. *Armature losses*—this is the I^2R loss in the armature winding.

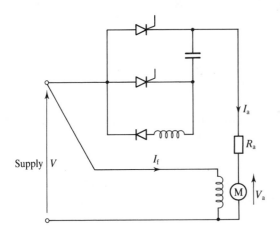

Figure 5.18 Speed control using thyristors.

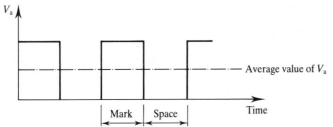

Figure 5.19 Voltage across armature terminals.

2. *Iron loss*—this loss is attributable to magnetic hysteresis and eddy currents in the armature and field cores.
3. *Commutator losses*—this loss is related to the contact resistance between the commutator brushes and segments. The total commutator loss is due both to mechanical friction and a voltage loss across the brushes.
4. *Excitation loss*—in shunt-wound machines, this power loss is to the product of the shunt current and the terminal voltage.
5. *Bearing friction and windage*—bearing friction is approximately proportional to the speed, but windage loss varies with the cube of the speed. Both of these losses are fairly minor unless the machine is fitted with a cooling fan, in which case the windage loss can be quite significant.

Despite the variety and nature of the losses associated with DC machines, they have a very good performance with overall efficiencies often in excess of 90 per cent.

Consider, for example, a shunt wound motor. The input power is given as the product of the terminal voltage V and the input current I. If the shunt current is denoted by I_s, then the armature current $I_a = I - I_s$. The loss in the shunt circuit is VI_s and the armature loss is $I_a^2 R_a$. Denoting the sum of the iron, friction and windage losses at C, the efficiency of the motor is given by

$$\text{efficiency} = \frac{\text{output}}{\text{input}} = \frac{\text{input} - \text{losses}}{\text{input}} = \frac{VI - I_a^2 R_a - VI_s - C}{VI} \tag{5.10}$$

The shunt, iron and friction losses are essentially independent of the load and since I_s can be considered negligible in comparison with I_a, then $I_a = I$. From Eq. (5.10), the efficiency is given approximately as

$$\text{efficiency} = \eta = 1 - IR_a/V - (VI_s + C)/(VI) \tag{5.11}$$

Differentiation with respect to I gives

$$d\eta/dI = -R_a/V + (VI_s + C)/(I^2 V) \tag{5.12}$$

and

$$d^2\eta/dI^2 = -2(VI_s + C)/(I^3 V)$$

Since the second derivative of η with respect to I is negative, then Eq. (5.12) gives the condition for the efficiency to be a maximum when the expression is equated to zero; i.e.

$$I^2 R_a = (VI_s + C) \tag{5.13}$$

Equation (5.13) shows that the efficiency of a motor is a maximum when the load is such that the variable loss $I^2 R_a$ is equal to the constant loss $(VI_s + C)$. The same conclusion can be drawn for a shunt-wound DC generator.

Example A 240 V shunt motor running on no-load at normal speed takes an armature current of 2.5 A. The field circuit resistance is 240 Ω and the armature resistance is 0.3 Ω. Calculate the motor output power and the efficiency when on load at normal speed, the armature current is 35 A.

On no-load the input power consumed $= VI_a = 240 \times 2.5 = 600$ W. This power is mostly required to overcome the iron, windage and friction losses, i.e. $C = 600$ W. Note however that there is an armature loss included in this total, ie.

$$I_a^2 R_a = 2.5^2 \times 0.3 = 1.875 \text{ W}$$

Therefore the iron, friction and windage loss is given by

$$C = (600 - 1.875) = 598.125\,\text{W}$$

Under loaded conditions, the current drawn is 35 A. $I_s = V/R_s = 240/240 = 1$ A and hence the field loss is $VI_s = 240 \times 1 = 240$ W and $I_a = I - I_s = 35 - 1 = 34$ A. The armature loss is $I_a^2 R_a = 34^2 \times 0.3 = 346.8\,\text{W}$.
The input power is $VI = 240 \times 35 = 8400$ W and the efficiency is

$$(VI - I_a^2 R_a - VI_s - C)/(VI) = (8400 - 346.8 - 240 - 598.13)/(8400)$$

i.e.

$$\eta = 0.859 = 85.9\%$$

Output power = input − losses, i.e.

$$8400 - 346.8 - 240 - 598.13 = 7215\,\text{W} = 7.2\,\text{kW}$$

5.5 AC MACHINES

Three-phase Alternators

Alternators are constructed with a stationary AC winding and a rotating field system. This reduces the number of slip-rings required to two and these have to carry only the field exciting current as opposed to the generated current. The construction is thereby simplified and the slip-ring losses are minimized. In addition the simpler arrangement enables heavier insulation to be used and in consequence much higher voltages can be generated. The robust mechanical construction of the rotor also means that higher speeds are possible and substantially higher power outputs can be generated with an alternator. A simple form of three-phase generator is depicted in Fig. 5.20.

The three coils on the stator are displaced by 120° and the rotor, which is a salient pole type, is supplied via the two slip-rings with a DC current. As the rotor is driven by some form of prime mover a rotating magnetic field is established and the e.m.f.s generated in the coils are displaced with a phase shift of 120°. The magntidue of the generated voltages are dependent on the flux produced by the rotor, the number of turns on the stator coils and the speed of rotation of the rotor. The rotor speed also dictates the frequency of the generated voltage.

The no-load and load characteristics of an alternator are very similar to those of the DC separately excited generator, Figs. 5.5 and 5.6, respectively. In constant speed operation, the

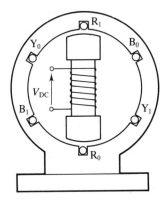

Figure 5.20 Simple three-phase generator.

terminal voltage exhibits a drooping characteristic where the decrease in terminal voltage is due to the resistance and reactance effects in the stator windings.

As the load on an alternator is increased then the speed of the prime mover drops. This is an unacceptable situation because the speed controls the frequency of the generated voltage. To maintain a constant frequency, the prime mover must be governed to run at constant speed over the entire range of expected loads. This is particularly important where many alternators are to be run in parallel to supply a distribution system such as the National Grid. In such cases the prime movers are always speed controlled and the output voltage is regulated to comply with the rated values. In the UK, alternators are usually two-pole machines driven as 3000 rev/min to produce the rated frequency of 50 Hz. In the USA a great deal of the electrical power consumed is generated from hydro-electric power stations. The water turbines used in these installations are fairly low-speed machines and the alternators, which are directly driven, are equipped with multiple poles to produce the rated frequency of 60 Hz. An alternator running at 240 rev/min, for example, would require to have 30 poles to give the rated output frequency.

The production of the rotating magnetic field may also be actioned using three, 120° displaced, rotor coils supplied with three-phase current. The rotational speed of the field is related to the frequency of the currents:

$$N_s = \frac{60f}{\text{number of pole pairs}} \tag{5.14}$$

where N_s is the speed of the field in revs/min and f is the frequency of the supply currents.

The speed of the rotating field is termed the 'synchronous speed', and for an equivalent single pair of poles, i.e. three coils, this is 3000 rev/min when the frequency of the supply currents is at 50 Hz.

The use of AC-excited rotor coils to produce the rotating magnetic field simplifies the mechanical construction of the rotor and greatly facilitates the dynamic balancing of the machine. An added advantage is that the waveform of the generated voltage is improved. The AC method of exciting the field is used extensively in large alternators. Salient pole rotors are normally restricted to the smaller machines.

Synchronous Motors

Synchronous motors are so called because they operate at only one speed, i.e. the speed of the rotating field. The mechanical construction is exactly the same as the alternator shown in Fig. 5.20. The field is supplied from a DC source and the stator coils are supplied with a three-phase current. The rotating magnetic field is induced by the stator coils and the rotor, which may be likened to a permanent bar magnet, aligns itself to the rotating flux produced in the stator. When a mechanical load is driven by the shaft, the field produced by the rotor is pulled out of alignment with that produced by the stator. The angle of misalignment is called the 'load angle'. The characteristics of synchronous motors are normally presented in terms of torque against load angle, as shown in Fig. 5.21.

The torque characteristic is basically sinusoidal with

$$T = T_{\max} \sin(\delta) \tag{5.15}$$

where $T_{\max}$ is the maximum rated torque and δ is the load angle.

It is evident from Eq. (5.15) that synchronous motors have no starting torque and the rotor must be run up to synchronous speed by some alternative means. One method utilizes a series of short-circuited copper bars inserted through the outer extremities of the salient poles. The rotating magnetic flux induces currents in these 'grids' and the machine accelerates as if it were a cage-type induction motor (see following section). A second method uses a wound rotor similar

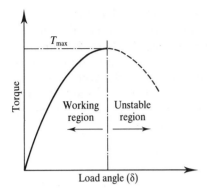

Figure 5.21 Torque characteristic for a synchronous motor.

to a slip-ring induction motor. The machine is run up to speed as an induction motor and is then pulled into synchronism to operate as a synchronous motor.

The advantages of the synchronous motor are the ease with which the power factor can be controlled and the constant rotational speed of the machine, irrespective of the applied load. Synchronous motors, however, are generally more expensive and a DC supply is a necessary feature of the rotor excitation. These disadvantages coupled with the requirement for an independent starting mode make synchronous motors much less common than induction motors.

Induction Motors

The stator of an induction motor is much like that of an alternator and in the case of a machine supplied with three-phase currents, a rotating magnetic flux is produced. The rotor may be either of two basic configurations which are the 'squirrel cage', or the slip-ring type. In the squirrel cage motor the rotor core is laminated and the conductors consist of uninsulated copper, or aluminium, bars driven through the rotor slots. The bars are brazed or welded at each end to rings or plates to produce a completely short-circuited set of conductors. The slip-ring machine has a laminated core and a conventional three-phase winding, similar to the stator and connected to three slip-rings on the locating shaft. Figure 5.22 shows a schematic representation of an induction motor having three stator coils displaced by 120°.

If the stator coils are supplied with three-phase currents a rotating magnetic field is produced in the stator. Considering the single rotor coil shown in the figure. At standstill the rotating field induces a voltage in the rotor coil since there is a rate of change of flux linking the coil. If the coil forms a closed circuit then the induced e.m.f. circulates a current in the coil. The

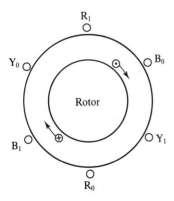

Figure 5.22 Schematic representation of an induction motor.

resultant force on the current carrying conductor is a consequence of Eq. 2.27 and this produces a torque which accelerates the rotor. The rotor speed increases until the electromagnetic torque is balanced by the mechanical load torque. The induction motor never attains synchronous speed because if it did there would be no relative motion between the rotor coils and the rotating field. Under these circumstances there would be no e.m.f. induced in the rotor coils and subsequently no electromagnetic torque. Induction motors therefore always run at something less than synchronous speed. The ratio of the difference between the synchronous speed and the rotor speed to the synchronous speed is called the 'slip':

$$\text{slip, } s = \frac{N_s - N}{N_s} \tag{5.16}$$

The torque–slip characteristic is shown in Fig. 5.23.

With the rotor speed equal to the synchronous speed, i.e. $s = 0$, the torque is zero. As the rotor falls below the synchronous speed the torque increases almost linearly to a maximum value dictated by the total of the load torque and that required to overcome the rotor losses. The value of slip at full load varies between 0.02 and 0.06. The induction motor may be regarded therefore as a constant speed machine. The difficulties in fact of varying the speed constitutes one of the inductor motors main disadvantages.

On start-up, the slip is equal to unity and the starting torque is sufficiently large enough to accelerate the rotor. As the rotor runs up to its full load speed the torque increases in essentially inverse proportion to the slip. The start-up and running curves merge at the full-load position.

Example A three-phase induction motor is wound for four poles and is supplied from a 50 Hz mains. Calculate the synchronous speed, the rotor speed when the slip is 4 per cent, and the required mains frequency to produce a rotor speed of 500 rev/min with the same value of slip.
From Eq. (5.14)

$$\text{synchronous speed} = 60f/p = 50 \times 60/2 = 1500\,\text{rev/min}$$

From Eq. (5.16) with 4 per cent slip, $0.04 = (N_s - N)/N_s = (1500 - N)/1500$, hence

$$N = 1500 - 0.04 \times 1500 = 1440\,\text{rev/min}$$

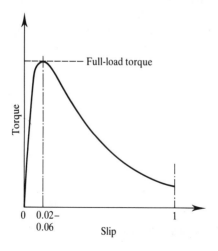

Figure 5.23 Torque–slip characteristic for an induction motor.

If the rotor speed is to be 500 rev/min with the same slip, then

$$0.04 = (N_s - 500)/N_s$$
$$N_s = 500/(1 - 0.04) = 521 \text{ rev/min}$$

Therefore

$$f = 521 \times 2/60 = 17.36 \text{ Hz}$$

5.6 STARTING AND SPEED CONTROL OF AC MACHINES

As with DC motors, the current drawn during starting of AC motors is very large, up to about five times full-load currrent. A number of devices are therefore employed to limit the starting current but they all involve the use of auxiliary equipment which is usually quite expensive.

Star–delta starter The star-delta switch, Fig. 5.24, is the cheapest and most common method employed. With the machine at standstill and the starter in the 'start' position, the stator coils are connected in the star pattern. As the machine accelerates up to running speed, the switch is quickly moved over to the 'run' position which reconnects the stator windings in the delta pattern. By this simple expedient, the starting supply current is reduced to one third of what it would have been had the stator windings been connected up in the delta pattern on start-up.

Auto-transformer starter The auto-transformer represents an alternative method of reducing the starting current drawn by an induction motor, Fig. 5.25.

Figure 5.25 shows a three-phase, star-connected auto-transformer with a mid-point tapping on each phase. The voltage supplied to the stator is therefore one-half of the supply voltage. With such an arrangement the supply current and the starting torque are both only one-quarter of the values which would be applied to the motor when the full voltage is supplied. After the motor has accelerated, the starter device is moved to the 'run' position thereby connecting the

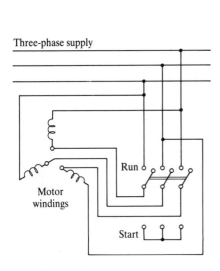

Figure 5.24 Star–delta starter.

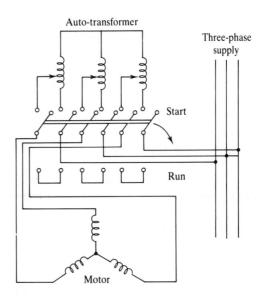

Figure 5.25 Auto-transformer starter.

motor directly across the supply and opening the star-connection of the auto-transformer. Unfortunately, the starting torque is also reduced and the device is generally expensive since it has to have the same rating as the motor.

Rotor resistance With slip-ring induction motors it is possible to include additional resistance in series with the rotor circuit. The inclusion of extra resistance in the rotor provides for reduced starting current and improved starting torque.

Braking Induction Motors

Induction motors may be brought to a standstill by either 'plugging' or by 'dynamic braking'.

1. *Plugging*. This refers to the technique where the direction of the rotating magnetic field is reversed. This is brought about by reversing any two of the supply leads to the stator. The current drawn during plugging is very large, however, and machines which are regularly plugged must be specially rated.
2. *Dynamic braking*. In this braking technique the stator is disconnected from the AC supply and reconnected to a DC source. The direct current in the stator produces a stationary uni-directional field and as the rotor will always tend to align itself with the field, it will therefore eventually come to a standstill.

Speed Control of AC Motors

Under normal circumstances, the running speed of an induction motor will be about 94 to 98 per cent of the synchronous speed, depending on the load. With the synchronous speed given by Eq. (5.14), it is clear that the speed may be varied either by changing the frequency of the supply current, or by changing the number of poles. Variable rotor resistance and variable stator voltage are also commonly used techniques for marginal speed control.

Change of supply current frequency Solid state variable-frequency drives first began to appear in 1968. They were originally applied to the control of synchronous AC motors in the synthetic fibre industry and rapidly gained acceptance in that particular market. In more recent times they have been used in applications to pumping, synchronized press lines, conveyor lines and to a lesser extent in the machine-tool industry as spindle drives. Modern AC variable-frequency motors are available in power ratings ranging from 1 kW to 750 kW and with speed ranges from 10/1 to 100/1.

The synchronous and squirrel cage induction motors are the types most commonly used in conjunction with solid-state, adjustable frequency inverter systems. In operation the motor runs at, or near, the synchronous speed determined by the input current frequency. The torque available at low speed, however, is decreased and the motor may have to be somewhat oversized to ensure adequate performance at the lower speeds. The most advanced systems incorporate a digital tachogenerator to supply a corrective feedback signal which is compared against a reference frequency. This gives a speed regulation of about 3 per cent. Consequently, the AC variable-frequency drive is generally used only for moderate to high-power velocity control applications, where a wide range of speed is not required. The comparative simplicity of the AC induction motor is usually sacrificed to the complexity and cost of the control electronics.

Change of number of poles By bringing out the ends of the stator coils to a specially designed switch it becomes possible to change an induction motor from one pole configuration to another. To obtain three different pole numbers, and hence three different speeds, a fairly complex switching device would be required.

Changing the number of poles gives a discrete change in motor speed with little variation in speed over the switched range. For many applications, however, two discrete speeds are all that is required and changing the number of poles is a simple and effective method of achieving this.

Changing the rotor resistance For slip-ring induction motors additional resistance can be coupled in series with the rotor circuit. It has already been stated that this is a common method used to limit the starting current of such machines. It can also be used as a method of marginal speed control. Figure 5.26 shows the torque characteristics of a slip-ring induction motor for a range of difference resistances connected in series with the rotor windings. As the external resistance is increased from R_1 to R_3, a corresponding reduction in speed is achieved at any particular torque. The speed range is increased at the higher torques.

The method is simple and therefore inexpensive, but the reduction in speed is accompanied by a reduction in overall efficiency. Additionally, with a large resistance in the rotor circuit, i.e. R_3, the speed changes considerably with variations in torque and the starting torque is considerably reduced.

Reduced stator voltage By reducing the applied stator voltage a family of torque-speed characteristics are obtained as shown in Fig. 5.27. It is evident that as the stator voltage is reduced from V_1 to V_3, a change in speed is effected at any particular value of torque. This is provided, of course, that the torque does not exceed the maximum load torque available at the

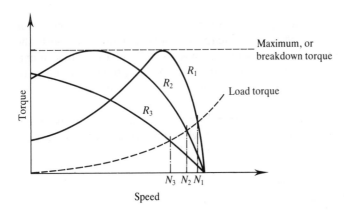

Figure 5.26 Torque–speed characteristics for various rotor resistances.

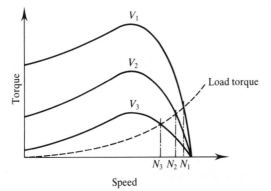

Figure 5.27 Torque-speed characteristics for various stator voltages.

reduced stator voltage. This latter point is obviously a limiting factor which places a constraint on this method of speed control. Generally, only very small speed ranges can be obtained using variable stator supply voltage.

5.7 SINGLE-PHASE INDUCTION MOTORS

The operation of an induction motor depends upon the creation of a rotating magnetic field. A single stator coil cannot achieve this and all of the so-called single-phase induction motors use some external means of generating an approximation to a two-phase stator supply. Two stator coils are therefore used and these are displaced by 90°. Ideally the currents which supply each coil should have a phase difference of 90°. This then gives the two-phase equivalent of the three-phase induction motor.

The shaded-pole motor The stator of the shaded pole motor consists of a salient pole single-phase winding and the rotor is of the squirrel cage type (Fig. 5.28).

When the exciting coil is supplied with alternating current the flux produced induces a current in the 'shading ring'. The phase difference between the currents in the exciting coil and the shading ring is relatively small and the rotating field produced is far from ideal. In consequence the shaded-pole motor has a poor performance and an equally poor efficiency due to the continuous losses in the shading rings.

Shaded-pole motors have a low starting torque and are used only in light duty applications such as small fans and blowers or other easily started equipment. Their advantage lies in their simplicity and low cost of manufacture.

The capacitor motor A schematic layout of a capacitor motor is shown in Fig. 5.29. The stator has two windings physically displaced by 90°. A capacitor is connected in series with the auxiliary winding such that the currents in the two windings have a large phase displacement. The current phase displacement can be made to approach the ideal 90° and the performance of the capacitor motor closely resembles that of the three-phase induction motor.

The universal motor These are small DC series-wound motors which operate at about the same speed and power on direct current, or on single-phase current with approximatley the same root

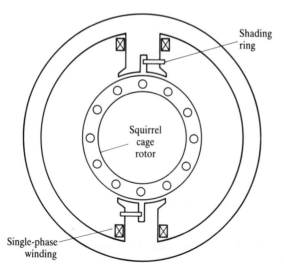

Figure 5.28 Shaded-pole motor.

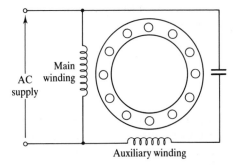

Figure 5.29 Capacitor motor.

Auxiliary winding

mean square voltage. If alternating current is supplied, the stator and rotor field strengths vary sinusoidally in magnitude but with the same phase relationship. As the applied voltage changes polarity, so also does the armature and field currents. Equation (5.9) indicates therefore that under these alternating current conditions, the applied torque will not reverse sign and will remain positive. The universal, or plain-series motor, is used mainly in small domestic appliances such as hair dryers, electric drills, vacuum cleaners, hedge trimmers, etc.

5.8 THE DC PERMANENT MAGNET (PM) MOTOR

The DC permanent magnet motor is a continuous rotation electromagnetic actuator which can be directly coupled to its load. Figure 5.30(a) shows the schematic representation of a DC permanent magnet motor along with the typical torque-speed characteristics for a range of input armature currents (Fig. 5.30(b)).

The PM motor consists of an annular brush ring assembly, a permanent magnet stator ring and a laminated wound rotor. They are particularly suitable for servo-systems where size, weight, power and response times must be minimized and where high position and rate accuracies are required.

The response times for PM motors are very short. The torque decreases linearly with speed but increases directly with the input current, independently of the speed or the angular position. Multiple pole machines maximize the output torque per watt of rotor power. Commercial PM motors are available in many sizes from 35 mN m at about 25 mm diameter, to 13.5 N m at

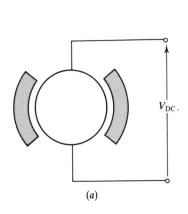

(a)

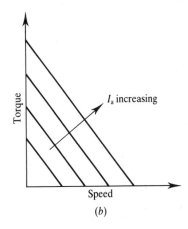

(b)

Figure 5.30 DC permanent magnet motor.

about 3 m diameter. Direct drive rate and position systems using PM motors utilize DC tachogenerators and position sensors in various forms of closed-loop feedback paths for control purposes.

5.9 THE STEPPER MOTOR

A stepper motor is a device which converts a DC voltage pulse train into a proportional mechanical rotation of its shaft. The discrete motion of the stepper motor makes it ideally suited for use with a digitally based control system such as a microcomputer.

The speed of a stepper motor may be varied by altering the rate of the pulse train input. Thus if a stepper motor requires 48 pulses to rotate through one complete revolution, then an input signal of 96 pulses per second will cause the motor to rotate at 120 rev/min. The rotation is actually carried out in finite increments of time but this is visually indiscernable at all but the lowest speeds.

Stepper motors are capable of driving a 2.25 kW load with stepping rates from 1000 to 20 000 per second in angular increments from 180° down to 0.75°.

There are three basic types of stepper motor, namely

1. *Variable reluctance.* This type of stepper motor has a soft iron multi-toothed rotor with a wound stator. The number of teeth on the rotor and stator, together with the winding configuration and excitation determines the step angle. This type of stepper motor provides small to medium-sized step angles and is capable of operation at high stepping rates.
2. *Permanent magnet.* The rotor used in the PM type stepper motor consists of a circular permanent magnet mounted onto the shaft. PM stepper motors give a large step angle ranging from 45° to 120°.
3. *Hybrid.* The hybrid stepper motor is a combination of the previous two types. Typically the stator has eight salient poles which are energized by a two-phase winding. The rotor consists of a cylindrical magnet which is axially magnetized. The step angle depends on the method of construction and is generally in the range 0.9° to 5°. The most popular step angle is 1.8°. The principle of operation of a stepper motor can be illustrated with reference to a variable reluctance, four-phase machine. This motor usually has eight stator teeth and six rotor teeth, Fig. 5.31.
   If phase 1 of the stator is activated alone then two diametrically opposite rotor teeth align themselves with the phase 1 teeth of the stator. The next adjacent set of rotor teeth in the

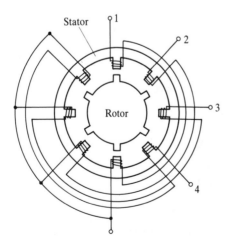

Figure 5.31 Variable reluctance stepper motor.

clockwise direction are then 15° out of step with those of the stator. Activation of the phase 2 winding on its own, would cause the rotor to rotate a further 15° in the anti-clockwise direction to align the adjacent pair of diametrically opposite rotor teeth. If the stator windings are excited in the sequence 1, 2, 3, 4 then the rotor will move in consecutive 15° steps in the anti-clockwise direction. Reversing the excitation sequence will cause a clockwise rotation of the rotor.

Stepper Motor Terminology

Pull-out torque. The maximum torque which can be applied to a motor, running at a given stepping rate, without losing synchronism.

Pull-in torque. The maximum torque against which a motor will start, at a given pulse rate, and reach synchronism without losing a step.

Dynamic torque. The torque developed by the motor at very slow stepping speeds.

Holding torque. The maximum torque which can be applied to an energized stationary motor without causing spindle rotation.

Pull-out rate. The maximum switching rate at which a motor will remain in synchronism while the switching rate is gradually increased.

Pull-in rate. The maximum switching rate at which a loaded motor can start without losing steps.

Slew range. The range of switching rates between pull-in and pull-out in which a motor will run in synchronism but cannot start or reverse.

The general characteristics of a typical stepper motor are given in Fig. 5.32.

During the application of each sequential pulse, the rotor of a stepper motor accelerates rapidly towards the new step position. However, on reaching the new position there will be some overshoot and oscillation unless sufficient retarding torque is provided to prevent this happening. These oscillations can cause rotor resonance at certain pulse frequencies resulting in loss of torque, or perhaps even pull-out conditions. As variable reluctance motors have very little inherent damping, they are more susceptible to resonances than either of the permanent magnet, or the hybrid types. Mechanical and electronic dampers are available which can be used to minimize the adverse effects of rotor resonance. If at all possible, however, the motor should be selected such that its resonant frequencies are not critical to the application under consideration.

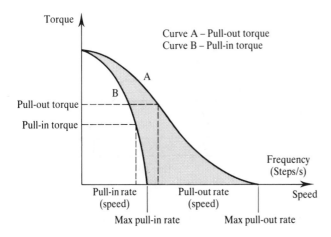

Figure 5.32 Stepper motor characteristics.

Owing to their unique characteristics, stepper motors are widely used in applications involving positioning, speed control, timing and synchronized actuation. They are prevalent in X–Y plotters, punched tape readers, floppy disc head drives, printer carriage drives, numerically controlled machine tool slide drives and camera iris control mechanisms. The most severe limitation on the purely electric stepper motor at present, is its limited power handling capability.

Example Figure 5.33 shows part of a mechanism which is driven by a stepper motor through a belt and pulley transmission system. The pulleys have an effective diameter of 240 mm. The belt conveys a mass of 500 kg which has to be accelerated uniformly up to a velocity of 0.1 m/s in a period of 2 s. This maximum velocity is then held constant for 4 s before being decelerated uniformly back to zero velocity in 2 s. Friction in the system requires a constant force of 100 N acting effectively through the mass. On completing the cycle, the motion is reversed through the same velocity–time history to return the mass to the orginal starting position. The stepper motor operates with 200 pulses per revolution and is directly coupled to the driven pulley.
Determine

(a) the pull-in torque at start up;
(b) the pull-out torque at constant velocity;
(c) the stepping rate required for the constant velocity;
(d) the power required at constant velocity.

The force required has to overcome friction in the mechanism and accelerate the mass. At start-up

$$\text{force} = \text{mass} \times \text{accel.} + \text{friction} = 500 \times (0.1/2) + 100 = 125\,\text{N}$$

Starting torque required is therefore

$$125 \times 0.12 = 15\,\text{Nm}$$

This is the minimum torque, or pull-in torque required at start-up. As the system accelerates, this torque will be constantly required until the steady velocity is reached. During steady motion, there is no force required for acceleration. Running torque during steady motion is

$$100 \times 0.12 = 12\,\text{Nm}$$

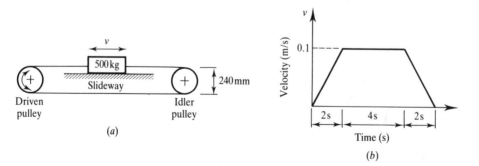

Figure 5.33 Stepper motor driven mechanism.

This lower value of torque is the minimum value allowable which the motor must be capable of providing without losing synchronism when running at the constant speed, i.e. the pull-out torque.

Since the peripheral velocity of the pulley is $v = \pi DN$, then the rotational speed of the pulley is

$$N = v/(\pi D) = 0.1/(\pi 0.24) = 0.133 \text{ rev/s}$$

The required stepping rate is

$$200 \times 0.133 = 26.5 \text{ steps/s}$$

The power required at this speed is given by

$$2\pi NT = 2 \times \pi \times 0.133 \times 12 = 10 \text{ W}$$

5.10 BRUSHLESS DC MOTORS

These motors have position feedback of some kind so that the input waveforms can be kept in the proper timing with respect to the rotor position. Solid-state switching devices are used to control the input signals and the brushless DC motor can be operated at much higher speeds with full torque available at those speeds. The brushless motor can normally be rapidly accelerated from zero to operating speed as a permanent magnet DC motor. On reaching operating speed, the motor can then be switched over to synchronous operation.

The brushless motor system consists of a wound stator, a permanent magnet rotor, a rotor position sensor and a solid state switching assembly. The wound stator can be made with two, or more input phases. Figure 5.34 shows the schematic representation of a two-phase brushless motor.

The torque output of phase A is

$$T = I_A(Z\Phi/2\pi)\sin(p\theta/2) = I_A K_T \sin(p\theta/2) \tag{5.17}$$

where I_A = current in phase A
$K_T = (Z\Phi/2\pi)$, is the torque constant of the motor
p = number of poles
θ = angular position of the rotor

In the expression for the torque constant, Z is the total number of conductors and Φ is the magnetic flux.

In a similar manner, the torque output of phase B is

$$T_B = I_B K_T \cos(p\theta/2) \tag{5.18}$$

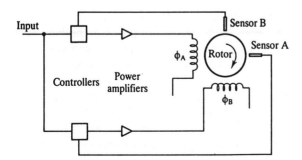

Figure 5.34 Two-phase brushless motor.

If the motor currents are arranged to be supplied in the following relationships:

$$I_A = I\sin(p\theta/2) \text{ and } I_B = I\cos(p\theta/2)$$

then the total torque for a two-pole motor becomes:

$$T = T_A + T_B = IK_T[\sin^2(\theta) + \cos^2(\theta)]$$
$$= IK_T \tag{5.19}$$

Equation (5.19) shows that if all of the above conditions are satisfied then the brushless DC motor operates in a similar manner to the conventional DC motor, i.e. the torque is directly proportional to the armature current. Note that the armature current in this context refers to the stator windings. Excitation of the phases may be implemented with sinuosidal, or square-wave inputs. The sine-wave drive is the most efficient but the output transistors in the drive electronics must be capable of dissipating more power than that dissipated in square-wave operation. Square-wave drive offers the added advantage that the drive electronics can be digitally based.

The brushless DC motor duplicates the performance characteristics of a conventional DC motor only if it is properly commutated. Proper commutation involves exciting the stator windings in a sequence that keeps the magnetic field produced by the stator approximately 90 electrical degrees ahead of the rotor field. The brushless DC motor therefore relies heavily on the position feedback system for effective commutation. It might also be apparent that the brushless motor as described is not strictly a DC machine, but a form of AC machine with position feedback.

The further development of the brushless DC motor will depend to a large extent upon future advances in semiconductor power transistor technology. It is likely, however, that within the next decade the true brushless DC motor, using solid state switching, will become commercially viable and will progressively dominate the DC servo-system market.

5.11 MOTOR SELECTION

In selecting an electric motor for a particular application, the first step is to determine the power required to drive the load. This is not always easy since, for a prototype artifact, the working torque/speed characteristics may not be well documented, or even very well understood. Other factors for consideration are the requirement for the motor to have enough starting torque to enable it to overcome static friction, accelerate the load up to full working speed and to handle the maximum overload. The motor must either satisfy the mechanical requirements, or give up trying. Giving up would be manifested in the form of the motor becoming disconnected from the supply by automatic circuit breakers responding to the excessive current being drawn by the motor in its attempt to fulfill the mechanical requirements.

The operating speed of the motor is fixed by the point at which the power or torque that the motor can supply electromagnetically intersects with the power or torque that the load can absorb mechanically. Figure 5.35 shows the torque–speed characteristics of an induction motor. Superimposed on the figure are the typical torque–speed characteristics of a driven load such as a centrifugal pump.

The intersection point of the two characteristics determines the final operating speed of the coupled driver and its load. Note also that on start-up, the motor furnishes sufficient excess torque to that required by the load on start-up. This ensures that the load will be rapidly accelerated up to the operating speed. In some applications it is inadvisable to provide too much

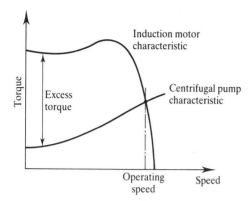

Figure 5.35 Matching of an induction motor to a load.

excess torque on start-up as this can result in a violent initial acceleration and could be quite dangerous if the driven machine is some form of hand-held device. On the other hand, if the motor cannot provide excess torque on start-up, then the load cannot be run up to the operating speed. Note that this applies even if the motor can supply the required torque at the operating speed. In such a case the additional torque required for start-up would have to be supplied from some additional external source.

Driven Machine Characteristics

Correct matching of a motor to a driven machine can be accomplished only if the torque–speed characteristics of the driven machine are known. Very often the full characteristics are simply not available and some kind of estimate has to be made. This estimate might be based on a single measurement of the driven machine torque at rated speed and a knowledge of the typical torque–speed curves for that particular type of machine. Typical torque–speed curves for a variety of driven loads are illustrated in Fig. 5.36.

Friction devices like sanders, buffers and industrial floor polishers have a torque–speed characteristic as shown in Fig. 5.36(a). The difference between the static and the dynamic friction accounts for the initial drop in torque as the speed increases from zero. Fans and blowers have torque–speed characteristics as shown in Fig. 5.36(b). These machines require very little torque for start-up but the running torque essentially increases with the square of the speed.

The torque–speed characteristic for a small reciprocating compressor is shown in Fig. 5.36(c). Because of the high torque required at start-up, many of these machines are fitted with a pressure relief valve which can be left open while the machine is started. This means that the driving motor does not have to compress gas at the same time as running the machine up to operating speed. Once the compressor has reached operating speed, the pressure relief valve is closed and the machine functions normally. The broken line indicates the torque–speed characteristic for a compressor fitted with a pressure relief valve.

High inertia devices, for example machine tool drives, rolling mills and electric trains require a very high torque at start-up in order to overcome the inertial loads. As these machines reach their operating speed the inertial load decreases and the torque required to continue the steady speed generally decreases. The torque–speed characteristics of high inertia devices is typical of that depicted in Fig. 5.36(d).

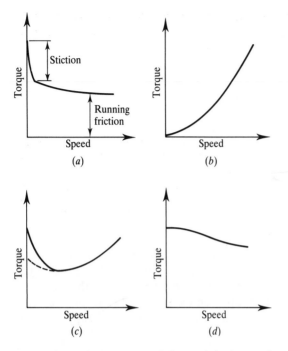

Figure 5.36 Typical torque–speed characteristics for a variety of driven loads: (*a*) friction devices; (*b*) fans and blowers; (*c*) reciprocating compressor; (*d*) high inertia devices.

Acceleration Time to Operating Speed

In some applications the time required for the motor to accelerate the load up to the operating speed is an important aspect in the design considerations. The acceleration time may be estimated from the torque–speed characteristics of the motor and the load, in conjunction with the relation:

$$J \, d\omega/dt + F\omega = \Delta T \tag{5.20}$$

where J = moment of inertia of the driven load, kg m^2
  ΔT = difference between the motor torque and any resisting torque provided by the load, N m
  F = frictional damping constant of the system
  ω = angular velocity, rad/s
  Rearranging Eq. (5.20) gives

$$dt = \frac{J \, d\omega}{\Delta T - C\omega}$$

Integration gives a relation for the time required to accelerate the load up to operating speed:

$$t = J \int_0^\omega \frac{d\omega}{\Delta T - C\omega} \tag{5.21}$$

Example A conveyor belt system has a torque–speed characteristic as shown in Fig. 5.37. The equivalent moment of inertia of the conveyor system and the motor output shaft is $0.4 \, \text{kg m}^2$. The motor chosen for the drive has the torque–speed characteristic also shown in the figure. The low value of excess torque on start-up is a requirement to satisfy the need for a soft start. Assuming that the system friction is negligible, determine the time taken for the motor to accelerate the load up to operating speed and the power consumed under normal operating conditions.

Since the friction is effectively zero then

$$\text{time} = J \int_0^\omega (1/\Delta T)\, \mathrm{d}\omega$$

From the machine characteristics given, the value of the integral can be determined using a simple numerical techique. This consists of evaluating the average value of the parameter $(1/\Delta T)$ over equal increments in speed, $\Delta\omega$. The total area under the curve, which is the integral, is then the sum of the areas of the elemental strips. The results are shown in Table 5.1.

The function $(1/\Delta T)$ is plotted against speed in Fig. 5.37.

Area under curve of $1/\Delta T$ is

$$(1/\Delta T)_{\text{average}} \times \Delta\omega = 2.4715 \times 20.9 = 51.76$$

Time is given by

$$J \times \text{ area under curve} = 0.4 \times 51.76 = 20.7\, s$$

Table 5.1 Numerical integration results.

Speed, rev/min	ω, rad/s	ΔT, N m	$1/\Delta T$, $(\mathrm{N\,m})^{-1}$	$(1/\Delta T)_{\text{average}}$ $(\mathrm{N\,m})^{-1}$
0	0	1	1	
				0.8125
200	20.9	1.6	0.625	
				0.5125
400	41.9	2.5	0.4	
				0.347
600	52.8	3.4	0.294	
				0.3195
800	83.8	2.9	0.345	
				0.480 (estimate)
1000	104.7	0	infinity	
			Total	2.4715

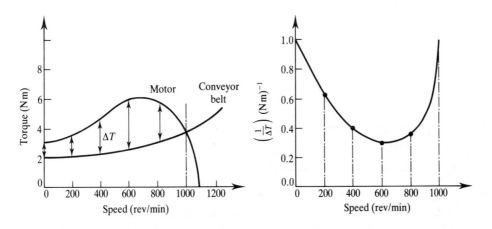

Figure 5.37 Torque–speed characteristics for a motor and driven load.

The above shows that the system will take about 21 s to run up to operating speed. At the normal operating speed the motor and load torques are equal to 3.55 N m. The power consumed is therefore

$$2\pi NT = 2\pi(1000/60)3.55 = 371\,\text{W} = 0.37\,\text{kW}$$

Note also that the maximum torque is 6 N m and this is produced when the speed is 700 rev/min. The power required at this point in the run-up is

$$2\pi(700/60)6 = 440\,\text{W} = 0.44\,\text{kW}$$

Similarly the power requirements over the run-up period are:

Speed, rev/min	200	400	600	700	800	900	1000
Power, W	75	193	358	440	477	471	371

Note that the maximum power and the maximum torque are not necessarily coincident at the same speed. The motor must therefore have a power rating of at least 0.5 kW to be able to cope with the driven load without overheating.

Aspects of Speed Control

Many mechanical applications require some form of speed control in an electrical drive system. This can have important ramifications on the choice of drive motor since the method of speed control can influence the resultant torque–speed characteristics of the machine. Figure 5.38 shows the torque–speed characteristics for a series-wound DC motor using (*a*) variable armature resistance for speed control and (*b*) solid state voltage control. Also shown in the

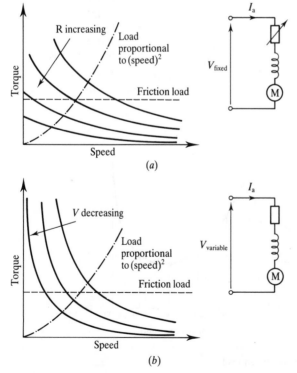

Figure 5.38 Torque–speed characteristics for a series DC motor with speed control: (*a*) variable armature resistance; (*b*) variable voltage.

figure are the torque–speed characteristics for a friction load and a load, like a fan or a blower, which is proportional to the square of the speed.

It might be apparent that armature resistance is more suitable for the load which is proportional to the square of the speed and that solid state voltage control is more suited to the friction load.

If we use variable armature resistance as a means of speed control while driving the friction load, then as we increase the resistance to obtain lower speeds there is barely enough torque available to drive the load. Similarly, if we were to use solid state voltage control to vary the speed while driving the load, which is proportional to the square of the speed, then as we decrease the voltage to reduce the speed we see that the load requires less driving torque while the motor actually supplies more driving torque. The motor characteristics are therefore quite incompatible with this load.

If in some other application the source of power were derived from a battery, say for example, a golf cart, then it would be unwise to use armature resistance as a means of speed control. The battery would still dissipate and waste considerable power through the extra resistance in the armature circuit. The ideal variable speed drive for a battery-operated vehicle would be a series DC motor with its direct drive and high starting torque, using solid state voltage control for economic speed regulation.

Variable speed in AC motors is more limited but can be implemented by using variable rotor resistance in a slip-ring induction motor, or variable stator voltages. Both of these methods will give a range of speed regulation for suitably matched loads. The most effective method of speed control for induction motors, however, is the use of a variable frequency power supply. The resulting torque speed characteristics for an induction motor with a variable frequency supply is shown in Fig. 5.39.

Adjustment of the supply frequency can alter the speed while maintaining the normal operating condition at which the slip is about 4 per cent.

Example Figure 5.40 shows the torque–speed characteristics for a disc sander and the torque–speed characteristics for two motors which are being considered for the drive. Discuss the starting and running conditions to be expected for each motor.

When motor A is used the sander will start very quickly and accelerate rapidly up to operating speed. The machine will not easily stall if the operator uses excessive thrust, or if the material being sanded is sticky. The excess torque, however, especially at start-up, might

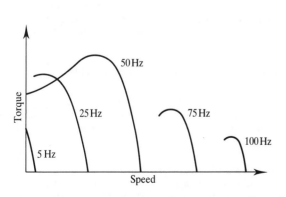

Figure 5.39 Torque–speed characteristics for an induction motor with a variable frequency power supply.

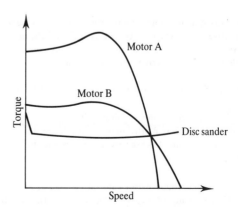

Figure 5.40 Torque–speed characteristics for disc sander and drive motors.

surprise the unwary operator and there might be a tendency for the machine to jerk out of the operators hands on start-up.

When motor B is used there will be no violent jerk on start-up but the motor may stall if the sander is pressed too heavily against the surface. The operator may have to lift the sander clear of the surface on start-up to allow the machine to run up to operating speed.

FURTHER READING

Bell, E. C. and R. W. Whitehead (1987) *Basic Electrical Engineering & Instrumentation for Engineers*, 3rd edn, Granada, London.
Fitzgerald, A. E., D. E. Higginbotham and A. Grabel (1981) *Basic Electrical Engineering* 5th edn, McGraw-Hill, Auckland.
Gray, C. B. (1989) *Electrical Machines and Drive Systems*, Longmans Scientific and Technical, Harlow.
Kenjo, T. and S. Nagamori (1985) *Permanent Magnet and Brushless DC Motors*, Monographs in Electrical and Electronic Engineering, Clarendon Press, Oxford.
Orthwein, W. (1990) *Machine Component Design*, West Publishing, St Paul, Minnesota.
Sen, P. C. (1989) *Principles of Electric Machines and Power Electronics*, Wiley, Chichester.
Wildi, T. (1981) *Electrical Power Technology*, Wiley, New York.

EXERCISES

5.1   A DC motor takes an armature current of 100 A at 440 V. The resistance of the armature circuit is 0.3 Ω. The machine has four poles and the armature is lap-wound with 860 conductors. The flux per pole is 0.05 Wb. Calculate the motor speed and the torque developed.

[572 rev/min, 684.5 N m]

5.2   A series motor runs at 500 rev/min when taking 90 A from a 240 V supply. The resistance of the armature and series windings are 0.2 Ω and 0.03 Ω, respectively. Calculate the motor speed when the current is 40 A. Assume that the useful flux per pole at 40 A is 65 per cent of that at 90 A.

[810 rev/min]

5.3   A shunt wound motor supplied with 230 V runs at 900 rev/min when the armature current is 30 A. The resistance of the armature circuit is 0.5 Ω. Calculate the value of a resistance required in series with the armature to reduce the speed to 500 rev/min, assuming that the armature current is then 18 A and that the field excitation remains constant.

[5.64 Ω]

5.4   When running at its rated load, a 40 kW series motor takes 74 A at 550 V. The rated speed is 750 rev/min. The armature and series field resistances are 0.35 Ω and 0.15 Ω, respectively. When the load torque is double the rated value, the current is 110 A. Determine the motor speed and the power output at 100 per cent torque overload.

[538 rev/min, 57.4 kW]

5.5   (a) A shunt wound motor runs off a 240 V supply and has field and armature resistances of 320 Ω and 0.2 Ω, respectively. The armature current is 50 A and the motor speed is 950 rev/min. Assuming a straight line magnetization curve, calculate the value of an additional resistance required in the field circuit to increase the speed to 1100 rev/min, while the armature current remains constant.

[35.7 Ω]

(b) Calculate the speed of the machine with the original field current and an armature current of 90 A.

[917 rev/min]

5.6   A DC series motor running at 700 rev/min takes a current of 60 A from a 420 V supply. Calculate the value of a resistor which, when inserted in series with the motor will reduce the speed to 500 rev/min, the torque then being one-half of its original value. Take the armature resistance to be 0.2 Ω and assume that the field flux is directly proportional to the field current.

[3.37 Ω]

5.7   A shunt wound motor runs on no load at 800 rev/min from a 230 V supply taking an armature current of 2 A. Calculate the value of resistance required in series with the shunt winding such that the motor may run at 1000 rev/min, when taking an armature current of 30 A. Take the field and armature resistances as 140 Ω and 0.3 Ω, respectively and assume that the flux is directly proportional to the field current.

[41.6 Ω]

5.8   (a) The resistance of the armature of a 200 V shunt motor is $0.2\,\Omega$ and its full load speed is 900 rev/min. Calculate the value of the resistor required in series with the armature to reduce the speed, with full load torque, to 600 rev/min, the full load armature current then being 30 A.

[$2.16\,\Omega$]

(b) If the load torque is now halved, determine the speed at which the motor will run.

[764 rev/min]

5.9   The current taken by 415 V shunt motor when running on no load is 6 A. The resistance of the armature and field circuits are 0.2 and $220\,\Omega$, respectively. Calculate the output power and efficiency when the machine draws a current of 120 A when running at normal speed under load. Calculate the armature current when the machine runs at maximum efficiency.

[44.52 kW, 89.4%, 111.6 A]

5.10   The speed of a shunt wound DC motor can be controlled by using a field regulator, by varying the armature resistance, or by using a thyristor circuit to control the armature voltage. Discuss the advantages and limitations of these three methods of speed control for a given application.

5.11   Write a summary report on the variety of methods of speed control applicable to induction motors, indicating the main advantages and disadvantages of each method.

5.12   A gas engine drives a six pole three-phase alternator at 1800 rev/min. The alternator is connected to a four pole three-phase induction motor running at 6 per cent slip. Determine the speed of the induction motor.

[2538 rev/min]

5.13   A three-phase induction motor runs at 1200 rev/min on no load and at 1140 rev/min on full load. Power is supplied from a 60 Hz three-phase line. Determine how many poles the motor has and the percentage of slip at full load conditions.

[six, 5%]

5.14   A stepper motor operating with 48 pulses per revolution is required to drive a geared system with an output speed of 10 rev/min. If the overall gearing ratio is a step down from 30 to 1, determine the required stepping rate.

[240 pulses/s]

5.15   The torque–speed characteristics for a load and two possible drive motors are tabulated below:

Speed (rev/min)	0	200	400	600	800	1000	1200	1400
Load torque (N m)	1	1.05	1.2	1.4	1.85	2.5	3.6	6
Motor A (N m)	8	8.35	9.1	10	9.8	7.5	0	—
Motor B (N m)	3	3.2	3.7	4.6	5	4.3	2.75	0

$(a\,2\quad b)$

Plot the torque–speed characteristics and determine the operating speed for each motor. If the effective inertia of the system is $1.4\,\text{kg m}^2$ and the system damping can be assumed to be zero, calculate the time taken for the system to run up to this speed using each motor. Determine also the maximum power consumed by each motor during run-up.

[1140 rev/min (both), 26.8 s, 75.7 s, 835 W, 450 W]

5.16   The torque–speed characteristic of a rotary mixer for thixotropic paints is given approximately by the relation:

$$T = 0.6 + 3/N, \text{ where } T \text{ is the torque in N m and } N \text{ is the speed in rev/s.}$$

This relation applies in the speed range of 1–60 rev/s and the mixer would normally be operating at 50 rev/s.
Plot the mixer torque–speed characteristic and select a suitable electric motor for the drive. Your choice of motor should be based on the starting and running torques and the start-up time.

5.17   A company wishes to market a power assisted lifting machanism for 'up-and-over' type garage doors. Estimate the expected torque–speed characteristics for the door and specify a suitable type of motor drive for the system, giving reasons for your choice.

NB. Some consideration should be given to the safety aspects, for example the event of a child attempting to 'ride' the door.

SIX

ELECTRO-PNEUMATIC AND ELECTRO-HYDRAULIC SYSTEMS

6.1 BASIC PRINCIPLES

There are three basic means of providing the necessary drive power in a mechatronic system. These are mechanical, electrical and fluid. Fluid systems comprise either gas (air for pneumatics) or liquid (oil for hydraulics). There are many advantages, disadvantages and limitations of each and a combination of all three may be employed in order to obtain the maximum benefit for any specific application.

In automation systems the intelligence and flexibility can be enhanced by employing a microprocessor-based controller, but the required movement and holding of components is invariably carried out using either pneumatic or hydraulic circuits. The sequential control of such systems is easily achieved by incorporating solenoid activation of the fluid power control valves, and hence the terminology electro-pneumatics and electro-hydraulics.

There is probably no manufacturing or assembly process that cannot be broken down into a cyclic series of relatively simple movements and functions, and the handling and control arrangement can be designed to suit. The complexity of the process usually determines the drive source, and in many cases there is little to choose between each and it almost certainly becomes a matter of personal preference. An advisable strategy is to carefully define the basic movements required in the process and work backwards to develop an actuation system. Once this is done, the selection of a controlling arrangement follows naturally. Microprocessor-based controllers certainly enhance the intelligence which can be embedded into the system but it should be noted that in many cases there may be no need to incorporate microelectronic devices. The choice is dependent upon the complexity of the system being developed and a large degree of personal preference of the designer.

The mechanical elements common to most systems comprise such parts as cams, gears, pulleys, belts, sprockets, chains and linkage mechanisms. Pure mechanical control is generally restricted to situations where a load is exerted over a short distance. The main disadvantages are the limitation on speed and the space requirement.

Electric systems are very versatile and are widely used in many industrial applications. They can be accurately controlled and the control hardware used is cheaper than that used with pneumatic and hydraulic systems. A simple ON/OFF electric switch is cheaper than a pneumatic or hydraulic valve used for the same function. The main advantages of electric drive systems are:

1. Electricity is easily supplied to the actuators via cables.
2. Electricity is easily controlled.
3. Electricity is clean.
4. Electrical faults are usually easy to diagnose and repair.

The main disadvantages are:

1. It is difficult and expensive to use in fire hazard areas.
2. There is not the same variety of actuator motion as there is with pneumatics and hydraulics.
3. The actuators are not too good at low speed applications with a high torque requirement.
4. They often need complex mechanisms to transform shaft rotation into the required movement.

Details of typical electrical actuators are given in Chapter 5.

Pneumatic Systems

Compressed air is readily available as a standard ring main service in industry and the utilization of electro-pneumatics for applications related to automation is high. The method is most suited for light loads at high speed with low cost. The load limitation is basically due to the pressure available from the source and is usually 5 to 6 bar (approximately $80\,lbf/in^2$). With the increased emphasis on automation, pneumatics is ideal for a wide range of pick-and-place cyclic operations and most industries in some way apply the technology.

The compressed air is usually made available from an air receiver which is charged by a reciprocating or rotary air compressor. Before being piped to the pneumatic control circuit the air is conditioned to remove moisture and solid contaminants which may cause problems with valve operation. The advantages in using pneumatics are:

1. The systems can be used in high-temperature environments.
2. There is no mess when leaks occur.
3. The components used in the system design are relatively cheap and easy to maintain.

The disadvantages are:

1. Air is compressible and accurate positioning is difficult.
2. Air is expansive and explosive type accidents are possible.
3. Large forces cannot be applied due to the low working pressures.

Pneumatic technology has developed significantly since the introduction of microelectronic controllers and a black box systems thinking approach can be adopted for pneumatic elements in much the same way as for microelectronic elements. This attitude lays more emphasis on what elements and components can do rather than what they comprise and importance is placed on providing a solution concerned with satisfying overall system objectives.

In 1964 the European Oil Hydraulic and Pneumatic Committee (CEETOP—Comite Europeen des Transmissions Oleohydrauliques et Pneumatiques) published a proposal for a range of graphical symbols for hydraulic and pneumatic components. This was recognized by the International Organisation for Standardisation (ISO) and is detailed in ISO 1219 (1976). The standard also formed the basis of BS 2917 (1977).

Hydraulic Systems

Oil hydraulic equipment is used in an ever increasing range of applications in modern industry and there are a number of highly specialized firms who produce a variety of related components for the system designer. The complexity of hydraulic systems vary depending upon the application but they are all essentially the same. The main components are: a power pack comprising a tank to hold the hydraulic oil with a positive displacement pump driven by an electric motor, valves to control fluid pressure and flow, and an actuator to convert the fluid energy into useful work. Hydraulic circuits can be tailored to produce practically any combination of force and motion.

Hydraulic systems operate at much higher pressures than pneumatic systems and hence their application where large forces are needed. Typical working pressures are 200–800 bar ($3000–12\,000\,\mathrm{lbf/in^2}$). Also, since oil is virtually incompressible, i.e. very little density change accompanying a large pressure change, hydraulic systems can be used in applications where precision movement is necesssary.

There are a number of basic properties which make oil hydraulic systems acceptable for fluid power transmission. These may be summarized as follows:

1. Good power to weight ratio with excellent acceleration of loads.
2. Infinitely variable speed transmission possible in hydrostatic power transmission systems with a rotary positive displacement pump supplying a rotary positive displacement motor.
3. Ability to combine with other forms of power transmission.
4. Safety can be relatively easily ensured due to the inexpansive nature of oil under pressure.

The disadvantages associated with such systems are:

1. They are much more expensive than pneumatic systems.
2. They are messy if a leak develops.
3. They are a potential fire hazard.
4. They usually must include oil cooling facilities.

The actuators and valves are basically similar to those used in pneumatics except that they are designed to withstand much higher pressures. The graphical symbols adopted to show the type or function of a component also conform to BS 2917 (1977).

6.2 ACTUATORS

The purpose of the actuator in a fluid power system is to convert the fluid energy into mechanical work and this may involve either a linear or a rotary device. A number of mechanical handling and automatic processing applications require a linear motion, and pneumatic and hydraulic cylinders are ideally suited. They are basically simple in construction and have the ability to withstand severe overloads. A typical cylinder consists of the barrel, end covers, piston and piston rod together with the appropriate sealing. Cylinders come in two design types:

1. Single acting with a single port. This has a power stroke in the outward direction only and the return of the piston is usually by means of a spring. Alternatively, the return can be achieved through the load.
2. Double acting with a port at each end of the cylinder barrel. They are occasionally required with a piston rod on both sides of the piston to ensure an equal thrust in both directions.

The graphical symbols for both these cylinders are shown in Fig. 6.1.

Most cylinders are available with a device that slows down the piston as it approaches the end of the stroke in order to reduce the shock encountered through a sudden stop. This is referred to as cushioning and is usually desirable in a pneumatic or hydraulic circuit. Rodless cylinders in which the internal piston is sealed by end caps are also available. The load mounting moves as the piston moves and the complete arrangement has the necessary control valves as an integral attachment to each end of the cylinder. This design provides an extremely compact and flexible component for various applications in automation systems.

An alternative to the linear actuator in a fluid system is the rotary type, in which the fluid energy in the form of pressure is transformed into mechanical energy in the form of a rotating shaft. These actuators are referred to as air motors in pneumatics and hydraulic motors in hydraulics. For both systems they are of similar positive displacement construction with a precise amount of fluid transported through the motor for one revolution of the shaft. The graphics symbols used for fixed and variable displacement machines are shown in Fig. 6.2.

The air motor is usually of fixed capacity and is relatively inefficient by comparison with an electric motor. However, they have the advantage of compactness and they can be overloaded or even stalled without damage. There is no need for elaborate protective devices. The most common designs for air motors are the vane, radial piston and axial piston. They each operate on the same basic principle and differ only in the way that the force is transmitted to the rotating shaft. The shaft output speed of a fixed displacement machine can be altered only by changing the rate of air flow or the supply pressure. They are used in relatively low power applications and a typical operating speed range is 500 to 6000 rev/min although speeds up to around 15 000 rev/min can occur in small portable air tools such as grinders. Typical torque/speed and power/speed characteristics for an air motor are shown in Fig. 6.3.

Hydraulic motors are generally used in situations where low speed and high torque are required. They are more expensive than air motors but hydrostatic power transmission with a variable speed drive compares favourably with electric systems. They are extremely rugged, can endure overload and are quite efficient with values in the order of 80 to 90 per cent. Many hydraulic motors can be used as pumps with little or no modification. The three most common types are the gear, the sliding vane and the piston. The piston design is further divided into radial and axial types.

The operation of a gear type motor is shown in Fig. 6.4. Both gears are driven but only one is connected to the output shaft. The fluid output from the pump enters the motor inlet and

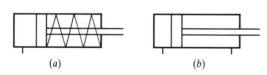

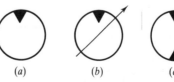

(a)   (b)   (a)   (b)   (c)

Figure 6.1 Linear actuators in fluid systems: (a) single-acting return spring; (b) double-acting.

Figure 6.2 Rotary actuators in fluid systems: (a) uni-directional (fixed displacement); (b) uni-directional (variable displacement); (c) bi-directional (fixed displacement).

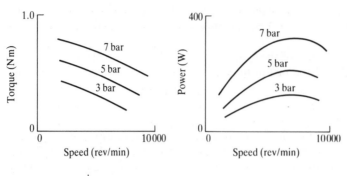

Figure 6.3 Air motor characteristics.

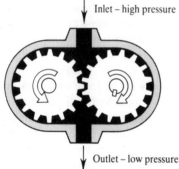

Figure 6.4 A gear type hydraulic motor/pump.

flows in both directions around the surface of the casing thus forcing the gears to rotate as shown. This rotary motion is then available as a torque at the output shaft. The application of gear motors is usually limited to an output power of around 10 kW. They are used when relatively high speed, up to 400 rev/min, and low starting torques are required. In a gear pump oil is drawn into the inlet from the supply tank and carried around the surface of the housing to the outlet. One gear is driven by an external prime mover and the rotary energy is transformed into fluid energy in the form of pressure. The pressure generated will, of course, be dependent upon the magnitude of the load on the pump from the hydraulic system being supplied. A close fit of the gear teeth within the housing is required to provide a seal between the inlet and outlet sides in order to minimize internal leakage.

The vane-type hydraulic motor has a number of vanes in a rotor which rotates in a cam ring within the motor housing. As the rotor turns the vanes follow the surface of the ring forming sealed chambers which carry the oil from the inlet to the outlet. Torque is developed by the differential fluid pressure acting on the surface of the vanes. Figure 6.5 illustrates the general principle of operation and the arrangement can be used as a pump by externally driving the rotor and connecting the inlet port to the supply tank. As the space enclosed by the vanes, rotor and housing enlarges a vacuum is created and the oil is forced into the space. With the rotation of the rotor the space is reduced in size and the oil is forced from the outlet port at the delivery pressure.

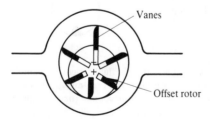

Figure 6.5 Principle of a vane-type hydraulic motor/pump.

Various vane-type of machines exist and include a variable displacement design along with one in which the pressure over the rotor is balanced by having two inlet and two outlet ports diametrically opposite each other. Hence any side loads which are generated oppose and cancel each other.

Piston-type hydraulic motors can operate at very high speeds and pressures. They are very efficient and have an excellent power to weight ratio. The torque is generated through pressure on the ends of reciprocating pistons operating in a cylinder block and the design can be either a radial or axial piston arrangement. Variable displacement can be achieved by varying the stroke length of the pistons. In the axial or in-line machine this is achieved by varying the angle of the swash-plate which is mounted on a swinging yoke. The angle can be changed by using a simple manual lever or a sophisticated servo-control system. Reducing the angle results in a speed increase with an accompanying torque decrease. Minimum angle stops are usually provided so that torque and speed are held within operating limits. The basic principle of the axial motor/pump is shown in Fig. 6.6

Details of typical maximum operating pressures and speeds for the common types of hydraulic motors are given in Table 6.1.

Formulae for hydraulic motors and pumps The volumetric capacity per revolution of a motor or a pump (C_m or C_p) governs the relationship between the oil flow rate (Q) and the speed of operation (N_m or N_p). The capacity is measured in volume per revolution of the shaft and can be expressed in units of cm^3/rev, litres/rev, millilitres/rev or in^3/rev.

$$1\,cm^3 = 10^{-6}\,m^3 = 10^{-3}\,litres = 1\,millilitre = 0.061\,in^3$$

The relationship between C, Q and N is given theoretically by

$$Q = CN$$

However, due to internal leakage the machines have a volumetric efficiency η_v which is defined as

$$\eta_{vm} = C_m N_m / Q$$

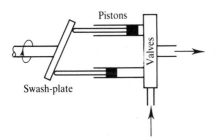

Figure 6.6 Principle of the axial piston type hydraulic motor/pump.

Table 6.1 Typical maximum pressures and speed for hydraulic motors.

Motor type	Typical maximum operating pressure (bar)	Operating speeds (rev/min)
Gear	250	400–6000
Vane	150	100–4000
Axial piston	400	50–4000

for a motor, and

$$\eta_{vp} = Q/C_p N_p$$

for a pump.

The leakage increases with pressure and can be related to a leakage coefficient λ in the form:

$$q_m = \lambda_m \Delta P_m \qquad \text{and} \qquad q_p = \lambda_p \Delta P_p$$

for a motor and a pump, respectively. ΔP_m and ΔP_p are the pressure drop over the motor and pressure rise over the pump, respectively. Hence the flow rate Q is given by

$$Q_m = C_m N_m + \lambda_m \Delta P_m$$
$$Q_p = C_p N_p - \lambda_p \Delta P_p$$

The volumetric efficiencies can then be written as

$$\eta_{vm} = \frac{1}{(1 + \lambda_m \Delta P_m / C_m N_m)}$$
$$\eta_{vp} = 1 - \lambda_p \Delta P_p / C_p N_p$$

Volumetric efficiencies are typically in the range of 85–95 per cent and are pressure dependent. The mechanical efficiency η_{mech} can be defined as follows:

For a motor:

$$\eta_{mechm} = \text{output power/'indicated' input power}$$
$$\text{output power} = 2\pi N_m T_m$$

where T_m is the torque generated

$$\text{'indicated' input power} = (C_m N_m)\Delta P_m$$

Hence

$$\eta_{mechm} = \frac{2\pi T_m}{C_m \Delta P_m}$$

For a pump:

$$\eta_{mechp} = \text{'indicated' output power /input power}$$

where T_p is the input torque

$$\text{'indicated' output power} = (C_p N_p)\Delta P_p$$

$$\text{input power} = 2\pi N_p T_p$$

Hence

$$\eta_{mechp} = \frac{C_p \Delta P_p}{2\pi T_p}$$

Peak mechanical efficiencies are typically in the range 85–95 per cent. The overall efficiency η_o can be defined as

$$\eta_o \text{ for a motor} = \text{output power/actual input power}$$
$$\eta_o \text{ for a pump} = \text{actual output power/input power}$$

For a motor, the actual input power $= Q_m \Delta P_m = C_m N_m \Delta P_m / \eta_{vm}$, hence

$$\eta_{om} = \frac{\eta_{vm}2\pi T_m}{C_m \Delta P_m}$$

$$= \eta_{vm}\eta_{mechm}$$

Similarly for a pump

$$\eta_{op} = \frac{\eta_{vp}C_p \Delta P_p}{2\pi T_p}$$

$$= \eta_{vp}\eta_{mechp}$$

Example A motor has a capacity of 50 ml/rev and a speed of 1500 rev/min with a pressure drop of 200 bar. Using a volumetric efficiency of 92 per cent and a mechanical efficiency of 95 per cent calculate:

(a) the actual flow rate of oil into the motor in litres/minute;
(b) the actual torque developed by the motor;
(c) the actual power developed by the motor in kW.

Actual flow rate into motor, $Q_m = C_m N_m / \eta_{vm}$, where $C_m = 50 \times 10^{-3}$ l/rev. Thus

$$Q_m = 50 \times 10^{-3} \times 1500/0.92$$

$$= 81.5 \, l/min$$

Actual torque developed by the motor is

$$T_m = \frac{(C_m N_m)\Delta P_m \eta_{mechm}}{2\pi N_m}$$

where $C_m = 50 \times 10^{-3}$ l/rev $= 50 \times 10^{-6}$ m^3/rev. Thus

$$T_m = \frac{50 \times 10^{-6} \times 200 \times 10^5 \times 0.95}{2\pi}$$

$$= 151.2 \, Nm$$

Overall efficiency is

$$\eta_o = 0.95 \times 0.92$$

$$= 0.872$$

Actual power developed by the motor is $Q\Delta P_m \eta_{om}$

$$= (81.5 \times 10^{-3}/60) \times 200 \times 10^5 \times 0.874$$

$$= 23.8 \, kW$$

Alternatively, the power could be calculated from

$$2\pi N_m T_m = 6.284 \times (1500/60) \times 151.2$$

$$= 23.8 \, kW$$

The output torque and power variation with speed characteristics of a hydraulic motor are dependent upon the nature of the pump/motor drive arrangement and this is covered in Sec. 6.5.

The characteristics of a fixed capacity positive displacement pump running at a constant speed are shown in Fig. 6.7.

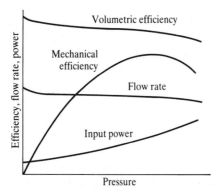

Figure 6.7 Characteristics of a typical positive displacement pump.

6.3 CONTROL VALVES

The fluid, air or oil, supplied to any actuator or any combination of actuators must be admitted or exhausted in a positive and reliable manner. This is ensured by the correct design of valve. The BS or ISO symbols take no account of the valve design or size and are basically a functional representation which indicates the flow connections. Valves are used in pneumatic and hydraulic circuits to:

1. Control the direction of motion of an actuator.
2. Control the speed of an actuator.
3. Control the limiting pressure in a system.

Directional Control Valves

Directional control valves are used to control the path of the fluid flow into an actuator mainly with respect to start, stop and direction of flow. They are classified according to their principal characteristics which include:

1. *Type of internal valving arrangement*   rotary spool or sliding spool.
2. *Number of flow paths*   two-way, three-way, four-way etc.
3. *Method of actuation*   mechanical lever, spring, push-button, plunger, pilot pressure, electric solenoid or a combination of these and others.

Figure 6.8 illustrates the principles of operation of a sliding-spool-type four-port, two-position valve (4/2-way). The spool-type valve is the most widely used as it is easy to operate and the

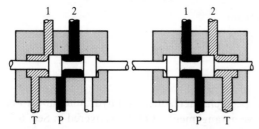

Flow P → 2, return 1 → T   Flow P → 1, return 2 → T   **Figure 6.8** Principle of operation of a 4/2-way sliding spool directional control valve.

design permits many variations in the internal flow paths while maintaining the same outward configuration. In electro-pneumatic or electro-hydraulic systems the activation of the valve is achieved by solenoids. An alternative method to purely activating a solenoid for switching the valve from an electrical supply is to employ a small pilot operator to make the compressed air do the main work of operating the valve spool. The air is directed to a piston actuator by the solenoid-enabled pilot operator which is only required to operate against light forces. Where direct solenoid operation is used, the solenoids are much larger, more expensive and differ for different sizes of main valves. If no main line pilot pressure is conveyed onto the piston of the sliding spool in the valve to enable the change in flow path to be made, then the solenoid must be held on when switching is required. For valve operation with solenoid and pilot pressure it is only necessary to pulse (on/off) the solenoid in order to effect the switching.

Figure 6.9 illustrates the graphical symbols adopted to indicate various methods for valve activation.

Directional control valves are classified as two-way, three-way, four-way or five-way, which is indicative of the number of connecting ports on the valve. The five-way valve is similar to the four-way except that it has an additional exhaust port which performs no other function. The number of successive squares used in the graphics symbol indicates the number of switching or control positions of the valve. Thus a valve designated as a 4/2-way type shows that it has four primary connections on the outside of the valve body with four ports inside the valve and two possible switching positions.

Various techniques are adopted by different manufacturers to denote the input and output port connections on the valve. These have included letters, numbers or a combination of both. Current BS and ISO practice is to use a numerical code but not all manufacturers have adopted it. An example of port identification for a 4/2-way valve is as follows:

Common method		BS/ISO standard	Other
P (for pressure)	= main supply port	1	P
1	= normal outlet port	2	A
2	= normal outlet port	4	B
T (for tank)	= normal exhaust port	3	T

This coding is used in Fig. 6.10 with the graphical symbol for a 4/2-way valve with solenoid actuation accompanied by pilot pressure. The standard symbols for an air supply on connection P and a vent to atmosphere on connection T are included on the figure.

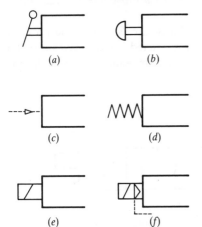

Figure 6.9 Valve activation symbols: (*a*) lever; (*b*) push button; (*c*) pilot pressure; (*d*) return spring; (*e*) solenoid; (*f*) solenoid and pilot pressure.

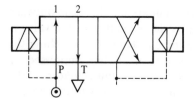

Figure 6.10 4/2-way directional control valve.

One of the simplest types of valve is the 2/2-way which can be operated in either a normally open or normally closed mode. It is basically an on/off switching device and for normally open operation the sliding spool in the valve does not permit fluid to flow from the supply to the outlet when the valve is not actuated. When the valve is switched on fluid flow occurs. A normally closed valve operates in the opposite manner. The symbol for a 2/2-way on/off valve with solenoid actuation and spring return is shown in Fig. 6.11.

Directional control valves for pneumatic and hydraulic systems operate on basically the same principle except that compressed air does not have to be returned to a reservoir tank when it has completed it's work. It is simply vented to the atmosphere. For solenoid-operated valves, which have only two possible switching positions, the flow path adopted at the initial system switch-on state will be dependent upon the last setting of the valve. If this is unsatisfactory, as is usually the case in hydraulic systems, then a 'spring-centred' arrangement can be used to return the valve spool to an open-centred position. This interconnects all ports and the pump delivery can flow back to tank at low pressure when no valve actuation takes place. Various centred configurations for 3-way valves are available for different applications. The graphical symbol for a solenoid operated 4/3-way valve with spring operation to return the spool to an open-centred position is shown in Fig. 6.12.

There are numerous arrangements for directional control valves but the graphics symbol is a useful way for indicating the function of the device according to the concepts outlined.

Flow Control Valves

The speed control of a pneumatic or hydraulic actuator is achieved by regulating the flow rate to the machine. This is usually done by adjusting the area of an orifice-based valve in the circuit. Although the basic principles of applying a restriction to the flow in order to increase the pressure at some point in the system are the same in pneumatics and hydraulics, there are fundamental differences. These are with respect to the fact that air is compressible and oil is virtually incompressible. Air from the system is also exhausted to atmosphere whereas oil is returned to the supply tank.

The general rule in pneumatics is to solely restrict the exhaust air. Study of the pressure changes occurring in a cylinder during operation show that a restricted exhaust gives a better speed stability, particularly towards the end of the stroke. With inlet air regulation at the driving

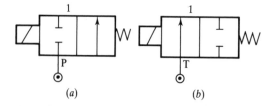

(a)   *(b)*

Figure 6.11 2/2-way on/off valve.

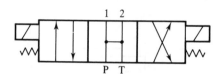

Figure 6.12 4/3-way spring-centred valve.

end, stability is not so good and is particularly unstable towards the end of the cylinder stroke, especially when the cylinder is unloaded or only slightly loaded.

By positioning a restriction in the actuator exhaust flow there will be a build up in back pressure in order to force the air through the orifice of the flow regulator. This results in a thrust on the piston that opposes the thrust due to the main supply pressure thus decreasing the pressure differential across the piston, and hence an appreciable reduction in piston speed occurs. To obtain a further reduction in speed, the resistance to exhaust flow can be increased by a corresponding decrease in orifice area. With a double-acting cylinder the air lines must act as both supply and exhaust, and it is therefore necessary to incorporate a uni-directional feature in the flow control valve design. This allows unrestricted air to enter the cylinder at either end and produces a resistance to the exhaust flow. This arrangement involves a parallel flow design with a restriction in one path and a uni-directional check valve in the other. The principle of operation is illustrated in the flow control valve symbol as shown in Fig. 6.13.

In hydraulic systems the actuator speed is determined by its displacement capacity C and the volumetric flow rate of fluid available Q. This is as formulated in Sec. 6.2 on actuators. A variable capacity pump or motor can be used to vary the motor speed but the use of fixed delivery machines and a flow control valve makes a more flexible circuit and is much less expensive. In order to vary the speed of a fixed capacity actuator using a fixed capacity pump it is necessary to divert some flow back to tank prior to it entering the actuator. This involves the use of a variable-orifice-type restriction flow control valve to cause a pressure increase which will enable oil to be prematurely returned to the supply tank. Various speed control techniques can be used and these are outlined in detail in Sec. 6.5 on hydraulic circuits.

The pressure developed in the system will depend upon the load on the actuator and a load change will cause the pressure drop across the flow control valve orifice to vary. Since the flow rate Q is proportional to the square root of the pressure drop over the orifice (Sec. 4.11), Q will therefore be dependent upon the load. For relatively steady loads, or when changes in actuator speed can be tolerated, a simple flow restrictor is sufficient. However, when precise speed control is required under varying load conditions it is necessary to maintain a constant pressure drop over the orifice. A variety of designs of flow control valves for hydraulic circuits are available which compensate for system pressure changes and ensure that the flow rate through the valve is kept constant. After the valve has been set for the desired flow rate, the orifice created by the pressure compensator within the valve automatically varies in size to compensate for any variations in load.

Pressure Control Valves

The control of pressure in a fluid system is actuated directly or indirectly by the pressure in some part of the circuit. This involves either limiting the pressure in the complete system or directing fluid to different parts of the system when the pressure level reaches a set value. This regulated

Unrestricted free flow

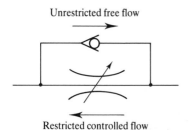

Restricted controlled flow   **Figure 6.13** Flow control valve.

pressure is always less than the system supply pressure. The valves associated with these functions are classified as pressure-control or pressure-regulating valves.

Relief valves Pressure-relief valves limit the system pressure to a preset value in any part of a circuit. In a pneumatic system if the pressure activated switch controlling the air compressor fails to shut down the compressor when the maximum working pressure is reached then the relief valve opens and discharges excess air to atmosphere. For safety the valve should be capable of discharging more air than the compressor is capable of supplying. These valves are usually placed at the immediate compressor discharge or in the air receiver tank which supplies the system. Protection is provided in a hydraulic system by a relief valve fitted to the pump outlet. When a pressure build-up occurs due to excessive load, or say a linear actuator reaching the end of the stroke, then the valve will open and direct oil back to the supply tank. The valve setting should be slightly in excess of the maximum load pressure expected. Hence, if the full pump flow is to tank through the relief valve then the fluid energy will be converted into heat with a consequent temperature rise in the oil. For this reason the supply tank should be designed to ensure that adequate natural cooling of the oil can take place prior to being delivered back into the system. In some cases it may be necessary to include a separate heat exchanger to cool the oil if relief valve actuation occurs regularly as is the case for some speed control circuits (see Sec. 6.5).

The simplest form of relief valve is the spring operated poppet type which is termed a direct acting relief valve. This basically consists of a poppet held down on a valve seat by the action of a spring. The spring force can be adjusted by a screw arrangement in order to set the valve to operate at a range of pressures. The valve is teed into the circuit and when the pressure is insufficient to overcome the spring force no flow will occur through the valve. When the pressure exceeds the adjusted spring force the poppet is forced off its seat and the valve opens. The re-direction of flow prevents further build up of pressure in the system. The valve closes when the system pressure drops below the valve setting. The principle of operation is illustrated in Fig. 6.14, together with the graphics symbol.

For this type of valve it is seen that the flow rate through the valve is dependent upon the magnitude of the pressure. The pressure at which the valve starts to open is termed the 'cracking pressure' and the pressure at which the full rated flow passes through the valve is termed the 'full flow pressure'. In some designs this 'pressure override' can be quite substantial and may be a disadvantage. For low values of pressure override there are a number of designs available which increase the pressure setting sensitivity by incorporating an additional low-rate control spring with a fixed main spring to provide the direct acting force against the valve element.

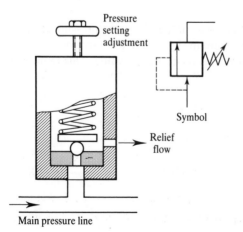

Figure 6.14 Direct acting pressure relief valve.

Pressure reducing valves A pressure level limit in any part of a fluid system can be set by means of a pressure reducing valve. In pneumatic systems they are often referred to as pressure regulators and although there are a number of designs available they all have the same basic operating principles. While a relief valve opens with an increase in system pressure, a regulator valve closes. The valve mechanism, which contains a spring-adjusted diaphragm or spool, provides a normally open flow passage from the supply side to the outlet side. The outlet pressure is sensed and the valve tends to close as it reaches the set value. If the main supply pressure is below the valve setting then fluid will flow freely from the inlet to the outlet. When the outlet pressure rises to the valve setting a throttling device used in the design moves to partly block the outlet port with a resulting drop in pressure.

In a pneumatic system, pressure regulating valves are usually located at the outlet of high-pressure air receiver tanks or on individual pieces of pneumatic equipment in order to provide close control of the air pressure. When operating they control or limit the pressure and do not exhaust compressed air into the atmosphere as do pressure relief valves.

It is generally accepted that pneumatics and hydraulics technology has reached a state of maturity in component hardware but there is a growth in the design and supply of system packages for a variety of industrial automation applications. This trend is combined with the more widespread use of microelectronic devices associated with the sensing and control functions.

6.4 PNEUMATIC CIRCUITS

The components which are used to make up a pneumatic circuit have been outlined in the previous sections and the required hardware must first be selected and assembled before it can be put to practical use. Due to the advent of thermoplastic flexible tubing, with simple push-in fittings, the components necessary for a fluid system can be connected together with the same ease as the laying of electric cables. The pneumatic mains network provides a storage capacity which can be drawn upon in the same way as an electricity supply. main. With modern sophisticated processes being used more and more in engineering industries, many machines are designed to operate with pneumatic power drives. The potential of pneumatics for the control of power is being increasingly realized and used for automatically controlled plant and machinery.

The design of a pneumatic system calls for a careful analysis of the task to be achieved, and this requires the preparation of a detailed specification in the initial stages. It is important that the pneumatic and mechanical aspects of the system be considered together. The circuitry is basically quite simple, and the most complex of circuits are generally composed of small individual circuits which are suitably interconnected. The design of basic circuits incorporate common pneumatic components.

The pneumatic control of plant and machines usually employ a sequential control strategy where the completion of each step provides a command to initiate the next step. Feedback from the point of operation may be pneumatic or electrical. All-pneumatic control has the advantage of simplicity but with increasing mechanization, solenoid operated pilot valves are popular by virtue of their ability to interact with modern microprocessor-based controllers such as the programmable logic controller (PLC) (Sec. 13.5). This combination enhances the flexibility and intelligence which are predominant features of mechatronic systems. Flexibility is the ease with which the system can be adjusted to a new environment and intelligence is associated with its control functions.

Wherever labour is being used to move, hold or form material repetitively there is a reason for automating the process by utilizing air cylinders which are the basic tool of pneumatic operations. Whenever components have to be moved from one place to another pneumatically operated mechanisms can be employed. Air cylinders can be used for operating levers, hoppers, conveyors, doors, gates and a variety of clamping operations. They are invaluable in automatic assembly machines and can be used when a steady thrust force is required, as in bending, drawing, crimping or stretching processes.

Simple Reciprocating Circuit

A reciprocating double-acting cylinder can be controlled using a variety of valves and one configuration is illustrated in Fig. 6.15. This circuit incorporates a solenoid-operated 2/2-way on/off valve (solenoid 1) which switches the air from the supply into the 4/2-way double solenoid (solenoid 2 and solenoid 3) operated directional control valve that feeds the cylinder (A). Adjustable flow control valves are fitted to the cylinder pressure lines with the restriction in the exhaust side. The sequence of operation is as follows:

1. When solenoid 1 is activated by an electrical start switch, air is supplied to the directional control valve. If solenoid 1 is deactivated then the air supply to the system is switched off.
2. When solenoid 2 is activated air is allowed to enter the left-hand side of cylinder A and the piston extends until the end of stroke is reached. Air is exhausted via the control valve from the right-hand side of the cylinder. This part of the motion is represented as A +. It should be noted that the solenoid is held on during this part of the cycle. If the valve had been solenoid pilot operated then it would have been necessary to activate the solenoid for only a short period of time to enable the air pilot pressure to be switched in to actually do the work in moving the valve spool.
3. Once the end of the stroke is reached solenoid 2 is switched off and solenoid 3 is activated. This allows air to enter the right-hand side of the cylinder and the piston retracts until the end of the stroke is reached. This is represented as A−.

Hence this simple sequence is represented as A +, A−.

In order to give an indication of when the directional control valve solenoids are to be energized, sensors must be placed in such a way that the end-of-stroke conditions can be detected. These sensors may be limit switches, optical switches, or capacitive/inductive proximity switches, which are triggered somehow by the end of stroke condition. Alternatively, magnetic-type sensors could be attached to the actual cylinder barrel.

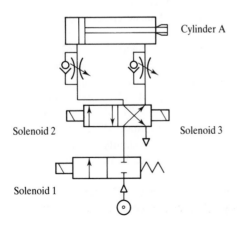

Cylinder A

Solenoid 2

Solenoid 3

Solenoid 1

Figure 6.15 Simple reciprocating electro-pneumatic circuit.

To control this system automatically using a microelectronic digital control device, three inputs including the on/off switch, and three outputs would be required of the controller.

Example Consider a transport system which requires a component to be lifted from one conveyor to another at a different level. Manual lifting can be eliminated by using a double-actuator pneumatic circuit with interlocked controlling action. The system is shown diagrammatically in Fig. 6.16.

The pneumatic system requirements, excluding flow control valves and an electrically switched start/stop valve, are basically:

2 double-acting cylinders
2 4/2-way or 5/2-way solenoid pilot operated directional control valves.
4 digital sensors. Two to detect the start and end of stroke condition for the lift cylinder A (S2 and S3), one to detect the end of stroke for the push cylinder B (S4) and one to detect when a component is in place to be lifted (S1). A sensor to detect when cylinder B is in the retracted position would also be useful as a safety measure although it is unnecessary with respect to requirements for the controlled sequence.

The pneumatic circuit using 5/2-way directional control valves is shown in Fig. 6.17. The basic control strategy is as follows:

1. With sensor S1 on, the lift of the component is started by extending cylinder A.
2. When S2 is activated cylinder B is extended.
3. When S4 is activated cylinder A is retracted.
4. When S2 is activated cylinder B is retracted.

The sequence is therefore A+, B+, A−, B−.

A displacement timing diagram for the sequence is often useful as a design and fault-finding aid. This is shown in Fig. 6.18 for the specified transport strategy.

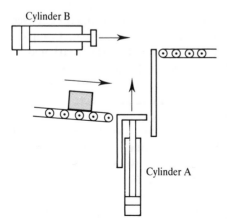

Cylinder B

Cylinder A

Figure 6.16 Lifting and transferring transport system.

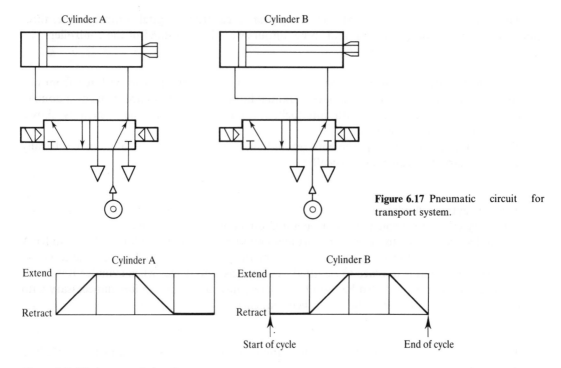

Figure 6.17 Pneumatic circuit for transport system.

Figure 6.18 Displacement timing diagram.

For a double cylinder arrangement, assuming that the sequence always starts with both pistons retracted and cylinder A starts first, other possible sequences for a two cylinder arrangement are

$$A+, \ A-, \ B+, \ B-$$

and

$$A+, \ B+, \ B-, \ A-$$

Simulation

Software packages are commercially available to build up pneumatic circuits using a PC-based menu-driven CAD package and to simulate the running operation of the system. Complete circuits can be stored on disk and retrieved as required. The package PNEUSIM marketed by Norgen Martonair Limited is one such pneumatic simulation package. It has been designed for both educational and industrial purposes and the library holds a comprehensive stock of pneumatic and electrical components which can be used to build circuits. Electrical control circuits consisting of switches, relays, timers, counters and solenoids can be displayed alongside the pneumatics. Electric feedback signals from toggle switches, limit switches or magnetic switches attached to cylinders power the movement of linear or rotary actuators through solenoid-operated control valves. Once the complete circuit has been developed the simulation mode can be entered and the automatic cycling of the system viewed. Faults in the circuit are identified by a halt in the simulation sequence. These can be edited and further tests made until a fully successful circuit is achieved.

Other facilities include mouse control, edit with cut, copy and paste, zoom, plot and file transfer to a computer-aided draughting package such as AUTOCAD. The package is an extremely useful student-centred learning aid and is appropriate to pneumatic circuit design with associated microelectronic control devices such as PLCs.

6.5 HYDRAULIC CIRCUITS

The basic elements of most oil hydraulic power circuits are a fluid reservoir, a pump, an actuator which performs the useful work, valves to control the direction, fluid flow rate and to limit the pressure, together with the pipework necessary to connect these components in the most efficient manner. They can be combined in a variety of arrangements to form speed drives for an almost unlimited range of applications.

Once an assessment has been made of the forces or torques, speed and mechanical requirements for an application, the particular type of actuator to be used can be selected. A typical adjustable speed hydrostatic power transmission drive consists of a fixed or variable delivery pump supplying oil to a fixed or variable capacity motor. The output motor speed may be controlled by either varying the delivery from the pump or varying the displacement of the motor. An arrangement using a variable capacity pump and a bi-directional fixed capacity motor is shown in Fig. 6.19. The hydraulic power pack comprising the pump and drive electric motor, pressure relief valve and supply tank is identified.

Consider a constant speed, variable capacity pump driving a fixed capacity motor as shown in Fig. 6.19. Neglecting leakage, the pump output flow rate $Q = C_p N_p$. Q is also the flow rate into the motor $= C_m N_m$. Hence

$$N_m = N_p(C_p/C_m)$$

For constant load, and neglecting frictional losses, the pressure rise over the pump will be equal to the pressure drop over the motor, i.e.

$$\Delta p_p = \Delta p_m$$

Therefore, the motor output power is given by

$$P_m = Q_m \Delta p_m = (C_m N_m)\Delta p_m$$
$$= 2\pi N_m T_m$$

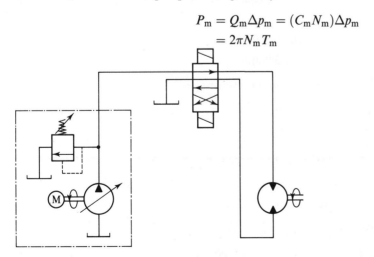

Figure 6.19 Basic hydrostatic power transmission system.

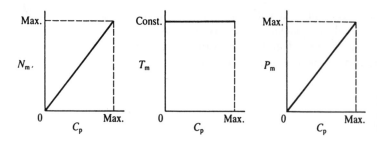

Figure 6.20 Characteristics of a variable capacity pump/fixed capacity motor drive.

Hence motor torque

$$T_m = (C_m \Delta p_m)/2\pi = \text{a constant}$$

The characteristics of this drive configuration giving motor speed, torque and power variation with pump capacity is shown in Fig. 6.20.

An alternative, but less common, arrangement is to use a fixed capacity constant speed pump to drive a variable capacity motor. In this case the motor output power is constant and its speed tends to infinity as the capacity tends to zero. Any torque/speed characteristic can be obtained to suit the specific application by using a variable pump and a variable motor.

Example A variable capacity pump directly coupled to an electric motor running at a fixed speed of 1440 rev/min has a maximum capacity of 115 ml/rev and supplies oil to a fixed displacement motor of 150 ml/rev capacity. The maximum circuit pressure is 80 bar.
Taking a mechanical efficiency of 92 per cent and a volumetric efficiency of 95 per cent for both the pump and the motor and neglecting pressure losses in the transmission system, calculate:

(a) the maximum motor speed;
(b) the motor maximum power output and torque,
(c) the overall efficiency of the complete system.

(a) Theoretical pump flow $= C_p N_p = 0.115 \times 1440 = 165.6\,l/min$. Actual flow out of pump into motor is $C_p N_p \times \eta_{vp}$

$$= 165.6 \times 0.95$$
$$= 157.3\,l/min$$

but this flow $= C_m N_m / \eta_{vm}$, hence the maximum motor speed is

$$157.3 \times 0.95/0.15$$

$$= 996\,rev/min$$

(b) Motor output power $= \Delta p \times$ flow rate into motor $\times \eta_{mech_m} \times \eta_{v_m}$

$$= 80 \times 10^5 \times (157.3 \times 10^{-3}/60) \times 0.92 \times 0.95$$

$$= 18.34\,kW$$

Also, the motor output power $= 2\pi N_m T_m$, therefore motor torque

$$T_m = 18.34 \times 10^3/(2\pi \times 996/60)$$

$$= 175.8\,N\,m$$

(c) Pump input power $= (C_p N_p)\Delta p/\eta_{\text{mech}}$

$$= (165.6 \times 10^{-3}/60) \times 80 \times 10^5/(0.92)$$

$$= 24 \text{ kW}$$

The overall efficiency of the system $= 18.34/24$

$$= 0.76$$

alternatively, the overall efficiency $= \eta_{o_p} \times \eta_{o_m}$

$$= (0.92 \times 0.95) \times (0.92 \times 0.95)$$

$$= 0.76$$

Speed Control Using Fixed Capacity Machines

The use of fixed capacity machines and flow control valves makes a more flexible and economical circuit than employing variable capacity pumps and motors. With such an arrangement some portion of the pump delivery must be diverted back to tank by using the system relief valve or via a flow control valve teed into the actuator supply line. Since the pressure generated alters with the load there is a varying pressure drop across the flow control valve. This results in varying flow rates into the actuator with a corresponding speed change and hence the need for pressure compensation within the flow control valve to maintain a constant speed. Various designs of valve exist which maintain a constant flow independent of the load pressure.

The three basic types of control valve installation relative to the actuator are termed 'meter-in', 'meter-out' and 'bleed-off'.

For the meter-in method of speed control the valve is installed in the pressure line connected to the actuator inlet. By increasing the restriction, pressure builds up at the valve entry until the condition is reached when the main system relief vale cracks open and diverts flow back to the tank. This reduces the flow to the actuator with a consequent reduction in speed. This method of speed control is applied in situations where the load always opposes the actuator motion, such as in table feeds on grinding and milling machines. One disadvantage of this technique is the tendency for the actuator to 'run away' when subjected to a load which assists the motion. A one-way check valve with a low cracking pressure installed in the actuator exhaust line helps stabilize this situation.

Although negative loads can be counterbalanced it is more effective to use a flow control valve in the actuator exhaust line. This is the basis of the meter-out method of speed control and the role of the main system relief valve is similar to that of the meter-in technique. This arrangement is a must where the load has a tendency to run-away and it is generally favoured in low-speed applications.

Both of these methods, where the flow is metered at either the actuator inlet or outlet, use the relief valve to vary the oil flow to the actuator. This diverted flow rate experiences a pressure drop corresponding to the relief valve setting with a consequent rise in oil temperature. Although the methods provide accurate speed control with pressure compensated flow control valves they can result in an extremely hot system during operation and an external heat exchanger for cooling the oil may be necessary.

The bleed-off method of speed control as illustrated in Fig. 6.21 is more efficient than the previous two methods but it is not as accurate in variable load applications. The flow control valve is teed into the main pressure line and is used to divert flow from the actuator back to tank at the load pressure thus generating less heat. It is more suited to applications where the load

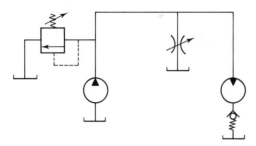

Figure 6.21 The 'bleed-off' method of speed control.

opposes the motion and is relatively constant. Under lightly loaded conditions a check valve should be installed in the exhaust line. The method is particularly suited to hydrostatic transmission drives.

Example In a hydraulic power transmission system the maximum load requires a system pressure of 100 bar and the relief valve is set at 10 per cent higher value.

In a meter-in speed control circuit a particular operating condition requires a flow of 1 l/min to be diverted back to tank. Calculate the temperature rise of the oil flowing through the relief valve. Take the relative density and the specific heat capacity for the oil as 0.86 and 2.15 kJ/kg K, respectively.

The fluid energy dissipated due to the pressure drop through the relief valve is given by

$$\rho Q(\Delta p/\rho)$$

$$= Q\Delta p$$

where ρ is the oil density. This energy is converted into heat

$$(\rho Q)C_{\mathrm{p}}\Delta T$$

where ΔT is the temperature rise and C_{p} is the specific heat capacity. Hence

$$\Delta T = \Delta p \,(\rho C_{\mathrm{p}})$$

where $\Delta p = 1.1 \times 100 = 110$ bar and density $\rho = 0.86 \times 1000 = 860 \,\mathrm{kg/m^3}$.
Temperature rise is

$$110 \times 10^5/(860 \times 2.15 \times 10^3)$$

$$= 6°C$$

Unloading Circuit

In a clamping operation with a hydraulic cylinder there is a requirement for a large flow with low pressure during the approach, and a small flow accompanying high pressure for the actual clamping. This can be achieved by a combination pump unit and relief valves as illustrated in Fig. 6.22. All the necessary components may reside within a single housing. During the advance part of the cycle the combined flow from the high-volume/low-pressure pump is delivered to the actuator. Once the system pressure exceeds the setting of the unloading relief valve associated with the high-volume pump the discharge from this machine is returned directly to tank at low pressure and the one-way check valve closes. The low-volume pump continues to deliver oil to the system up to the main relief valve setting at which time all the flow is returned to tank while maintaining the required pressure for the clamping process.

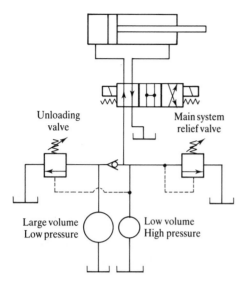

Figure 6.22 Combination pump unit in an unloading circuit.

Unloading valve

Main system relief valve

Large volume Low pressure

Low volume High pressure

With an increased emphasis on the need to automate in order to increase productivity and enhance competitiveness the designer must be aware of the potential benefits of fluid power and be able to design reliable, safe and economical systems by taking advantage of the technology. Practically every type of machine, large and small, simple and complex, can be controlled by fluid circuits. New developments in hardware and microprocessor-based controllers for these systems will continue into the future and make them more versatile, more reliable, easier to use, and less expensive.

6.6 ELECTRO-HYDRAULIC SERVO-SYSTEMS

The influence of external disturbances in a system can be minimized by utilizing servo-control, which monitors the output and forces it to quickly and accurately follow an input requirement. Electro-hydraulic servo-systems are generally associated with the control of speed and position. The closed-loop system usually employs a servo-valve which is essentially a directional control valve that has the ability to control the oil flow to the actuator. This has the effect of controlling the actuator position or speed to a preset value. A typical closed-loop servo-system is shown in Fig. 6.23.

Electro-hydraulic servo-valves operate from an electrical signal to a torque motor which directly or indirectly positions the spool in the valve such that the oil flow to the actuator and the flow diverted back to tank are such as to move the load to a specific position or acquire a specific velocity. The signal relayed to the torque motor is generated by the amplification of the error signal comprising the difference in the requirement and the current condition, as measured by a transducer. This error signal then effectively sets the spool position within the valve to achieve the required setting.

The torque motor basically replaces the solenoids on a conventional control valve and it has two coils and an armature held centred by a torsion bar. Increasing the current in one coil and reducing it in the other causes the armature to swing off-centre by an amount linearly proportional to the change in current. The valve spool is connected to the armature by a mechanical linkage and the spool movement is therefore also directly proportional to the input signal. The total armature movement is only a few minutes of arc and this corresponds to a

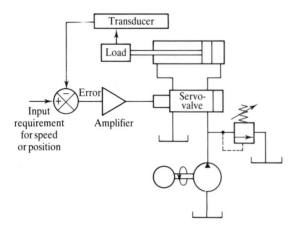

Figure 6.23 Closed-loop electrohydraulic servo-system.

spool movement in either direction of the order 0.25 mm. The design of such an electro-hydraulic device allows for an adjustment of flow rate, with a good frequency response, by varying the input electrical signal to the torque motor.

The servo-valve effectively combines the functions of a directional valve and a flow control valve. The fixed capacity pump supplies a greater flow rate than that required by the actuator and the system may sustain, by virtue of a large pressure drop over the control orifice, a power loss with a consequent rise in temperature.

The single-stage spool valve as described is really only suitable for low flow rates and pressures of the order 25 l/min and 70 bar, respectively. For large values a two-stage valve is used. Although this is of a more complex design, the basic concept is the same with the flow to the valve ports connected to the actuator being proportional to the electrical signal in the form of a voltage applied to the torque motor.

A similar type of control valve in which the movement of the spool is proportional to an input electrical signal is the so-called proportional valve. These devices utilize a solenoid-actuated force operating against a spring to position the valve spool. The force exerted is dependent upon the solenoid current and hence the spool movement is proportional to this input in the form of a current applied to the solenoid windings. These valves can be used for position, flow and pressure control. Their response time and maximum operating frequency are not so favourable as those for a servo-valve, which is best suited for fast response and good control characteristics. They are, however, a satisfactory alternative for many applications since they are less expensive and are much more dirt tolerant.

FURTHER READING

McCord, B. E. (1983) *Designing Pneumatic Circuits*, Marcel Dekker, New York.

Parr, E. A. (1987) *Industrial Control Handbook, Techniques, Vol. 2*, BSP Professional Books, Oxford.

Pessen, D. W. (1989) *Industrial Automation—Circuit Design & Components*, Wiley, New York.

Pinches, M. J. and J. G. Ashby (1989) *Power Hydraulics*, Prentice-Hall, Englewood Cliffs, New Jersey.

Pippenger, J. J. (1984) *Hydraulic Valves and Controls—Selection and Application*, Marcel Dekker, New York.

Reed, E. W. and I. S. Larman (1985) *Fluid Power with Microprocessor Control—An Introduction*, Prentice-Hall, Englewood Cliffs, New Jersey.

EXERCISES

6.1   Discuss the comparative advantages and disadvantages of using electro-mechanical, pneumatic and hydraulic technology for industrial automation systems.

6.2   In a manufacturing process components are to be clamped using a pneumatically operated clamping device. By operating an electrical switch the moveable clamping jaw is pushed forward and the component is clamped. By de-activating the switch the clamping jaw is returned to its start position.

Using standard symbols draw the pneumatic circuit using a single acting cylinder with a spring-return as the clamping actuator.

6.3   In a stamping machine, components are pushed out of a hopper into the stamping station by means of a pneumatic cylinder as shown in Fig. Q6.3. When the components are in position the stamping head, which is also controlled by a pneumatic cylinder, moves down to perform the stamping process. This cylinder then retracts and signals the hopper cylinder to retract. The forward stroke of the hopper cylinder is speed controlled and the cycle is initiated by operating an electric switch to supply air to the system.

Draw the pneumatic circuit and specify the input/output requirements if the system is to be controlled by a microprocessor-based controller.

Also draw the timing diagram for the cycle.

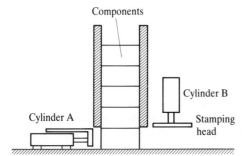

Figure Q6.3 Arrangement for pneumatically controlled stamping machine.

6.4   In a hydraulic system with a fixed displacement pump the motor speed is controlled using the 'bleed-off' method of speed control. The relief valve setting is 200 bar and at a particular steady state load the system operating pressure is 120 bar. At this load the flow control valve is set to return 10 litres of oil per minute back to tank in order to run the motor at the required speed. If the tank capacity is 40 litres of oil calculate the rate at which the temperature in the tank would increase when operating at this condition. Neglect all external heat losses from the tank and take the oil density and specific heat capacity as $850\,\text{kg/m}^3$ and $2.2\,\text{kJ/kg K}$, respectively.

[1.6°C/min]

6.5   A variable displacement pump directly coupled to an electric motor running at a constant speed of 1440 rev/min has a maximum capacity of $164\,\text{cm}^3/\text{rev}$ and supplies oil to a fixed displacement rotary motor. The maximum circuit pressure is 100 bar and this is to correspond to a motor torque of 270 N m.

Taking an overall efficiency of 89 per cent and a leakage coefficient of $70\,\text{cm}^3/\text{min}$ per bar for both the pump and the motor, calculate the necessary motor capacity. Neglect viscous friction losses in the transmission system.

[$184\,\text{cm}^3/\text{rev}$]

6.6   The hydraulic motor in a variable displacement pump and fixed displacement motor circuit is to supply a constant torque of 220 N m at speeds between 100 and 400 rev/min. The pump is driven at a constant speed of 1440 rev/min. The relief valve is set to give a maximum motor inlet pressure of 60 bar and the motor back pressure with a spring operated check valve in the exhaust line is 2 bar. The pump and motor each have a mechanical efficiency of 95 per cent and a volumetric efficiency of 90 per cent.

Calculate:
  (*a*) suitable pump and motor capacities;
  (*b*) the overall efficiency of power conversion if the pressure drop between the pump and the motor due to hydraulic losses is 3 bar.

[Pump: maximum = 85.8 ml/rev; minimum = 21.5 ml/rev, Motor: 250 ml/rev, 67%]

SEVEN

DIGITAL ELECTRONICS

While analogue systems involve currents and voltages which are infinitely variable, digital systems operate between two possible states which can be considered as either 'on' or 'off'. As such, digital systems are essentially discrete in operation with the circuits either conducting or not conducting. Boolean algebra has been developed to perform the analysis of such systems involving two state logic variables.

7.1 BOOLEAN ALGEBRA

The basic rules of Boolean algebra are conveniently described with reference to simple manually switched circuits. In the binary notation, a '0' denotes the switch as off and a '1' denotes the switch as on. The 0 and 1 can also be taken to represent the absence, or presence, respectively, of a voltage or a current. In TTL circuitry a nominal 5 V is used to denote a logic level 1, or on and a nominal 0 V used to denote a logic level 0, or off.

Logical AND

Figure 7.1 shows a simple AND circuit. The logical functions may also be represented in a tabular form known as a 'truth table'. The truth table indicates the output generated for all possible combinations of the inputs. Figure 7.1 also shows the truth table for the logical AND.

Obviously the lamp will light only when both switch A AND switch B are closed. Writing this as a Boolean expression:

$$F = A \text{ AND } B \tag{7.1}$$

A, B and F are Boolean variables denoting the switches A, B and the lamp, respectively. The logical operator AND is denoted by a dot thus:

$$F = A.B$$

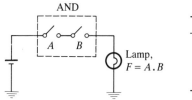

A	B	A.B
0	0	0
0	1	0
1	0	0
1	1	1

Figure 7.1 Simple AND circuit.

or

$$F = AB \qquad (7.2)$$

Logical OR

Figure 7.2 shows the simple OR circuit and its corresponding truth table.

It is clear that the lamp will light in the OR circuit when either switch A OR switch B is closed. As a Boolean expression, the OR function is written:

$$F = A \text{ OR } B$$
$$F = A + B \qquad (7.3)$$

The '+' sign is used to denote the logical OR and must not be confused with the arithmetical meaning.

The AND and the OR are the basic logical functions and quite complex switching circuits can be represented in Boolean form using them.

Logical NOT

The NOT function is the inverse complement, or negation of a variable. The negation of the variable A is $\overline{A}$. Thus if $A = 1$, then $\overline{A} = 0$ and vice versa.

Logical NAND

The NAND function is the inverse of AND.

Logical NOR

In similar fashion, the NOR is the inverse of OR.

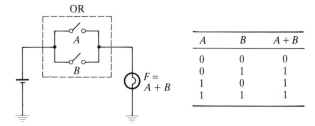

A	B	A + B
0	0	0
0	1	1
1	0	1
1	1	1

Figure 7.2 Simple OR circuit.

A	B	C	A.B.C	$\overline{A.B.C}$
0	0	0	0	1
0	0	1	0	1
0	1	0	0	1
0	1	1	0	1
1	0	0	0	1
1	0	1	0	1
1	1	0	0	1
1	1	1	1	0

Figure 7.3 Truth table for AND and NAND operators with three inputs.

Table 7.1 Boolean identities.

$A + 0 = A$	$A.A = A$
$A + 1 = 1$	$A + \bar{A} = 1$
$A.0 = 0$	$A.\bar{A} = 0$
$A.1 = A$	$\bar{\bar{A}} = A$
$A + A = A$	$\overline{A + B} = \bar{A}.\bar{B}$
	$\overline{A.B} = \bar{A} + \bar{B}$

Exclusive-OR

In Fig. 7.2 it can be seen that the lamp will also light when both switches A and B are closed. The exclusive-OR is a special function which does not enable an output when both switches are closed. Otherwise the exclusive-OR functions as the normal OR operator. The notation used for an exclusive-OR is the plus sign enclosed within a circle, i.e. $\oplus$.

Figure 7.3 illustrates the truth table for the AND and NAND operators with three inputs A, B and C. Using the basic logical functions, the Boolean identities are specified in Table 7.1. In Table 7.1 a '0' can be taken to represent an open circuit while a '1' represents a short circuit. Using a truth table, it is easy to prove the validity of various logical expressions by evaluating both sides, e.g.

$$A.(B + C) = A.B + A.C$$
$$(A + B).(A + C) = A + B.C$$
$$A + \overline{A}.B = A + B$$

The first example shows that brackets may be removed by multiplying out as in normal arithmetic. The second two examples have no arithmetic counterpart. The proofs of these second two identities are outlined in the examples which follow.

A useful manipulation technique is due to De Morgan. De Morgan's theorem states that in any logical expression, AND can be replaced by OR and vice versa, provided that each term is also replaced with its inverse complement. The resulting expression is then the inverse of the original.

Example From $A.B.C$ we negate to

$$\overline{A.B.C} = \overline{A} + \overline{B} + \overline{C}$$

Hence

$$A.B.C = \overline{\overline{A} + \overline{B} + \overline{C}}$$

Example From $F = A.B + C.D$ we negate to

$$\overline{F} = (\overline{A} + \overline{B}) + (\overline{C} + \overline{D})$$

Applying De Morgan again

$$F = \overline{(\overline{A} + \overline{B}).(\overline{C} + \overline{D})}$$

The equivalence of the original and the final expressions in the above two examples may be checked using a truth table.

Example Simplify the expression $(A + B).(A + C)$.
Applying De Morgan gives

$$\overline{(\overline{A + B}) + (\overline{A + C})}$$

Applying De Morgan again gives

$$\overline{\overline{\overline{A.\overline{B}}} + \overline{\overline{\overline{A}.\overline{C}}}} = \overline{\overline{A}.\overline{B} + \overline{A}.\overline{C}}$$

Since $\overline{A}$ is common to both terms, then

$$\overline{\overline{A}.(\overline{B} + \overline{C})}$$

Thus applying De Morgan again gives

$$A + (\overline{\overline{B} + \overline{C}})$$

Finally we arrive at

$$A + B.C$$

Therefore

$$(A + B).(A + C) = A + B.C$$

Example Simplify the expression $A + \overline{A}. B$.
Applying De Morgan gives

$$A + \overline{(\overline{A} + \overline{B})} = \overline{\overline{A}.(\overline{A} + \overline{B})}$$

Multiplying out gives

$$\overline{\overline{A}.\overline{A} + \overline{A}.\overline{B}}$$

Since $\overline{A}.A = 0$ and $\overline{0 + \overline{A}.\overline{B}} = \overline{\overline{A}.\overline{B}}$, then the expression simplifies to

$$\overline{\overline{A}.\overline{B}} = \overline{\overline{A} + \overline{B}} = A + B$$

Thus

$$A + \overline{A}.B = A + B$$

7.2 DIGITAL ELECTRONIC GATES

The principles of Boolean algebra have been considered with respect to manually switched circuits. In modern digital systems the switches are formed with transistors for speed of operation and they are generally referred to as 'gates'. Over the years various technologies have been developed in the manufacture of logic gates. The earliest forms of electronic gate were based on the unidirectional conduction properties of diodes. Diode logic gates have now been superseded by transistor–transistor logic gates, TTL, or the recent CMOS family of logic gates.

The internal construction and operation of modern logic gates may be quite complex but this is of little interest to the digital systems designer. Generally, all that the designer needs to know are the power supply voltages, the transient switching times, the 'fan out' and the 'fan in'. Fan out refers to the number of similar gates which can be driven from the output of one gate. Fan in, on the other hand, refers to the number of similar gate outputs which can be safely connected to the input of one gate.

TTL

The TTL family is based on the bipolar junction transistor and was the first commonly available series of logic elements. TTL logic gates are rapid switching devices, the SN7400, for example, takes just fifteen nanoseconds to change state. The standard power supply is 5 V with a low tolerance band of 0.5 V. This in turn necessitates a reliable power supply regulation which is reasonably facilitated through the numerous variety of supply regulators which are now available in integrated circuit form. For the SN74 series TTL ICs, the fan out is about 10.

A TTL-based system can place quite large instantaneous loads on a power supply and this can result in substantial interference 'spikes' on the power lines. Since the spikes can upset the normal operation of the system it is common practice to connect small capacitors directly across the power lines, as close to the TTL ICs as possible. One capacitor, 0.1 μF to 10 μF, per five ICs is sufficient in most instances.

TTL circuits are continually being improved and a major recent advance has been the introduction of the low power 'Schottky' TTL circuits. These use the same generic code numbers as the standard series, but have 'LS' inserted before the type code, e.g. SN74LS00. The operating speed is about twice as high and the power consumption is about 20 per cent of the standard series. Schottky devices are, however, slightly more expensive.

CMOS

The problematic features of the power supply associated with the TTL family of logic devices has been largely responsible for the growth of its major competitor, CMOS. CMOS ICs are based on the field effect transistor and can operate from a range of power supply voltages between 3 V to 18 V. CMOS devices dissipate very little power, are very cheap and are simple in operation. The fan out is about 50 and they have a far greater immunity to power supply noise. The noise immunity of CMOS devices means that there is no requirement for smoothing capacitors to the extent that they are generally found in TTL circuitry.

There are also some disadvantages associated with CMOS devices. The main one being that CMOS is slower than TTL, roughly about one tenth of the equivalent TTL circuit. CMOS ICs are also very sensitive to electrostatic voltages. Manufacturers do build in some safety features to reduce the electrostatic sensitivity, but CMOS devices must still be handled with due care. Table 7.2 gives a brief comparison between TTL and CMOS devices.

Gate Symbols

Having defined a system output in terms of a Boolean expression, the actual circuit can be constructed using the required gates selected from the logic family chosen. Generally, the design will be centred round the more readily available NAND and NOR logic gates. In laying out a

Table 7.2 Comparison between TTL and CMOS devices.

Property	TTL	CMOS
Power supply	5 V ±0.25 V	3 V to 18 V
Current required	mA	μA
Input impedance	low	very high
Switching speed	fast, 10 ns	slow, 300 ns
Fan out	10	50

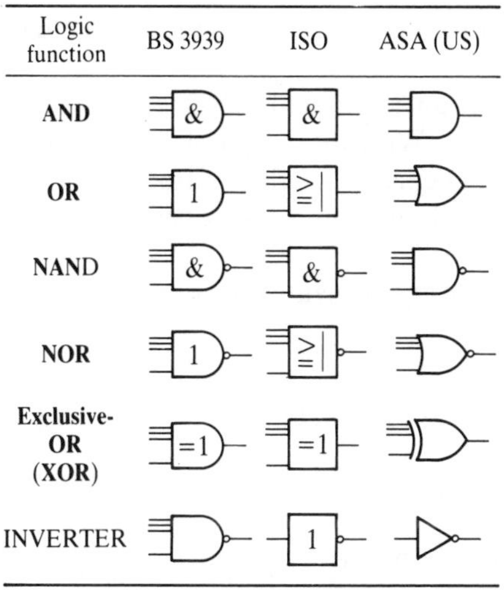

Logic function	BS 3939	ISO	ASA (US)
AND	&	&	
OR	1	≥1	
NAND	&	&	
NOR	1	≥1	
Exclusive-OR (XOR)	=1	=1	
INVERTER		1	

Figure 7.4 Gate symbol systems in current use.

gate interconnection diagram, standard symbols are used to represent the individual gates. Unfortunately no universal set of symbols has emerged and several systems are in current use. Figure 7.4 summarizes the most common gate symbol systems.

7.3 COMBINATIONAL LOGIC SYSTEMS

Logic Systems Using Simple Gates

A vending machine which dispenses either tea or coffee serves as an illustrative example. The logic circuit may be realized using AND gates as shown in Fig. 7.5.

The money input is common to both gates, and the system, although workable, has a minor fault in that if both buttoms are pressed after the money criterion is satisfied, then the output

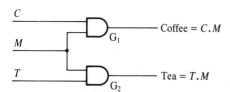

Figure 7.5 Logic circuit for drinks vending machine.

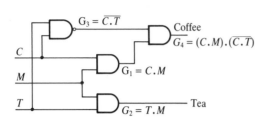

Figure 7.6 Extended logic circuit for drinks machine.

Inputs			Outputs	
C	M	T	Coffee	Tea
0	0	0	0	0
0	0	1	0	0
0	1	0	0	0
0	1	1	0	1
1	0	0	0	0
1	0	1	0	0
1	1	0	1	0
1	1	1	0	1

Figure 7.7 Truth table for drinks vending machine.

will be both tea and coffee. This fault can be designed out of the system by extending the logic circuit as shown in Fig. 7.6.

The extended system incorporates a NAND gate and an additional AND gate. If both buttons are now pressed then the output from G_3 will be 0. With the output 1 from G_1, the output from G_4 will be 0 and the machine will dispense tea. On pressing either button on its own and satisfying the money input criterion, the correct drink will be output. The operation of the extended system is verified in the truth table shown in Fig. 7.7.

By inspection of Fig. 7.6, the system can be represented in Boolean expressions as

$$coffee = (C.M).(\overline{C.T}) \qquad (7.4)$$

$$tea = T.M \qquad (7.5)$$

C, T and M represent the coffee button, tea button and money input, respectively, and the overscore represents the inverse complement as usual.

Using De Morgan's theorem the system may alternatively be written as

$$coffee = \overline{(\overline{C} + \overline{M}) + (\overline{\overline{C} + \overline{T}})} \qquad (7.6)$$

$$tea = \overline{\overline{T} + \overline{M}} \qquad (7.7)$$

Thus the same logic system can be implemented using one OR and three NOR gates as shown in Fig. 7.8. The validity and equivalence of Eqs. (7.4) and (7.7) may easily be checked using a truth table. Four logic gates are again required but the circuit operates with inverted input signals. This means that three inverters are also required in the circuit as shown. It is apparent that the logical function can be realized in several different ways; e.g.

$$coffee = (\overline{\overline{C} + \overline{M}}).(\overline{C} + \overline{T}) \text{ and } tea = T.M$$

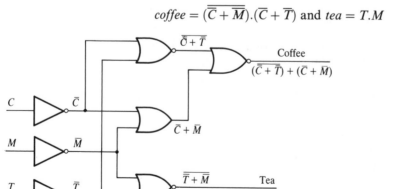

Figure 7.8 Logic circuit for drinks vending machine using OR and NOR gates.

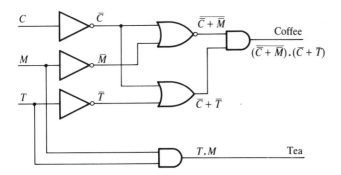

Figure 7.9 Alternative logic circuit for drinks vending machine.

Using the above realization, the circuit takes the form shown in Fig.7.9.

Logic Systems using NAND and NOR Gates only

Logic gates are packaged as arrays of the same gate type in IC form. A typical example is SN7408, which is a 14-pin DIL package containing four separate 2-input AND gates. Because the logic gates are marketed in this particular form it is advantageous to design the logic circuit using only one type of gate. This normally minimizes the number of IC packages required. Figure 7.10 shows a 2-input NAND gate driving into a single-input NAND gate.

For the 2-input NAND gate, the Boolean expression is

$$F = \overline{A.B}$$

Since F is then fed into a single-input NAND gate, which operates as an inverter, the final output is

$$F_o = \overline{F} = \overline{\overline{A.B}} = A.B$$

It is apparent therefore that the circuit given in Fig. 7.10, using NAND gates, performs the same function as the logical AND operator. Figure 7.11 shows two single-input NAND gates with their outputs driving into a 2-input NAND gate.

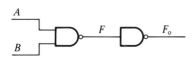

A	B	A.B	$\overline{A.B}$	$\overline{\overline{A.B}}$
0	0	0	1	0
0	1	0	1	0
1	0	0	1	0
1	1	1	0	1

Figure 7.10 AND realization using NAND gates.

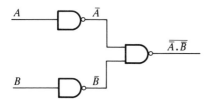

A	B	$\overline{A}$	$\overline{B}$	$\overline{A}.\overline{B}$	$\overline{\overline{A}.\overline{B}}$
0	0	1	1	1	0
0	1	1	0	0	1
1	0	0	1	0	1
1	1	0	0	0	1

Figure 7.11 OR realization using NAND gates.

Following through the truth table it can be seen that the circuit performs the logical OR function. If the output F is then fed to another single-input NAND gate, not shown in the figure, then the function performed will be a logical NOR.

It can be seen therefore that suitable combinations of NAND gates can be made to perform the logical functions AND, OR and NOR. In a similar manner, it can be shown that the AND and OR functions can be realized using NOR gates only. This is illustrated in Fig. 7.12.

The conclusion which can be drawn is that any logic circuit can be realized using NAND gates, or NOR gates alone. Considering again the drinks vending machine depicted in Fig. 7.8. The single OR gate may be replaced with a 2-input NOR gate which then feeds directly into a single-input NOR gate. This is shown in Fig. 7.13.

Note that NOR gates are also used in place of inverters in the input signal lines. By inspection of the circuit diagram, the governing Boolean expressions are

$$coffee = \overline{\overline{(\overline{C} + \overline{M})} + \overline{(\overline{C} + \overline{T})}}$$
$$= (\overline{C} + \overline{M}) + (\overline{C} + \overline{T}) \tag{7.8}$$

$$tea = \overline{\overline{T} + \overline{M}} \tag{7.9}$$

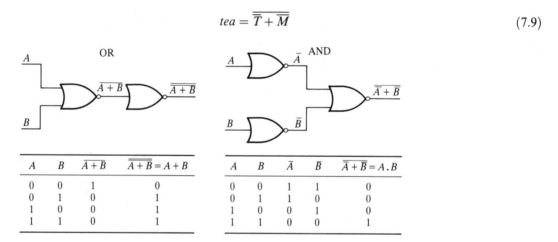

A	B	$\overline{A+B}$	$\overline{\overline{A+B}} = A+B$
0	0	1	0
0	1	0	1
1	0	0	1
1	1	0	1

A	B	$\overline{A}$	$\overline{B}$	$\overline{\overline{A}+\overline{B}} = A.B$
0	0	1	1	0
0	1	1	0	0
1	0	0	1	0
1	1	0	0	1

Figure 7.12 OR and AND realizations using NOR gates only.

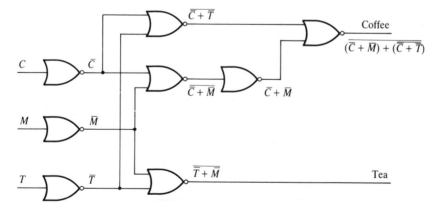

Figure 7.13 Logic circuit using NOR gates only for drinks vending machine.

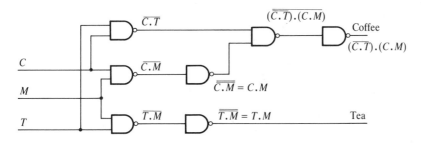

Figure 7.14 Logic circuit using only NAND gates for drinks vending machine.

Equations (7.8) and (7.9) are identical to Eqs (7.6) and (7.7), respectively. This, of course, must be true since the circuits from which the expressions were deduced perform identical logical functions.

Similarly the circuit in Fig. 7.6, involving one NAND and three AND gates, may be replaced by an equivalent circuit using only NAND gates. This equivalent circuit is shown in Fig. 7.14. Inspection of the circuit gives the Boolean expressions

$$coffee = \overline{(\overline{C.M}).(\overline{C.T})}$$
$$= (C.M).(\overline{C.T}) \tag{7.10}$$

$$tea = (\overline{\overline{T.M}}) = T.M \tag{7.11}$$

As expected, the Boolean expressions are identical to Eqs (7.4) and (7.5), which were deduced from the logic circuit of Fig. 7.6. The realization of Boolean expressions in either all NAND, or all NOR gates can be stated in the following simple rules:

1. *NAND realization.* First obtain the required Boolean expression in AND/OR form and construct the circuit required. The final output gate must be an OR gate. Replace all gates with NAND gates and, starting with the output gate, number each level of gates back through to the inputs. The logic level at the inputs to all 'odd' level gates must be inverted.
2. *NOR realization.* Obtain the required Boolean expression in OR/AND form. The final output gate must be an AND gate. Replace all gates with NOR gates and number each level of gates from the output back through to the input. The logic level at all inputs to 'odd' level gates must be inverted. Application of these rules is best illustrated by an example.

Example NAND realization of $F = A.B + C.(D + E)$.
Figure 7.15 shows the realization of the function in AND/OR form.
As inputs D and E appear at an odd level of gate input, they must be inverted. In terms of the actual circuit this means that inputs D and E are inverted, using NAND gates, prior to entering the NAND gate at level 4. A similar procedure is adopted for a NOR realization of a Boolean expression. The exclusive-OR function serves as an interesting example. Written as a Boolean expression, the exclusive-OR is

$$F = A.\overline{B} + \overline{A}.B \tag{7.12}$$

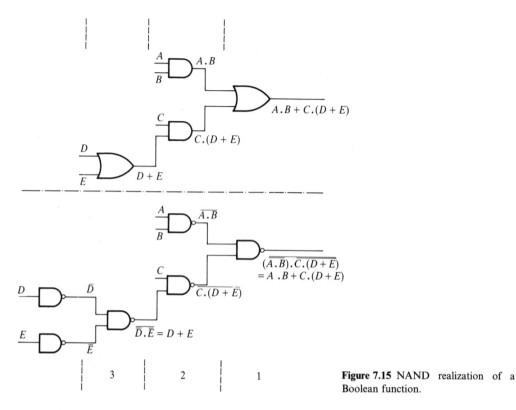

Figure 7.15 NAND realization of a Boolean function.

For the NOR realization, however, it is necessary that the final output gate is an AND. The exclusive-OR function must therefore be manipulated such that the final logical function in the expression is an AND. Using De Morgan's theorem:

$$F = \overline{(\overline{A.\overline{B}}).(\overline{\overline{A}.B})}$$
$$= \overline{(\overline{A} + B).(A + \overline{B})}$$

Multiplying this expression out gives

$$F = \overline{\overline{A}.A + \overline{A}.\overline{B} + A.B + B.\overline{B}}$$

Since $\overline{A}.A = B.\overline{B} = 0$, the expression simplifies to

$$F = \overline{\overline{A}.\overline{B} + A.B}$$
$$F = (\overline{\overline{A}.\overline{B}}).(\overline{A.B})$$

Using De Morgan again gives

$$F = (A + B).(\overline{A} + \overline{B}) \tag{7.13}$$

The realization of Eq. (7.13) is shown in Fig. 7.16.

Example Construct a logic circuit, using NOR gates only, to convert an input 3-bit Gray code into an output 3-bit binary code. The relationship between binary and Gray code is that the most significant bit of the binary code, B, is equal to the most significant bit of the

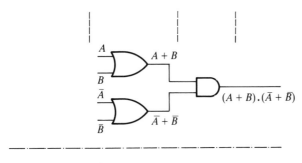

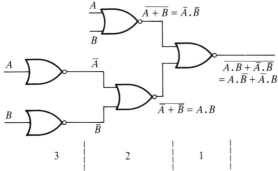

3   2   1

Figure 7.16 NOR realization of the exclusive-OR function.

Gray code, G. Thereafter, the relationship has the form:

$$B_n = G_n \oplus B_{n+1} \tag{7.14}$$

where n denotes the bit numbers.

A circuit which will implement the functional relationship using exclusive-OR gates is shown in Fig. 7.17.

Consideration of the seven unique signal combinations on the input side confirms the equivalent binary pattern produced on the output side. This relationship is also tabulated in Fig. 7.17. However, we have to implement the conversion using NOR gates only. Equation (7.13) and the implementation of this equation, shown in Fig. 7.16, indicates how the circuit might be constructed. Basically any two consecutive input signal lines are fed to a NOR gate. The inverted signal lines are also fed to a NOR gate. The outputs from these NOR gates are then fed to another NOR gate which produces the desired output signal. The inversion of the original input signals may also be performed using single-input NOR gates. A suitable circuit is shown in Fig. 7.18.

The circuit, extended to any number of bits as required, might be used as a hardwired conversion interface to generate an n-bit binary coded signal from an input n-bit Gray signal. This can be very useful when a digital computer, which operates with binary numbers, is accessing signals from a digital shaft encoder. Alternatively, if processing speed is not important, the conversion could be performed through an algorithm embedded within the computer software.

Unused Inputs

Multi-input gates are also commonly available. In practical circuits however, it is important that any unused inputs are tied, i.e. they are either connected to the positive voltage supply, or to the

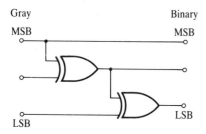

Gray	Binary	Decimal
000	000	0
001	001	1
011	010	2
010	011	3
110	100	4
111	101	5
101	110	6
100	111	7

Figure 7.17 Gray to binary conversion circuit using exclusive-OR gates.

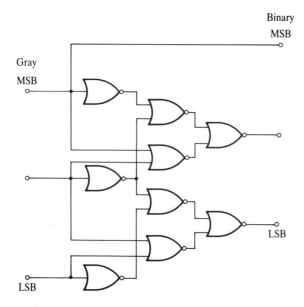

Figure 7.18 Gray to binary conversion circuit using NOR gates only.

zero voltage supply. The unused inputs are therefore set at either logic level 1 or at logic level 0, as required. In connecting an unused input to the positive supply, the connection should be made through a $1\,k\Omega$ resistor. Failure to connect any unused inputs can result in intermittent malfunction of the circuit, or in harmful oscillations with attendant overheating.

Latches

It is often useful to 'freeze' a particular binary sequence and devices called 'latches' are used for this purpose. Normally the outputs assume the same state as the inputs, however, when a control signal, known as a 'strobe' input, is taken to logic 1, the outputs are locked in whatever state they were at the instant of the strobe input going high. This enables the binary sequence to be 'captured' without affecting the ongoing processes, whatever they may be. The latch therefore serves as a temporary state recording device which may subsequently be referred to during various interrupt operations.

The Karnaugh Map

The Karnaugh map provides an alternative representation of a Boolean expression for all possible Boolean input combinations. In some respects the Karnaugh map is like a truth table in that identical logical expressions display an identical pattern on a Karnaugh map. The Karnaugh map, however, also has great utility in simplifying Boolean expressions in a systematic manner.

The Karnaugh map consists of a set of boxes in which each box represents one possible combination of the Boolean input variables. The boxes are assigned either a 1 or a 0 to indicate the value of the Boolean expression for the particular combination of input variables that the box represents. The number of boxes required is 2^n, where n is the total number of input variables. Although any number of input variables can be represented, a practical limitation is about seven. Figure 7.19 shows the Karnaugh map for a four-input system.

Within each box the unique Boolean input combination is represented by assigning each variable the logic values indicated along the horizontal and vertical axes. These values conform to the Gray code in which adjacent consecutive characters differ in only one variable. This imparts this property to the Karnaugh map that adjacent squares, vertically or horizontally, differ in only one variable.

As an example, the Boolean expression $F = \overline{A}.\overline{B}.C.D + A.\overline{B}.C.\overline{D} + \overline{A}.B.\overline{C}.D$, is represented by the Karnaugh map given in Fig. 7.20.

The maps are drawn up by placing a 1 in each box for which the combination of input variables makes the logical expression have a value of 1. All the other boxes represent the combination of input variables which make the expression have a logical value of 0. Usually the 0 is not entered in the box. A second example for consideration is $F = \overline{A}.\overline{B}.C.D + A.C + \overline{C}.\overline{D}$. The Karnaugh map for this expression is shown in Fig. 7.21.

It can be seen that the term $A.C$ includes all four squares in which both A and C are included. Similarly the term $\overline{C}.\overline{D}$ also encompasses four squares on the map. It may be concluded that in a four-variable expression, any term which contains the four variables will

CD \ AB	00	01	11	10
00	$\overline{A}.\overline{B}.\overline{C}.\overline{D}$	$\overline{A}.B.\overline{C}.\overline{D}$	$A.B.\overline{C}.\overline{D}$	$A.\overline{B}.\overline{C}.\overline{D}$
01	$\overline{A}.\overline{B}.\overline{C}.D$	$\overline{A}.B.\overline{C}.D$	$A.B.\overline{C}.D$	$A.\overline{B}.\overline{C}.D$
11	$\overline{A}.\overline{B}.C.D$	$\overline{A}.B.C.D$	$A.B.C.D$	$A.\overline{B}.C.D$
10	$\overline{A}.\overline{B}.C.\overline{D}$	$\overline{A}.B.C.\overline{D}$	$A.B.C.\overline{D}$	$A.\overline{B}.C.\overline{D}$

Figure 7.19 Karnaugh map for a four-input system.

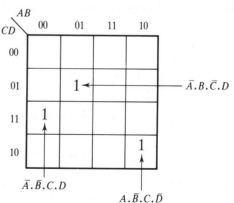

Figure 7.20 Karnaugh map for a Boolean expression (1).

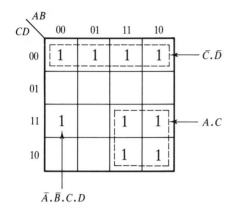

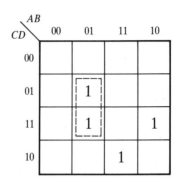

Figure 7.21 Karnaugh map for a Boolean expression (2).

Figure 7.22 Karnaugh map for an arbitrary expression.

occupy one square on the Karnaugh map. Any term which contains only three of the variables will occupy two squares and any term which contains only two of the variables will occupy four squares. A term containing only one of the variables will occupy eight squares in the Karnaugh map.

The Karnaugh map may be used in a reverse mode to deduce the Boolean expression. This technique is applied to the map given in Fig. 7.22. The expression may be read off as

$$F = \overline{A}.B.\overline{C}.D + \overline{A}.B.C.D + A.B.C.\overline{D} + A.\overline{B}.C.D$$

Alternatively there is an obvious grouping of 1s which can be taken together giving

$$F = \overline{A}.B.D + A.B.C.\overline{D} + A.\overline{B}.C.D$$

In grouping 1s like this, the term, or terms, which are dropped out are always the ones which are represented both as 0 and 1 within the grouping. The procedure has resulted in two possible Boolean expressions, both of which are correct. The second expression, however, is simpler and this technique forms the basis of using the map to minimize Boolean expressions.

Minimization Principles

The principle of minimization is based on the Boolean identity $A + \overline{A} = 1$. Thus

$$F = A.B.C.D + A.B.C.\overline{D} = A.B.C.(D + \overline{D}) = A.B.C \quad (7.15)$$

The grouping of squares along any axis therefore enables the minimization which is typified by Eq. (7.15). An extension of this principle is shown in Fig. 7.23. The Boolean expression depicted in Fig. 7.23 can be written as

$$F = A.B.\overline{C}.\overline{D} + A.B.C.\overline{D} + \overline{A}.\overline{B}.C.D + A.\overline{B}.C.D$$
$$= A.B.\overline{D}.(\overline{C} + C) + \overline{B}.C.D.(\overline{A} + A)$$
$$= A.B.\overline{D} + \overline{B}.C.D$$

Minimization in the above examples reduces the four terms in the expression to two terms, each involving three variables. The groupings in the example are akin to the idea of rolling the map into a cylinder about either axis to complete the two groupings as shown. In extending the minimization principle to five variables, the number of squares required is $2^5 = 32$. This is best

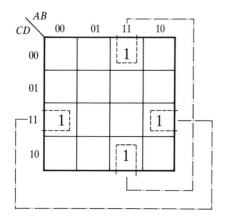

Figure 7.23 Extended minimization principle.

handled as two sets of 16 squares in a top and bottom arrangement. The 16 square layers represents the first four input variables and each layer accommodates the two possible input combinations for the fifth variable. Higher numbers of input variables can be dealt with, but the map becomes increasingly more difficult to handle.

In certain situations involving a number of input variables, particular combinations of the variables never actually occur in practice. Under these circumstances the output which would occur with these combinations of variables is irrelevant. The output can therefore have any value. Such input combinations are called 'don't care' conditions and they can be incorporated into a system to allow a simpler circuit realization. The principle can be illustrated by means of an example:

$$F = \overline{A}.\overline{B}.\overline{C}.D + \overline{A}.\overline{B}.C.D + \overline{A}.B.\overline{C}.D$$

It is stated that the combination $\overline{A}.B.C.D$ will never occur. Including the don't care condition into the expression gives:

$$F = \overline{A}.\overline{B}.\overline{C}.D + \overline{A}.\overline{B}.C.D + \overline{A}.B.\overline{C}.D + \{\overline{A}.B.C.D\}_x \qquad (7.16)$$

The don't care combination is usually enclosed within brackets and subscripted with either an x or 0. The Karnaugh representation for the expression is shown in Fig. 7.24. The don't care condition is clearly indicated in the figure. By ignoring the don't care condition, minimization of the expression results in

$$F = \overline{A}.\overline{C}.D + \overline{A}.\overline{B}.D \qquad (7.17)$$

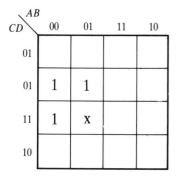

Figure 7.24 Karnaugh representation of Eq. (7.16).

If the network output is allowed to be 1 for the don't care condition, the minimization yields

$$F = \overline{A}.D \tag{7.18}$$

The example shows that considerable savings in the realization of an expression can be made by including a relevant don't care condition. It is also worth bearing in mind that although the Karnaugh map can yield a minimum gate solution to a given problem, it might not be an optimum solution. In the real world other considerations may well dictate in terms of parts, design, assembly costs and the number of IC packages required. Hazard considerations may also take precedence over circuit minimization.

Hazard Conditions

In any logic circuit where two or more signals change state while being input to a subsequent gate there is a possibility of circuit malfunction if the inputs do not change state at the same time. During a change of state of say the variable A, the Boolean relations $A + \overline{A} = 1$ and $A.\overline{A} = 0$, do not hold. Hazard conditions can occur therefore if either, or both of these relations momentarily exist during a change of state. For example the relation $F = A.C + B.\overline{C}$ might be prone to a hazard condition if during a change of state, A and B are both momentarily equal to 1. In this event the circuit reduces to $F = C + \overline{C}$ which would temporarily upset the Boolean relation. To avoid possible hazard conditions the expression should be examined to make sure that it cannot be momentarily reduced to $A + \overline{A}$, or $A.\overline{A}$. The prevention of hazards and circuit minimization techniques are essentially conflicting, however, good practice should be aimed at minimization of the circuit first and then elimination of potential hazard conditions.

Example Derive an alternative function for the potentially hazard-prone relation $F = A.C + B.\overline{C}$.
Using De Morgan we can write

$$F = \overline{(\overline{A} + \overline{C})} + \overline{(\overline{B} + C)}$$

Similarly

$$F = \overline{(\overline{A} + \overline{C}).(\overline{B} + C)}$$

Multiplying the expression out gives

$$F = \overline{\overline{A}.\overline{B} + \overline{A}.C + \overline{C}.\overline{B} + \overline{C}.C} = \overline{\overline{A}.\overline{B} + \overline{A}.C + \overline{C}.\overline{B}}$$

Further manipulation using De Morgan gives

$$F = \overline{(\overline{\overline{A}.\overline{B}}).(\overline{\overline{A}.C}) + (\overline{C}.\overline{B})}$$

$$= \overline{(\overline{A}.\overline{B})}.\overline{(\overline{A}.C)}.\overline{(\overline{C}.\overline{B})}$$

$$= (A + B).(A + \overline{C}).(C + B)$$

Multiplying out the above gives

$$F = A.A.C + A.B.C + A.\overline{C}.C + B.\overline{C}.C + A.A.B + A.B.B + A.B.\overline{C} + B.B.\overline{C}$$

$$= A.C + A.B.C + A.B + A.B + A.B.\overline{C} + B.\overline{C}$$

$$= A.C + A.B.(C + \overline{C}) + A.B + B.\overline{C}$$

$$= A.C + A.B + B.\overline{C}$$

In this particular version the relation cannot be reduced to the form $C + \overline{C}$ and the potential hazard condition has been eliminated. The equivalence of the original and the final relations can be checked using a truth table.

Positive and Negative Logic

In considering the digital logic systems so far, no particular significance has been made of the logic levels in terms of the actual voltages applied. Two possibilities exist to differentiate between logic 1 and 0. In a positive logic system, logic level 1 is represented by a more positive voltage level than logic level 0. Both logic voltage levels could actually be negative, but many digital systems operate with a voltage between 0 V and 0.8 V denoting logic level 0 and a voltage between 2.4 V and 5 V denoting logic level 1.

In a negative logic system, logic level 1 is represented by a less positive voltage than logic level 0. This standard applies to data transmission interfaces where a voltage in the range -3 V to -15 V denotes logic 1 and a voltage in the range $+3$ V to $+15$ V denotes logic 0. The large differentiation between 0 and 1 ensures good immunity to electrical noise. These voltages, however, are not compatible with either TTL or CMOS devices and interconversion ICs are required within the data transmission interface.

As an alternative to using the terms logic 1 and logic 0, the terms 'high' and 'low' are often substituted. In a positive logic system a transition from logic 0 to logic 1 can be termed a transition from low to high.

The logic level definitions also influence the function of the logic device. Figure 7.25 shows two types of 2-input NOR gates. In Fig. 7.25(a) the inputs are negative logic and the output is positive logic. The NOR gate therefore performs the logical AND function. In Fig. 7.25(b) the inputs are positive logic while the output is negative logic. This NOR gate therefore performs the logical OR function.

Tri-state Logic

Tri-state logic does not represent three logic levels but denotes three states which may be logic 1, logic 0, or 'unconnected'. A separate 'enable' input determines whether the output behaves as a normal output, or goes into the third, open circuit state. Tri-state devices are used in applications where different logic devices are required to be connected into output lines which are common to other logic devices, for example computer data buses. While one set of logic devices are transmitting signals, the other set of devices are temporarily disconnected, or disabled.

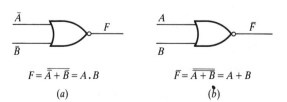

$$F = \overline{\overline{A} + \overline{B}} = A.B$$

(a)

$$\overline{F} = \overline{\overline{A + B}} = A + B$$

(b)

Figure 7.25 NOR gates using positive and negative logic systems.

7.4 SEQUENTIAL LOGIC SYSTEMS

The logic circuits so far considered are all examples of combinational logic systems where the output is determined by the combination of input variables present at that time. Sequential logic circuits are those in which the outputs depends upon the sequence of prior inputs. The main difference between sequential and combinational logic systems is that the former circuits must possess some semblance of 'memory'. The basic memory element in sequential logic systems is provided by one of several 'bistable' gates, so called because of the two different, but stable outputs which the gates produce.

The SR Bistable (flip-flop)

The term 'flip-flop' is traditionally used with respect to basic memory elements and in the SR flip-flop the 'S' denotes Set and 'R' denotes Reset. The SR flip-flop was an early development, commonly constructed using discrete transistors. The internal operation, in which two transistors alternate between the cut-off and saturated states, is of less importance than the external function which the device performs. Using the systems approach, the SR flip-flop can be represented as shown in Fig. 7.26.

The system shows the two inputs S and R and the two output lines traditionally denoted as Q and $\overline{Q}$. For sequential circuits the truth table is more usually called a state table. The state table for the SR flip-flop is given in Fig. 7.27. Each set of input variable values is considered for both possible states of the output. This is necessary because the output values do not depend uniquely on the input variable values, but also on the current values of the outputs themselves. The operation of the SR flip-flop may be summarized as follows:

With $S = 0$ and $R = 0$, the output is not affected and remains as it was.
With $S = 1$ and $R = 0$, the output will change to $Q = 1$ if previously Q was 0.
Q will remain at 1 if previously Q was 1.
With $S = 0$ and $R = 1$, the output will change to $Q = 0$ if previously Q was 1.
Q will remain at 0 if previously Q was 0.

In all cases considered, the output $\overline{Q}$ will be the inverse complement of Q.

The SR flip-flop may be constructed using cross-coupled NOR, or NAND gates as shown in Fig. 7.28.

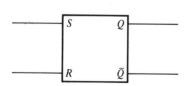

Figure 7.26 The SR flip-flop.

Inputs		Output changes	
S	R	$Q_n \rightarrow Q_{n+1}$	$\overline{Q}_n \rightarrow \overline{Q}_{n+1}$
0	0	$0 \rightarrow 0$	$1 \rightarrow 1$
0	0	$1 \rightarrow 1$	$0 \rightarrow 0$
0	1	$0 \rightarrow 0$	$1 \rightarrow 1$
0	1	$1 \rightarrow 0$	$0 \rightarrow 1$
1	0	$0 \rightarrow 1$	$1 \rightarrow 0$
1	0	$1 \rightarrow 1$	$0 \rightarrow 0$
1	1	NOT AVAILABLE	
1	1		

Figure 7.27 State table for the SR flip-flop.

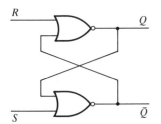

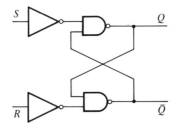

Figure 7.28 SR flip-flop using cross-coupled gates.

The T (Trigger) flip-flop

The T flip-flop is another bistable circuit having two outputs, Q and $\bar{Q}$, but only one input, T. The T flip-flop changes state on every T input signal and then remains in that state while the T input remains low.

The JK flip-flop

The JK flip-flop uses integrated circuit technology and since it can perform both of the SR and T flip-flop functions, it has become the most common flip-flop in current use. Figure 7.29 gives the state table and logic symbol for the JK flip-flop.

The state table is identical to the SR flip-flop with the exception that the input condition $J = 1$, $K = 1$ is allowed. For these latter inputs the JK flip-flop functions as a T flip-flop using an input clock signal, in the form of a pulse train, as the trigger.

The JK flip-flop operates in a clocked, or synchronous mode. In synchronous mode, the J and K inputs do not in themselves initiate a change in the logic outputs, but are used to control inputs to determine the change of state which is to occur. A pulse input to the clock terminal, CK, then determines the timing of the state changes. The clocked mode allows for precise timing of the state changes in a sequential circuit.

JK flip-flops may also be provided with additional Set, S, and Clear, C, inputs which can be used to set output Q to 1, or clear output Q to 0 at any time. Multiple J and K inputs are also commonly available to enable logical ANDing of multiple input signals.

A slightly more complicated flip-flop arrangement is the JK master–slave flip-flop. This consists of a pair of SR flip-flops connected together by various logic gates as shown in Fig. 7.30. The JK master–slave flip-flop differs from the simpler arrangement in that if the clock pulse is at logic 1, a logic 1 applied to either J or K will not set the outputs. The new data however is accepted by the 'master'. When the clock pulse returns to 0, the master is isolated from the inputs but its data is transferred to the slave with the result that Q and $\bar{Q}$ can then change state. In a circuit involving many such flip-flops, the advantage of the master–slave arrangement is that it can allow for synchronization of all the output state changes.

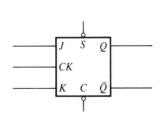

Inputs		Outputs
J	K	$Q_n \rightarrow Q_{n+1}$
0	0	$0 \rightarrow 0$
0	0	$1 \rightarrow 1$
0	1	$0 \rightarrow 0$
0	1	$1 \rightarrow 0$
1	0	$0 \rightarrow 1$
1	0	$1 \rightarrow 1$
1	1	$0 \rightarrow 1$
1	1	$1 \rightarrow 0$

Figure 7.29 JK flip-flop and corresponding state table.

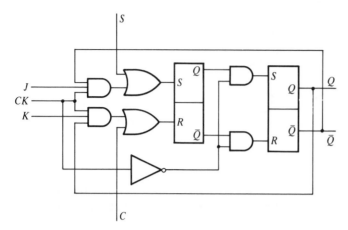

Figure 7.30 The JK master slave flip-flop.

Registers and Counters

In the previous section it was shown that a logic level of 1 on a particular input line to a flip-flop can set an output line to 1. In this way the flip-flop can perform an elementary memory function. For a binary signal of length n bits, n flip-flops are required to construct a memory device for the n-bit input signal. A group of flip-flops used together in this manner constitutes a 'register'.

Data may be entered into the register in a serial, or a parallel manner. In the parallel method the n-bit binary 'word' is available on n input lines. Each line is connected to its own flip-flop and the n data bits are entered simultaneously into the register. In the serial entry method, the data is available on only one input line in a time sequence. The data is entered consecutively and is timed into the register by a system clock. Serial entry registers are also called the 'shift' registers since the data bits are entered into the first flip-flop and moved consecutively along into the next flip-flop as the next data bit arrives at the first flip-flop and so on. The serial method of data entry requires as many shift and store operations as the number of bits in the binary word. This means that the serial entry method is much slower than the parallel method. Serial entry, however, is also much less expensive than parallel entry.

Yet another type of register is the counting register. These consist of a number of flip-flops arranged to store a binary word which is representative of the number of input pulses applied at the input terminal. Using n flip-flops, a total count of 2^n can be made.

Counting register, or 'counters', may be synchronous, in which the state changes in all the flip-flops occur simultaneously, or asynchronous, in which the state changes in various flip-flops do not occur at the same time. Figure 7.31 illustrates an asynchronous, 3-bit binary counter composed of JK flip-flops. All J and K inputs are held at logic level 1 and the input signal consists of a pulse train fed to the clock input of the first flip-flop. In this mode the JK flip-flop is operating as a T flip-flop. The output Q from the first flip-flop provides an input for the clock

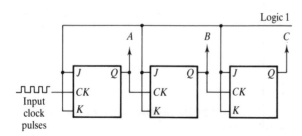

Figure 7.31 Asynchronous, 3-bit binary counter.

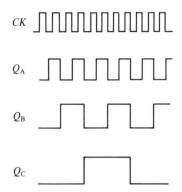

Clock	Flip-flop		
pulses	C	B	A
0	0	0	0
1	0	0	1
2	0	1	0
3	0	1	1
4	1	0	0
5	1	0	1
6	1	1	0
7	1	1	1
0	0	0	0

Figure 7.32 State table and timing diagram for a 3-bit binary counter.

of the second flip-flop and so on through the network. The outputs also form the binary representation of the counter where A is the least significant bit, increasing through to C which represents the most significant bit. The state table and timing diagram for the counter are shown in Fig. 7.32.

The state table shows that each flip-flop changes state when the next less significant flip-flop output changes from 1 to 0. The output signal from each flip-flop, moving through the network, is at half the frequency of that of the previous flip-flop. These output signals thus provide the correct binary count of the number of input pulses applied to the input. The 3-bit binary counter can count up to a maximum of 8 decimal. If a ninth pulse is applied at the input, the count reverts back to the initial zero setting and the count continues again as normal for further input pulses.

Asynchronous counters are also referred to as 'ripple' counters because of the way that the changes of state ripples through the network of flip-flops.

A synchronous version of the counter can also be realized using a network of JK flip-flops. The synchronous counter additionally uses the outputs Q and $\overline{Q}$ of each flip-flop, in logic gate networks, to produce the necessary control signals for the J and K inputs. This ensures that all flip-flops change state correctly to the desired state table for each clock pulse. The synchronous counter alleviates the problems associated with transient operation inherent in the asynchronous counter.

There are of course many other types of flip-flop available, but the only other one of significant practical importance is the D flip-flop (Fig. 7.33), where the 'D' refers to Data. In the D-type flip-flop, the D input is fed directly into the J input line and the inverse complement of D is fed to the K input line. This ensures that J and K are always the inverse complement of one another. A logic 0 or 1 on the data input will then flip, or flop, the outputs when the clock pulse is at logic 0.

Timers and Pulse Circuits

An essential feature of the flip-flop circuits described in the previous two sections was the provision of a pulsed clock signal. Although timers can be designed using discrete components, it is normal to design round the commonly available timers which are already available in IC

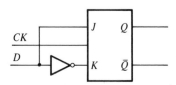

Figure 7.33 D-type flip-flop.

form. The most prevalent timer currently in use is the NE555, which is manufactured as an 8-pin DIL package. The CMOS equivalent to the TTL-based NE555 is the ICM7555. These packages are essentially identical and ICM7555 can be used to replace NE555, although the converse is not always applicable. The so called '555' timer is very versatile and can be used in either 'monostable', or 'astable' mode.

Monostable Figure 7.34 shows the 555 wired up for monostable operation. When the 'trigger' is taken from $+5\,$V to $0\,$V (i.e. high to low), the output goes high for a period determined by the values selected for R and C. The length of the output pulse is given by $1.1RC$. The timer can deliver currents of more than $100\,$mA and it can therefore be used to drive a DIL reed relay directly. When such a relay is switched off, however, the back e.m.f. generated by the relay coil could damage the timer. As a precaution a diode is normally connected in parallel with the relay coil, in the opposite direction to the current flow, to absorb the high induced voltage.

> **Example** Calculate the positive pulse width of a signal resulting from a $10\,$kHz clock triggering a monostable multivibrator with $R = 2\,$kΩ and $C = 0.001\,\mu$F.
> Clock signal period is given by
> $$1/f = 1/10\,000 = 10^{-4}\,\text{s} = 100\,\mu\text{s}$$
> Pulse width $= 1.1RC$, i.e.
> $$1.1 \times 2000 \times 0.001 \times 10^{-6} = 2.2\,\mu\text{s}$$

Astable Figure 7.35 depicts the 555 wired up for astable operation. The $100\,$nF capacitor is required only for TTL-based timers. In astable operation the output is a continuous pulse train. The ON and OFF times can be controlled independently within certain limitations, with

$$\text{ON time} = 0.693(R_1 + R_2)C \qquad (7.19)$$

$$\text{OFF time} = 0.693(R_2)C \qquad (7.20)$$

Obviously the ON time can only be equal to, or greater than the OFF time. The output signal, however, can always be inverted if, in a particular application, short duration positive pulses were required.

The maximum operating frequency for the 555 timer is about $500\,$kHz and the minimum frequency, limited by the leakage of the capacitor, is about one cycle per several hours.

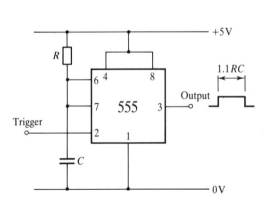

Figure 7.34 555 timer in monostable operation.

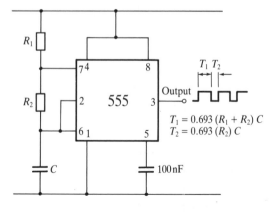

Figure 7.35 555 timer in astable operation.

Example Determine the frequency, the width of the positive pulse and the mark–space ratio for an astable circuit with $R_1 = 4.3\,\text{k}\Omega$, $R_2 = 5.6\,\text{k}\Omega$ and $C = 0.002\,\mu\text{F}$.
From Eq. (7.19),

$$\text{ON time} = 0.693(4.3 + 5.6)10^3 \times 0.002 \times 10^{-6} = 13.72\,\mu\text{s}$$

From Eq. (7.20),

$$\text{OFF time} = 0.693(5.6)10^3 \times 0.002 \times 10^{-6} = 7.76\,\mu\text{s}$$

Output signal period is

$$\text{ON time} + \text{OFF time} = 13.72 + 7.76 = 21.48\,\mu\text{s}$$

Output signal frequency $= 1/\text{period}$, i.e.

$$1/(21.48 \times 10^{-6}) = 46.55\,\text{kHz}$$

Positive pulse width is the ON time i.e. $13.72\,\mu\text{s}$, and the mark–space ratio is given by

$$\text{ON time}/\text{OFF time} = 13.72/7.76 = 1.77$$

Example A car alarm system operates when the ignition switch I is de-activated, when the alarm system A is activated and when either one, or all three doors D_1, D_2, D_3 are open. Before the alarm is sounded, however, there is a 15 s delay T, which allows the rightful owner time to enter the vehicle and de-activate the alarm system. All switching and timing signals can be assumed to be at logic level 1 when activated and at logic level 0 when de-activated.

(a) Select suitable circuit elements for a 555 timer, operating in monostable mode and triggered by the opening of any one door, to generate the 15 s delay.
(b) Derive appropriate Boolean expressions to implement the desired control functions and construct a suitable logic circuit.
(c) Construct alternative logic circuits: (i) using NAND gates only; (ii) using NOR gates only.

(a) Time ON pulse $= 1.1RC = 15\,\text{s}$. Choosing $C = 10\,\mu\text{F}$, then

$$R = 15/(1.1 \times 10 \times 10^{-6}) = 1.36\,\text{M}\Omega = 1.4\,\text{M}\Omega$$

(b) Consideration of the circuit requirement gives the logical expression:

$$\text{Alarm on IF}(D_1 \text{ OR } D_2 \text{ OR } D_3) \text{ AND } A \text{ AND NOT } T \text{ AND NOT } I$$

or, as a Boolean expression,

$$F = \bar{I}.\bar{T}.A.(D_1 + D_2 + D_3)$$

The implementation of this expression in a logic circuit is shown in Fig. 7.36.
With the alarm activated, $A = 1$ and with the ignition OFF, $I = 0$. An inverter is used to convert I to $\bar{I}$ as shown. Following the time delay generated by the 555 timer, the signal level at the output from the timer will be 0. An inverter is used again here to convert T to $\bar{T}$. Note that the trigger for the timer is taken from any one, or all three of the door switches D. The door switches are connected into a 3-input OR gate and the output from this gate will be 1 only when any, or all doors are opened. This event will furnish a logic level 1 for the final input to the 4-input AND gate. If this occurs then the alarm will be sounded. The 15 s time delay should give enough time for the car owner to enter the vehicle and de-activate the

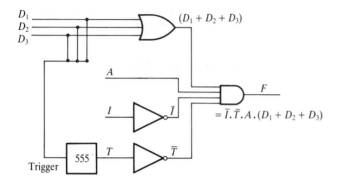

Figure 7.36 Circuit diagram for car alarm system.

alarm signal A. This, of course, will prevent the alarm from sounding which can only happen when all four inputs to the AND gate are at logic level 1.

The construction of the circuit using NAND gates only is shown in Fig. 7.37.

The resulting Boolean expression can be written as:

$$F = \overline{\overline{\overline{I.T.A.(\overline{\overline{D_1.D_2.D_3}})}}}$$

Consideration of the operation of the system shows that it performs the same essential functions as the circuit shown in Fig. 7.36.

Alternatively, the alarm system can be constructed using NOR gates only. This is shown in Fig. 7.38.

The resulting Boolean expression is

$$F = \overline{\overline{T} + \overline{I} + \overline{A} + \overline{(D_1 + D_2 + D_3)}}$$

Again, consideration of the normal signals on the input lines shows that the circuit performs the same functions as the two previous circuits.

Digital Computers and Microprocessors

No coverage of digital electronics can fail to give some cognizance to the impact of the digital computer and its associated microprocessor. The modern digital computer, although a complex digital system, consists of no more than the basic logical subsystems previously discussed. This includes AND, OR, NAND and NOR gates, registers, counters and communication interfaces. A detailed description of computer systems and microprocessors, with specific details related to microprocessor technology and number systems, is presented in Chapter 8.

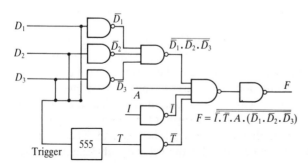

Figure 7.37 Circuit diagram for car alarm system using NAND gates only.

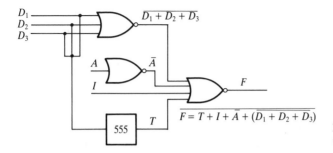

$$F = T + I + \overline{A} + (\overline{D_1 + D_2 + D_3})$$

Figure 7.38 Circuit diagram for car alarm system using NOR gates only.

The main advantages of the microprocessor-based system are that the logical functions for a particular application can be developed and implemented in software, as opposed to electronic hardware. In many instances the microprocessor-based system may actually be the cheaper alternative to a hardwired logic gate circuit. The software is easy to alter in the event of incorrect system operation and the complete system can be tested as a simulation before being committed.

For relatively small logical switching applications, up to say 32 inputs, the single-card microcomputer, or the single-chip microcomputer, represents an ideal low-cost solution. These microsystems can be used as dedicated devices where all of the system components reside on a single card or a single chip, respectively. The major applications for these devices are in the high-volume production markets such as automotive electronics, washing machines, bus ticket machines and time attendance recorders.

7.5 APPLICATION-SPECIFIC INTEGRATED CIRCUITS, ASICs

Application-specific integrated circuits are chips that have their internal configuration set by the user. This enables the designer to customize the device for specific applications. The technology developed substantially throughout the 1980s into a design tool with a large choice of software development packages and hardware programming devices. Such customization provides an enhancement of performance, reliability and compactness in addition to design security. The availability of devices which support this technology has resulted in a trend for designers of logic circuits to move away from the standard small scale integration (SSI—up to 100 transistors) and medium scale integration (MSI—up to 1000 transistors) logic components such as the 74 and 4000 series in the TTL and CMOS semiconductor families.

Although the design of semiconductor chip architecture is a highly specialized activity the ASIC simplifies the matter by providing a large number of semiconductor elements such as amplifiers, logic gates and switches, which can be interconnected as required, to provide the control or functions needed for a specific task. The uncustomized ASIC is common to a large number of applications and thus the cost of the integrated circuit package is low. In addition, since all the interconnection detail lies within the silicon structure, the design is relatively secure.

There are two main types of ASIC—the customized and the semi-customized. The customized ASIC can be built up from a library of pre-designed cells and requires specialized manufacturing processes. They can contain digital, analogue or mixed signal circuits. Many manufacturers provide a design and manufacture service for such devices which would normally be required for large volume production applications. Semi-customized ASICs are usually digital only, although some manufacturers class ASICs differently. They can be of two main types. The first is the mask-customized ASIC which is based on ROM technology. This type still needs to be produced by a specialized manufacturer but it is much cheaper than a customized design. The second type is a programmable logic device (PLD) which can be programmed by the designer with the use of appropriate software and hardware. The PLD is suitable for a one-off, a prototype or small production runs. Some PLDs can be programmed a number of times thus making them ideal for inexpensive prototyping. For large volume manufacture the designer should consider once-programmable PLDs or customized ASICs.

Programmable Logic Devices

The PLD has evolved over the years from ROM, PROM, EPROM and EEPROM technology. The basic PROM consists of a fixed logic AND-array and a programmable logic OR-array with fuses that can be blown or left intact for the required interconnections. By introducing a programmable AND matrix the PROM was developed such that it could be programmed by the logic circuit designer 'in the field'. Such devices, which were introduced in 1975, are termed field programmable logic arrays or FPLAs. In some texts they are referred to as programmable logic arrays (PLAs) which can cause some confusion with programmable array logic (PAL).

The PAL family architecture is also defined using fuse maps based on a programmable AND-array, as in the FPLA, and a fixed OR-array. The design also offers several features that make the family desirable over FPLAs in many applications. At the same time that PALs were introduced in 1978, a computer-based aid to assist in the logic design process became available. This logic language termed PALASM became almost universally accepted throughout the PLD design industry and PALs are generally the number one device in terms of sales. The PAL16L8 is a popular 20-pin device which is commonly used for general purpose decoding and logic applications. The security feature common in PLDs originated in the PAL family. This allows the designer to blow a security fuse which inhibits the device from being copied easily.

One problem with PALs is that they are once-only programmable and cannot therefore be altered. Developments in semiconductor technology led to electrically erasable cells which enabled generic array logic (GAL) PLDs to be produced. These devices can be reprogrammed and emulate existing PAL devices. They are ideal for prototype design or system upgrades without the need to discard the IC each time. GAL is a trade mark of Lattice Semiconductor and is used by companies such as National Semiconductors. Other companies provide similar devices under a host of names such as PEELs—programmable electrically erasable logic, and EPLDs—erasable programmable logic devices. The GAL16V8 is a popular 20-pin device for general logic designs. It has ten dedicated input pins and eight configurable I/O pins.

The Design Development Process

As with any other design methodology the first and most important step involved in the process is to obtain a clear definition of the problem to be solved. This is followed by generating a block diagram of the logic to be implemented. It is then necessary to express the design in terms of Boolean equations which are the basis of the fuse-blowing program for the PLD.

A variety of software packages, usually operating on a personal computer (PC), are available to help the designer produce designs based on PLDs. Tools termed logic assemblers or compilers translate a design source file into a fuse pattern which is ultimately stored in a JEDEC (Joint Electron Device Engineering Council) file. This standard was released in 1986 and JEDEC files are produced by almost all PLD development software and are accepted by all popular PLD programmers. Once the JEDEC file containing the fuse map has been created it is then transferred to a PLD programmer. Generally when using the programmer transfer software, the device type—such as a GAL16V8—must be selected. This is then followed by the name of the JEDEC file. Most PLD programmers are capable of handling a large selection of devices. If the PLD is a reprogrammable type it will first be erased and a screen display usually indicates the number of times that the device has been programmed. LED indication shows when the programming process is complete.

Thus the design implementation consists of selecting and using the necessary PC driven software and hardware tools to translate the logic design, expressed in a Boolean equation format, into a configured PLD. A summary of the steps to be taken are:

- PLD family and device selection
- Entry of Boolean equations into a source file
- Run development software and produce a fuse map JEDEC file
- Configure PLD programmer and transfer JEDEC file ·
- Device programmed

Traditionally, logic applications have used Karnaugh maps (Sec. 7.3) to manually minimize the logic requirement. These are extremely time consuming and tedious. However, a number of software development packages for producing PLDs incorporate minimization algorithms which are capable of transforming a set of Boolean equations into a smaller, but functionally equivalent set of equations. Generally, within the package, a facility also exists for checking that the device itself implements what was originally required with respect to input/output relationships. The technique involves either inputting by hand or generating automatically what is referred to as test vectors. These are then used in a simulation to check that the necessary truth table will be obeyed correctly.

Example The complete process of developing a PLD is best illustrated by means of a simple example. Consider the control of the water level in a waste water sump system as shown in Fig. 7.39.

The pump (P) is started when the upper level switch (LS1) is activated. The level then drops and LS1 is deactivated. The pump must remain on until the lower level switch (LS2) is activated.

Some form of latching is required to hold the pump on and, as for a digital control process, it is advisable to draw up a flow chart to define the operation of the system. This is illustrated in Fig. 7.40.

The Boolean equation which satisfies the control requirement is

$$P = (P.\overline{LS2}) + (LS1.\overline{LS2}) \tag{7.21}$$

which requires one NOT gate, two AND gates and one OR gate as arranged in the circuit shown in Fig. 7.41.

The arrangement can now be applied to a PLD and the example can be used to illustrate the procedure when using the following design tools:

1. PC-based software package, PLAN from NATIONAL SEMICONDUCTORS, Santa Clara, California, for assembling the source file which contains the Boolean equation(s).

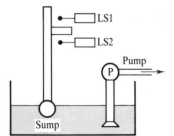

Figure 7.39 Waste water level control system.

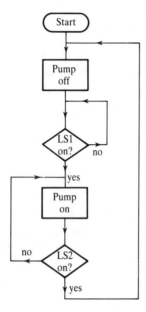

Figure 7.40 Flow chart illustrating waste water level control system operation.

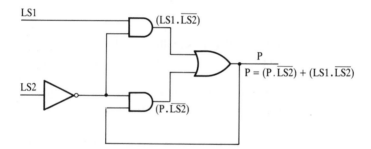

Figure 7.41 Logic circuit to control waste water level system.

2. PC-based PLD programmer PLD-1100 from **BP MICROSYSTEMS**, Houston, Texas, for the programming hardware.

The test file which must have the extension .BEQ, for it to be read by the PLAN software, can be created by any text editor that can produce an ASCII text file. The file must contain such information as the device type, pin I/O list and the Boolean equation(s).

All device pins must be accounted for and any unused pins must be labelled NC. The standard method is used to specify the power supply pins—VCC and GND. The pin list is contrained on two lines of the file starting with pin 1. If a chosen arrangement is omitted by leaving two blank lines then the software assigns pins for all I/O requirement and displays the configuration at the assembly stage.

For the waste water level control system the source code, WWLC.BEQ, is

```
GAL 16V8; Waste water level control system
LS1 LS2 NC NC NC NC NC NC NC GND
NC NC NC NC P NC NC NC NC VCC
T1.TERM=P*/LS2     ;Pump AND NOT LS2
T2.TERM=LS1*/LS2   ;LS1 AND NOT LS2
P=T1+T2            ;Complete Boolean equation
```

This ASCII text file is now converted into a fuse blowing JEDEC file using the PLAN assembler program:

```
PLAN WWLC<CR>
```

This produces the JEDEC file—WWLC.JED—which is also in ASCII format and can be viewed or printed.

A diagram of the chip with the I/O pinout connections is also displayed on the screen at this stage.

It now remains to take this fuse map file and program the PLD by using the logic programmer PLD1100 which connects into a PC through the parallel printer port:

```
PLD1100<CR>
```

Using the displayed menu, the device GAL16V8 must be SELECTed then the file WWLC.JED LOADed through the BUFFER option on the main menu. The PLD device is now inserted into the ZIF socket in the programmer, the DEVICE option is selected and the < CR > key activated to program the GAL16V8. The gate configuration is now blown onto the PLD and can be tested.

These basic concepts apply irrespective of the software and hardware development tools selected.

It can thus be seen that one of the most useful ASIC devices for the digital logic designer is the programmable logic device. The PLD allows the designer to implement his own designs on a single integrated circuit. This is ideal for prototypes, system upgrades or small batch production runs. In comparison the customized ASIC requires a much greater degree of expertise with respect to both software and hardware development tools.

FURTHER READING

Alford, R. C. (1989) *Programmable Logic Designer's Guide*, Howard V Sams & Company, Indianapolis, Indiana.
Horowitz, P. and W. Hill (1989) *The Art of Electronics*, 2nd edn, Cambridge University Press, Cambridge.
Kaufman, M. and R. H. Seidman (1988) *Handbook of Electronics Calculations for Engineers and Technicians*, 2nd edn, McGraw-Hill, New York.
Watson, J. (1983) *Mastering Electronics*, Macmillan, London.

EXERCISES

7.1 Using De Morgan's theorem, prove that

(a) $A.\overline{B} + \overline{A}.B = \overline{\overline{A.B} + \overline{A}.\overline{B}}$;

(b) $A.(B + \overline{C}) = \overline{\overline{A} + \overline{B}.C}$.

7.2 Simplify the Boolean expression $[A.(\overline{A.\overline{B}}).(\overline{C.D})]$.

$$[\overline{A.B} + C.D]$$

7.3 A simple burglar alarm is to be wired up in a house which has two access doors, A and B. Microswitches are used to detect whether the doors are open or closed with a logic level 0 detected when a door is closed and a logic level 1 transmitted when a door is open. The alarm system can also be activated ON or OFF through a concealed manual switch

S. With the system activated, a logic level 1 is transmitted through switch S. A logic level 0 through switch S indicates that the system is OFF. Derive an appropriate Boolean expression to represent the sounding of the alarm F when the system is activated and either, or both, of the doors are opened.

$$[F = A.S + B.S, \text{ or } F = S.(A + B)]$$

Construct a circuit diagram for the alarm system and deduce the appropriate Boolean functions:

(a) using NAND gates only;

(b) using NOR gates only.

$$[F = \overline{(\overline{A.S}).(\overline{B.S})} : F = \overline{\overline{(\overline{A+B})} + S}]$$

7.4   A level control system operates with two float switches, S_1 and S_2, which are set at the minimum and the maximum levels, respectively. These switches produce logic signals of 0 and 1 depending on whether they are tripped or not. The level in the tank is to be kept within the minimum and maximum values while some fluid is constantly being drawn off. A small pump P is used to supply fluid and excess fluid can be drained through a solenoid operated valve V. Both the pump and the solenoid operated valve are switched ON by logic level control signals, where a logic 1 switches the devices ON and a logic level 0 switches the devices OFF. Derive appropriate Boolean expressions to implement the desired control functions and construct suitable logic circuits:

(a) using NAND gates only;

(b) using NOR gates only.

$$[P = \overline{S}_1, \ V = S_1.S_2 : \ P = \overline{S}_1, \ V = \overline{\overline{S_1.S_2}} : \ P = \overline{S}_1, \ V = \overline{\overline{S}_1 + \overline{S}_2}]$$

7.5   Minimize the Boolean expressions:

(a) $F = \overline{A}.\overline{B}.\overline{C}.D + A.\overline{B}.\overline{C}.\overline{D} + A.\overline{B}.\overline{C}.D + A.\overline{B}.C.\overline{D}$.

(b) If the combination $A.\overline{B}.C.D$ can be included as a 'don't care' condition in (a), determine the new minimization.

(c) $F = B.C + C.D + D.B + B.C.D$.

$$[F = \overline{B}.(A.\overline{D} + \overline{C}.D) : \ F = \overline{B}(A + \overline{C}.D) : \ F = B + C.D]$$

7.6   In order to assess the heat losses from a building it is required to record the room temperature every half-hour over a period of 24 h. The temperature transducer which is to be used can be tripped to record using a positive logic level pulse with a minimum duration of 5 s. Using a 555 timer, in astable mode, select suitable values for the circuit elements to produce the approprate pulse duration and frequency. Hint: the output from the circuit will require to be inverted.

$$[\text{For } C = 10\,\mu\text{F}, \ R_1 = 129\,\text{M}\Omega, \ R_2 = 370\,\text{k}\Omega]$$

The output signal used to trigger the temperature sensor is also to be used to drive a ripple counter based on JK flip-flops. Determine how many JK flip-flops are required to totalize the number of temperature readings taken over the sampling period.

[six]

7.7   A combination of switches are to be used as a security device for a wall safe. There are six switches A, B, C, D, E and F and the correct combination is 101001. To open the safe a start signal is activated by a key and the switches must then be set. A timing device is incorporated into the system, triggered by the start signal which allows the user 20 s to set the correct combination on the switches. If this is done correctly the safe will open automatically.

(a)   Select suitable circuit elements for a 555 timer operating in monostable mode to generate the required delay time.

$$[C = 10\,\mu\text{F}, \ R = 1.8\,\text{M}\Omega]$$

(b)   Derive an appropriate Boolean expression to implement the desired control function and construct a suitable logic circuit.

$$[F = A.\overline{B}.C.\overline{D}.\overline{E}.F.T]$$

(c)   Construct alternative logic circuits:

(i)   using NAND gates only;

(ii)   using NOR gates only.

$$[F = \overline{\overline{A.\overline{B}.C.\overline{D}.\overline{E}.F.T}} : \ F = \overline{\overline{A} + B + \overline{C} + D + E + \overline{F} + \overline{T}}]$$

EIGHT

MICROPROCESSOR TECHNOLOGY

8.1 INTRODUCTION

Since its appearance on the market in 1971 the microprocessor has revolutionized the flexibility and intelligence which can be incorporated into a variety of consumer products and industrial systems. Typical examples include automatic cameras, camcorders, video recorders, calculators, toys, cash registers, washing machines, automatic bank teller machines, robots, automobiles and CNC machine tools. Flexibility refers to the ease with which a system can be adjusted to suit altered requirements or situations. The intelligence level of a system is determined by its control functions. Both flexibility and intelligence are greatly enhanced by employing microprocessor technology and software algorithms play a dominant role in designing how these systems will behave.

Designers of both products and manufacturing systems who have taken advantage of the opportunities offered by the use of microprocessors dominate in the market place and ultimately reap the potential benefits associated with doing things better, faster and cheaper than before. Each microprocessor-based system involves both hardware and software. Hardware refers to the physical components in the system, and software is the set of instructions, or program, which instructs the system on how to perform. The main categories of application are associated with office information systems and industrial, or process, control. The underlying technology in both of these applications is identical and there is considerable overlapping of the boundaries.

The forerunner of the modern computer is reputed to be the mechanically based analytical engine conceived by Charles Babbage, which underwent development from about 1836 to 1871. The concept of storing the program on punched cards was taken from Jacquard's automatic loom which used such a system to control the pattern to be woven.

The transition from a mechanical to an electrical means of calculation is accredited to Herman Hollerith. His machine was developed in the 1880s and was used for processing the data for the 1890 US census. Any further advancement was dependent upon the introduction of electronic concepts and this did not take place until the 1930s when a computer type machine, which employed electro-mechanical relays and Boolean algebra, was designed. This computer was based on binary rather than decimal arithmetic and was used to perform mathematical calculations. Very large computing machines soon followed, using electronic valve technology, and one such example was the Colossus which was operational in 1943. The Colossus was used extensively for breaking communication codes during the Second World War. At about the same time projects were initiated in the USA to build an electronic numerical integrator and calculator (ENIAC), and an electronic discrete variable computer (EDVC). The latter is attributed to von Neumann and the specification for its design defined the basic requirements which laid down the ground rules for all subsequent computer architectures. The first truly commercial computer of the late 1940s and the early 1950s, which used an electronically stored program, was the British Ferranti Mark 1.

The first revolutionary breakthrough on reduction in size and power consumption was the invention of the transistor at the Bell Laboratories in 1948. The device was capable of being used as a logic switching element to replace the electronic tubes, or valves, in a computer. There then followed the technique for producing a number of transistors onto a miniature circuit of semiconductor material. The first integrated circuit (IC or chip), was developed for Texas Instruments in 1958. The natural progression of increasing the complexities of ICs ultimately led to the development of the first microprocessor, or central processing unit (CPU), for a microcomputer by Intel in 1971. This was the numerically named 4004 which was a 4-bit processor with 4096 4-bit memory locations and 45 different programming instructions. The '4-bit' refers to the group of binary logic signals handled by the microprocessor during the transfer of data to the memory. The 4004 had only limited application and in the same year Intel released an 8-bit version microprocessor, the 8008. With a memory of 65 536 8-bit locations and more programming instructions, many more advanced applications were possible.

The first of the modern 8-bit microprocessors appeared in 1973 with the Intel 8080. Other manufacturers such as Motorola, MOS Technology and Zilog followed suit with processors such as the 6800, 6502 and Z80, respectively. These devices were capable of accessing more memory and executing more instructions faster than ever before. This availability of 8-bit processing power led to the appearance of a variety of desktop microcomputers such as the Commodore PET, the Apple, the BBC micro and the Sinclair ZX81. The first three were very popular in the educational environment and their manufacturers favoured the 6502 microprocessor. The relatively inexpensive ZX81, however, used a Z80 microprocessor. One self-evident problem was the lack of standardization between the manufacturers and there was virtually no compatability between the various commercially marketed machines.

Among the first of the new generation of 16-bit devices, the 8086 was launched by Intel in 1978/79. This heralded the arrival of machines which were able to compete directly with the larger minicomputers used in business, science and engineering applications. The 8088 followed shortly afterwards but it is debatable whether the 8088 was a true 16-bit device, since it still had an 8-bit external data bus. The advent of these microprocessors led to IBM entering into the microcomputer market with their PC. This first appeared in 1981 and the processor used was the 8088, in order to make use of the many 8-bit auxiliary chips that were available at that time. The programming instruction set for the 8088 is, in fact, identical to that of the more recent 8086. The IBM PC was a great commercial success with huge sales on a world-wide basis. Other manufacturers soon started to produce compatible machines to compete in this lucrative market. This has helped to achieve some standardization for microcomputer applications. The main rival to the IBM PC is the Apple MacIntosh which is built around the Motorola 68000 microprocessor.

It has been general policy in the past to classify IBM machines and compatibles as either 'PCs' (personal computers), 'XTs' (extended technology), or 'ATs' (advanced technology). These basically refer to microcomputers built around 8088/8086 microprocessors with floppy disk drive(s), 8088/8086 microprocessors with a hard disk drive and 80286 microprocessors, respectively. The continuous development of the 8086, with what is termed the 80X86 family of microprocessors, now makes the terminology somewhat meaningless although an 'AT' may be regarded as anything which uses an 80286, or further development.

The Intel 8086/8088/80X86 family is a series of 16-bit and 32-bit microprocessors which share a common internal architecture. The devices include the 8086, 8088, 80186, 80188, 80286, 80386 and 80486. The 286 processes its data as parallel lines of 16 bits whereas the 386 and 486 both have a 32-bit internal bus structure. These powerful microprocessors have real-time, multi-user, multi-tasking and memory management facilities with a downward compatibility in applications software.

Microprocessors have had a substantial impact on enhancing the embedded intelligence within products and systems and continual developments will ensure higher speeds, improved flexibility, adaptability, consistency and reliability. These features provide extensive capabilities for analysis, data storage, display, control and communications. The increasing power and sophistication of microcomputers built around modern microprocessors results in a computing facility which is increasingly attractive to the designer of engineering systems.

8.2 DATA CODES

The storage and manipulation of data within microprocessors and other integrated ciruits is achieved by devices which operate between two discrete states. These are termed binary digits, or bits, and they take the form of either a high state (logic '1'), or a low state (logic '0'). This binary number system is the basis of the technology of digital information processing.

In an actual computer system the bits are represented by voltage levels, ideally 0 V is equivalent to a logic '0' and 5 V is equivalent to a logic '1'. However, in reality the logic levels are dependent upon the binary signal being input to a device or output from a device. Another influencing factor is the logic family used for the construction of the device. Different types of logic circuitry can be used to construct logic devices as found in microprocessor systems. The most popular ones used are transistor–transistor logic (TTL) and complementary metal oxide semiconductors (CMOS). The logic levels 0 and 1 are characterized by the following voltage values:

TTL

Inputs:	Low 0–0.8 V	High 2.0–5.0 V
Outputs:	Low 0–1.5 V	High 3.5–5.0 V

CMOS

Inputs:	Low 0–1.5 V	High 3.5–5.0 V
Outputs:	Low 0 V	High 5 V

It is seen that these two families are not compatible with respect to the logic level definitions.

In the processing of digital data a number of bits are grouped together and the resulting sequence of 1s and 0s is referred to as a byte, or a word. A byte is always taken as a group of 8 bits, but a word can generally be either 8, 16 or 32 bits. The definition of a 'word' for a particular computer is depedent upon the number of bits transmitted in parallel from place to place along the data bus inside the system. The data bus is the electrical conducting path for the data on which the system is to operate. Each wire carries one of the bits and the complete group makes up the data word.

In order to understand digital systems an acquaintance with the binary number system is necessary. Other number systems of interest are the hexadecimal (hex) and binary coded decimal

(BCD). Hex is a number system which has a base of 16 and is essentially a convenient shorthand way of representing pure binary numbers. The BCD method of representing binary data is to display pure binary patterns for the decimal values of 0 through to 9 only, with each number being composed of four binary digits. In microprocessor technology the emphasis on the use of number systems is to provide a means of pattern, or code recognition.

An 8-bit word can be interpreted in several possible ways. The most obvious being that of a numerical binary number which converts into a decimal range of 0–255. The number of binary variations of an n-bit word being 2^n and commencing from zero, the range is therefore 0 to $(2^n - 1)$. Another possible interpretation is to regard the group of bits as a code which can either be used to represent say alpha-numeric data in a standard binary format, or as an instruction to a microprocessor to do something. The latter would form the basis of the instruction set for a particular family of microprocessors. A sequential list of such instructions constitutes a program.

When binary information is transmitted using 8-bit words it must first be encoded by the transmitter into a succession of bytes and then decoded by the receiver. The most common binary code used in systems for representing alpha-numeric symbols, together with all the punctuation marks and control characters, is the American Standard Code for Information Interchange, usually referred to as ASCII. A summary of some of the more common ASCII codes is given in Appendix A.

Binary/Decimal and Decimal/Binary Conversion

All number systems follow the same rules and operate to a specific base number. The binary system is based on two digits and the decimal system on 10. The only numbers allowed in binary are 0 and 1. In the decimal system, the numbers 0, 1, 2, 3, 4, 5, 6, 7, 8 and 9 are all valid. Microprocessor technology utilizes the binary system, regardless of the normal decimal presentation, and emphasis is placed on the use of the number system as a means of displaying specific binary patterns. These patterns are representative of codes that are meaningful within the context of data transmission in a digital system.

Direct, or pure, binary is used to encode integer quantities and a byte is denoted by each bit numbered from the least significant bit (LSB), or bit 0, through to the most significant bit (MSB), or bit 7. This presents the binary range:

$$00000000 \text{ to } 11111111$$

or generally:

$$B_7 \ B_6 \ B_5 \ B_4 \ B_3 \ B_2 \ B_1 \ B_0$$

As in any number system, the weighting represented by any particular number value in a group is evaluated by raising the number system base to a power indicated by the number's position in the group. In the decimal system, base 10, the weighting of the number 3 within the group 5324 is 10^2 or 100. In the binary system, base 2, the weighting of bit 3 within an 8 bit number is 2^3 or 8. Hence the decimal equivalent of an 8-bit binary number is

$$(B_7 \times 2^7) + (B_6 \times 2^6) + (B_5 \times 2^5) + \ldots \ldots (B_0 \times 2^0)$$

To assist in this process a conversion aid can be utilized in the form:

	MSB							LSB
bit	7	6	5	4	3	2	1	0
	128	64	32	16	8	4	2	1

The binary value of   1   0   0   1   1   0   0   1
will convert to   128 +   16 + 8 +   1

= 153 decimal

and the decimal value of 93 will convert to a binary value of

0   1   0   1   1   1   0   1

In the BCD number system direct binary patterns for the decimal values 0 to 9 are used. Each decimal value is represented by four binary digits. Hence the decimal number 5324 would be represented by a BCD number

0101   0011   0010   0100

BCD coding is used to represent decimal values directly as a binary format. This is the system adopted for number manipulation in a hand-held calculator. In contrast, the direct or pure binary system is generally used in computers.

It can be seen that for larger numbers the direct binary system becomes somewhat unwieldy and some abbreviated or shorthand method for representing binary numbers is essential. This is achieved by dividing a byte into two 4-bit nibbles and using one alpha-numeric character for each nibble. The 4 bits in a nibble allows 16 unique symbols to be represented. This number system is termed hexadecimal, or hex for short, and operates on a base of 16. It is universally adopted for use in microprocessor systems since it uses only two symbols to encode 8 bits. The 16 symbols used are 0 to 9 and A to F inclusive. A conversion table is shown at Table 8.1.

Table 8.1 Conversion table: Decimal/Binary/Hex/BCD.

Decimal	Binary	Hex	BCD
0	0000	0	0000
1	0001	1	0001
2	0010	2	0010
3	0011	3	0011
4	0100	4	0100
5	0101	5	0101
6	0110	6	0110
7	0111	7	0111
8	1000	8	1000
9	1001	9	1001
10	1010	A	0001 0000
11	1011	B	0001 0001
12	1100	C	0001 0010
13	1101	D	0001 0011
14	1110	E	0001 0100
15	1111	F	0001 0101
16	10000	10	0001 0110
17	10001	11	0001 0111
18	10010	12	0001 1000
19	10011	13	0001 1001
20	10100	14	0001 0000

For numbers larger than one byte the grouping is sub-divided into bytes, with 16-bit numbers having two bytes and 32-bit numbers having four bytes. The weighting of any particular byte being 256 raised to the power of the byte position. For example, consider a 24-bit number which will represent a decimal value in the range of 0 to 16 777 215, i.e. $0 - (2^{24} - 1)$. The relative weightings are 1 for the least significant byte, 256 for the middle byte and 65 536 for the most significant byte. Hence the hex number.

$$14 \quad 3A \quad FF$$

is equivalent to

$$(20 \times 65\,536) + (58 \times 256) + (255 \times 1)$$
$$= 1\,325\,823 \text{ decimal}$$

The converse of translating decimal numbers into hex numbers is performed by sub-dividing the numbers and the remainder quantity if necessary, by 256^n where n represents the byte position.

Example Convert the decimal number 43119 into a binary and a hex representation. Observation indicates that the number can be accommodated on two bytes. Hence the most significant byte and the least significant byte are

$$44\,119/256 = 168(\text{MSB}) \text{ remainder } 111(\text{LSB})$$

Hence the binary form is

$$1010 \quad 1000 \quad 0110 \quad 1111$$

and the hex form is

$$A \quad 8 \quad 6 \quad F$$

Some common bit patterns are listed below:

Binary	Decimal	Hexadecimal
11111111	255	FF
1 00000000	256	100
100 00000000	1024	400
1000 00000000	2048	800
10000 00000000	4096	1000
11111111 11111111	65535	FFFF

A large number of bytes is usually referred to in terms of kilo (K), or mega (M), where 1 K is $2^{10} = 1024$ and 1 M is $2^{20} = 1\,048\,576$. Thus the number of bytes in 64K is 65 536.

In the binary system, negative numbers are denoted by assigning the most significant bit of the number as the sign bit. A 1 is used to represent a negative value and a 0 a positive value. Thus in a signed binary notation for an 8-bit number the format is

sign	msb						lsb
B_7	B_6	B_5	B_4	B_3	B_2	B_1	B_0

The range of decimal values is now $+127$ to 0 and -1 to -128 as compared with 0 to 255 in direct binary.

The two's complement technique, which is used almost exclusively in microprocessor-based systems, is utilized to represent signed binary negative numbers. Positive numbers are represented as previously indicated with the MSB of the number being a 0.

The technique is best illustrated by means of an example to represent say -7 as a signed binary value:

$+7$ as an 8 bit binary number is	0000 0111
complement	1111 1000
Add 1 to the complement	$+1$
Result	1111 1001

Hence -7 in decimal is represented by F9 in hex using the two's complement method for signed binary conversion. The conversion from signed binary to decimal is performed in the same way.

Example Convert the 16-bit signed binary number presented as A000 in hex into the decimal equivalent.

A000 is:	1010 0000	0000 0000	in binary

It should be noted that the MSB is a 1 which denotes a negative number.

Complement	0101 1111	1111 1111
Add 1		1
Result	0110 0000	0000 0000

Hence the decimal number is

$$-[(256 \times 96) + (0)] = -24\,576$$

It should be noted that the rules for binary arithmetic addition are:

$$0 + 0 = 0$$
$$0 + 1 = 1$$
$$1 + 0 = 1$$
$$1 + 1 = 0 \text{ and CARRY } 1$$

The CARRY denotes that an additional 1 is added to the next most significant bit in the binary group.

8.3 MICROCOMPUTER ARCHITECTURE

The function of a computer is to execute a series of stored instructions according to specified rules. The instructions are referred to as the computer program and this generally performs arithmetic and logical operations on a set of data. The computer system consists of two parts; hardware and software. The hardware element comprises all the electronic circuits and mechanical devices, and the software comprises the programs which are to be processed by the hardware.

Although the technology associated with digital computers is continually progressing, whether they be mainframe, minicomputer or microcomputer, the general organization has basically remained unchanged for several decades. The architectural features of microcomputers are similar but not necessarily identical. The features are invariably related to the particular family of microprocessor to which the microcomputer belongs and the design and organization of the constituent elements may differ considerably from one model to another.

A computer system based on a microprocessor is termed a microcomputer and the system consists of the microprocessor plus whatever additional elements are required to make it function in any given situation. Due to the variety of applications possible, the physical appearance can change considerably. This is evident when considering microprocessor-based controllers in the form of a personal computer (PC), a programmable logic controller (PLC), or a single-chip microcomputer, or microcontroller (SCM). There is, however, irrespective of appearance, a basic norm for a microcomputer with respect to its internal structure.

System Structure

The main constituents of the microcomputer system are the microprocessor, the memory and the input/output (I/O) interface. These three elements of hardware, which exist in integrated circuit form, are connected by three buses. The buses carry digital information between the units in a binary format. Their functions are to communicate:

1. the data associated with the processing function of the microprocessor (this is termed the data bus);
2. the address of a specific memory location for the accessing of stored data (this is termed the address bus);
3. the control actions related to the microprocessor and the memory devices (this is termed the control bus).

This basic arrangement of the three units with the interconnecting buses is shown in Fig. 8.1. It should be noted that this configuration indicates the I/O connected into the system in a similar manner to that of the memory devices and this is referred to as a 'memory mapped' I/O organization. An alternative is to connect the microprocessor directly to the I/O interface with a dedicated bus structure. This is referred to as a 'dedicated', or 'port addressed', I/O organization.

The data bus is used to transport a computer word between the memory, or I/O interface, to and from the microprocessor. While typical word lengths in PCs are 16 or 32 bits today,

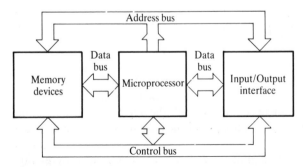

Figure 8.1 A typical microcomputer system.

microcontrollers may have words of only 4 or 8 bits. Each wire in the bus carries a binary signal (a 0 or a 1), and an 8-bit data bus is numbered as:

D_0 first data bus wire or least significant bit (LSB)
D_1 second data bus wire
⋮   ⋮
D_7 eighth data bus wire or most significant bit (MSB)

The larger the data bus the more powerful the computer with respect to speed and computing capability.

The address bus is used to provide an address for the memory to select a particular location for connection to the data bus. In a 'memory mapped' I/O arrangement the address bus may also be used to select individual input or output ports where the binary signals can be connected to external devices. Normally the address bus is an output from the microprocessor and the address data travels from the microprocessor to the memory. A typical 8-bit microcomputer has a 16-bit wide address bus with the wires numbered as A_0, A_1, A_2, . . . , A_{15}. This size of bus can access $2^{16} = 2^6 \times 2^{10} = 64K$ bytes $= 65\,536$ 8-bit data locations. Generally, 16-bit machines have an address bus with 20 wires giving 1M byte of addressable locations. When a particular memory location is selected, or enabled by placing its address on the bus, all other locations are deselected or disenabled. Thus the microprocessor communicates with one location at a time.

The control bus comprises the set of signals required to synchronize the operations of the separate elements of the microcomputer. For example, it is necessary for the microprocessor to inform the support devices in the system whether it needs to read data from an input device, or whether it needs to write data to an output device. This signal is referred to as the READ/ WRITE or $R/\overline{W}$ line. A logic 1 output from the microprocessor informs the system that a READ operation is to be performed from the location whose address is currently on the address bus. A logic 0 is indicative of a WRITE operation and this active low condition is illustrated by placing a horizontal bar above the $\overline{W}$ in the definition of the READ/WRITE control bus line, i.e. $R/\overline{W}$. Some I/O elements in the system can send signals to the microprocessor via the control bus and examples of this are the RESET and interrupts, which enable the system to be reset to some specific start condition or respond appropriately to some external event.

The most important signals on the control bus are the system clock signals, which generate the time intervals during which all system operations take place. The clock is crystal controlled and produces an on/off signal that repeats continuously. Typical frequencies are within the range 1 to 30 MHz with a corresponding period of 1 to 0.0333 µs. The circuitry is usually built into the microprocessor and all actions such as fetching information and carrying out instructions are synchronized to this precise time source.

The physical form of a bus standard is represented by its mechanical and electrical characteristics. Such information as card dimensions, input and output pin-out connections, signal levels and loading capability are specified. Standard buses for microcomputers operate under such names as Euro-bus, Microchannel, Multibus, S-100 bus, STD bus, STE bus and PC bus.

Address Decoding

Excluded from the units indicated in Fig. 8.1 are the ICs related to how the microprocessor can fetch or send information to the correct location. This requires a logic circuit which decodes the address bus signals and selects the appropriate piece of hardware for communication. When the correct address appears on the bus the output from the decoding circuit changes to the logic level (usually a 0), necessary to activate the device which is to supply or receive data. This signal is generally called a chip select pulse (CS) or a device select pulse (DS).

A decoder is a combinational logic circuit which will decode an n-bit binary code. It has 2^n output lines and activates the output signals as a function of the state of the n-bit code applied at the input. A 2-bit code can encode up to four elements of information and a 3-bit code up to eight. Decoders are commercially available as an IC package and a typical example available from the 74 series of logic devices is the 74 LS138 which is a 3-to-8 decoder, i.e. a 3-bit input and an 8-bit output.

In a memory-mapped I/O the address decoder enables the I/O device by enabling its chip select (CS) input when the correct address is on the address bus. Data is then read or written as appropriate. If the R/$\overline{\text{W}}$ signal is high then a read operation takes place (i.e. read the state of an input port). If the R/$\overline{\text{W}}$ signal is low then a write operation takes place (i.e. output data to an output port).

The Microprocessor

The microprocessor IC package is the heart of the system. It contains a host of electronic devices and provides an almost infinite flexibility in application. The basic simple tasks that it is capable of performing can be executed quickly according to a specified sequence of instructions related to the solution of a particular problem. It is generally referred to as the 'central processor unit' or CPU, and it has two basic functions. Primarily it is responsible for executing arithmetic and logic operations which involves the handling of the binary data being processed. Additionally it controls the timing and sequence of operations in the microcomputer system. In addition to the arithmetic and logic unit (ALU) and the control unit, the CPU contains a number of registers in which data manipulation can take place. The term 'register' is used to denote a set of electronic switches which can store bits until such time as they are required. They are somewhat similar to memory locations except that they are inside the microprocessor itself. Their function extends beyond simply storing data since they participate in the role of program execution. The internal arrangement of a typical microprocessor is shown in Fig. 8.2.

The ALU is responsible for performing the actual data manipulation operations. The arithmetic functions include binary addition, subtraction, and in some cases multiplication and division. The logic functions are AND, OR, NOT and exclusive OR. The unit comprises a number of circuits organized to define an arrangement of logic gates. The gates accept binary inputs and supply outputs appropriate to the program instruction codes. An instruction which specifies a simple addition of two numbers arranges for each number to be fed to the necessary ALU gate inputs. The gates in this case are arranged as a binary adder circuit and produce an output result from the addition process. The numbers are represented in binary format as previously outlined in Sec. 8.2.

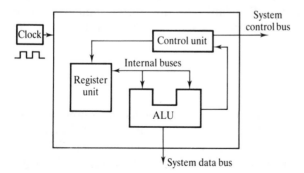

Figure 8.2 Internal arrangement of a typical microprocessor.

The control unit within the microprocessor controls the timing of operations within the system. A major part of its function is to generate the timing signals required to *fetch* a program instruction from memory and *execute* it. The process of fetching and executing an instruction is referred to as the instruction cycle. The CPU hardware that executes instructions must wait until the instruction is fetched, decoded and the ALU set up to perform the required operation. A lot of time is spent in waiting for instructions to be fetched. The design of the Intel 16-bit processors has eliminated this wasted time by dividing the CPU into two independent functional units. These are the bus interface unit (BIU) which fetches the instruction from memory and the execution unit (EU) which executes previously fetched instructions. After having completed an execution the next instruction is immediately available without delays caused by instruction fetching.

The register unit within the processor contains a group of registers which hold the internal data that the processor is currently using while executing the program. This information includes the state of the processor and a program counter (PC), or instruction pointer (IP), to allow the processor to keep track of its current position in the program. From the programmer's viewpoint the most important register in the chip is the accumulator (A) since it is involved in all the data transfer functions associated with conducting arithmetic and logic operations. A description of the various registers in the Intel 8086 and their specific function is given in Sec. 9.3, on 8086 assembly language programming.

The programming model of the 8-bit 6502 microprocessor, with respect to register availability, is shown in Fig. 8.3, while that for the 16-bit 8086 is dealt with in Sec. 9.3.

There are numerous different types of microprocessors, far more than is generally appreciated. However, a few have achieved particular recognition via the personal computer market. The common 8-bit devices are:

1. The MOS-Technology 6502 used in the Commodore PET, the Apple and the BBC microcomputer.
2. The Zilog Z80 used in Cromenco, Tandy, and Sinclair ZX81 and Spectrum machines.
3. The Intel 80X86/8088 used in IBM PCs and compatibles.
4. The Motorola 68000 and later developments used in the Apple MacIntosh microcomputer.

Memory Devices

The microcomputer system must include memory devices to store binary data. The data may represent program instruction codes, numbers or operands to be used in computation, and the results of computation. The memory takes the form of one or more integrated circuits

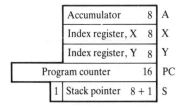

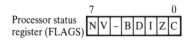

Figure 8.3 Programming model for the 6502 microprocessor.

depending upon how much is required and it may be regarded as a block of pigeon holes with each holding a byte of data. In order to locate the correct piece of information, each has to have a unique address. The size of memory available within a system is determined by the number of electrical connection lines in the address bus controlled by the microprocessor. This is generally 64K for 8-bit systems and upwards of 1M for 16-bit and above.

If data can be written to a memory device, as well as being read from it under program control, then the device is referred to as random access memory, or simply RAM. It can be further classified as either static or dynamic and this refers to the way that the memory cell is constructed. Static devices are addressed only when data is written or read. With dynamic devices it is essential that the entire RAM be refreshed frequently. Dynamic devices require less space than their static equivalent and also use less power. RAM type memory is volatile and held data is lost when the power supply is withdrawn. Usually, with microprocessor-based industrial controllers, the RAM has a battery backup so that data will not be lost if the main power supply was to fail. This type of memory is normally used as a general notepad facility for the temporary storage of data prior to transference to a more permanent media.

The memory device which is only capable of being read is referred to as read only memory, or ROM. This is also random access but attempting to write new information into ROM is not possible. The idea of ROM is that of a secure information store which, once configured, cannot be overwritten. Programs that are known to be satisfactory are put into ROM at the manufacture stage. The quantity produced must be high for economic reasons and the data codes cannot be changed. In most microcomputer systems an initialization program, which operates automatically once the machine is switched on, or when a reset button is pressed, is stored in ROM to form what is generally called a monitor program. The monitor program is designed by the manufacturer and stored in non-volatile memory so that the program is not lost when the power supply is removed. The monitor program generally permits the user to address any memory location, modify data stored in RAM, take control of the microprocessor by means of a program and return control back to the monitor as required.

The basic concept of ROM is inflexible and accordingly there have been many developments aimed at overcoming this problem. A variety of devices are available for general use, with the EPROM being the most popular programmable integrated circuit. EPROM is an erasable and programmable ROM which is supplied uncommitted, the bits of each byte all being high, and can be configured using an EPROM programmer. The process involves developing the necessary codes in a PC file and transferring the corresponding data held in RAM to an EPROM programmer connected into the PC. The uncommitted EPROM connected into the programmer is then blown to contain the codes held in the file. For all practical purposes the result is permanent. However, the device can be returned to its uncommitted state by exposing it to intense UV light in an EPROM eraser for about 20 minutes. A small visible window is fitted to the EPROM IC package for this purpose. The device is thus reusable.

One disadvantage of the EPROM is the need to completely erase the device and to reprogram it when an alteration to the code is to be made. An alternative memory device which alleviates this problem is the electrically erasable and programmable ROM, EEPROM or E^2PROM. This chip can be reprogrammed without removing it from the system, by applying an external voltage on a programming pin on the IC as necessary to alter any particular piece of information. Applications as diverse as engine management and video recorder remote control benefit from the advantages of an E^2PROM. Such benefits include the storage of user-programmed and calibrated data, and the storage of fault condition information for subsequent analysis. Every E^2PROM cell does, however, have a finite lifetime and after a number of programming and erasing operations a cell may fail to function correctly. The operating temperature and voltage can also have significant effects on the operation and life of the device.

Memory Organization

At the design stage of the complete microcomputer system the address range within available memory is allocated to specific functions appropriate to RAM and ROM requirements. This is generally referred to as the system address map or memory map. It shows the whole address range from 0000 at the bottom, to FFFF at the top of a typical 8-bit system with a 16-bit address bus. The corresponding range for a 16-bit system with a 20-bit bus is 00000 to FFFFF. Blocks or addresses are then marked into the map to show how they are used. Although a very simple idea, it is essential that users of any microprocessor-based system understand how the manufacturer has utilized the available memory. A typical memory map for an 8-bit system is shown in Fig. 8.4.

The operating system, which ensures that the facilities of the machine are coordinated, is located at the top of the memory. This area also contains the information regarding the start address for routines which are executed at the system reset, or when an external interrupt is experienced. These locations are referred to as the reset or interrupt vectors.

Programs available to the user for developing software may also be supplied in ROM. These can take the form of translating user-prepared programs into the machine code appropriate to the particular microprocessor on which they are to be executed.

The visual display unit (VDU) screen supported by the system can also be memory mapped, with any particular location on the screen being defined by a specific memory address in the video RAM. The size of the RAM allocated to this task is dependent upon the resolution requirements for graphics applications and the number of colours supported.

The operating system requires some RAM and the user should be careful not to use any of this allocated space. Part of this memory is referred to as the system stack where data can be temporarily stored on a last in/first out basis as necessary. The system automatically uses the stack for storing the return address after the execution, for example, of code associated with a subroutine which is called within the sequencing of the main program codes. The stack area of RAM may be automatically set up by the system, or in some cases it must be declared by the user. The stack pointer is a register in the CPU which contains the address of the next available memory location in the stack. On start-up, or reset, the stack pointer is initialized to the address corresponding to the start of the stack area of RAM.

The 16-bit 8086 microprocessor uses a 20-bit address bus which can access 1Mbyte of memory. The subsequent 32-bit developments can support an addressable physical memory space of 16Mbytes with the capacity to provide up to one gigabyte (10^9) of virtual memory space for the user. The memory structure of IBM PCs and compatibles with 80X86 microprocessors is

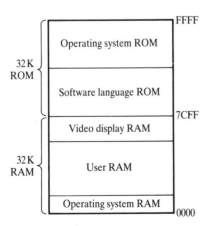

Figure 8.4 Typical memory map for an 8-bit microcomputer system.

more complex than that for typical 8-bit systems. References are often made to conventional, high, extended, expanded, real and virtual memory.

The conventional memory is the actual working memory in which the program code is executed. Owing to the design of the PC it is restricted to a maximum of 640K. High memory is the 384K between the 640K and 1M. It is normally used by the system hardware such as the video adapter and the Basic Input/Output System (BIOS). Extended memory is memory above the 1M boundary. It can only be accessed by 80286 or higher processors when switched to a protected operational mode. Expanded memory may be accessed by PC compatibles and requires a software driver. Owing to its method of application it is slower to use than extended memory. In the default real address mode the microprocessor's physical memory is 1Mbyte whereas the protected mode offers virtual memory space above those of the real address locations. The additional 16Mbytes of virtual memory behaves in a similar manner to the working base volatile RAM and can be used to store program machine codes and data. Software device drivers, usually referred to as 'memory managers', allow access to the various types of memory. The overall system memory map for a PC with 1Mbyte of addressable locations is as shown in Table 8.2. The memory is rigidly structured with certain address locations allocated for specific functions.

The PC handles its address space in 64K blocks, or segments. To address 1Mbyte, the microprocessor has to generate a 20-bit address, but to keep the chip reasonably simple the registers only handle 16-bit quantities. The segment register file holds the key to the wide address range of the 80X86 devices and introduces the concept referred to as segmented addressing. There are four segment registers available which give simultaneous access to 256Kbytes of memory at any one time, and 1Mbyte by reloading one or more of the segment registers. Each of the four segment registers has a specific function so that it may be used to form an absolute address within the 1Mbyte range. The segments are

1. The code segment (CS) for holding the instruction codes.
2. The data segment (DS) for holding the program data.
3. The stack segment (SS) for use in stack operations.
4. The extra segment (ES) gives an all purpose data area.

The 16-bit segment registers are used to point to the base of the four 64K segments of addressable memory. Hence in the real address mode of operation the absolute 20-bit address within the system is automatically computed by multiplying the appropriate segment register setting by 16 and adding the 16-bit offset.

Table 8.2 System memory map (all numbers expressed in hex).

Address Range	Function
00000-9FFFF	The first 600 bytes of RAM are used by the system
(640K)	The rest is available to the user
A0000-BFFFF	RAM
(128K)	Video display buffer
	The CGA video buffer is 32K of screen memory,
	B8000-BFFFF
C0000-DFFFF	ROM
(128K)	Reserved for I/O adapters
E0000-EFFFF	ROM
(64K)	For expansion purposes
F0000-FFFFF	ROM
(64K)	Operating system

$$\text{Absolute address} = (\text{segment value} \times 16) + \text{offset}$$

Hence the 640K of user RAM expressed in a segmented address format is

$$0000 : 0000 - 9000 : FFFF$$

and an address expressed as

$$B800 : 0900$$

is an absolute address

$$
\begin{array}{r}
B8000 \\
+0900 \\
\hline
= B8900
\end{array}
$$

For 32-bit processors such as the 80386 and above, the memory management registers provide the means of support for multi-user operating systems. The addressable memory within a PC has contributed both to its success and its universal acceptance for a large variety of applications.

Input/Output Organization

Microcomputers need to be connected to a large variety of different devices. The I/O interface enables the connection of devices such as sensors and transducers to feed data from the outside world into the microprocessor system. The I/O interface also enables the sending of data from the system for the switching of such external devices as relays and solenoids.

One method of connecting the microcomputer to an external device is to make the I/O interface appear as a memory location within the system. This is termed memory mapped I/O and if data is read from the address then it is an input to the system from the external device. Alternatively, if data is written into a memory address associated with the interface then it is an output to an external device. These data input and output locations are usually referred to as I/O ports. Most microcomputer systems are built around chips from the same family and the most popular memory mapped I/O interface device used is the 6522 versatile interface adapater (VIA), which is associated with the 8-bit 6502 microprocessor. Boards based on this chip are, however, also available for use with 80X86 machines. Such interfaces are programmable and can be set up to operate in different modes. This flexibility gives them a wide range of extra facilities which enhance the capabilities of the microcomputer. They are housed in an IC which is usually in a dual-in-line package with 40 pins and it is of comparable physical size to the microprocessor.

The 6522 VIA is a complex and powerful integrated circuit which provides a wide range of interface functions that include:

1. Two bi-directional 8-bit I/O ports, A and B.
2. Two data direction registers used for setting the ports as either input or output, DDRA and DDRB.
3. Two 16-bit programmable timer/counters, T1 and T2.
4. Four handshaking control lines, CA1, CB1, CA2 and CB2 (handshaking is a procedure for controlling the transfer of data from one device to another).

The VIA also includes the following 8-bit registers which are used in the setting up of the mode of operation for the timers and control lines:

1. The auxiliary control register (ACR).
2. The peripheral control register (PCR).
3. The interrupt flag register (IFR).
4. The interrupt enable register (IER).

The most commonly used function is the use of the ports with bits PA_0–PA_7 from port A and PB_0–PB_7 from port B. The two 8-bit DDRs are responsible for controlling the direction of data flow to and from each of these ports. Each port line is directly associated with the corresponding bit in the DDR and individual lines may be configured as either input or output according to the following convention:

A logic 0 placed in a DDR bit will assign that line in the corresponding port as input.
A logic 1 placed in a DDR bit will assign that line in the corresponding port as output.

Thus to make the 8 lines in port A all as input and the 8 lines in port B all as output, then a 0000 0000, i.e. 0 decimal, is placed in DDRA and a 1111 1111, 255 decimal, is placed in DDRB.

The timers can be set up to operate in difference modes by loading the ACR with a particular control value. The different modes include:

1. Generating a single time interval (T1 and T2).
2. Counting high to low transitions on PB_6 (T2 only).
3. Generating continuous time intervals (T1 only).
4. Producing a single pulse, or continuous pulses on PB_7 (T1 only).

The handshaking control lines can be set up to operate in different modes by loading the PCR with a particular control value. The different modes include:

1. High to low transition detection on all lines.
2. Low to high transition detection on all lines.
3. Pulse output from CA2.
4. Pulse output from CB2.

Memory mapped addressing results in a decrease in the number of locations available for RAM and ROM. Some microprocessors such as the Intel 80X86 series use a different organization known as I/O mapped port addressing. The I/O is connected to separate data and control buses and the processor has dedicated instructions which place an 8-bit address on the lower byte of the address bus and activate a control line. This allows 256 I/O addresses which are independent of memory location addresses. This method of I/O is quicker and cheaper in decoding circuitry.

The most commonly used I/O interfacing device in 80X86 family systems is the 8255 Programmable Peripheral Interface (PPI). Most of the digital and analogue I/O expansion cards available for use in PCs are based on this low-cost integrated circuit. It has 24 pins for I/O providing three ports A, B and C, that can be used in three separate modes of operation. The A and B ports are each 8 bits wide and port C, although it appears as an 8-bit wide port, is in reality two 4-bit wide ports. The 24 I/O lines are programmable in two groups of 12, designated as Group A and Group B. Group A programs port A and the upper nibble of port C, while Group B programs port B and the lower nibble of port C. The configuration of the ports as either inputs or outputs is controlled by the control register.

An I/O interface card for a PC can generally be switch-selected to some appropriate base address (BA) which defines the addresses of the ports on the dedicated I/O bus. The addresses are as follows:

$$
\begin{aligned}
\text{Port A} &= \text{BA} \\
\text{Port B} &= \text{BA} + 1 \\
\text{Port C} &= \text{BA} + 2 \\
\text{Control Register} &= \text{BA} + 3
\end{aligned}
$$

The control register is a write only register which, at power up, is initialized such that all ports are designated as inputs. This is a safety measure since, if the ports had been set as output then any connected external peripheral devices could be initialized in an unpredictable manner, which could result in a dangerous situation.

The most common mode of operation is mode 0 which sets up the ports for standard I/O applications. The function of the ports is established by writing an 8-bit control word to the control register data bits D_0–D_7. The format of the word is as follows:

D_7 = 0:   Bit set/reset active (for port C)
     = 1:   Mode definition active

D_6, D_5 = 0 0:   Group A ports selected to mode 0
     = 0 1:   Group A ports selected to mode 1
     = 1 X: Group A ports selected to mode 2
           (X = '0' or '1')

D_4 = 0:   Port A set for output
     = 1:   Port A set for input

D_3 = 0:   Port C (upper nibble) set for output
     = 1:   Port C (upper nibble) set for input

D_2 = 0:   Group B ports selected to mode 0
     = 1:   Group B ports selected to mode 1

D_1 = 0:   Port B set for output
     = 1:   Port B set for input

D_0 = 0:   Port C (lower nibble) set for output
     = 1:   Port C (upper nibble) set for input

Example Establish the control word which is to be placed in the control register of an 8255PPI in order to establish standard I/O with port A as input and ports B and C as outputs.
Set up mode 0 for both Group A and Group B. The control word is

D7	D6	D5	D4	D3	D2	D1	D0
1	0	0	1	0	0	0	0

Thus a value of 144 decimal, or 90 hex, is to be placed into the control register to configure the ports as specified.

Mode 1 is often referred to as strobed I/O and is used to set up independent 8-bit I/O buses with handshaking capabilities. Ports A and B provide the data buses whilst port C provides the handshaking lines. Mode 2 provides the facility of a strobed bi-directional bus mode using Group A. Port A becomes bi-directional and allows data to be transmitted or received through the same 8 bits. The upper nibble of port C is used for the handshaking lines and port B can be used in either Mode 0, or Mode 1, within the same arrangement if required.

Interrupts

In the operation of a microcomputer system it is essential that the processor can respond to requests for service from external devices as required. These requests are generally received in an 'asynchronous' manner. Asynchronous is a communications protocol where information can be transmitted at an arbitrary unsynchronized point in time without synchronization or reference to a timer or clock. The two techniques used to provide this service are referred to as 'polling' and 'interrupt'.

Polling is a means of attracting the attention of the processor which then acts accordingly. In this arrangement the input ports are checked regularly by the program at designated intervals to determine whether any connected device needs attention. If this is the case then an appropriate subroutine is activated. A program with an embedded polling routine contains instructions that poll periphral hardware devices and perform all other tasks. The appropriate program can be written in any programming language using normal programming skills. The method is basically simple, but has the disadvantage that the processor must always be able to execute the entire loop fast enough to be able to keep up with the demands of the peripherals. If too many devices are to be serviced then the polling routine loop may occasionally fail.

An alternative peripheral servicing technique is to use interrupts which utilize sophisticated circuitry within the processor itself. When the external device requires attention it applies a change in logic level to a special interrupt request pin on the microprocessor chip. When this occurs the CPU completes the execution of the current instruction in the main program then control is transferred to the execution of an interrupt service routine appropriate to the external device. This routine behaves very much like a subroutine within a program except that it is initiated by hardware rather than called from within the software.

It is important that the interrupt does not lead to a loss of data and an interrupt handling routine must be incorporated into the software. This includes the storing on the stack of the state of all the processor registers and the last address accessed in the main program. At the end of the interrupt service routine the contents of the stack are restored to the processor so that it can continue execution from where it was interrupted.

Hardware interrupt logic generally includes three characteristically different types:

1. The IRQ, or INTR, interrupt which can be enabled or disenabled by the setting of an interrupt flag in the processor status, or flag register. This usually requires knowledge of assembly language programming although some high-level languages, such as C, provide interrupt handling capabilities.
2. The NMI, non-maskable interrupt, which cannot by definition be disenabled and must execute the appropriate service routine when activated. This is given priority over the maskable interrupts.
3. RES is the system reset and when this is activated, usually by a logic 0, then all activity in the system stops and a system start-up routine is executed.

When any of the above service routines are to be executed then the start address of the code must somehow be specified. Since the interrupt is initiated by an external event, and is not called from within a program, then an alternative method in specifying the start address of the service routine must be employed. The mechanism for this is to store the start address in dedicated locations in memory. These locations are termed 'vectors' and two locations are required to hold a 16-bit address. They are usually held in ROM, with the reset vectors in 8-bit systems often residing in the last two locations—FFFE and FFFF. The exact details of what happens when a system is first switched on, or reset, vary from one computer to another although the general principles are very much the same and apply to all. When the reset mechanism is activated, typically by applying a logic 0 to the microprocessor reset pin, the contents of the reset vectors are loaded. These vectors specify the start address of the routine which is to be executed and the CPU starts to run the program. The same process applies to the IRQ/INTR and NMI interrupts.

In the case of a PC, the interrupting device supplies an 8-bit 'interrupt code' which indicates the type of interrupt that is taking place. This code references a look-up table of interrupt vector addresses which point to the start address of up to 256 interrupt handling routines. The interrupt display table (the IDT) is located right at the bottom of RAM. For example, the NMI is referenced as interrupt number 2 (INT 02), and the IDT gives a start address for the NMI routine displayed as four bytes—offset low and high bytes, followed by the segment low and high bytes.

The idea of an interrupt, in which the normal operation of a program execution is suspended and some special action taken, is a useful concept but need not necessarily be initiated by an external event. The method of calling a routine resident within the system memory by means of a special instruction, other than a 'jump to subroutine' at a specified start address, is known as a software interrupt. The most common applications of this facility is the break instruction which is useful for implementing breakpoints when debugging a program. In a PC, a breakpoint can be inserted into the program codes with the one byte long software interrupt call of INT 3. Another useful PC-based software interrupt is INT 21 (21 in hex), which can terminate the execution of a machine code program and return control to the disk operating system (DOS).

It must be emphasized, however, that using interrupts is not always preferable to polling and the optimum strategy is dependent upon the application.

Software Considerations

Computers process information according to a sequential list of instructions termed a program. The only way that the early computers could be programmed was to enter the binary 0s and 1s by hand into the memory. A program in this format is referred to as machine code. This method of programming was obviously tedious and the next step involved the use of mnemonics that represented, in readable form, a list of instructions that could be translated on a one-to one basis by a program termed an 'assembler'. The mnemonics and corresponding machine code vary for each microprocessor family. For example, consider the instructions necessary to place a binary value of 1111 1111, i.e. 255 decimal or FF hex, into a specified memory location.

For the Intel 80X86 family the instructions

$$\text{MOV} \quad \text{AL, FFH}$$
$$\text{MOV} \quad \text{[400H], AL}$$

will transfer the data into a memory location defined by an offset of 0400 hex relative to the code segment set up (see section on 'memory organization' within this chapter). The mnemonic codes translate directly to

$$\text{B0 FF A2 00 04}$$

This is in contrast to the 6502 microprocessor, which has a corresponding set of instructions as

LDA#FF

STA 0400

that translate directly to

A9 FF 8D 00 04

Languages like these are called low-level or assembly languages, and they are still used for programming microcomputers. The main attraction of using machine code for a particular application is its speed of operation and efficiency in memory usage. It is more common, however, as appropriate, to use languages which provide a high level of resemblance to the English language and mathematical notation. These so called high-level languages make programming easier by allowing the programmer to describe what the program is to do without having to make reference to the internal operation of the microcomputer system. Program instructions written in these high-level languages, termed source code, must still be converted into the machine code format peculiar to the microprocessor being used. Such translation programs are termed 'interpreters' or 'compilers'.

The language BASIC is the most commonly used interpreted high-level language. The PC versions are BASICA and the compatible version GW-BASIC. The source code consists of line-numbered instructions which are written in an understandable form. During the execution of the program, using the 'RUN' command, each line is converted in turn into machine code and executed. No complete machine code translation of the complete source code program is formed and the execution is relatively slow. One advantage of the interpretation method is the ease with which the program instructions can be altered by simply replacing, editing, adding or deleting lines of code.

The majority of the high-level languages are of the compiled variety and include languages such as ADA, C, FORTH, FORTRAN and PASCAL. The source codes are first developed using a wordprocessor/editor according to the syntax, or specified rules of the language. The compilor program is then used to translate the source program into a machine code format which is termed an 'object code'. This in turn is then linked to language library facilities and any associated subroutines which are called from within the program. The resulting code is now in an executable machine code state. The main advantage of compiled high-level language programs is the transportability of the codes between different makes of microcomputers with the same family of microprocessor. The debugging of the program, which invariably involves the altering of the source code, can prove to be somewhat tedious but nevertheless it is usually well worth the effort. Compilers generally, however, produce inefficient code in terms of size and speed of execution in comparison with a pure machine code program produced from an assembler.

The choice of a computer language is a very personal thing and people who are using computer technology for specific applications become quite attached to a particular language. All high-level languages have good and bad points but the majority of engineering industrial applications still appear to be written in some dialect of BASIC. The most common being the interpreted BASICA/GW-BASIC and the compiled QuickBasic by Microsoft. BASIC generally comes with the software available for use with a PC. The trend recently has been a move towards the language C which offers some of the advantages associated with an assembly language. A brief overview of some of the more popular high-level languages used in engineering applications follows.

ADA (after Ada Lovelace) Programming in ADA is quite different from most of the other high-level languages. Its introduction in the 1980s was due to the requirement of the US Department of Defense to develop and maintain software for embedded computer systems. Embedded systems are used in both military and civilian applications where they are part of a much larger system. Typical examples include spacecraft, military aircraft, missiles, traffic control, robots and process systems. With no language standards for military systems and the widespread use of numerous languages, compatibility was a major problem. Hence the need arose for some commonality of software and the starting point for the new language ADA was to use a PASCAL syntax. Strict criteria for compilers were specified in order to achieve good portability of software. For this reason few compilers are available and the use of the language is almost entirely restricted to US military contracts. Although ADA has been developed specifically for control applications, it is slightly cumbersome for general use and has thus lost ground to other languages.

BASIC (beginner's all-purpose symbolic instruction code) The language was developed in the 1960s in Dartmouth, New Hampshire, USA and now appears in a variety of interpreted (I) and compiled (C) formats. Some of the more popular versions include BASICA/GWBASIC (I), BBCBASIC (I), TURBOBASIC/POWER BASIC (C) and Microsoft's QUICKBASIC (C). The early BASICs were somewhat restrictive in available facilities for the writing of concise and well structured programs but the more up-to-date versions are quite powerful and can equally well handle the manipulation of alpha-numeric string data as well as numerical data for number crunching exercises. BASIC is commonly used in engineering applications and specific interpreted dialects are available for control applications such as CONTROL BASIC and RT-BASIC. Modern compiled-type BASICs are equally appropriate to most engineering applications as the other popular high-level languages.

Memory reads and writes are easily performed in BASIC using the keywords PEEK and POKE. The format of the read memory content command is

$$I = PEEK \text{ (memory address)}$$

which returns the integer value for I in the range $0 < I < 255$. The corresponding instruction to place a byte of data in memory is

$$POKE \text{ memory address, value}$$

where 'value' is within the range 0–255.

When applied to a PC with segmented addressing, it is first necessary to set up the segment address with a 'DEF SEG' definition and then specify the offset as required with the PEEK or POKE command.

Example Define the code segment to commence in RAM at a hex address of &H1000 (the &H is used to denote a hexadecimal number) and insert the data &HAA into an offset address of zero.
The instructions in BASIC are

```
DEF SEG = &H1000
POKE 0,&HAA
```

This puts AA hex into an absolute address of 10000 hex, which is equivalent to placing 170 decimal into a decimal address of 65536.

The data can then be read with the instructions

PRINT PEEK(0) which returns a 170 on the screen

or

PRINT HEX$(PEEK(0)) which returns AA

The PEEK and POKE instructions also apply to the setting up of ports, the reading of the status of a port, and the outputting of data to a port in a memory mapped I/O arrangement. For a dedicated port addressed I/O the corresponding keywords are INP and OUT. The format of the read port status command is

I = INP(port address)

and for outputting a byte from a port

OUT port address,value

Example Write the instruction in BASIC which would configure on 8255 PPI as port A input, port B output and port C output. The base address is set as &H1B0.

The address of the control register used to configure the ports is &H1B3 and, as shown previously for the arrangement specified, a value of &H90 must be placed into this address. The instruction in BASIC is

OUT &H1B3,&H90

All the foregoing instructions are appropriate and easily implemented for data acquisition and control applications using a microcomputer.

C The language C is generally growing in popularity for both commercial and industrial applications. It is a language which cannot be truly classified as either high-level or low level. It has all the features expected of a high-level language but it additionally has the speed and direct access to microprocessor-related hardware that is usually associated with a low-level language. There are a number of versions of C available but the accepted standard is that of Kernighan and Ritchie. The basic language is quite small compared with other languages. Features such as input/output, mathematical functions and supporting graphics are not contained within the C compilor but are available in associated library routines which can be included by declaration within a program as necessary. In practice this philosophy has worked well and results in efficiently produced machine codes with an emphasis on programmer flexibility.

FORTH FORTH is an interpreted threaded language developed specifically for control applications. The instructions which constitute an application are stored as a list of previously defined routines. This list is threaded together during the entry of source code from either the computer keyboard or the mass storage buffers. The process of producing the list is often termed compilation, but this is not strictly correct since the result of the true compiling of source code produces pure machine code. It is a most unusual language since arithmetic calculations do not follow traditional methodologies. Before calculations can be made it is first necessary to understand how the stack operates in FORTH. Most high-level languages use one or more stacks for their internal operations but they are generally designed so that the user does not have to understand how the stack actually functions. FORTH allows the user full control of the values stored in the stack and their manipulation.

FORTH is based on a memory-resident dictionary of software procedures called words and its essence of operation is to work its way through a hierarchy of the routines of words until it reaches the fundamental definitions that can be executed. Programs can be typed in at the keyboard and executed directly but to save programs for execution at a later date the mass storage buffers and the FORTH editor must be used. Unlike other languages FORTH performs only a limited number of error checks. The errors detected are those which are most likely to cause the system to crash if allowed to pass undetected. The main reason for the lack of error checking is that it would slow FORTH down. Since the main use of FORTH is in time critical control situations, this would be prohibitive.

FORTRAN (FORmula TRANslator) This language was one of the first to be written and has remained popular in engineering number crunching applications. Although there have been successive improvements to the language over the years, such as FORTRAN 77, it has now somewhat lost ground to developments such as C. With the early FORTRANs the basic input/ output of numerical data was quite cumbersome. This has been improved with the later versions which allow a free format entry and exit of data. The main strength of FORTRAN is it's ability to execute a wide range of mathematical operations. It has always been regarded as a language which is more suited to sicientific applications but is not too appropriate for system control work. With the exception of BASIC, FORTRAN has probably been the most widely used and supported high-level language and one of its main features is its high degree of portability. A vast array of subroutines for specific mathematical tasks, such as the numerical solution of differential equations, are readily available for linking with main source programs. This greatly facilitates the role of the programmer who can concentrate on the structure of the program to solve the problem, rather than get involved in detailed mathematical manipulation routines.

PASCAL (after Blaise Pascal) PASCAL originated in 1969 and its structure was influenced by the then popular language ALGOL. All variables and constants are declared at the start of the program and the structure adopted results in a modular and easily read source code. The well-ordered software is relatively easily debugged and PASCAL programs help keep maintenance costs down considerably. PASCAL is a language which helps gain more insight into methods of organizing large programs and managing software projects. Although generally regarded as a good educational language, there are deficiencies with respect to some I/O handling which is a disadvantage in many engineering applications. While it is readily applicable for number crunching and data processing, it is rarely used for the control of systems. For this reason the language MODULA, and the revised version MODULA-2, were developed. The syntax is similar to that of PASCAL and these languages readily support the implementation of modules written by different programmers. There are very few variations available and the codes are generally portable.

It should be noted that irrespective of the language used, the design and implementation of a computer program should include the study of the problem specification, the formulation of the algorithm, and an appraisal of the hardware. This is then followed by the preparation of the source code in the particular choice of language to be used, with subsequent translation into the machine code specific to the microprocessor-related hardware. The most important aspect is undoubtedly a thorough understanding of the problem to be solved and effort expended at this stage will facilitate the latter stages of the exercise, which are more concerned with software development. Next in the line of importance is the algorithm. This is the procedure that the microprocessor uses to determine the output requirements in response to the input conditions. The process is one of breaking the problem down into a series of small steps until a detailed strategy for solving the overall problem is produced. One of the most widely used methods of illustrating the operation of a computer program is the flowchart which shows the step-by-step sequence to be carried out, and the way in which the program passes from one task to the next. Only then, after the problem is thoroughly understood and a strategy formulated for a solution, should the development of the actual program codes commence.

8.4 DIGITAL DATA COMMUNICATION STANDARDS

Various standards have been drawn up to define the protocol for the transmission of binary data from within the microcomputer bus structure to external devices such as monitors, printers, plotters and other peripheral equipment. Most microcomputers are already equipped with these facilities and manufacturers of data measurement and control instrumentation usually offer an external communication port as an added extra.

The most commonly accepted standards are those defined by the American Electronic Industries Association (EIA) and the Institute of Electrical and Electronics Engineers (IEEE). The standards fall into the two main categories of 'serial' and 'parallel' data communication. The difference between the two relates to the number of bits of information transmitted simultaneously between the communicating devices. The serial method is the slower of the two, where the bits denoting the characters of information travel sequentially along a single path. In the parallel method, the data word is sent as a parallel code, invariably 8 bits wide, resulting in a bit parallel, byte serial transmission of information. The parallel transmission is much faster than serial transmission, but requires more hardwired connections in the transmission interface.

In a typical microcomputer system the data transmission interface between the keyboard, or mouse, and the computer is a serial link. The data transmission interface between the computer and a printer, or plotter, is usually a parallel link. For normal computing and wordprocessing, the user need not be concerned, or even aware, of these communication standards. For instrumentation and control applications, however, it is often necessary to set up these communication interfaces in a particular way. It becomes necessary therefore to have a basic knowledge on how the interfaces work, how they can be set up for particular applications and how they can be controlled.

Serial Communication

In its simplest form serial transmission needs only a pair of cables (the signal path and an earth return), which minimizes the cost. Data within a computer, however, is stored in a parallel form which has to be converted into a serial form for transmission. Conversely, data received over a serial line has to be reformatted into parallel form before being processed in a computer. The basis of these conversion processes is a shift register into which data is loaded in parallel and then clocked out serially, or into which data is clocked serially and when full is read out as a parallel word.

A number of special integrated circuits are marketed to perform the conversion from the parallel data format found inside a computer system, to the serial data format for transmission. The common devices are:

UART   – universal asynchronous receiver transmitter
ACIA   – asynchronous communications interface adaptor
USART – universal synchronous/asynchronous receiver transmitter
SIO   – serial input output device

The basic function of all of these devices is depicted in Fig. 8.5.

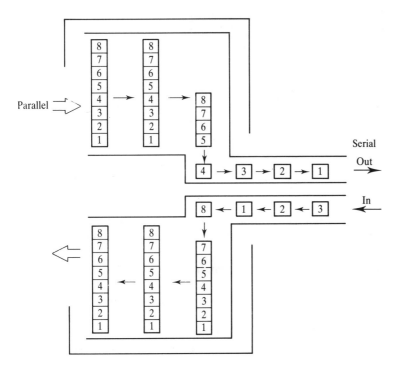

Figure 8.5 UART—universal asynchronous receiver transmitter.

The shift register (or a multiplexer) feeds parallel data, sent to an output buffer, out as a serial stream of bits. When receiving, the bits from a serial stream are collected to form a single byte at an input buffer. Along with these basic features, most UARTs support a number of additional control lines to ensure the safe transfer of data.

While there have been several communication standards, the most widely used is EIA RS232C. The Recommended Standard, number 232, revision C, RS232C, has become the accepted standard for serial transmission. Originally this was defined to connect a terminal to a modem (modulator/demodulator) to provide a universal method of connecting computer peripherals to a telephone line. It has, however, been adopted for connecting terminals into a computer system. RS232C defines a 25-way plug–socket in which every pin is allocated a signal whose meaning and direction are written into the standard. Pin 2, for example, is given the label XMIT DATA and is meant to convey information from the terminal to the modem. RS232C also defines the electrical characteristics for the signals in terms of voltage levels, maximum transmission line length and speeds of data transfers (Table 8.3). In practice the voltages associated with the two logic levels have been standardized on ± 12 V.

Table 8.3 Primary characteristics of the RS232C interface.

Parameter	Value
Maximum line length	100 feet
Maximum bits/second	2×10^4
Data '1' -marking	-1.5 to -36 V
Data '0' -spacing	$+1.5$ to $+36$ V

The Modem should have a FEMALE connector and the terminal a MALE. The EIA has never defined the type of connector to be used with RS232C, but the industry has itself standardized on the 25-way D-type.

The Comité Consultatif International Téléphonique et Télégraphique (CCITT) has established standards that correspond to RS232C. Whilst these standards, CCITT V.24 and CCITT V.28, are very similar to RS232C they are not identical. By not making use of all the circuits defined in both RS232C and CCITT V.24, a data communications interface can conform to both RS232C and CCITT V.24 without any modification to the interface. The circuits which are utilized vary with different applications and with different modems.

The main pin functions are listed in the table as follows:

Function Table

Pin 1   Protective ground. Electrical equipment frame and AC power ground.

Pin 2   Transmitted data. Data originated by the terminal to be transmitted via the sending modem.

Pin 3   Received data. Data from the receiving modem in response to analogue signals transmitted from the sending modem.

Pin 4   Request to Send. Indicates to the sending modem that the terminal is ready to transmit data.

Pin 5   Clear to Send. Indicates to the terminal that its modem is ready to transmit data.

Pin 6   Data Set Ready. Indicates to the terminal that its modem is not in a test mode and that modem power is ON.

Pin 7   Signal ground. Establishes common reference between the modem and the terminal.

Pin 20 Data Terminal Ready. Indicates to the modem that the associated terminal is ready to receive and transmit data.

In practice it is rare to find a secondary channel in use. When used as a communications channel between a computer and a terminal, it is often found that only the four handshake lines, Request to Send, Clear to Send, Data Terminal Ready and Data Set Ready, are used to control information flow. The simplest interface for a send/receive terminal uses only Signal ground, Transmit data and Receive data. Equipment at one end of the line might, however, expect to see Clear to Send at the correct signal level before it allows data to be sent. If the signal is not produced by the system on the opposite end of the cable, then it has to be hardwired into the connector to fool the device that it has received a handshake signal from the other end. The device sends out a handshake signal which is linked back into its own connector as a received handshake to its signal. Both connectors may be terminated in this way, which is referred to as the auto loop-back connection. Figure 8.6 illustrates this simplest of RS232C interconnections.

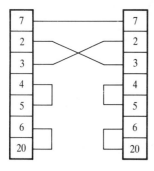

Figure 8.6 Auto loop-back connections.

Serial transmission protocols RS232C provides a common means of implementing a communications channel between a computer and peripherals. Before information can be passed between two such systems, however, both must be configured to send and accept data at the same rates, and in a format which both have been programmed to accept.

The most prevalent coding technique which allows alpha-numeric and control codes to be passed between systems is the 7-bit ASCII code. With few exceptions, this is universally used for the transmission of data over serial communication links.

If we accept ASCII and implement RS232C, there only remains the problem of deciding the order in which the information is to be sent. This order is called the transmission protocol and governs not only the order in which the code for a character is sent, but also the control bits needed to synchronize both ends of the line. The receiving end has to be informed when a character begins, where it ends and also needs some means of determining if any error has occurred during transmission. There are basically two forms of transmission technique in wide use called synchronous and asynchronous transmission. The former is used for sending blocks of characters at a time over a serial line while the latter only allows one character to be sent at a time. Synchronous transmission protocols are much more complex than asynchronous, and do not apply to the RS232C standard.

Asynchronous transmission requires that an initial start bit is sent from the transmitter to the receiver to inform it that a character is about to be sent. When ASCII code is used, the 7-bit code for the character is then transmitted in reverse order. Thus the least significant bit is sent first and the most significant bit is sent last. Following these 7 bits, an error checking, or parity, bit is then sent. The way in which the parity bit is implemented differs between systems. Parity may be ignored altogether and no bit sent, or even/odd parity may be used. If, say, even parity is in use, then the transmitter counts all the logic 1 bits sent in the ASCII coded character and if they add up to an even number, then parity is sent as a logic 0 level. If, however, the bits add up to an odd number, the parity bit is sent as a logic 1 level so that the total number of logic 1 bits transmitted to the receiver is always an even number. Odd parity simply implements the converse of even parity. The single error checking bit can be used to detect all single-bit errors in transmission, but can be duped by multiple-bit errors. The receiver counts the number of logic 1 states it receives and flags an error if they disagree with the type of parity in use. After the parity bit, the line is allowed to idle for one, one and a half, or two clock periods before another character may be sent. These stop bits are a carry-over from the days when most peripherals were electro-mechanical devices which could not respond instantly to another character and needed a dwell time between them. The format for asynchronous data transmission is given in Fig. 8.7. Prior to any character being transmitted the line idles at $+12\,\text{V}$, which in RS232C represents the logic 0 state. If through some misfortune the line is severed, or becomes disconnected at either end, its potential will fall to the ground which can be detected at the receiver to indicate a line failure.

The transmitter clocks out information onto the line using its own clock, while the receiver clocks information into itself using a separate clock which conventionally runs 16 times faster. The first negative transition on the line is taken to be the start bit and the receiver counts 8 of its clock pulses and then samples the state of the line. This should place it in time half-way into the

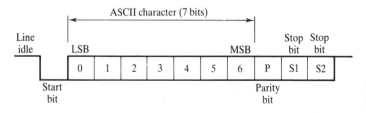

Figure 8.7 Asynchronous transmission protocol.

start bit pulse. If the receiver samples a low-voltage state, then it takes the signal to be a valid start pulse, otherwise it assumes a glitch and resets itself for a valid start pulse edge.

If a valid start pulse is detected, the receiver then counts a series of 16 pulses of its own clock which will cause it to sample the state of the line mid-way into each character bit and the parity bit. The sampled states are clocked into a shift register, which when full can be read, in parallel, into the computer system. If as an example the upper case alphabetic character 'A' is being transmitted, this has a hexadecimal code of 41 in ASCII. Assuming that even parity is being applied, then the parity bit will be sent as a logic 0 to ensure that the total number of logic 1 bits sent are even. The binary pattern for 'A' is 1000001 as a 7-bit code, which when sent in reverse order with the parity bit included forms the sequence 10000010. Viewed on an oscilloscope, the transmitted character 'A', with even parity, looks as shown on Fig. 8.8.

Baud rates The rate at which characters are transmitted is quoted in bits/second or baud. A speed of 2400 baud corresponds to $2400/11 = 218$ characters/s, since there are 11 bits required to transmit one character.

RS422 and RS423 RS232C provides a communication port which is primarily intended for short communication links of up to about 15 m. Longer links can be achieved if low-loss cables and connectors are used. Generally the total load capacitance must not exceed 2500 pF.

RS422 and RS423 are the successors to RS232C and they have extended communication distances and increased transmission speeds. RS423 is compatible with RS232C in that it uses a single transmission line. RS423, however, allows for communication over 1500 m at 9600 baud or 15 m at 100 kbaud.

Implementing an RS232C communications link It must be noted that while the voltages and signal connections for the plug are defined in the standard, the data protocol is not defined. This must therefore be known for the devices which are to be connected and can be set accordingly by software. The requirements are:

1. baud rate;
2. number of bits in the ASCII group;
3. odd, even or no parity;
4. number of stop bits.

Both the source and the destination must be set to the same mode of operation.

The IBM-PC and compatibles The serial port on the IBM-PC and compatible machines is the standard 25-way D-plug denoted as 'COM1' or 'COM2'. The IBM-PC defaults to serial transmission with 1 start bit, 7 data bits, even parity and one stop bit for baud rates other than

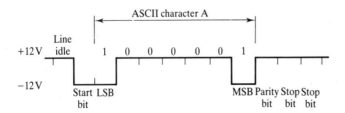

Figure 8.8 ASCII coded 'A' viewed on a serial line.

110. The format can be altered either using the MS-DOS command MODE, or the BASIC command OPEN, e.g.

MODE COM1:baud, 'o' or 'e' parity, data bits, stop bits

i.e.

MOD COM1: 9600,o,8,1

or

OPEN COM1:baud, 'o', 'e' or 'n', data bits, stop bits, FOR INPUT/OUTPUT AS X

i.e.

OPEN 'COM1:9600,n,8,1,rs,cs,ds' FOR OUTPUT AS #1

NB: The parameters rs, cs and ds are usually followed with a number to denote the number of milliseconds to delay before a 'device timeout' error is detected. By leaving these unspecified the RTS (request to send), CTS (clear to send) and DSR (data set ready) handshaking lines are disabled.

Example To set up two IBM compatible PCs where one acts as a transmitter and the other as a receiver and to send data over the serial transmission link.

Program 8.1 RS232C character transmitter program.

```
10 OPEN"COM1:9600,n,8,1,rs,cs,ds"FOR OUTPUT AS #1
20 INPUT A$
30 PRINT #1,A$
40 GOTO 20
```

Program 8.2 RS232C character receiver program.

```
10 OPEN"COM1:9600,n,8,1,rs,cs,ds"FOR INPUT AS #1
20 INPUT#1,A$
30 PRINT A$
40 GOTO 20
```

With these programs running on the transmitter and receiver, respectively, any keyboard input at the transmitter will be displayed on the screen of the receiver.

The above can be altered to send a complete computer program between the two machines. The program listing, TEST.BAS, must first of all be written and saved as an ASCII file to disk Thus:

Program 8.3 RS232C file transmitter program.

```
10 OPEN "TEST.BAS" FOR INPUT AS #2
20 OPEN"COM1:9600,n,8,1,rs,cs,ds"FOR OUTPUT AS #1
30 LINE INPUT #2,A$
40 PRINT #1,A$
50 GOTO 30
```

Program 8.4 RS232C file receiver program.

```
10 OPEN"COM1:9600,n,8,1,rs,cs,ds"FOR INPUT AS #1
20 LINE INPUT#1,A$
30 PRINT A$
40 GOTO 20
```

Using the above, the transmitted program will appear listed on the screen of the receiver. NB: LINE INPUT allows a complete line of ASCII characters up to a carriage return line feed, to be input as the ASCII string.

Parallel Communication Standards

The rate at which data can be transferred from one system to another can be dramatically increased if it is sent in a parallel format rather than serial. The complexity of the interface, and the interconnecting cabling costs, however, rapidly increase as we include more and more lines in the connecting bus. A compromise scheme may use say eight lines as a bus with a few others to control bus transfers. Such a scheme was proposed by Hewlett-Packard to interconnect test equipment and was developed by them as the Hewlett Packard Interface Bus (HPIB). The bus has come into widespread use and is alternatively known as:

- The general purpose interface bus (GPIB):IEEE-488 1975 standard which was revised in 1978 as the IEEE-488 1978 standard.
- The ANSI bus (American National Standards Institute standard MCI.1-1975).
- The IEC 625-1 standard (International Electrotechnical Commission).

The GPIB standard for parallel data transfers sets out both electrical and mechanical requirements; signal levels are TTL compatible, but the current drive requirements exceed that of any standard TTL component. However, ICs are readily available which satisfy all aspects of the standard. Data transfer rates can be up to 1 Mbit/s and up to 15 major devices can be connected onto the bus at any one time. Within each major device, up to 32 secondary addresses can be referred to. A secondary address may relate, for example, to the DC voltmeter section of a digital multimeter, while another may relate to the ohmmeter. Physically, devices connected on the bus must not be more than 4 m apart, with a maximum transmission length of 20 m, or twice the number of devices on the bus, quoted in metres, whichever is the least. Thus if only three devices are connected, the maximum transmission length reduces to 6 m. The IEEE-488 standard defines a 24-way connector, which is a combined plug and socket. These connectors are stackable and allow either a star or radial configuration of devices. It should be noted that the European standard IEC 625-1 specifies a 25-way connector, and to interconnect instruments designed to this particular standard onto an IEEE-488 bus, adaptors are necessary. The bus is intended to interconnect programmable instruments along with the bus controller, which manages all data transfers. Data transfers do not have to pass through the controller, but can be put onto the bus by one instrument and taken off it by several others under the supervision of the controller. The GPIB uses a parallel bus structure containing 16 signal lines and 8 ground lines. Each device on the bus is given a unique identity, or address.

Talkers, listeners and controllers GPIB Devices can be listeners, talkers and/or controllers. A digital voltmeter, for example, is a talker and may be a listener as well. A talker sends data messages to one or more listeners, which receive the data. The controller manages the flow of information on the GPIB by sending commands to all devices. The GPIB is a bus like an ordinary computer bus except that where a computer has its circuit cards interconnected via a backplane, the GPIB has stand-alone devices interconnected via a cable. The role of the GPIB controller can be compared to the role of the computer's CPU, but a better analogy is to compare the controller to the switching centre of a city telephone system. The switching centre (controller) monitors the communications network (GPIB). When the centre (controller) notices that a party (device) wants to make a call (send a data message) it connects the caller (talker) to the receiver (listener). The controller usually addresses, or enables, a talker and a listener before the talker can send its message to the listener. After the message is transmitted, the controller usually unaddresses both devices. Some GPIB configurations do not require a controller. For example, one device may always be a talker (called a Talk-only device) and there may be one or more listen-only devices. A controller is necessary when the active or addressed talker or listener must be changed. The controller function is usually handled by a computer. A large number of devices have both talk and listen capability. For example, a programmable multimeter may be a listener which will accept instructions selecting the required function and range, or it may be a talker, allowing it to reply with the measurement. Figure 8.9 shows a typical GPIB cluster.

GPIB signals and lines The GPIB interface system itself, Fig. 8.10, consists of 16 signal lines and 8 ground return, or shield drain lines. The 16 signal lines, discussed below, are grouped into data lines (8), handshake lines (3), and interface management lines (5). The eight data lines, DIO1 through DIO8, carry both data and command messages. All commands, and most data, use the 7-bit ASCII or ISO code set, in which case the eighth bit, DIO8, is either unused, or used for parity checking.

Handshake lines Three lines asynchronously control the transfer of message bytes between devices. The process is called a three-wire interlocked handshake and it guarantees that message bytes on the data lines are sent and received without transmission error.

NRFD (not ready for data). NRFD indicates when a device is ready, or not ready, to receive a message byte. The line is driven by all devices when receiving commands and by listeners when receiving data messages.
NDAC (not data accepted). NDAC indicates when a device has, or has not, accepted a message byte. The line is driven by all devices when receiving commands and by listeners when receiving data messages.
DAV (data valid). DAV tells when the signals on the data lines are stable (valid) and can be accepted safely by devices. The controller drives DAV lines when sending commands and the talker drives DAV lines when sending data messages.

All data transfers make use of the three handshake lines. The handshaking protocol used by these three lines ensures that valid data is not removed from the bus until all devices

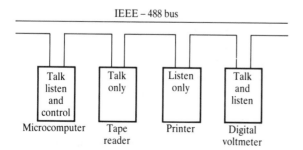

Figure 8.9 Typical GPIB group.

programmed to accept it have captured and stored it. All data transfers take place at a speed dictated by the slowest device on the bus.

Handshaking protocol A simplified handshake timing diagram for these lines is given in Fig. 8.11. The DAV line is controlled by the talker, while the NRFD and NDAC lines are controlled by the activated listeners on the bus. DAV is used to indicate when valid data has been placed on the bus. NRFD indicates when listeners are ready or not to accept data and NDAC indicates when the listeners have received and accepted the data. Assuming that the controller has set up a talker and programmed all the listeners, then all the listeners raise the NRFD line as shown by position 1 in Fig. 8.11. The talker monitors the NRFD line and when it is raised high, is aware that all listeners are ready to accept the data that the talker will place on the bus. The talker then places its data onto the bus and allows a short time interval to allow the new line states to stabilize. After this time the talker pulls the DAV line low to inform all the listeners that the data on the bus is valid. This state is shown by position 2 in Fig. 8.11. All listeners sense the DAV line going low, and pull the NRFD line low when it is ready to accept the data. After each listener has stored the data into its internal buffers, it releases the NDAC line to show that it has accepted the data. Only when the slowest listener has released the NDAC line can the sequence continue. This is indicated by position 4 in the diagram. The talker senses that the NDAC line has been pulled high (false) and raises the DAV line to show that the data on the bus is no longer valid. Each listener in turn detects the DAV line going high and drops NDAC low to acknowledge the fact that data has been removed from the bus. This is indicated by position 6 in Fig. 8.11. Each listener then raises NRFD high (false) to indicate that it is ready to receive the next byte of data send down the bus. The sequence is now complete, with all listeners waiting for the next data byte. This sequence is the essence of all data and address transfers over the bus and allows for signal propagation delays and listener processing time.

Interface management lines Five lines are used to manage the flow of information across the interface.

ATN (attention). The controller drives ATN true when it uses the data lines to send commands, and false when it allows a talker to send data messages.
IFC (interface clear). The system controller drives the IFC line to initialize the bus.
REN (remote enable). The system controller drives the REN line, which is used to place devices in remote or local program mode.
SRQ (service request). Any device can drive the SRQ line to asynchronously request service from the controller.

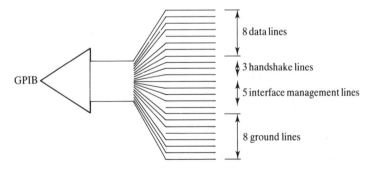

Figure 8.10 GPIB signal lines.

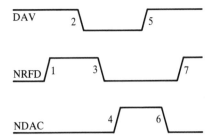

Figure 8.11 Simplified GPIB handshake procedure.

EOI (end or identify). The EOI line has two purposes. The talker uses the EOI line to mark the end of a message string. The controller uses the EOI line to tell devices to identify their response in a parallel poll.

The five interface management lines form a control bus performing a number of interface housekeeping functions. Attention (ATN) is driven only by the controller and monitored by all other devices. When true (logic 0), the interface is in the command mode with the data lines holding interface command codes or station addresses. In the false condition (logic 1), the interface is in data mode, with the active talker passing data to the active listener(s). Remote enable (REN) is another controller only output used to place a device under remote control. Service request (SRQ) acts like an interrupt line, allowing instruments that have either just completed a measurement or encountered a problem (e.g. a printer that has run out of paper) to demand attention from the controller.

Talk and listen addresses Each device on a GPIB cluster has a unique device address in the range 0 to 30. Normally this address can be selected by small in-line switches, positioned either inside or on the rear panel of the device. Corresponding to each device address are two address codes called the talk address and the listen address (Table 8.4). Prior to any transaction between a talker and listeners, the controller uses these address codes to enable the participants. The selection is carried out with the bus in command mode (i.e. ATN true), with each device keeping a lookout for its own talk or listen address code. For example, if a controller wished to set up a transaction between a paper tape reader (talker) at device address 21, a printer (listener) at device address 16, and a video display (listener) at device address 4, it would place the following code sequence on the data lines while holding ATN true:

> 55H – talk address device 21
> 30H – listen address device 16
> 24H – listen address device 4

When ATN was released by the controller, each device would adopt its proper role in the subsequent data exchange.

Commands and data From the address table it can be seen that the maximum talk and listen addresses are 5EH and 3EH, respectively. The following two codes, 5FH and 3FH, are given special functions, namely as the untalk (UNT) and the unlisten (UNL) commands. The former can be used by the controller to 'unaddress' or silence the current talker. This command is not often used since addressing any device to talk automatically unaddresses all the others. The unlisten command is, however, frequently used as a means of ensuring that only those devices meant to listen, do listen, i.e. there are no eavesdroppers left from some previous transaction. The concept of unlistening eavesdroppers is crucial to efficient operation of the bus as the data

Table 8.4 Relationship between device address and listen/talk codes.

Device address (decimal)	Listen address (hex)	Talk address (hex)
0	20	40
1	21	41
2	22	42
3	23	43
4	24	44
5	25	45
6	26	46
7	27	47
8	28	48
9	29	49
10	2A	4A
11	2B	4B
12	2C	4C
13	2D	4D
14	2E	4E
15	2F	4F
16	30	50
17	31	51
18	32	52
19	33	53
20	34	54
21	35	55
22	36	56
23	37	57
24	38	58
25	39	59
26	3A	5A
27	3B	5B
28	3C	5C
29	3D	5D
30	3E	5E

handshake, described earlier, forces transfers to take place at a speed suited to the slowest listener. Hence the need to ensure that no unnecessary slow device is enabled. For example, if a printer was left eavesdropping while a disk system transferred data into a microcomputer's memory, then all the data transfers would take place at a rate governed primarily by the printer.

In operation a GPIB alternates between the command and data modes in a manner similar to the fetch and execute cycles performed by a microprocessor. The similarity also extends to the use of mnemonics for the various bus commands. The commands can be divided into two groups: universal commands and addressed commands, which are listed below.

ATN	Attention
DCL	Device clear
GET	Group execute trigger
GTL	Go to local
LAG	Listen address group
LLO	Local lockout

MLA	My listen address
MTA	My talk address
PPC	Parallel poll configure
PPU	Parallel poll unconfigure
PPE	Parallel poll enable
PPD	Parallel poll disable
SCG	Secondary command group
SDC	Selected device clear
SPD	Serial poll disable
SPE	Serial poll enable
TCT	Take control
UNL	Unlisten
UNT	Untalk

The universal commands are directed at all instruments on the bus that contain the necessary functions to obey them. They take the form of either a special code on the data lines (a multi-line command), or activation of one or more of the bus management lines (a uni-line command). Addressed commands are similar except that they are directed as specific addressed devices. All addressed commands have a multi-line format. When the GPIB enters the data mode (ATN false), information changes hands between a talker and listeners. The format and nature of the data depends on each instrument and lies outside the GPIB interface standard. A simple device, such as a printer, would probably receive its data in the form of a string of ASCII characters forming a text file, whereas a digital multimeter would make use of ASCII code sequences to select function and range.

Polling The service request (SRQ) management line allows devices to signal the controller that they are in need of attention. On detecting a service request, the controller then carries out a polling procedure to determine who requested service and why. The GPIB standard supports two methods of polling: serial and parallel. Only devices with talker capability can be serial polled, with the controller addressing each device in turn with an SPE command (serial poll enable). The polled device replies, sending a status byte on which a logic 0 in bit 7 confirms that it was responsible for activating the SRQ line. The remaining bits normally display a device-dependent code that reflects why the SRQ line was set. Performing a serial poll of the requesting device causes it to release the SRQ line. A parallel poll is often used to provide a rapid check on the status of up to eight devices at the same time (e.g. to determine which instruments are ready to send or receive data). Before making use of a parallel poll, the controller carries out a configure procedure in which each device is assigned one of the eight data lines. The poll itself is initiated by the controller simultaneously asserting the ATN and EOI management lines. Polled devices then use their assigned bit to report their status. If more than eight devices are in use, a parallel poll can still be carried out but some data lines have to be shared.

4–20 mA Current Loop

In both the serial and the parallel communication standards there are restrictions on the maximum length that the transmission cables can be extended to. The length restriction is related to the voltage loss in the cables and increasing capacitive effects with length. In many industrial applications, however, there is a need to accommodate longer transmission lines for remote sensing and control. In such applications the most common communication standard is the so-called 4–20 mA current loop. This system uses a current level as opposed to a voltage level

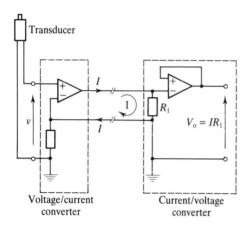

Voltage/current converter

Current/voltage converter

Figure 8.12 4–20mA current loop circuit.

to transmit information along a single wire. A current of 4 mA equates to a value of zero while a current of 20 mA represents full scale.

An additional advantage associated with the 4–20 mA current loop is its essential immunity to contamination through voltage 'spikes' which are ever present in the industrial environment. The current loop is also allowed to 'float', i.e. it is not tied to a reference earth, and this improves its noise immunity.

Most transducers and electrical display devices operate with voltage levels and it becomes necessary to convert transducer outputs from voltage to current before transmission. At the receiving device, the transmitted current must be re-converted back to a voltage prior to display, or conversion from analogue to digital form. Figure 8.12 shows a schematic representation of a typical 4–20 mA current loop.

Fibre-optics

Fibre-optics may be used to implement a very high speed, low noise data communication link between devices. The data can either be in digital form, or may be frequency modulated allowing more than one signal to be carried through the link simultaneously. Fibre-optic communication links are intrinsically safe since there is no electrical current present, they are, however, generally more expensive than other methods.

In an optical communication system the 'carrier' is in the form of infra-red light. This is generated from either light-emitting diodes, or from semiconductor lasers. Amplitude modulation is achieved by varying the intensity of the light. If the information is digitally coded, this essentially means that the light source is simply switched on and off. A general optical communication system is depicted in Fig. 8.13.

Modern optical fibre cables have very low attenuation rates and transmission distances of up to 100 km are possible before the signal requires to be regenerated. The optical link is immune to electromagnetic interference and this makes it an ideal communication link in electrically noisy environments. Also, since the signal carried by the fibre cannot be easily tapped, then the optical system provides a very high degree of security.

Information transmitted through the optical fibre can be in analogue or digital form. The common light sources have a linear response over part of their current–light output characteristic and this enables the light intensity to function as an analogue type of signal. Current technology utilizes 256 separately identifiable levels of light intensity. Although analogue transmission is useful in some applications, most optical communication systems are designed to carry digital information in the form of an on/off type of signal.

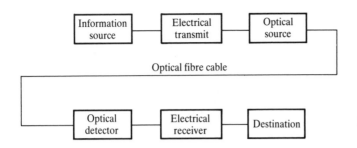

Figure 8.13 General optical communication system.

The potential for optical communication systems are vast and there are already available RS232C and 4–20 mA communication interfaces which use light, as opposed to voltage or current, as the information carrier.

FURTHER READING

Brey, B. (1991) *The Intel Microprocessors: 8086/8088, 80186, 80286, 80386 and 80484: Architecture, Programming and Interfacing*, 2nd edn, Merrill, Macmillan, New York.

Downton, A. C. (1988) *Computers and Microprocessors—Components and Systems*, 2nd edn, Van Nostrand Reinhold, London.

Feuer, A. and N. Gehani (eds) (1984) *Comparing and Assessing Programming Languages—Ada C Pascal*, Prentice-Hall, Englewood Cliffs, NJ.

Fraser, C. J. and J. S. Milne (1990) *Microcomputer Applications in Measurement Systems*, Macmillan, London

Kernighan, B. W. and D. M. Ritchie (1978) *The C Programming Language*, Prentice Hall, Englewood Cliffs, NJ.

Lam, H. and J. O'Malley (1988) *Fundamentals of Computer Engineering—Logic Design and Microprocessors*, Wiley, New York.

Sayers, I. L., A. E. Adams, E. G. Chester and A. P. Robson (1991) *Principles of Microprocessors*, CRC Press, Boca Raton, Florida.

EXERCISES

8.1 Compare and contrast the characteristics of TTL and CMOS semiconductor families.

8.2 Give the main reason for choosing the hex code to represent binary numbers.

8.3 Express the following unsigned 8-bit binary numbers in decimal, hexadecimal and BCD formats:
(a) 1001 1001; (b) 1100 1100; (c) 0001 0001; (d) 0111 1111.

[(a) 153 99 99; (b) 204 CC —; (c) 17 11 11; (d) 127 7F —]

8.4 Convert the following hex numbers into decimal values:
(a) A9; (b) CE4; (c) 7FFF; (d) FFFFF.

[(a) 169; (b) 3300; (c) 32767; (d) 1 048 575]

8.5 Convert the following decimal numbers into hex values:
(a) 193; (b) 571; (c) 23592.

[(a) C1; (b) 23B; (c) 5C28]

8.6 Convert the BCD code 0111 1000 1001 0010 into a decimal number.

[7892]

8.7 Convert the following signed decimal numbers into binary numbers:
(a) −1; (b) −100; (c) −317; (d) −25000.

[(a) FFFF; (b) FF9C; (c) FEC3; (d) 9E58]

8.8 Convert the following signed binary numbers into decimal numbers:
(a) 1000 0000; (b) 1111 0000; (c) 1000 1111 1010 1010

[(a) −128; (b) −16; (c) −28758]

8.9 Write the ASCII codes appropriate to your name using both upper and lower case letters.

8.10 Illustrate how the CPU and memory devices are related to the I/O interface in a dedicated port addressed organization.

8.11 The NMI routine for an IBM PC compatible starts at a segmented address of 0B9E: 0016. Express this address as an absolute value.

[0B9F6]

8.12 A microcomputer has a memory mapped I/O based on a 6522 VIA with the following decimal addresses:

Port B-2304; Port A-2305; DDRB-2306; DDRA-2307

Write the necessary instructions in BASIC which would configure port A as input, and the bits in port B as PB_0 output and PB_{1-7} as input.

[POKE 2307,0 : POKE 2306,1]

8.13 A card for use with a PC is based on an 8255 PPI and is set for a base address of 700 hex. Write the instruction in BASICA which would configure port A and port B as input and port C as output.

[OUT &H703,&H92]

8.14 Compare and contrast the 6522 VIA and the 8255 PPI interface chips.

8.15 Explain the function of the IRQ/INTR and NMI pins on the microprocessor.

8.16 Explain the sequence of events which occur once a microprocessor RESET has been activated.

8.17 Using the program DEBUG which is supplied with DOS on a PC determine the start address of the NMI routine. Then examine the codes starting at this address.

8.18 Using the appropriate BASICA instructions read the last 16 bytes in a PC system ROM, i.e. from FFFF0 to FFFFF.

8.19 Try POKEing data to ROM and view the result. Start with a segment address of F000.

8.20 The screen memory on a PC starts at a segment address of &HB800 with the top left hand corner corresponding to an offset of 0. POKE the ASCII codes appropriate to your name such that it appears about the middle of the screen. Note: start with an even offset address and increment the address by two for each character code value. Work in BASICA/GW-BASIC.

8.21 Explain what is meant by a syntax error in programming.

8.22 Compare and contrast the relative merits of high- and low-level programming languages.

8.23 Sketch and describe the pin connections required in an auto loop-back serial communication link.

8.24 Define the essential data transfer protocols which must be specified for devices connected via an RS232C serial communication link.

8.25 Describe the functions of the electronic device termed a 'UART'.

8.26 The three handshaking lines in a parallel communication interface are denoted NRFD (not ready for data), NDAC (not data accepted) and DAV (data valid). Using an illustrative sketch of the line signals, describe the handshaking protocol which is carried out in the transmission of a single character on the data lines.

8.27 Describe the relevant advantages and disadvantages of optical fibres as a means of digital communication.

HIGH- AND LOW-LEVEL PROGRAMMING

9.1 OPERATING SYSTEMS

The basic function of a computer's operating system (OS) is to provide a means by which a user may manipulate files and execute computer programs. It is essentially a system control program which acts as an interface between the user and the computer hardware. The ultimate purpose is to provide a service to the user and all computers are provided with some type of operating system.

The physical or hardware resources managed by the OS include the central processing unit, the main memory, the I/O devices, the secondary data storage media such as disk drives, and internal devices such as clocks and timers. Software resources such as all types of computer files are also managed by the OS. Some popular computer systems which are supplied as a package from a single source include editors and other software tools as part of the OS. However, the kernel of the OS is the collection of the resource management procedures which typically are resident in memory and are entrusted with the privileges that the hardware can provide. For this reason the OS and the computer architecture have a great deal of influence on each other.

A special form of OS is the ill-defined real-time operating system or RTOS. It is often just associated with the high throughput of transaction processing. While in control applications real-time operating systems means not missing any event, even if the system is busy doing something else, and responding appropriately in time. In a full priority scheduled real-time system, the executing task is always the one with the highest priority that is ready to run. The UNIX operating system, which is written in C, saves space by hashing tasks on to a small set of priority queues and lets the processor search through the list for the highest priority runnable process. This is one of the reasons why conventional UNIX is less deterministic than an RTOS. There are however real-time versions of UNIX which get around this and other problems.

The well-established industry standard OS-9 operating system provides the real-time, speed-critical responses which modern embedded control applications demand. This multi-tasking RTOS is applied to almost every field of real-time control, from consumer electronics, through industrial control to aerospace. It is written almost entirely in assembly language and offers a lean, fast solution for control systems based on a variety of popular buses. A version, mostly written in C, is available for running on a PC with all preconceived limits, such as a 640K memory availability, eliminated.

The rise of windowing systems has done much to improve the role of the industrial systems integrator. Packages such as Microsoft Windows running on ruggedized hardware makes it possible to create easy to use graphical interfaces. Additionally, Microsoft's Visual Basic has become a key prototyping tool for PC-based interface screens.

Types of OS Services

The operating system functions provided for the convenience of the user include such services as:

1. Program execution
2. Input/output operations
3. File manipulation
4. Error detection

The file system is the most visible aspect of the OS. It is of particular interest since it is usually required to read, write, create, copy, rename, print, list and delete files by name. Files store data and computer programs in a variety of formats. They are normally organized into directories so that they can be managed in a logical and accessible manner.

The creator of the file defines the nature of the information stored. These may be, for example, source programs, object programs or simply text with ASCII characters separated by carriage returns and line feeds. A file is referred to by its name which generally includes an extension that is indicative of the nature of the file. For example, an extension '.BAS' indicates a source program written in BASIC; '.OBJ' indicates a relocatable object code file which can be linked to other routines to produce an executable file with a '.EXE' extension.

MS-DOS

With the introduction of the IBM PC in the early 1980s a 'disk operating system' (DOS) was required to provide an interface between the computer and the disk drives. The initial intention was to use Digital Research's CP/M operating system (Computer Program for Microcomputers) which was the industry standard at that time. However, for various reasons, Microsoft Disk Operating System 1.0 with the further developed IBM PC-DOS 1.0 was used with the introduction of the IBM PC in October 1981. The operating system for PCs has been continuously developed with DOS 3.3 introduced in April 1987 for the PS/2 series which supported 1.44 Mb and DOS partitions. DOS 4.0 arrived in August 1988 and the current version (1992) available is DOS 5.0.

DOS consists of four components:

1. *The boot record.* This begins on track 0, sector 0, side 0 of every formatted disk or on the first sector of the DOS partition for a hard disk. Its function is to produce an error message if an attempt is made to boot up (start) the system with a non-system disk.
2. *The ROM BIOS interface* (IBMBIO.SYS or IO.SYS). This file provides a low-level interface to the ROM basic input/output system device routines.
3. The DOS program (IBMDOS.COM or MSDOS.SYS). This provides a high-level interface for application programs and contains the file management routines.

4. The command processor (COMMAND.COM). This interpreter file, COMMAND.COM, is the part that the user interacts with on the screen command line and a resident portion accommodates all standard DOS error handling routines.

The system is initialized by either a software reset (CTRL-ALT-DEL), a hardware reset (reset button), or by switching the computer on. The system prompt such as A > or C > indicates that DOS is at the command level, ready to accept commands from the user. The letter in the system prompt identifies the current drive. The current drive, such as C, can be changed by typing the new drive letter, followed by a colon and pressing the Enter key.

C>A:<CR>

would select drive A.

Before a disk is used it must first be divided up into locatable 'tracks' and 'sectors' which can be identified by the operating system. This is achieved by a formatting program—FORMAT.COM—which is available with the DOS facilities. To format a disk placed in drive A:

C>format a:<CR>

In most cases today this will attempt to formalize a high-density disk to give a 1.44 Mbyte storage availability. If, however, a double-sided double-density disk is used then it can be formatted to 720 Kbyte with

C>format a:/n:9/t:80<CR>

or, with DOS 5,

C>format a:/f:720<CR>

The system files can be transferred at the formatting stage by adding the switch "/s" at the end of the instruction. This has the effect of producing a disk which can be used for the start-up of the system (boot).

Other useful MS-DOS commands are:

CD\DATA < CR >	changes the current directory from the root
DIR < CR >	displays a directory listing of files in the current drive
DIR A: < CR >	displays a directory listing of files on drive A
DIR/P < CR >	displays a directory listing of files, one screenful at a time
DIR *.BAS < CR >	displays a directory listing of files with the extension '.BAS'
TYPE FILE.BAS¦MORE < CR >	displays the contents of an ASCII-type file 'MORE' allows a display of 23 lines at a time
PRINT FILE.TXT < CR >	prints a file to a prompted device e.g. PRN which is the default
DEL FILE.EXE < CR >	deletes a specified file
COPY C:FILE.DOC A: < CR >	copies a file from one drive to another, e.g. C to A
COPY C:\PROGS\FILE.BAS B: < CR >	copies a file from a specified directory on to another drive
RENAME A:FILE.C PROG.C < CR >	changes the name of a file, from–to
MD LETTERS	makes a new directory on the current drive

RD LETTERS	removes a specified directory which must be empty
CLS < CR >	clears the screen and displays the system prompt

There are a number of MS-DOS commands but the above are probably the most commonly used.

9.2 REAL-TIME CONTROL LANGUAGES

'Real-time control' is one of those jargon terms which mean different things to different people. Real-time computer systems are found in many diverse areas, from automobile engine management to a variety of manufacturing processes such as automatic assembly machines, paper making machines, chemical plants and steel rolling mills. The most imaginative applications are undoubtedly those associated with space technology such as rocket launching, space craft orbiting and vehicle landing. There are of course many more mundane applications associated with a vast number of consumer products.

It is quite difficult to define exactly what is a real-time system and what is not, but all real-time computer systems do share several common features. The most important of which are:

1. The computer's response time (i.e. the time that elapses between an event occurring and the computer system's response to it) must be sufficiently fast to affect the functioning of the system being controlled.
2. The execution of the controlling computer program is synchronized with the operation of the system being controlled.

The first of these requirements is largely dependent upon the nature of the system being controlled. For example, a response time of a few minutes may be acceptable for a boiler-house application but in the case of a missile homing in on its target the response time of the controller must be of the order of a few milliseconds. In the past, although computers were fast compared to other technologies, they did not produce information as fast as it was needed. One example of this was the situation in a bank where a customer required an immediate cash withdrawal transaction. The data generally took a long time to reach the customer and the computer operations were often carried out sequentially and thus lead to long delays.

Modern machines do however have much faster reponse times with multi-tasking capabilities. Such machines can action instant by instant control of what is happening. In addition, the live interactions now possible between humans and computers, however distant, are extremely effective. This is evident in modern financial self-service machines with highly sophisticated graphical user interfaces (GUIs).

The second required feature of the real-time system is closely linked to the problem of connecting the computer to the real world where events do tend to take place in real time. Some of the most relevant properties expected of the real-time programming language for the control of an external system or process are:

1. The computer must be able to time the duration of a process or make the process run for a specified time. This requirement necessitates access to timer facilities within the language.
2. The external controlling actuators for altering the state of the process should be able to be turned on and off easily through the software. This should be within a specified response time which is dictated by the system being controlled.
3. It should be easy to ascertain whether external sensing devices are on or off at any particular time.

4. The program should be able to respond to external events as they occur. This often requires interrupt handling as outlined in Sec. 8.3.
5. The controller should be able to handle a number of tasks simultaneously.

The first real-time application programs were written in machine code to obtain the benefits of speed and running efficiency. Today many low-level applications are still implemented using assembly code with the assistance of quite sophisticated software and hardware development support tools to produce the necessary machine code. The trend now is usually for real-time programs to be written in a high-level language with blocks of machine code inserted appropriately for certain tasks. BASIC, FORTRAN, PASCAL, MODULA and C have all been used and are still being used in this way.

Languages such as MODULA-2 and ADA are much more suited to real-time applications since they have the necessary features designed into them rather than patched into them as with the real-time versions of BASIC and FORTRAN. However, the most important aspect is really the scale and nature of the process being controlled. In many cases the speed of program development using a real-time BASIC with a small single-board microprocessor-based controller offsets the inefficiencies of the language for a single application or low production runs.

Although the PC was hardly designed as a real-time engine, the amount of software written for the platform makes it an enticing way of bringing user interfaces and communications to real-time control systems. Due to the significant degree of standardization among PC and data acquisition and control manufacturers, a large variety of hardware and software tools with applications packages have appeared on the market. The result is that a data acquisition and control system can be set up within a fraction of the time and expense that was formerly required. PCs invite innovation and it is now practical to tailor highly effective solutions to quite unique applications. This type of innovation has revolutionized a variety of products and manufacturing processes.

9.3 PROGRAMMING FOR DATA ACQUISITION AND CONTROL APPLICATIONS

The first digital computers were developed specifically for performing routine arithmetical calculations. It was soon appreciated, however, that they embodied the potential for much more than just calculation engines. Today they are being used to control mechanisms and greatly enhance the intelligence and flexibility embedded in a large variety of products and processes. The high-level intelligence is achieved through the software which is becoming more of an engineering activity. The practice of conceiving, designing, writing, testing and documenting software constitutes a large element of the necessary resources associated with developing mechatronic products which meet market needs. Flexibility and intelligence are predominant features of mechatronic systems.

Programming is a means of communicating with the computer in order to elicit a response according to set criteria. The communication must be exact and precise so that the programmed instructions are executed in an unambiguous manner. This identifies the need for computer programming languages. Programs should, where possible, be written in a high-level language and a summary of some of these is given in Sec. 8.3. Where memory space or speed of execution is an important factor then it may be necessary to write all or part of the program in assembly language. The choice of language is often left to the designer, or programmer, and it is preferential to use a language which helps to produce structured, modular code. Structured programming is a discipline which encourages the programmer to direct thought to the organization of the programming process and the problem-solving process in general.

BASIC is available on most machines and a large number of engineering application programs are still being written in this language. Although the early BASICs were quite primitive the modern compiled versions such as POWER BASIC and Microsoft's QUICKBASIC are gifted with powerful tools for producing structured programs and executable codes efficiently. These are somewhat compatible with the interpreted versions of IBM's Advanced Basic (commonly referred to as BASICA) and Microsoft's GWBASIC. There are of course some minor differences and the compiled versions contain many extensions. The modern trend, however, has been a move towards the application of the language C. In addition to being used to write the programs for operating systems, spreadsheet calculators and database management systems, C is being used extensively for industrially related data acquisition and control applications. It is a very flexible language and the programs are very transportable.

With the dominance of the PC on the industrial scene and the move towards a PC platform as a standard for control applications some knowledge of 80X86/88 assembly language is useful. These Intel processors, which have an extremely powerful instruction set, are probably the most widely used computing devices adopted by industry today.

Hence, within an engineering context, for applications related to data acquisition and control a working knowledge of BASIC, C and 8086/8088 is desirable. On this basis the requirements of the language include:

1. The input and output of data
2. Arithmetic and logic operations
3. Conditional statements
4. Looping statements
5. Functions and subroutines
6. Timing operations
7. File handling
8. Graphics

Programming in QUICKBASIC

Input/Output Within the BASIC language, numerical or alpha-numeric data (strings) can be input by using the key statements INPUT and READ.

INPUT. Prepares the program for an input from the keyboard during the program execution.
READ. Used to read values from an inbuilt DATA statement and assign them to variables.
Although the DATA statements can be placed anywhere within the program it is good practice to place them immediately prior to the END statement. The data values are accessed in order and they can be re-read from the start if necessary by the use of the RESTORE instruction.

The PRINT statement is used to display information to the screen. PRINT USING can be used for printing to a specified format, e.g.

```
150 PRINT USING "pressure = ###.#kN/m^2";PA
```

will print out the numerical value of the variable PA to one decimal place and up to three digits before the point.

Example Perform various arithmetical operations on two real numbers X1 and X2, which are input interactively at the keyboard.

Program 9.1 Arithmetical operations in BASIC.

```
CLS : REM clear screen
INPUT "first number = "; x1
INPUT "second number = "; x2
sum = x1 + x2
diff = x1 - x2
prod = x1 * x2
div = x1 / x2
pow = x1 ^ x2
PRINT : PRINT : PRINT
PRINT "sum of "; x1; " and "; x2; " = "; sum
PRINT "difference ="; diff
PRINT "product = "; prod
PRINT "division = "; div
PRINT x1; " to the power of "; x2; " = "; pow
END
```

If the variables X1 and X2 are to be assigned numerical values by a READ statement then the INPUT statements are replaced by

READ X1,X2

Immediately prior to the END statement the following is added:

DATA <the two numerical values separated by a comma>

The arithmetic operators are

$$+,-,/,*,\hat{}$$

as illustrated in the example.

The logic operators, for bit manipulation or Boolean operations are

AND, OR, NOT, XOR

The functional/trigonometric operators are

SQR, SIN, COS, TAN, ATN

e.g. $Y = SQR(X)$ gives the square root of X. $Z = ATN(Y)$ gives $\tan^{-1}$ of Y with Y expressed in radians.

Note: some languages give an assigned variable, usually PI, for the numerical value of π. If this is not the case then PI can be evaluated from a statement built into the program:

$PI = 4*ATN(1)$

I/O for memory locations PEEK returns the byte (integer in the range 0–225) stored at a specified memory location. POKE writes a byte into a memory location. Note: with the IBM PC and compatibles the location in memory is treated as an offset from the specified DEF SEG statement (see Sec. 8.3).

I/O for ports with dedicated port addressing INP returns the byte read from a port; OUT sends a byte to a port (see details in Sec. 8.3).

Example A digital I/O card for a PC is configured for a base address of &H1B0. Write a program which would continuously monitor the state of input port A and put the value out onto output port B.

Program 9.2 Illustration of input/output via ports.

```
        BA = &H1B0
        PORTA = BA: PORTB = BA + 1: CR = BA + 3
        OUT CR, &H90: REM PORTA input and PORTB output
more:
        I = INP(PORTA)
        OUT PORTB, I
        GOTO more
```

Note the use of the 'GOTO' statement for an unconditional jump to a specified label.

Conditional statements The purpose of the IF statement within a program is to make a decision regarding a diversion in the program flow based on some conditional expression. The single-line form of the statement is used for straight-forward tests where only one action is taken. The form is either

IF<conditional expression>THEN<action 1>

or if necessary

IF<conditional statement>THEN<action 1>ELSE<action 2>

The conditional operators are

equal to	=
not equal to	< >
greater than	>
less than	<
greater than or equal to	>=
less than or equal to	<=

The actions may be either a statement regarding some variable's numerical value or the control of the program's execution. This can be redirected through either a GOTO instruction or by activating a subroutine. The GOTO statement provides a way to branch to another part of the program. It is a very useful facility but should be handled with care since it does not generally lead to good structuring principles.

The compiled BASICs offer a more structured form of IF blocks which can virtually eliminate the need to implement GOTO instructions. This can involve a nested structure, illustrated as follows:

```
If<condition 1>THEN
      <block of statements>
ELSE
      IF<condition 2>THEN
            <block of statements>
      ELSE
            <block of statements>
      END IF
END IF
```

Example Consider an ON/OFF control strategy implemented in software for a temperature control application. The strategy is simply:

If the temperature in a room is greater than or equal to the required setpoint value then the heater is switched off else the heater is switched on.

In practice the actual room temperature would be read from a sensor and input to the microprocessor-based controller via an analogue-to-digital converter interface. In addition, the heater would be switched on and off by means of an output logic signal from a port to a power switching digital interface. However, for simulation purposes it is sufficient to input the current room temperature value at the keyboard and print the heater ON/OFF requirement onto the display screen. A suitable program is shown in Program 9.3.

Program 9.3 Use of conditional statement for ON/OFF temperature control.

```
          CLS
          INPUT "setpoint in deg C= "; setpoint
heatoff:
          LOCATE 12, 30
          PRINT "heater off"
readtemp:
          LOCATE 4, 15
          INPUT "room temperature in deg C= "; temp
          IF temp >= setpoint THEN GOTO heatoff
          LOCATE 12, 30
          PRINT "heater on "
          LOCATE 4, 15
          PRINT "                              "
          GOTO readtemp
```

In the design of a program, particularly for control applications, it is essential to draw up a flow chart which clearly and logically maps out the train of thought appropriate to the formulation of the rules that govern the sequence of requirements in a particular application. A flow chart is composed of symbols of different shapes, which are meant to indicate different operations. Descriptions of the operations are written within each shape. The description should be clearly expressed and not include any reference to computer code. Arrows are used to connect the shapes to indicate the order in which operations are to be executed within the flow of the program. The two main symbols used are:

1. The input/output operation and the general processing symbol—these can be represented by a rectangular shape.

2. The decision symbol which is used to indicate branches in a program flow—this is represented by a diamond shape. The condition tested is described in the symbol with one input and two possible outputs which may be either true or false (Yes or No).

Once the process that is to be controlled is thoroughly understood and a flow chart drawn up according to some chosen strategy, then it is relatively easy to translate the sequence of operations into computer code.

> **Example** Consider the temperature control of a room by means of a hot water radiator supplied by a gas-fired boiler with an electrically driven pump. The room temperature and boiler water temperature settings are specified and the control strategy is as follows:
> If the room temperature is greater than or equal to the room setting, then both the pump and the boiler are to be switched off.
> If the boiler temperature is greater than or equal to the boiler setting, then the pump is to be switched on and the boiler off.
> If both the room and the boiler are below the set values, then both the pump and the boiler are to be switched on.
> A suitable flow chart for the continuous operation of the system is shown in Fig. 9.1.
> A program listing which implements the strategy using keyboard input and a print to screen for output is given in Program 9.4. Although the program functions correctly it employs a number of GOTO statements and is not too well structured. A more structured solution is presented later.

Looping statements There are number of ways by which a program can repetitively execute a number of operations. The simplest is the GOTO statement combined with a conditional statement to redirect the sequential execution of lines of code to a specified line in the program.

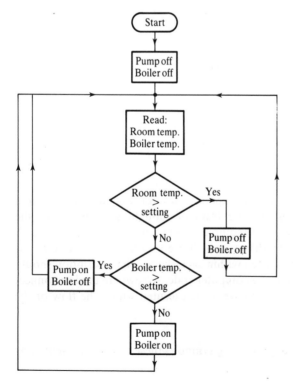

Figure 9.1 ON/OFF control of room and boiler temperatures.

Program 9.4 ON/OFF control for room and boiler temperatures.

```
        CLS
        INPUT "required room temperature in deg C= "; roomset
        INPUT "required boiler temperature in deg C= "; boilerset
        CLS
        LOCATE 12, 25
        PRINT "boiler OFF and pump OFF"
again:
        LOCATE 3, 10
        INPUT "room temperature in deg C= ", roomtemp
        LOCATE 4, 10
        INPUT "boiler temperature in deg C= ", boilertemp
        IF roomtemp >= roomset THEN GOTO poffboff
        IF boilertemp >= boilerset THEN GOTO ponboff
        LOCATE 12, 25
        PRINT "pump ON  and boiler ON  "
        GOTO again
poffboff:
        LOCATE 12, 25
        PRINT "pump OFF and boiler OFF"
        GOTO again
ponboff:
        LOCATE 12, 25
        PRINT "pump ON  and boiler OFF"
        GOTO again
```

The most common way of performing loops is through a FOR/NEXT statement. This takes the form:

> For < counter = initial value > TO < final value > STEP < increment >
> < statements in loop >
> NEXT counter value

If the STEP < increment > is not specified then the increment is assumed to be unity. This is usually the case

A FOR/NEXT loop can be placed within another FOR/NEXT loop. This is referred to as nested loops. Each loop must have a unique variable name as its counter and I,J,K are commonly used.

Example In a test on a centrifugal pump running at a constant speed (RPM), the pressure rise (Δp) and the input torque (T) are measured for various flow rates (Q). The test data is to be processed to give the pump efficiency (η) from the relationship:

$$\eta = (Q\Delta p)/(\Omega T)$$

where $\Omega = 2\pi RPM/60$.

The test data is as follows:
Pump = 1500 rev/min.

Flow rate	$(l\,s^{-1})$	0	10.5	20.0	30.0	40.5
Pressure rise	$(kN\,m^{-2})$	182.2	190.2	191.2	183.3	152.9
Input torque	$(N\,m)$	22.6	34.6	44.4	53.2	57.0

A suitable program listing is given in Program 9.5.

Program 9.5 Processing test data for a centrifugal pump characteristic.

```
CLS
LOCATE 10, 20
INPUT "pump speed in rev/min= "; rpm
LOCATE 12, 20
INPUT "number of tests made= ", n
DIM q(n), dp(n), t(n), eta(n)
pi = 4 * ATN(1)
omega = (2 * pi * rpm) / 60
CLS
PRINT : PRINT : PRINT
PRINT "          centrifugal pump characteristic"
PRINT
PRINT USING "              pump speed = #### rev/min"; rpm
PRINT : PRINT
PRINT "        test     quantity    efficiency"
PRINT "                   l/s          %"
PRINT
FOR k = 1 TO n
READ q(k), dp(k), t(k)
eta(k) = (q(k) * dp(k)) / (omega * t(k))
PRINT USING "          ##        ##.#        ##.##"; k; q(k); eta(k) * 100
NEXT k
DATA 0,182.2,22.6,10.5,190.2,34.6
DATA 20.0,191.5,44.4,30.0,183.3,53.2
DATA 40.5,152.9,57.0
END
```

It should be noted that in this program the test variables are stored as array elements. This requires a DIM statement to declare the variables and allocate storage space for the specified number. It is good practice to put the DIM statements at the start of the program, outside of any loops. If the upper bound of the array is set as a constant then the array is said to be of a 'static' type. Whereas, if the limit is allocated when the program is run then the array is dynamic. This is the case in the example given.

Alternative methods for repeating a block of statements are the DO...LOOP and the WHILE...WEND statements. The DO LOOP is the more versatile of the two because it can test for a condition at the beginning or at the end of a loop. The forms of the DO LOOP are as follows:

```
DO < condition >
< statements in block >
LOOP
```

and:

```
DO
< statements in block >
LOOP < condition >
```

The 'condition' takes the form of (say)

```
WHILE roomtemp < = roomset
```

The WHILE/WEND loop executes a series of statements in a loop as long as a stated condition is true. The structure with an example condition is as follows:

```
WHILE roomtemp < = roomset
< statements in block >
WEND
```

Subroutines It is often the case in a computer program that a sequence of statements needs to be accessed a number of times. Rather than repeat the sequence in the program listing it is preferable to have them placed in a subroutine or subprogram. This is attached or linked to the main program from which it is called by a specified name. A subroutine may be called any number of times within a program and it may be called from within another subroutine. To prevent inadvertently entering a subroutine which follows the main program it should be immediately preceded by a STOP, END or GOTO instruction to direct the program control away from the subroutine.

The simplest form of subroutine operation is GOSUB...RETURN where the program execution is redirected to a specified label which qualifies the GOSUB instruction. The subroutine code terminates with RETURN. The format is as follows:

```
< main program statements >
GOSUB check
< main program statements >
END

check:

< subroutine statements >
RETURN
```

It should be noted that in this type of subroutine all variables are declared as global by default. This means that they can be accessed and used anywhere in the complete program which involves the main part and all associated subroutines.

An alternative and more powerful method for implementing subroutines, which allows a better structured approach to programming, is to use a subprogram which is called within the main routine by means of a defined global name. The format is as follows:

```
DECLARE SUB subname( < parameter list > )
< main program statements >
CALL subname( < parameter list > )
< main program statements >
END

SUB subname( < parameter list > )
< subprogram statements >
END SUB
```

The parameter list is an optional comma-delimited list of parameters that represent variables which are to be passed to and from the subprogram when it is called. Other variables within the subprogram are local variables unless specified as otherwise. Variables which are COMMON SHARED between the main program and any subprograms must be specified at the start of the main. Arrays are passed as follows:

$$\text{CALL name(x( ),y( ),n,m,c)}$$

where x and y are arrays, n is (say) the dimension of the array with m and c (say) output-derived values from the subprogram.

Example Consider the previous example given in Program 9.4 which dealt with the ON/OFF control of the temperatures of a room and the heating boiler. Say that the controller has a dedicated port addressed I/O (see Sec. 8.3). It is fitted with a digital I/O card set for a base address of 1B0 hex and an analogue input card set for a base address of 700 hex. The operation of both cards relate to an 8255 PPI.

Port B on the digital card is used to switch the pump and the boiler with a logic '1' denoting an ON condition and a logic '0' OFF. The pump interface (see Sec. 10.1) is connected to bit 0 on the port and the boiler gas supply solenoid to bit 1.

The 16-channel, 12-bit resolution analogue-to-digital converter card (see Sec. 10.2) is operated as follows:

1. The ports are configured as A and B set to input and C output.
2. The upper nibble of C is used to select the channel that is connected to the temperature sensor.
3. The conversion is started by toggling the LSB of port C low and high while keeping bit 1 high.
4. There is no end of conversion signal available but a small delay is sufficient before reading the 12-bit value that is representative of the temperature.
5. The 8 LSBs are read on port A and the 4 MSBs on the lower nibble of port B.

The full 12-bit value represents a temperature of 100°C while a zero represents 0°C and the relationship is linear.

A more structured program to that shown previously by using an 'IF/THEN/ELSE/END IF' arrangement is illustrated in Program 9.6. The analogue to digital conversion routine is shown as a subprogram with appropriate parameter passing and shared variables.

Program 9.6 ON/OFF control using a more structured approach..

```
            DECLARE SUB adc (chan%, i%)
            COMMON SHARED pa, pb, pc
            BAdig = &H1B0: BAan = &H700
            porta = BAdig: portb = BAdig + 1: CRdig = BAdig + 3
            pa = BAan: pb = BAan + 1: pc = BAan + 2: CRan = BAan + 3
            OUT CRdig, &H90: REM porta set as input, portb as output for digital I/O
            OUT CRan, &H92: REM ports A and B input and C output for analogue card
            OUT portb, 0: REM pump OFF and boiler OFF
            CLS
            INPUT "required room temperature in deg C = ", roomset
            INPUT "required boiler temperature in deg C = ", boilerset
            INPUT "channel number on analogue card for room temp = ", chanrt%
            INPUT "channel number on analogue card for boiler temp = ", chanbt%
DO
            CALL adc(chanrt%, i%)
            roomtemp = i% / 4095 * 100
            CALL adc(chanbt%, i%)
            boilertemp = i% / 4095 * 100

            IF roomtemp >= roomset THEN
                    OUT portb, 0: REM pump OFF and boiler OFF
            ELSE
                IF boilertemp >= boilerset THEN
                        OUT portb, 1: REM pump ON and boiler OFF
                ELSE
                        OUT portb, 3: REM pump ON and boiler ON
                END IF
            END IF
LOOP

            REM adc routine
            DEFINT A-Z: REM all variables set as integer

            SUB adc (chan, i)
            c1 = (chan * 16) + 2
            c2 = (chan * 16) + 3
            OUT pc, c1:               REM start conversion
            OUT pc, c2
            FOR k = 1 TO 10: NEXT k: REM small delay
            lsb = INP(pa):            REM read 8 LSBs
            msb = INP(pb) AND 15:     REM read 4 MSBs
            i = 256 * msb + lsb:      REM form 12 bit value
            END SUB
```

Example The 'best' gradient (m) and intercept (c) for a set of X, Y data points related by:

$$Y = mX + c$$

can be obtained from the formulae derived according to the least squares technique:

$$m = \frac{[\Sigma Y^* \Sigma X] - [N^* \Sigma XY]}{[\Sigma X^* \Sigma X] - [N^* \Sigma X^2]}$$

$$c = \frac{[\Sigma X^* \Sigma XY] - [\Sigma X^{2*} \Sigma Y]}{[\Sigma X^* \Sigma X] - [N^* \Sigma X^2]}$$

Apply to the data points:

Number of test points $= 5$

X	0	1	2	3	4
Y	0.9	3.2	5.1	6.8	9.0

A suitable program listing with a subprogram for the straight line fit routine is shown in Program 9.7.

Program 9.7 Least squares straight line fit.

```
DECLARE SUB slf (N, X(), Y(), gradient, intercept)
CLS
INPUT "nuber of X/Y points= ", N
DIM X(N), Y(N)
FOR K = 1 TO N
READ X(K), Y(K)
NEXT K
CALL slf(N, X(), Y(), m, c)
CLS
LOCATE 10, 10
PRINT "gradient= "; m
LOCATE 12, 10
PRINT "intercept= "; c
DATA 0,0.9,1,3.2,2,5.1,3,6.8,4,9.0
END

SUB slf (N, X(), Y(), gradient, intercept)
sumx = 0: sumy = 0: sumxy = 0: sumxx = 0
FOR K = 1 TO N
sumx = sumx + X(K)
sumy = sumy + Y(K)
sumxy = sumxy + (X(K) * Y(K))
sumxx = sumxx + (X(K) * X(K))
NEXT K
gradient = ((sumx * sumy) - (N * sumxy)) / ((sumx * sumx) - (N * sumxx))
intercept = ((sumx * sumxy) - (sumxx * sumy)) / ((sumx * sumx) - (N * sumxx))
END SUB
```

Functions A function procedure returns a string or numeric value which is related to the parameters passed in the same manner as a BASIC intrinsic function such as SQR, SIN, ATN etc. The routine is placed at the start of the main program and takes the form:

```
DEF FNfunctioname(<parameter list>)
    <function statements>
FNfunctioname = <expression>
END DEF
```

and it is called from within the main program by the instruction

$$\text{variable} = \text{FNfunctioname}(<\text{parameter list}>)$$

Example In a hydropower generating system the turbines are supplied with water at a known flow rate Q from a reservoir level H through a pipeline of length L.
The energy lost in the pipeline due to viscous friction is given by

$$E_f = 9.81H(1 - \eta_t)$$

where η_t is the energy transmission efficiency of the pipeline.
Once E_f is known for a given η_t value, the required diameter of the pipe can be calculated from

$$D = [(32fLQ^2)/(\pi^2 E_f)]^{0.2}$$

where the friction coefficient f is a function of the parameters

$$Re = (4Q)/(\pi \nu D)$$

and

$$KD = k/D$$

where ν is the kinematic viscosity of water ($10^{-6}\,\mathrm{m^2\,s^{-1}}$) and k is a measure of the roughness of the pipe (0.15 mm for galvanized steel).
The correlation between f and (Re, KD) is

$$f = \left[\left(\frac{8}{Re} \right)^{12} + \frac{1}{(A + B)^{1.5}} \right]^{1/12} \times 0.3557$$

where

$$A = \left[2.457 \ln \left(\frac{1}{[(7/Re)^{0.9} + 0.27(k/D)]} \right) \right]^{16} \times 10^{-6}$$

$$B = \left[\frac{37\,530}{Re} \right]^{16} \times 10^{-6}$$

It can be seen that an iterative solution is needed and hence a starting value is required to initiate the sequence. A typical value based on an understanding of the fluid dynamics is $f = 0.005$. The iteration is allowed to continue until a defined tolerance condition is reached. A suitable program listing expressing the relationship between f and (Re, KD) as a function is given in Program 9.8.

Program 9.8 Pipe-line design using a defined function and an iterative procedure.

```
DEF FNcorrelation (R, KD)
c1 = (7 / R) ^ .9
c2 = c1 + (.27 * KD)
c3 = 1 / c2
c4 = LOG(c3)
a = ((2.457 * c4) ^ 16) / 1000000
b = ((37530 / R) ^ 16) / 1000000
c5 = (8 / R) ^ 12
c6 = (a + b) ^ 1.5
c7 = 1 / c6
FNcorrelation = ((c5 + c7) ^ (1 / 12)) * .3557
END DEF



REM*************************************************************
REM calculates pipe diameter D(mm) from:
REM length L(m), flow rate Q(m^3/s), head H(m)
REM transmission efficiency ETA(%) and pipe roughness (k/D)
REM*************************************************************
CLS
READ l, q, h, K
nu = .000001: pi = 4 * ATN(1)
INPUT "transmission efficiency(%)= ", eta
ef = 9.81 * h * (1 - eta / 100)
REM start iteration with friction factor=0.005
f2 = .005
f1 = 0
WHILE ABS(f1 - f2) > .000001
f1 = f2
d = ((32 * f2 * l * q * q) / (pi * pi * ef)) ^ .2
Re = (4 * q) / (pi * nu * d)
KD = K / d
f2 = FNcorrelation(Re, KD)
WEND
CLS : LOCATE 10, 10
PRINT USING "pipe diameter for a transmission efficiency of ### %"; eta
LOCATE 12, 10
PRINT USING "is #### mm"; d * 1000
DATA 600,8.38,300,0.15e-3
END
```

Inputting various transmission efficiencies with $L = 600\,\text{m}$, $Q = 8.38\,\text{m}^3\,\text{s}^{-1}$, $H = 300\,\text{m}$ and $k = 0.15\,\text{mm}$ yields the following results:

transmission efficiency (%)	67	80	90	99
pipe diameter (mm)	861	949	1085	1696

Timing operations In control applications it is often the case that specific time delays are required within a sequence of events. Or alternatively, it is necessary to measure the time between two events. In PC BASIC this can be achieved, with somewhat limited accuracy, by means of the instruction TIMER. This returns the number of seconds, expressed in floating point format, elapsed since midnight or since the last system reset. Although TIMER cannot be set to zero, a variable can be made equal to the current value at any particular instant. Thus the time elapsed between two events can be easily obtained by a difference calculation.

Example Develop a program for measuring the reaction time in milliseconds to respond to a prompt printed to the screen. The prompt should be printed at some random time up to say 10 s from when the program is run. Once the prompt is displayed the keyboard spacebar should be pressed and the elapsed time printed to the screen. A suitable program listing is given in Program 9.9.

Program 9.9 Measurement of reaction time.

```
        CLS
        GOSUB delay
        CLS
        LOCATE 5, 5
        PRINT "press space bar now!!!!"
        t1 = TIMER
repeat:
        IF ASC(INPUT$(1)) <> 32 THEN GOTO repeat
        t2 = TIMER
        LOCATE 7, 5
        PRINT USING "time taken = #### ms"; (t2 - t1) * 1000
        END

delay:
        RANDOMIZE TIMER
        del = INT((RND * 10) + 1)
        t = TIMER
        WHILE (TIMER < (t + del)): WEND
        RETURN
```

The instruction ASC(INPUT$(1)) reads the ASCII character equivalent to the key pressed. The code for the spacebar is 32. In addition to being used to measure the elapsed time the TIMER instruction is also used to generate a random delay time which is called as a subroutine prior to the prompt being displayed. An audible prompt can also be included through the command BEEP. A typical good reaction time is of the order of 200 ms.

Example Consider the driving of a stepper motor (see Sec. 5.9) by generating pulses whose frequency governs the speed of rotation of the motor. A four-phase stepper motor would normally require four connections from an output port through some power switching interface. Each phase is then pulsed according to a prescribed sequence to make the motor rotate one step per pulse. If the driving sequence is reversed then the motor direction reverses. However, a driving interface (SAA 1027 (RS 300-237)) is available which allows a small four-phase two-stator stepper motor to be driven from two port connections. One connection (P) is used to supply the pulses. The other (D) specifies the direction of rotation with a '0' denoting clockwise and a '1' anticlockwise. The pulse train need not be a symmetrical square wave since it is the period which decides the speed of rotation.

The control system requirements for a 24 pulse/rev stepper motor, which is to rotate at a speed of approximately 25 rev/min, is as follows:

1. If bit zero of the controller input port is switched low (logic '0') then the motor is to rotate clockwise continuously.
2. If bit 1 of the input port is switched low then the motor is to rotate anticlockwise continuously.
3. If bit 7 of the input port is switched low then the motor is to stop rotating and control is to return to checking whether bit 1 or bit 2 have been activated.

All switches are of the normally open, spring return type (see Sec. 10.1). The controller I/O is based on an 8255 PPI with a base address of &H1B0. The port connections are illustrated in Fig. 9.2 and a flow diagram for the control requirements is given in Fig. 9.3.

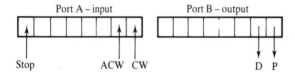

Figure 9.2 I/O port connections for driving the stepper motor.

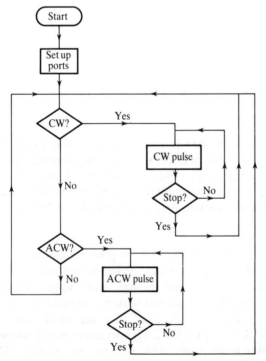

Figure 9.3 Flow diagram for stepper motor control.

The stepper motor requires 24 pulses/rev and the speed is to be approximately 25 rev/min. Hence the frequency of the pulse train is

$$f = 24(25/60) = 10\,\text{Hz}$$

and period $T = 1/f = 0.1$ s. This can be taken as the delay in the pulse train generation. The program listing, which follows the flow diagram, is given in Program 9.10.

Program 9.10 Driving a stepper motor.

```
        ba = &H1B0
        porta = ba: portb = ba + 1: cr = ba + 3
        OUT cr, &H90: REM porta input and portb output

        DO
        IF (INP(porta) AND 1) = 0 THEN GOSUB cw
        IF (INP(porta) AND 2) = 0 THEN GOSUB acw
        LOOP

cw:
        DO WHILE (INP(porta) AND 128) = 128
        OUT portb, 0
        GOSUB delay
        OUT portb, 1
        LOOP
        RETURN

acw:
        DO WHILE (INP(porta) AND 128) = 128
        OUT portb, 2
        GOSUB delay
        OUT portb, 3
        LOOP
        RETURN

delay:
        t = TIMER
        WHILE (TIMER - t) < .1: WEND
        RETURN
```

When this program is executed it is found that the motor rotates at 23 rev/min and not 25 rev/min as expected. This is due to the time taken to execute the BASIC statements in the motor driving loop which effectively decreases the frequency and thus decreases the speed. If a more accurate value of speed is required then the magnitude of the delay can be fine tuned on a trial and error basis.

Also note in the program listing the use of the logical AND instruction to detect when a particular bit on an input port has undergone a high to low transition. The technique involves the choosing of a 'mask' composed of zeros except for the bit to be examined. The port state is then ANDed with this mask and the result is indicative of whether an input switch has been activated.

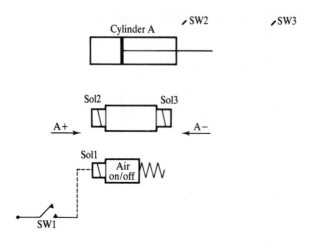

Figure 9.4 Circuit for the sequencing of a single pneumatic cylinder.

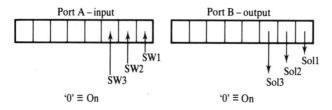

Figure 9.5 I/O port connections for the sequencing operation.

Example Consider the sequencing of a double-acting pneumatic linear actuator (A) as required in (say) a clamping operation as part of an automation process. Following the activation of a normally open start switch which switches air via a solenoid/spring return on/off valve into a double solenoid-operated directional control valve, the sequence for A is as follows:

A + ; 5 second delay; A − ; with the cycle repeating 10 times   (see Sec. 6.4)

The system is illustrated diagrammatically in Fig. 9.4.

The I/O requirements of the controller, which is again based on an 8255PPI with a base address of &H1B0, are three inputs and three outputs. The connections chosen are illustrated in Fig. 9.5 and the interfaces are such that a logic 0 denotes the activation state for both the inputs and the outputs.

A control program listing is shown in Program 9.11.

File handling Data can be held in an ASCII format in a created file. Sequential file handling techniques are a straightforward way to write to and read from disk files. The files are generally portable to other programs and they can be used with wordprocessors and text editors. They are particularly useful in data acquisition applications where physical data pertaining to process information such as temperatures and speeds are logged on a basis of regular time intervals. In fast-acting applications the raw data is primarily held in RAM and then transferred as a block to a more permanent storage medium such as a disk. The data can then be retrieved as required and processed as necessary. The basic principles behind sequential files is to write to them as if

Program 9.11 Sequencing of a pneumatic cylinder.

```
        ba = &H1B0
        porta = ba: portb = ba + 1: cr = ba + 3
        OUT cr, &H90: REM porta input and portb output

sw1:
        REM check for start switch being on
        IF (INP(porta) AND 1) = 1 THEN GOTO sw1
        REM switch on air and retract cylinder
        OUT portb, 250
        REM wait until cylinder fully retracted
check:
        IF (INP(porta) AND 2) = 2 THEN GOTO check

        REM complete 10 cycles
        FOR k = 1 TO 10
        REM extend cylinder and start delay once end of stroke is reached
        OUT portb, 252
sw3:
        IF (INP(porta) AND 4) = 4 THEN GOTO sw3
        GOSUB delay
        REM retract cylinder and check for end of stroke
        OUT portb, 250
sw2:
        IF (INP(porta) AND 2) = 2 THEN GOTO sw2
        NEXT k

        REM switch everything off
        OUT portb, 255
        END

delay:
        t = TIMER
        WHILE ((TIMER - t) < 5): WEND
        RETURN
```

they were the screen memory and read from them as if they were the keyboard. A file can be created and written to as follows:

1. Open the specified file in a sequential OUTPUT mode. The 'OUTPUT' refers to the transfer of data from the computer memory to the disk file, e.g.

OPEN"A:file.dat" FOR OUTPUT AS #1

The named 'file.dat' would in this case be created on drive A.

A file must first be opened before any I/O operation can be performed on it. If the file does not exist then a new one is created. If the file already exists then its current contents are erased and the file is treated as a new file.

The # precedes the file number which is usually between 1 and 255. This number associates an I/O buffer with a disk file and the association exists until the file is closed.

2. Data is then written to the file using PRINT# < file number > .
3. The file is then closed using CLOSE# < file number > .
   This releases all buffer space associated with the closed file.

Example Consider an application where the temperature of an environmental chamber is to be logged at approximately 10 s intervals. The temperature sensor analogue output is converted to a corresponding digital value using an A/D converter routine. Data is to be acquired for a total length of 1 h, which means that 361 pairs of readings indicative of time and temperature are to be stored. A program to perform this task is shown in Program 9.12. The A/D converter routine is not shown.

Program 9.12 Storing time/temperature data to a disk file.

```
        OPEN "temp.dat" FOR OUTPUT AS #1
        REM put number of test points onto the data file
        PRINT #1, 361
        time = 0
more:
        CALL adc(1, I%)
        PRINT #1, time, I%
        GOSUB delay
        time = time + 10
        IF time <= 360 THEN GOTO more
        CLOSE #1
        END


delay:
        t = TIMER
        WHILE (TIMER - t) < 10: WEND
        RETURN
```

The data held in a file can be read as follows:

1. OPEN the named file in a sequential INPUT mode. The 'INPUT' refers to the transfer of data from the disk file to the computer memory, e.g.

   OPEN"A:file.dat" FOR INPUT AS #1

2. Read data from the file using INPUT#1 < file number > .
3. Close the file.

Example Read the time/temperature data from the disk file previously created and store as array elements in RAM. The actual temperature values should be derived by taking 100°C as equivalent to the full 12-bit value. The appropriate program listing is given in Program 9.13.
If the number of test points (N) was not written to the disk file and there is uncertainty as to how much time/temperature data is held then a test can be made for the end-of-file condition. This is the EOF function which has the syntax of EOF(file number). For

Program 9.13 Reading and processing data from a disk file.

```
OPEN "temp.dat" FOR INPUT AS #1
INPUT #1, n
DIM time(n), temp(n)
FOR k = 1 TO n
INPUT #1, time(k), temp(k)
temp(k) = temp(k) * 100 / 4095
NEXT k
CLOSE #1
REM temperature/time data can now be processed as required
END
```

example, declare an array of size 1000 for time and temperature and test for the end-of-file using the following routine:

```
K=0
DO WHILE NOT EOF(1) AND K<=1000
INPUT#1,Time(K),Temp(K)
K=K+1
LOOP
```

Graphics There are many applications in data acquisition and control which can benefit from a graphical display of information. On the PC there are a number of screen display standards which can be set by an instruction within a program. The main graphics hardware standards for an IBM PC are:

CGA Colour Graphics Adapter
EGA Enhanced Graphics Adapter
VGA Video Graphics Adapter

The SCREEN statement is used to specify a screen mode which defines the resolution of the graphics and thus the clarity of the images produced. The screen display is composed of a grid of picture elements, termed pixels, and the larger the number of pixels the higher the clarity of the graphics produced. For example, SCREEN 1 gives a resolution of 320 pixels horizontally by 200 pixels vertically (320×200) with the coordinates measured relative to the top left hand corner of the screen. This screen mode supports CGA, EGA and VGA. SCREEN 9 gives a higher resolution of 640×350 but does not support CGA.

The background and foreground colours are set by the COLOR statement. In SCREEN 1 this has a unique syntax that includes a palette argument which is a 0 or a 1. Each palette has three defined colours with the default being palette 1 and colour white for the foreground graphics. The specification of COLOR 1 will set white graphics on a blue background.
The codes for the logical colours are:

0	black (default)	8	grey
1	blue	9	light blue
2	green	10	light green
3	cyan	11	light cyan
4	red	12	light red
5	magenta	13	light magenta
6	brown	14	yellow
7	white	15	high intensity white

In SCREEN 9 the syntax for the colour command is:

COLOR foreground, background

hence

COLOR 14,1

will produce yellow graphics on a blue background.

The graphics mode and the colour requirement can be defined appropriately within a program. Once this has been done it is then necessary to plot points, draw lines and add text. This must be done within the coordinate system chosen for the defined SCREEN. Hence, some scaling to define physical quantities which are to be plotted into the screen coordinate reference system must be performed.

The VIEW statement can be used effectively to define a graphics 'viewport' inside the screen boundary. All graphics then take place within this viewport and any graphics outside are ignored or 'clipped'. The syntax for VIEW is

VIEW $(x1,y1)-(x2,y2)$

where x1,y1 defines the top left-hand pixel coordinates of the viewport and x2,y2 defines the bottom right-hand corner.

Viewport coordinates can be redefined to suit a situation with actual x,y sizes using the WINDOW statement. This eliminates the need for scaling and makes the plotting of graphs easy. The statement allows a change in the way that pixels are addressed relative to the top left-hand corner, and any appropriate coordinate system can be chosen. The syntax for WINDOW is

WINDOW $(x1,y1)-(x2,y2)$

where x1 and x2 are real numbers which define the logical coordinates for the range of x values and y1 and y2 are those for the y axis.

Points can be drawn on the screen using the PSET instruction which takes the form:

PSET (X,Y),colour

where the colour code for the point is optional. If it is unspecified then the point will be plotted in the foreground colour defined. The x,y coordinates are absolute values and will conform to the screen pixel values if WINDOW has not been defined.

Lines can be drawn on the screen using the LINE instruction which takes the form

LINE $(x1,y1)-(x2,y2)$, colour

where the colour code for the line is optional. The x,y coordinates specify the end points of the line. An abbreviated form is:

LINE$-(x,y)$

which draws a line to the specified coordinates from the current cursor position (most recent point). The cursor can be positioned as required using the PSET command.

Text can be printed on the graph by first positioning the cursor to a specified location and printing text to the screen in the normal manner. The syntax is as follows:

LOCATE row, column
PRINT " < required text > "

The integer quantities of row and column generally require a trial and error process to obtain the desired location for the text.

Example Consider plotting the graph of

$$Y = X^2 + 5$$

between the limits of $0 < X < 3$.
A suitable program for a CGA graphics format is illustrated in Program 9.14.

Program 9.14 Display of graph in CGA graphics.

```
SCREEN 1:                      REM CGA graphics (320 x 200)
COLOR 1:                       REM white lines on a blue background
VIEW (50, 30)-(290, 170):  REM set up graphics window
WINDOW (0, 0)-(3, 15):     REM X axis is 0-3 and Y axis is 0-15
LINE (0, 0)-(3, 0):        REM draw X axis
LINE (0, 0)-(0, 15):       REM draw Y axis
PSET (0, 5):               REM position first point, X0,Y0
FOR x = .1 TO 3 STEP .1:   REM plot graph
y = x ^ 2 + 5
LINE -(x, y)
NEXT x
LOCATE 23, 20:             REM put text on graph
PRINT "x-axis"
LOCATE 12, 1
PRINT "y-axis"
LOCATE 3, 12
PRINT "graph of Y=X^2+5"
END
```

Example The differential equation which describes the variation in displacement (x) with time (t) for a spring/mass system with damping is

$$M\,d^2x/dt^2 + R\,dx/dt + Sx = 0$$

where M is the system mass, R is the damping coefficient and S is the spring stiffness.
The solution for light damping $(\zeta < 1)$ is

$$x = A\exp(-\zeta\omega_n t)\sin(\omega_d t + \phi)$$

with $\zeta = R/(2\,\text{sqrt}(SM))$
$\quad\omega_n = \text{sqrt}(S/M)$
$\quad\omega_d = \omega_n\text{sqrt}(1 - \zeta^2)$
$\quad\phi = \tan^{-1}[\omega_d/\zeta\omega_n)]$
$\quad A = x_o/\sin\phi$ where x_o is the initial displacement
The period of the oscillation is $2\pi/\omega_d$.
Display graphically the variation in x with t over four periods.
Use data of: $M = 1\,\text{kg}$; $S = 100\,\text{N\,m}^{-1}$; $R = 2\,\text{Ns\,m}^{-2}$ and $x_o = -200\,\text{mm}$.
A program listing is given in Program 9.15.

Programming in Turbo C

C is fast becoming one of the most popular programming languages for a range of industrial applications. It has excellent control and data structures which enable algorithms to be

Program 9.15 Display of a damped oscillation.

```
start:
      CLS
      INPUT "mass (M) in kg                = "; m
      INPUT "spring stiffness (S) in N/m   = "; s
      INPUT "damping cofficient (R) in Ns/m = "; r
      INPUT "initial displacement in mm    = "; x0

      xi = r / (2 * SQR(s * m))
      IF xi >= 1 THEN GOTO start
      wn = SQR(s / m)
      wd = wn * SQR(1 - xi ^ 2)
      phi = ATN(wd / (xi * wn))
      a = x0 / SIN(phi)

      period = 2 * 3.14159265# / wd
      tmax = 4 * period

      SCREEN 9: REM EGA/VGA graphics (640 x 350)
      COLOR 14, 1: REM yellow lines on a blue background
      REM define graphics window to be used
      VIEW (80, 30)-(600, 300)
      WINDOW (0, -x0)-(tmax, x0)
      REM draw axes
      LINE (0, 0)-(tmax, 0)
      LINE (0, -x0)-(0, x0)
      REM position the first point
      PSET (0, x0)

      dt = period / 50

      REM now plot graph of x=f(t)
      FOR t = dt TO tmax STEP dt
      x = a * EXP(-xi * wn * t) * SIN(wd * t + phi)
      LINE -(t, x)
      NEXT t

      LOCATE 12, 3
      PRINT "x-mm"
      LOCATE 14, 65
      PRINT "t-seconds"
      END
```

expressed concisely. The compiled codes are also very transportable. The language was developed at the Bell Laboratories in 1972 and is closely associated with the UNIX operating system. No computer programming language conforms to a 100% standard but the accepted definition for C is that by Kernighan and Ritchie (K&R). Most C compilors conform to this standard although porting code from one CPU architecture to another may cause problems. To overcome this the American National Standards Institute (ANSI) defined the ANSI C standard in 1989. This standard retains a large portion of the original language, as defined by K&R, and a number of areas which were not fully defined were formalized. Borland's Turbo C supports the ANSI standard and fully supports the K&R definition of the language. Turbo C comes as an integrated development environment which includes certain optional extensions for mixed language programming that allow the PCs capabilities to be exploited.

This section provides an overview of the basic C statements that make up a source program. Emphasis is placed on those statements which are invariably used in data acquisition and control applications. For illustrative and comparative purposes the examples will follow exactly the sequence portrayed in the section 'Programming in Quick Basic'.

C consists of a frugal central kernel with an extensive library of support routines. Turbo C is equipped with over 450 library routines that are called from within the source program. These included files perform a wide variety of tasks such as input/output, mathematical functions, timing operations and graphics. The header files are stated as required by a '#include < file.h >' statement at the start of the program. This adds the included files into the source code and the complete program is then compiled and linked to produce executable code.

Although there are many library routines only a few are actually required for all of the previous illustrative examples and details are as follows:

conio.h   used in calling the DOS console I/O routines such as the clearing of the text mode window and placing the cursor in the upper left hand corner (CLRSCR()).
dos.h   used to give declarations needed for DOS and 8086-specific calls. It is used for handling port I/O by calling macros to either read a port state or write data to an output port (inportb and outportb). In this context a macro may be defined as a self-contained module in assembly language. The various libraries contain a number of useful macro routines.
graphics.h used when calls are made for graphics functions.
math.h   used for handling mathematical functions.
stdio.h   used for standard I/O such as outputting text to the screen (printf) and reading values which are input at the keyboard (scanf).
time.h   used in time conversion routines.

The structure of a C program consists of a main function (main()) and possibly other functions which are called from within main. All variables used must be declared as a specified type before they are used. This is normally done at the start of a function and some examples of types are:

char	1 byte	-128 to 127
int	2 bytes	$-32\,768$ to $32\,767$
long	4 bytes	$-2\,147\,483\,648$ to $2\,147\,483\,647$
float	4 bytes	$3.4E^{-38}$ to $3.4E^{38}$ with 7 digit precision
double	8 bytes	$1.6E^{-308}$ to $1.6E^{308}$ with 15 digit precision

Variables which are declared outside a function are taken as global to all functions which follow the declaration. If variables are declared within a function then they apply only to that function.

Input/output In the C language the input of data from the keyboard and the printing of data to the screen requires the < stdio.h > library functions along with the key statements of printf and scanf.

printf. Writes a specified output to the screen which may include formatted numerical values. Formatted integer values are specified as %d and a field width of say 4 would be %4d.

Formatted floating point values are specified as %f and a field width of say 10 with 2 decimal places is %10.2f. The field width includes the decimal point but not the sign of the number, e.g.

```
printf(''\n\npressure=%5.1fkN/m^2'',pa);
```

The \n indicates a new line and note that each statement in a function ends with a semi-colon. The omission of this semi-colon is perhaps the most common syntax error highlighted at the compilation stage.

scanf. Scans and formats input data as specified. The formatted input is then stored at an address which is passed to it as an argument following the format specification. A %d indicates that the variable is of an integer type (int) and a %f is used for floating point values (float). The variable list in a scanf statement is a list of pointers which indicate where the inputs are to be placed. An & indicates that the address or location of the variable is referred to rather than the variable itself.

Example Perform various arithmetical operations on two floating point numbers, X1 and X2, which are input interactively at the keyboard.

A listing is given in Program 9.16. Note that comments are contained between /*.........*/.

Program 9.16 Arithmetic operations with input/output.

```
#include <stdio.h>      /* standard functions for screen I/O */
#include <conio.h>      /* for DOS console I/O routines-clrscr() */
#include <math.h>       /* math functions - 'pow', x to the power y */

main()                  /* start of main function */

{
        float x1,x2,sum,diff,prod,div,power;
        clrscr();       /*  clear the screen */
        printf("first number = ");
        scanf("%f",&x1);
        printf("\n\nsecond number = ");
        scanf("%f",&x2);

        sum=x1+x2;
        printf("\n\n\nthe sum of %f and %f is %f",x1,x2,sum);
        diff=x1-x2;
        printf("\n\nthe difference of %f and %f is %f",x1,x2,diff);
        prod=x1*x2;
        printf("\n\nthe product of %f and %f is %f",x1,x2,prod);
        div=x1/x2;
        printf("\n\nthe division of %f by %f is %f",x1,x2,div);
        power=pow(x1,x2);
        printf("\n\n%f to the power of %f is %f",x1,x2,power);

}
```

Unlike BASIC, data cannot be read from a data statement. However, a data block of numerical values can be declared explicitly at the head of a function along with the other variable declarations for int and float values, e.g.

```
float x[]={0,1.1,1.9,3.0,4.1};
float y[]={1.1,2.9,8.7,19.3,33.1};
```

would assign values to array elements for x and y in the range of 0–4.

The arithmetic operators are:

$$+, -, /, *$$

as illustrated in the example. x^y is indicated by the function 'pow' in the math.h library, i.e. pow(x,y).

It should be noted that calculations involving integers and floating point numbers may produce incorrect answers and decimal points should be used with all floating point calculations as necessary. For example, if 'temp' is declared as type float and 'I' as type int then the following would be used to calculate temp from a known I value:

```
temp=100.0*(I/4095.0);
```

The logical operators, for bit manipulation or Boolean operations are

& is a bitwise AND
| is a bitwise OR

The functional trigonometric operators are

sqrt, sin, cos, tan, asin, acos, atan

e.g.

y = sqrt(x);   /*square root of x */
z = atan(y);   /*tan^{-1} of y */

I/O for memory locations
peek   examines a memory location addressed by segment:offset and returns a word. It takes the form: peek(segment,offset).
peekb   similar to peek but a byte is returned.
poke   stores a word at a given memory location addressed by segment:offset. It takes the form: poke(segment,offset,value).
pokeb   same as poke except that a byte is deposited instead of a word.

I/O for ports with dedicated addressing
inportb   reads a byte from a specified port and takes the form: inport(port address).
outportb   writes a byte to a specified port and takes the form: outportb(port address, value).

All of these instructions are unique to the 8086 family of microprocessors and require the dos.h library to be included.

Example Consider the example given in Program 9.2 where an input port is continuously monitored and its state is output to an output port. The comparative program in C is given in Program 9.17.

Program 9.17 Illustration of input/output via ports.

```
#include <dos.h>
main()
{
        int ba=0x1b0;
        int porta,portb,cr,i;

        porta=ba;
        portb=ba+1;
        cr=ba+3;

        outportb(cr,0x90);
more:
        i=inportb(porta);
        outportb(portb,i);
        goto more;
}
```

Note that hexadecimal numbers are preceded with a'0x'.

Conditional statements The general form of this statement is

```
if(conditional expression)
    statement 1;
else
    statement 2;
```

The 'if' instruction can be used without the 'else' and when the 'conditional expression' is FALSE the next program instruction is obeyed directly.

A number of statements can be governed by the 'if' and 'else' provided that they are bracketed with { and }. When necessary an 'if . . . . else if' type of structure can be used as follows:

```
if (conditional expression 1)
{
        statements;
}
else if (conditional expression 2)
{
        statements;
}
else if (conditional expression 3)
{
        statements;
}
else
{
        statements;
}
```

The conditional operators are:

```
==  equal to
!=  not equal to
>   greater than
<   less than
>=  greater than or equal to
<=  less than or equal to
```

Example Consider the software-generated ON/OFF thermostat with the listing given in Program 9.3. The corresponding program in C is shown in Program 9.18.

Program 9.18 Use of conditional statement for ON/OFF temperature control.

```c
#include <stdio.h>
#include <conio.h>
main()
{
        float setpoint,temp;
        clrscr();
        printf("setpoint in deg C = ");
        scanf("%f",&setpoint);
heatoff:
        clrscr();
        printf("\n   heater OFF");
readtemp:
        printf("\n\n\n room temperature in deg C = ");
        scanf("%f",&temp);
        if (temp>=setpoint)
        goto heatoff;
        clrscr();
        printf("\n   heater ON ");
        goto readtemp;
}
```

Example Now consider the flow chart shown in Fig. 9.1 which is illustrative of the problem on the control of a room and boiler temperature. The BASIC program is shown in Program 9.4 and the corresponding listing in C is given in Program 9.19.

Program 9.19 ON/OFF control of room and boiler temperatures.

```c
#include <stdio.h>
#include <conio.h>
main()
{
        float roomset,boilerset,roomtemp,boilertemp;
        clrscr();
        printf("required room temerature in deg C = ");
        scanf("%f",&roomset);
        printf("\n\nrequired boiler temperature in deg C = ");
        scanf("%f",&boilerset);
```

```
        clrscr();
        printf("\n boiler OFF and pump OFF");
again:
        printf("\n\n\n   room temperature in deg C = ");
        scanf("%f",&roomtemp);
        printf("\n\n   boiler temperature in deg C = ");
        scanf("%f",&boilertemp);
        if (roomtemp >=roomset)
        goto poffboff;
        if (boilertemp>=boilerset)
        goto ponboff;
        clrscr();
        printf("\n boiler ON and pump ON");
        goto again;
poffboff:
        clrscr();
        printf("\n pump OFF and boiler OFF");
        goto again;
ponboff:
        clrscr();
        printf("\n pump ON and boiler OFF");
        goto again;
}
```

The same unstructured approach has been adopted as for Program 9.4 and a more elegant solution follows later.

Looping statements Loops for repeating sections of code include the FOR, WHILE and DO/WHILE formats. They operate in basically the same way as those available in QUICKBASIC. A summary of the syntax follows:

```
(a)  for (counter=1;counter<=maximum;counter++)
     {
             loop statements;
     }
```

The 'counter + +' indicates the incrementing of the counter by 1 after using its value. To increment in steps of 2 then 'counter + 2' would be used. The FOR loop can also be used with floating point variables, e.g.

```
     for (time=0.0;time<=4*period;time+dt)
     {
             loop statements;
     }
```

would perform all loop statements for the variable time = 0 to time = (4*period) in steps of dt. If the limiting condition is removed then an infinite loop is obtained, e.g.

$$\text{for } (k = 0;;k + +)$$

```
(b)  while (condition)
     {
              loop statements;
     }
(c)  do
     {
              loop statements;
     }
     while (conditional expression);
```

Example Use a FOR loop to process a set of pump characteristic test data as given in the example with the listing in Program 9.5. A version in C is shown in Program 9.20 and note (i) how arrays are declared and (ii) how a data block can be presented.

Program 9.20 Processing test data for a centrifugal pump characteristic.

```c
#include <stdio.h>
#include <conio.h>
#include <math.h>

/*---------------------------------------------------*/

main()

{

int k,speed;
float eta[20],omega;

float q[]={0,10.5,20.0,30.0,40.5};
float dp[]={182.2,190.2,191.1,183.3,152.9};
float t[]={22.6,34.6,44.4,53.2,57.0};

clrscr();

printf("pump speed in rev/min= ");
scanf("%d",&speed);
omega=2.0*3.14159*speed/60.0;

for (k=0;k<=4;k++)
  {
    eta[k]=(q[k]*dp[k])/(omega*t[k]);
  }
clrscr();

printf("          Centrifugal Pump Characteristics\n");
printf("          --------------------------------\n\n");
printf("             Pump Speed= %4d rev\min\n\n\n",speed);
```

```
printf("              Test    Quantity  Efficiency\n");
printf("                       L/s         %\n");
for (k=0;k<=4;k++)
  {
   printf("\n             %2d %10.1f %10.2f",k,q[k],eta[k]*100);
  }
}
```

Subroutines All subroutines in C are known as functions and by using functions it is possible to produce a better structure to a program. The function must be declared by name as a type 'int' or 'float' in the main program depending upon the nature of the value returned from the function to the main program body. Alternatively, if a function returns no value at all then it is declared as type 'void'. If a parameter list is included then the variables must be declared either locally or globally. This can also be done within the parameter list, e.g.

```
float simpson(int n, float dx, float xmin)
```

The value which is to be returned from the function is specified in a 'return' statement at the end of the routine as follows:

$$return(answer);$$

and the function is called from within the main program by

$$answer = simpson(n,dx,xmin);$$

The overall structure of a C program could take the form:

```
#include <all necessary library routines>
declaration of any global variables and functions ();
main ()
{
        declaration of any local variables and functions ();
        program statements;
}
type function(parameter list if any)
declaration of local variables or functions;
{
        function statements;
}
```

Other functions can be added as required.

Example Consider the ON/OFF control application illustrated by the flow diagram in Fig. 9.1. A structured program in QUICKBASIC is given in Program 9.6. A subroutine is used for returning the analogue to digital converter value which is representative of the room or boiler temperature. A comparative listing in C is given in Program 9.21.

Although a number of parameters can be passed into the function only one value is returned. In applications where more than one parameter is evaluated within the called function a different approach must be employed. This involves the use of pointers to hold the address of the parameters which are to be passed from the function to the main program. Most variables in

Program 9.21 ON/OFF control using a more structured approach.

```c
#include <stdio.h>
#include <conio.h>
#include <dos.h>
        int i;
main()
{
        int chanrt,chanbt,adc();
        float roomset,boilerset,roomtemp,boilertemp;
        outportb(0x1b3,0x90);    /* set up digital I/O ports */
        outportb(0x703,0x92);    /* set up ports for analogue I/O card */
        outportb(0x1b1,0);       /* pump OFF and boiler OFF */
        clrscr();

        printf("\n\n required room temperature in deg C= ");
        scanf("%f",&roomset);
        printf("\n\n required boiler temperature in deg C= ");
        scanf("%f",&boilerset);
        printf("\n\n channel number on analogue card for room temp= ");
        scanf("%d",&chanrt);
        printf("\n\n channel number on analogue card for boiler temp= ");
        scanf("%d",&chanbt);
do
{

        i=adc(chanrt);
        roomtemp=100.0*(i/4095.0);
        i=adc(chanbt);
        boilertemp=100.0*(i/4095.0);
        if (roomtemp>=roomset)
                outportb(0x1b1,0);       /* pump OFF and boiler OFF */
        else if (boilertemp>=boilerset)
                outportb(0x1b1,1);       /* pump ON and boiler OFF */
        else
                outportb(0x1b1,3);       /* pump ON and boiler ON */
}
while(1);                                /* infinite loop */
}
/*************************************************************/
        int adc(int chan)                /* A/D converter routine */
        {
        int c1,c2,k,lsb,msb;
        c1=(chan*16)+2;
        c2=(chan*16)+3;
        outportb(0x702,c1);                 /* start conversion */
        outportb(0x702,c2);
        for (k=0;k<=100;k++);               /* small delay */
        lsb=inportb(0x700);                 /* read 8 LSBs */
        msb=(inportb(0x701) & 15);          /* read 4 MSBs */
        i=256*msb+lsb;                      /* evaluate 12 bit number */
        return(i);
```

a program hold the actual data information that the program manipulates. However, it is often the case that it is necessary to note where the data is held rather than just its value. This requires the use of pointers. A pointer is effectively a variable that holds the address of some data, rather than the actual data itself.

Example Evaluate the gradient and intercept for a set of straight line X,Y data using the least squares formulae previously presented. The corresponding QUICKBASIC program listing is given in Program 9.7. When a function that evaluates the gradient and intercept is called from 'main' then these values have to be passed. This can be achieved by using pointers. The appropriate variables are preceded by a '*' and for the call instruction they correspond to the addresses which are denoted by an '&' in the same way that the scanf instruction operates.

Since the function in this case does not explicitly return anything then it is of type 'void'. It must be declared and for the example in question this might take the form:

```
void slf(int N, float *X, float *Y, float *M, float *C);
```

It should be noted that the N X/Y array elements must also be declared in pointer form. The pointers for the gradient and the intercept, evaluated within the routine, are respectively, *M and *C.

The call within the main program is basically as before except that the address of the M and C held data are used, i.e.

slf(N,X,Y,&M,&C);

The numerical results are then simply the M and C values. A program listing is given in Program 9.22.

Program 9.22 Least squares straight line fit.

```
#include <stdio.h>
#include <conio.h>
main()
{
        void slf(int N, float *X, float *Y, float *M, float *C);
        int n=5;
        float m,c;
        float x[]={0,1,2,3,4};
        float y[]={0.9,3.2,5.1,6.8,9.0};

        slf(n,x,y,&m,&c);

        clrscr();
        printf("\n\n gradient = %f",m);
        printf("\n\n intercept= %f",c);
}
/***********************************************************/

        void slf(int N, float *X, float *Y, float *M, float *C)
{
        int k;
```

```
      float sumx=0;
      float sumy=0;
      float sumxy=0;
      float sumxx=0;

      for (k=0;k<=N-1;k++)      /* note that arrays are numbered from 0 */
{
      sumx=sumx+X[k];
      sumy=sumy+Y[k];
      sumxy=sumxy+(X[k]*Y[k]);
      sumxx=sumxx+(X[k]*X[k]);
}
      *M=((sumx*sumy)-(N*sumxy))/((sumx*sumx)-(N*sumxx));
      *C=((sumx*sumxy)-(sumxx*sumy))/((sumx*sumx)-(N*sumxx));
}
```

Example Now consider, for comparative purposes, the example on iteration to calculate the necessary pipe diameter in a hydraulic power transmission system for a given transmission efficiency. The QUICKBASIC listing is Program 9.8 and the corresponding C listing is shown in Program 9.23. Note the iteration procedure and the use of the function to evaluate the pipe friction coefficient from the Reynolds number and the pipe roughness value.

Program 9.23 Pipe-line design using an iterative procedure.

```
      #include <stdio.h>
      #include <math.h>
      #include <conio.h>

/*-------------------------------------------*/
      main()
  {
      float eta,ef,fold,fnew,d,re,kd,f_factor();
      float h=300.0;
      float L=600.0;
      float q=8.38;
      float k=0.15e-3;
      float nu=1.0e-6;
      float pi=3.14159;

      clrscr();

      printf("\n\n\n     Transmission Efficiency (%) = ");
      scanf("%f",&eta);

      ef=9.81*h*(1-eta/100.0);
      fnew=0.005;

  do
  {
```

```
            fold=fnew;
            d=pow(((32.0*fold*L*q*q)/(pi*pi*ef)),0.2);
            re=(4.0*q)/(pi*nu*d);
            kd=k/d;
            fnew=f_factor(re,kd);
        }
        while (fabs(fnew-fold)>1.0e-6);

        printf("\n\n\n    pipe diameter= %.1f mm",d*1000.0);
    }


    /*--------------------------------------------------------------*/

        float f_factor(reno,roughfactor)
        float reno,roughfactor;


    {
        float c1,c2,c3,c4,c5,c6,c7,a,b;
        float fnew;

        c1=pow(7.0/reno,0.9);
        c2=c1+(0.27*roughfactor);
        c3=1/c2;
        c4=log(c3);
        a=pow(2.457*c4,16)/1e6;
        b=pow(37530.0/reno,16)/1e6;
        c5=pow(8.0/reno,12);
        c6=pow(a+b,1.5);
        c7=1/c6;
        fnew=pow(c5+c7,0.083333)*0.357;
        return(fnew);
    }
```

Timing operations A delay of a specified number of milliseconds (n) can be inserted into a program by the instruction:

$$delay(n);$$

If the time interval between two events is required then the instruction 'clock', which determines the processor time, can be used in conjunction with the macro CLK_TCK as follows:

```
    #include<time.h>
    #include<stdio.h>
    main ()
    {
        clock_tT1,T2;
        T1=clock();
        /* code to be timed goes here */
        T2=clock;
        printf"\n\n\n time taken=%f seconds",(T2-T1)/CLK_TCK);
    }
```

Note that the use of the timing facility requires the library 'time.h' and that clocked variables are declared as clock_t values.

Example The example outlined in Program 9.9 with the corresponding listing in Program 9.24 is illustrative of the use of some of the timing functions. The input corresponding to the keyboard key character pressed is obtained through the instruction 'getch' which is available within the conio library.

Program 9.24 Measurement of reaction time.

```
#include <stdio.h>
#include <stdlib.h>  /* random functions are in this library */
#include <conio.h>
#include <time.h>

void randomdelay();

main()
{
        clock_t t1,t2;
        clrscr();
        randomize();
        printf("\n press SPACE BAR when prompted\n");
        randomdelay();
        printf("\n\n\n\n Press SPACE BAR NOW!!!\n");
        t1=clock();
        while (getch() != ' ');
        t2=clock();
        printf("\n\n time taken = %f ms",1000*(t2-t1)/CLK_TCK);
        exit(0);        /* return to the operating system */
}

void randomdelay(void)
{
        int wait;
        wait=random(11); /* returns an integer between 0 and 10 */
        delay(wait*1000);
}
```

Example Now consider the driving of a stepper motor according to the flow diagram given in Fig. 9.3 with the I/O port connections displayed in Fig. 9.2. The QUICKBASIC listing is in Program 9.10 and the corresponding self-explanatory listing in C is given in Program 9.25.

Program 9.25 Driving a stepper motor.

```c
#include <dos.h>
#include <conio.h>

int porta=0x1b0;
int portb=0x1b1;
int conreg=0x1b3;

void cw(void);
void acw(void);

main()
{
        outportb(conreg,0x90);   /* set up ports- A input and B output */
        do
        {
        if ((inportb(porta) & 1)==0)    /* check for CW rotation */
        cw();
        if ((inportb(porta) & 2)==0)    /* check for Anti-CW rotation */
        acw();
        }
        while(1);
}

void cw(void)                           /* CW driving routine */
{
        while ((inportb(porta) & 128)==128) /* check for STOP condition */
        {
        outportb(portb,0);
        delay(100);
        outportb(portb,1);
        }
}

void acw(void)                          /* Anti-CW driving routine */
{
        while ((inportb(porta) & 128)==128) /* check for STOP condition */
        {
        outportb(portb,2);
        delay(100);
        outportb(portb,3);
        }
}
```

Example The next example relates to the sequencing of a pneumatic cylinder, as shown diagrammatically in Fig. 9.4. The cycle which is to be repeated 10 times is

$$A+; \text{ 5 second delay; } A-$$

The I/O port connections chosen are given in Fig. 9.5 and the QUICKBASIC listing is Program 9.11 The corresponding listing in C is given in Program 9.26.

Program 9.26 Sequencing of a pneumatic cylinder.

```
#include <dos.h>

        int porta=0x1b0;
        int portb=0x1b1;
        int conreg=0x1b3;
        int count;
main()
{
        outportb(conreg,0x90);   /* set up ports- A input and B output */

        while ((inportb(porta) & 1)==1);  /* check for start switch on */
        outportb(portb,250);             /* retract cylinder */
        while ((inportb(porta) & 2)==2);/* check for retracted position */

        for (count=1;count<=10;count++)  /* repeat 10 times */
        {
        outportb(portb,252);             /* extend cylinder */
        while ((inportb(porta) & 4)==4);/* wait for end of stroke */
        delay(5000);                     /* 5 second delay */
        outportb(portb,250);              /* retract cylinder */
        while ((inportb(porta) & 2)==2);/* wait for start of stroke */
        }
        outportb(portb,255);             /* switch everything off */

}
```

File handling The basic principles of writing to an opened sequential file and reading data from the file using C are the same as those used in QUICKBASIC. The file name is specified as a string of characters, e.g. 'tempdata' or 'tempdata.dat'. Once the transfer of data to the file is complete the file is closed with a file pointer fp, e.g.

$$fclose(fp\_tempdata);$$

Example The previous example where temperature data is logged at 10 s intervals is shown in the C format in Program 9.27. The program includes a short routine to check if the specified file can be opened for information to be written to it (w), and if not, due to say insufficient disk space, then the program is terminated. Writing data to the file is the instruction 'fprintf' which is equivalent to 'PRINT#' in QUICKBASIC.

Data held in the file can be read and processed as necessary by using the 'fscanf' instruction associated with the address (&) of the data to be read. This is illustrated in Program 9.28.

Program 9.27 Storing time/temperature data to a disk file.

```
#include <stdio.h>
#include <conio.h>
#include <dos.h>
int i;

main()
{
        int time;
        int n=361;
        FILE *fopen(),*fp_tempdata;

        if (( fp_tempdata=fopen("tempdata","w"))==NULL)
        {
        printf("\n cannot open file 'tempdata' for writing \n");
        printf ("PROGRAM IS TERMINATED");
        exit();
        }

        fprintf(fp_tempdata,"%d\n",n);
        time=0;
        while (time<=360)
        {
        adc(1);   /* call A/D converter routine */
        fprintf(fp_tempdata,"%d %d\n",time,i);
        delay(10000);
        time=time+10;
        }

        fclose(fp_tempdata);
}

{ A/D converter routine goes in here as in program 9.21 }
```

Program 9.28 Reading and processing data.

```
#include <stdio.h>
#include <conio.h>

main()
{
        int k,n,i;
        int t[500];
        float temp[500];

        FILE *fopen(),*fp_tempdata;
        if ((fp_tempdata=fopen("tempdata","r"))==NULL)
        {
        printf("\n cannot open file 'tempdata' for reading\n");
```

```
printf("PROGRAM IS TERMINATED");
}

clrscr();
fscanf(fp_tempdata,"%d\n",&n);
for (k=1;k<=n;k++)
{
fscanf(fp_tempdata,"%d %d\n",&t[k],&i);
temp[k]=i*100.0/4095.0;
printf("\n %d       %f",t[k],temp[k]);
}
fclose(fp_tempdata);
}
```

Graphics The basics of applying graphics routines in Turbo C are similar to those already outlined for QUICKBASIC. A large number of library routines are included in the header file < graphics.h >. The graphics standard adopted is automatically detected by using the instructions 'graphdriver' and 'graphmode' within a graph initialization function. This is set up as follows:

```
#include<graphics.h>
int graphdriver;
int graphmode;

graphdriver=DETECT;
initgraph(&graphdriver,&graphmode,"");
```

Colour control is achieved by setting the background and foreground colours with the instructions 'setbkcolor(colour code)' and 'setcolor(colour code)'. For a CGA the numerical colour codes are the same as those used in QUICKBASIC. On the EGA standard the colours can be called by name, e.g.

> setbkcolor(EGA_BLUE);   /* blue background */
> setcolor(EGA_WHITE);   /* white graphics */

Relative to the top left-hand screen position (0,0) the X axis is 0–640 pixels and the Y axis is 0–460 pixels. Within this framework the instructions to move the cursor, draw a line and print text are, respectively:

> moveto(X,Y);
> lineto(X,Y);
> outtextxy(X,Y,"text to be printed");

Unlike QUICKBASIC there is no WINDOW command which configures to the screen to suit the numerical values appropriate to a physical problem. It is therefore necessary to scale the actual values to the overall screen coordinates.

Example Consider the plotting of the graph $Y = X^2 + 5$ with $0 < X < 3$.
Suppose that the X axis is taken as 500 pixels long and starting at 60 pixels in from the left-hand side of the screen. The Y axis is taken as 350 long and starting 60 up from the bottom of the screen. Bearing in mind that the screen origin (0,0) is the top left-hand corner then the

relationships between the pixel values (X, Y) and the actual values (x, y) are:

$$X = 100 + (x/x_{max}) \times 500$$
$$Y = 400 - (y/y_{max}) \times 350$$

where x_{max} and y_{max} are the maximum physical values to be plotted. (For the example given $x_{max} = 3$ and $y_{max} = 14$.) A program listing for this example is shown in Program 9.29.

Program 9.29 Display of graph in EGA graphics.

```
#include<graphics.h>
#include<math.h>

main()
{
int graphdriver;                              /*include these*/
int graphmode;                                /*for graphics*/
float x,y,xmax,ymax,dx,X,Y;
/*------------------------------------------*/

graphdriver=DETECT;                           /*automatic detection*/
initgraph(&graphdriver,&graphmode,"");  /*of graphics driver*/
setbkcolor(EGA_BLUE);                             /*blue background*/
setcolor(EGA_YELLOW);                            /*yellow foreground*/

xmax=3.0;
dx=0.1;
ymax=pow(xmax,2)+5.0;
                                                 /*draw axes*/
moveto(100,50);
lineto(100,400);
lineto(600,400);

moveto(100,125);                             /*move to first X,Y posit*/

for (x=0.0;x<=xmax+dx/3;x=x+dx)              /*for x=0 to xmax step dx*/
{
y=pow(x,2)+5.0;
X=100.0+(x/xmax)*500.0;                      /*draw graph of y=x^2+5 */
Y=400.0-(y/ymax)*350.0;                      /*note scaling*/
lineto(X,Y);
}

outtextxy(20,230,"y-axis");
outtextxy(300,440,"x-axis");
outtextxy(250,50,"graph of y=x^2+5");                    /*put text on graph*/
}
```

Example Now consider the example illustrated in Program 9.15 which plots the solution to the second-order ordinary differential equation that describes a lightly damped spring/mass system. The corresponding C program is shown in Program 9.30.

Program 9.30 Display of damped oscillation.

```c
#include<stdio.h>
#include<conio.h>
#include<math.h>
#include<graphics.h>

main()
{
int graphdriver;
int graphmode;
float x,t,r,wn,wd,phi,xi,a,period,dt,tmax,X,T;
float m=1.0;
float s=100.0;
float x0=0.2;
float xmax=0.25;
float pi=3.14159;

clrscr();
printf("\n\n\nDamping Coefficient (in Ns/m) = ");
scanf("%f",&r);

xi=r/(2*sqrt(s*m));
wn=sqrt(s/m);
wd=wn*sqrt(1.0-pow(xi,2.0));
phi=atan((wd*x0)/(xi*wn*x0));
a=x0/sin(phi);
period=2.0*pi/wd;
tmax=4.0*period;
dt=period/50.0;

graphdriver=DETECT;
initgraph(&graphdriver,&graphmode,"");
setbkcolor(EGA_BLUE);
setcolor(EGA_YELLOW);

moveto(100,50);
lineto(100,410);
moveto(100,230);
lineto(600,230);

X=230.0-(x0/xmax)*180.0;
moveto(100,X);

for (t=0.0;t<=tmax;t=t+dt)
{
```

```
        x=a*exp(-xi*wn*t)*sin((wd*t)+phi);
        X=230.0-(x/xmax)*180.0;
        T=100.0+(t/tmax)*500.0;
        lineto(T,X);
        }
    }
```

It should be noted that there are many more powerful graphics statements within the C graphics library but those mentioned here provide a basis for incorporating graphical displays into general data acquisition and control applications.

Programming in 8086 Assembly Language

Machine code is the programming language that the computer can execute directly. These instructional codes within a program are a sequence of binary values which are understood specifically by the microprocessor used. For convenience the codes are generally expressed in a hexadecimal format and they relate to such operations as:

data transfer	the moving of data within memory
arithmetic	add, subtract, multiply and divide
logic	bitwise AND and OR
compare	compare two data values
shift program control	

       (i)   conditional of result of a comparison
      (ii)   jump to another area of memory
    (iii)   jump to a subroutine

Programming directly in machine code is difficult and tedious. A step up to make low-level programming easier is to program in an assembly language directly appropriate to the microprocessor being used. This allows the use of mnemonic operation codes, labels and names to refer to numerical equivalents. These memory provoking mnemonic codes, usually comprising three letters, translate directly into the machine code equivalent. This requires the use of an assembler program to translate the mnemonic operation codes and names into their machine code format. The assembler also assigns places in memory for data values and the program instruction codes.

There are a number of assemblers available for 8086/8088 processors such as Borland's Turbo-Assembler, Intel's ASM86, Microsoft's MASM and A86 from the Shareware author Eric Isaacson. The programs listed here have been written for assembling with A86. It is a very fast assembler, over a thousand lines of code per second, and it is complemented by a useful debugging program, D86. However, most assemblers accept much the same style of source code and the differences are usually quite small.

Low-level programming is generally associated with execution speed. It should be noted, however, that this is dependent upon the skill of the programmer in writing efficient and effective code. A well written compiled C program will run faster than a badly written assembly program. Good programming at low level will result in compact codes which can be blown directly into say an EPROM for executing within a small microcontroller without the need for a keyboard or display screen. Hence, the application and the microprocessor-based hardware which is to be used generally dictate whether a low-level or a high-level language should be employed. In a project which requires a large complex program with say graphical displays then it is much cheaper to use a high-level language because of the time factor involved in the writing

Table 9.1 Program numbering for chosen examples.

Example	QUICKBASIC Program number	C Program number	8086 Program number
ON/OFF temperature control	9.3	9.18	9.32
ON/OFF control of room and boiler temperatures	9.4/9.6	9.19/9.21	9.33
Driving a stepper motor	9.10	9.25	9.34
Sequencing of a pneumatic cylinder	9.11	9.26	9.35

and debugging of the instruction codes. It is interesting and useful, however, to have some knowledge of assembly language programming and for comparative purposes some of the previous programs written in QUICKBASIC and C will be developed in 8086 assembly language. The examples chosen are related to simple ON/OFF and sequential control applications. Table 9.1 displays the examples and their corresponding program numbers for QUICKBASIC, C and 8086.

Data Transfer

The transfer of data within a microprocessor is performed through the use of dedicated registers within the chip. The general purpose 16-bit registers within the 8086 are designated as AX, BX, CX and DX. Each is composed of two 8-bit registers termed high byte (H) and low byte (L). Thus AX is composed of AH and AL. The primary function of each is as follows:

AX (accumulator)   Holds one operand and, subsequently, the result of most arithmetic and logic operations.

BX (base)   Used frequently as a base register for referencing a block of data held in memory. It holds the start address and specific locations are referenced by adding an offset value.

CX (count)   Holds a 16-bit counter for a group of instructions that relate to the repeating of a particular sequence.

DX (data)   Used to hold the addresses of I/O ports within an 8255PPI during IN and OUT operations which involve external devices.

The mnemonic instruction associated with moving data is 'MOV' and it takes the following general form for transferring data from a source to a destination:

MOV destination, source

For example, to configure the ports in an 8255 PPI set for a base address of 1B0 hex the assembly language codes are

```
MOV DX,1B3H   ;load control register into DX
MOV AL,90H    ;load 90 hex into AL
OUT DX,AL     ;put 90 hex into the control register
```

The assembled version is

BA B3 01 B0 90 EE

These codes would configure the ports as A input, B output and C output. Note that an address is translated into machine code in the order of low byte followed by high byte.

The destination and source can each be of a different type such as a register, a memory location or an immediately specified value. These combinations are referred to as addressing modes and examples are as follows:

Register addressing

MOV AX,DX	;moves the contents of the 16-bit DX register into the 16-bit AX register
MOV AH,CL	;moves the contents of the 8-bit CL register into the 8-bit AH register

Immediate addressing

MOV DX,1B3H	;moves the value of 1B3 hex into the 16-bit DX register
MOV AL,3	;moves the value of 3 into the 8-bit AL register
MOV CX,0FFFFH	;moves the value of FFFF hex into the 16-bit CX register
MOV w[300H],0FFFH	;moves FF hex into location 300 hex and 0F hex into location 301hex

Direct addressing

MOV AL,b[200H]	;moves the contents held in location 200 hex into the 8-bit AL register
MOV AX,w[300H]	;moves the contents of location 300 hex into AL and the contents of ;301 hex into AH
MOV b[250H],CL	;moves the contents of CL into address 250 hex

It should be noted that the specified square bracketed addresses are offsets from the appropriate segment. Hex values starting with a letter should always be preceded by a zero in order to avoid confusion with registers or data values. When referring to data which is to be held or transferred to an address then the address should be preceded appropriately by a 'b' to indicate a byte (8 bits) or a 'w' to indicate a word (16 bits).

As described in Sec. 8.3 on 'memory organization', the addressable memory space available within a PC at any time is divided up into four 64K segments. These are referred to as the code segment which contains the program codes, the data segment which contains the program data values, the stack segment for holding stack data and the extra segment which can be used as an additional data area. All of these areas may overlap. Segment registers, CS, DS, SS and ES are used to hold the base address of the four addressable segments of memory. The segments should be set up as necessary within the assembly program to ensure that program data values, if used, are kept separate from the program codes. Although it is good practice to set a stack allocation of memory (see Sec. 8.3) the PC's operating system automatically assigns an area of RAM for the stack use.

The 8086/8088 internal architecture supports other registers which have some significance to varying degrees in assembly language programming and for completeness they are detailed as follows:

SP   This is the 'stack pointer' which points to the location of the top of the stack area of memory. Data is pushed on to the stack with the instruction PUSH and retrieved from the stack with the instruction POP.

BP   This is the 'base pointer' which is used to point to the start address of a block of data within the stack area of memory.

SI   This is the 'source index' register which is used in an indirect addressing mode.

DI   This is the 'destination index' register which is also used in certain indirect addressing modes.

IP   This is the 'instruction pointer' or program counter which keeps a check on the instruction codes in memory during the execution process. It holds the address of the next instruction which is to be executed by the microprocessor.

The last register is termed the 'flag register' or processor status register. This register contains a number of flags that reflect the result of an arithmetic or logic operation that has just occurred. The most important flags appropriate to control applications are the zero flag (ZF), the carry flag (CF) and the sign flag (SF). Details of these flags are as follows:

ZF This flag is set (logic 1) when the result of an operation is zero.

CF This flag is set when an operation, such as an addition or subtraction, results in a carry or a borrow into the leftmost bit position of the 8 or 16-bit result.

SF This flag is set when the high-order bit of the result is a logic 1, which is indicative of a negative number (see Sec. 8.2).

Figure 9.6 diagrammatically illustrates the internal registers of the 8086/8088 microprocessor.

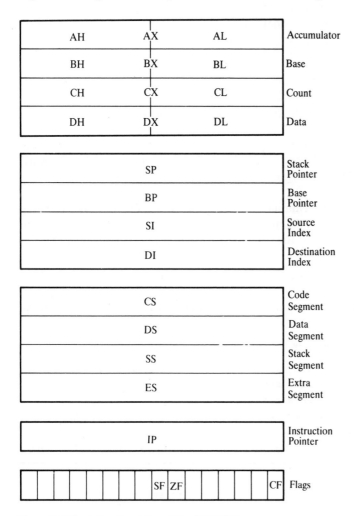

Figure 9.6 The internal registers of the 8086/8088.

Arithmetical Operations

The basic addition, subtraction, multiplication and division mnemonics are

1. ADD destination, source
    puts destination + source data into the destination, e.g.

    > ADD AL,25
    > ADD AX,CX
    > ADD b[300H],8
    > ADD AX,0FFFH

2. SUB destination, source
    puts the destination–source data into the destination, e.g.

    > SUB AL,25
    > SUB b[300H],8
    > SUB AX,OFFFH

3. MUL source
    this is the unsigned multiplication of a source operand data and the accumulator A. For a byte source, AX holds the product of AL times the source data, e.g. MUL b[400H] would store the result in AL of the product of the byte held at 400H with the data initially held in AL.
    For a word source then AX,DX (low byte, high byte) holds the product of AX times the source data, e.g. MUL w[400H] would store the result as AX,DX of the product of the word stored at 400H (low byte), 401H (high byte) and the initial data held in AX.

4. DIV source
    performs an unsigned division of the accumulator (AX) by the source operand. If the source operand is a byte then AX/source gives the quotient in AL and the remainder in AH. If the operand is a word then AX/source gives the quotient in AX and the remainder in DX.

Example on addition Add two numbers of say 7 and 8. Allocate data locations for these values and the answer to the addition.

A layout for this exercise is shown in Program 9.31 and comments are added appropriately.

Program 9.31 Layout of an 8086 assembly language.

```
;program to illustrate the layout of a typical 8086 assembly program
dseg     segment           ;set up data segment address area
org      1000h             ;origin offset for data segment
num1     db       ?        ;allocate variable space as a byte, no initial value
num2     db       ?        ;......ditto.......
ans      db       00       ;initialise variable space as a byte with value zero
dseg     ends


sseg     segment           ;set up stack segment area of memory
org      1200h             ;start of stack is at 1200 hex
DW       600h     DUP(0)   ;set stack for 300 (hex) words initialised as 0
sseg     ends


cseg     segment           ;set up code segment area of memory
```

```
org      100h               ;offset of 100h as for a .COM file
assume ds:dseg,ss:sseg,cs:cseg  ;initialises all segments to the default
                                ;value set up by the PC at startup and all
                                ;addresses are offset relative to this.
;*****************************
begin:
         mov     num1,07       ;move values to be added into locations
         mov     num2,08       ;defined in the data segment
;*****************************
         mov     al,num1       ;move first number into accumulator (8-bit)
         add     al,num2       ;move second number into accumulator(8-bit)
         mov     ans,al        ;store answer to 8-bit addition
         mov     ax,4ch        ;clean return to operating system which is
         int     21h           ;supported by DOS 5
cseg     ends
         end
```

The addition could have been performed without declaring locations within the data segment as set up. Data values could have been used directly and the answer could be stored at a location which is well into the default segment, say at an offset of [200H]. The resulting complete program is simply:

```
MOV AL,7          ;move the value '7' into AL register
ADD AL, 8         ;add the value of '8' to AL data
MOV b[200H],AL    ;store answer as a byte at 200H
INT 21H           ;return to operating system
```

The result as 0FH can be viewed in location 200H by using the program DEBUG which is supplied with MS-DOS. This is done as follows:

First assemble the source code, say ex.asm, using an assembler, e.g.

A86 ex.asm

This produces a COM file with an offset of 100H from the segment set up by the system.

```
Now run DEBUG with:   debug <CR>
At the prompt, type: n        <followed by the name of the file 'ex.com'><CR>
then type:           1<CR><this loads the COM file>
A'u'<CR> displays the codes and their mnemonics for the program from 100H.
A'd100'<CR> displays the codes from 100H.
g=100<CR> will execute the codes at any time from 100H.
A'd200'<CR> will display the data codes held from 200H and the value of 0F will be
observed at this location.
Use 'q'<CR> to quit and return to DOS.
```

DEBUG is a useful tool for looking at data in memory but it must be borne in mind that the codes must actually be executed within the debug environment so that all codes and data values are relative to the common segment address set up by the system.

Example on subtraction Subtract FE0 hex from FF0 hex.

```
MOV AX,0FF0H
SUB AX,0FE0H
MOV w[200H],AX
INT 3
```

Note: the INT 3 instruction is useful when executing codes within DEBUG as it displays the state of the registers prior to returning to DOS. When the above program is assembled and its COM file executed within debug the answer of 10 hex is shown in the AX register and it can also be displayed at location 200H.

Examples on multiplication (i) Multiply 27 hex by 3.

```
MOV AL,27H
MOV BL,3
MUL BL
INT 3
```

The answer can be displayed in the AX register as 75 hex which is correct.
(ii) Multiply 1000 hex by 10 hex

```
MOV w[400H],1000H
MOV AX,10H
MUL w[400H]
INT 3
```

The answer is displayed in the AX and DX registers as 0000 and 0001, respectively. This indicates a result of 1 0000 hex which is correct.

Examples on division (i) Divide 7 by 2.

```
MOV b[400H],2
MOV AX,7
DIV b[400H]
INT 3
```

The answer is displayed in the AX register as 0103 which indicates 3 remainder 1.
(ii) Divide 1001 hex by 4.

```
MOV w[400H],4
MOV AX,1001H
DIV w[400H]
INT 3
```

The answer is displayed in the AX and DX register as 0400 and 0001, respectively which gives 400 hex remainder 1 which is correct.

Using the I/O ports on an 8255 PPI All of the I/O port activities are performed via the DX register which must first be loaded appropriately with the control register address or a port address prior to performing an OUT (output) or an IN (input) via the accumulator AL. For example, the instructions for setting up say port A as input and ports B and C as output are

```
MOV DX,conreg   ;load control register address into the DX register
MOV AL,90H      ;load 90 hex into the AL register
OUT DX,AL       ;transfer 90 hex into the control register address
```

Values are then output from say the B port with

```
MOV DX,portb    ;load port B address into the DX register
MOV AL,value    ;load byte value to be output into the accumulator
OUT DX,AL       ;output value from port B
```

and values are read into the accumulator, AL from say port A with:

```
MOV DX,porta    ;load port A address into the DX register
IN AL,DX        ;read state of port A into the accumulator
```

Logic operations The bitwise AND takes the form:

$$AND\ destination,source$$

which performs the logical 'AND' of the two operands which may be either in a byte or word format. The result is returned to the destination operand. For example, suppose that BX contains AC07H and CX contains 23F4H then the execution of the instruction AND BX,CX would produce a result of 2004H in the BX register while the data in the CX register is unaltered.

The bitwise OR takes the form:

$$OR\ destination,source$$

which performs the logical 'OR' of the two operands which may be in either a byte or a word format. The result is returned to the destination operand.

Both of these instructions can be used in the immediate, direct or register addressing modes previously outlined.

Jump and branch instructions A departure from the normal one-step incrementing through a sequence of program codes can be achieved by:

1. An unconditional jump (JMP) which transfers control to a specified location, usually represented by a label. It takes the form:

$$JMP\ label$$

2. A 'jump to subroutine' call which activates an out-of-line procedure. Once the procedure routine has been executed the return instruction at the end of the procedure (RET) transfers control back to the appropriate position within the main program immediately following the CALL. Use is made of the system stack for temporarily saving the return address. The mnemonic for the operation is

$$CALL\ procedure\_name$$

3. A conditional jump which takes place only if a condition holds. Arithmetic, logic, incrementing, decrementing and compare instructions all affect the state of the flags in the processor status register and the conditional jump instructions are based on the resulting flag states. In control applications the most important flags are invariably the zero flag (Z),

the carry flag (C) and the sign flag (S). A choice of mnemonic code is available in some cases and details are as follows:

JZ (or JE)   jump if Z flag set (1), result equals zero
JNZ (or JNE) jump if Z flag clear (0), result not equal to zero
JC (or JB)   jump if C flag set (1), or jump if below
JNC (or JAE) jump if C flag clear (0), or jump if above or equal
JS   jump if S flag set (1)
JNS   jump is S flag clear (0)

The conditional jump instructions take the form:

conditional jump instruction followed by a label

The label signifies a position within the program which is effectively an 8-bit relative offset following the conditional jump code. This offset instructs the microprocessor instruction pointer on how many bytes to jump forward ($+$) or backward ($-$) from its current location which will be two bytes ahead of the instruction being executed. This is termed 'relative addressing' and produces relocatable codes which are independent of the actual destination address. The assembler automatically performs the calculation of the offset from the IP position to the label referred to in the conditional jump statement.

Examples (a) Consider a small delay routine equivalent to a FOR/NEXT loop in BASIC or C. This might take the form of say loading a counter of value FF hex into the AL register and decrementing until the result is zero. At this stage the Z flag is set. The appropriate mnemonics and machine codes are:

```
        MOV AL,OFFH  ;load 255 into 8 bit accumulator
more:
        DEC AL       ;decrement value in the accumulator
        JNZ more     ;keep decrementing until the Z flag set

        B0 FF FE C8 75 FC
```

The code 'FC' indicates that the instruction pointer must jump back 4 locations (-4) when the conditional jump instruction is taken.

(b) Consider the case where a sequence of operations is dependent upon say bit 5 of an input portA experiencing a high to low transition. The corresponding mnemonic codes are:

```
        MOV DX, portA  ;load port A address into the DX register
check:
        IN AL,DX       ;transfer state of port A into the accumulator
        AND AL,20H     ;AND accumulator data with mask of 0010 0000
        JNZ check      ;keep checking if PA5 has not gone low
```

(c) Consider the case where two values are to be compared and a decision made according to the result. This uses the 'compare' instruction which takes the form:

CMP destination,source

This alters flags according to the result of the (destination (A)-source (M)) data. The operands may be bytes or words and their values are unchanged following the subtraction process. A summary of the result on the flags is

	Z	C	S
$A < M$	0	1	1
$A = M$	1	0	0
$A > M$	0	0	0

It is seen that if a test is to be made for the situation where the destination (A) is >= the source (M) the jump will be made with the instruction: JNC (or JAE) to a specified label.

All of the foregoing instructions are illustrated in Programs 9.32 and 9.33 which may be compared with their QUICKBASIC or C counterparts.

Program 9.32 ON/OFF temperature control.

```
        ;example on a "software thermostat"
        porta   equ     1b0h    ;addresses for digital I/O card
        portb   equ     1b1h
        conreg  equ     1b3h
        pa      equ     700h    ;addresses for analogue I/O card
        pb      equ     701h
        pc      equ     702h
        cr      equ     703h


        mov dx,conreg           ;set up digital I/O ports
        mov al,90h              ;B output to switch heater on/off
        out dx,al

        mov dx,cr               ;set up analogue I/O ports
        mov al,92h              ;A input, B input and C output
        out dx,al


off:
        mov dx,portb            ;switch heater off
        mov al,0
        out dx,al
more:
        mov al,1                ;read room temperature on channel 1
        mov dx,pc
        call AtoD               ;A/D converter subroutine
        cmp ax,819             ;evaluate (room temp-setpoint of 20 deg C)
        jnc off                 ;if temp>=setpoint then goto off
        mov dx,portb            ;if not then switch heater on
        mov al,1
        out dx,al
        jmp more                ;repeat on/off control loop
```

```
AtoD:

        shl al,4               ;select channel on upper nibble of portc
                               ;by shifting al value 4 bits to the left
        add al,2               ;start conversion on selected channel
        out dx,al
        add al,1
        out dx,al
        call delay             ;small delay for end of conversion
        mov dx,pa              ;read 8 LSBs in al from pa and the 4
        in ax,dx               ;MSBs in ah from pb-note 16 bit read
        and ax,0fffh           ;mask out upper nibble of 16 bit number
        ret                    ;ax now holds the room temperature

delay:                         ;small delay subroutine to allow
        mov cx,0ffh            ;the conversion to be complete
again:
        dec cx
        jne again
        ret
```

Program 9.33 ON/OFF control of room and boiler temperatures.

```
;example on room and boiler temperature control
        mov dx,1b3h    ;set up digital I/O ports
        mov al,90h
        out dx,al
        mov dx,703h    ;set up analogue I/O ports
        mov al,92h
        out dx,al
        mov dx,1b1h     ;boiler off and pump off
        mov al,0
        out dx,al
again:
        mov al,1       ;select A/D channel for room temperature
        mov dx,702h
        call AtoD      ;call A/D converter routine
        cmp ax,819     ;if roomtemp>=20 deg C then switch pump
        jnc poffboff   ;and boiler off
        mov al,2       ;select A/D channel for boiler temperature
        mov dx,702h
        call AtoD
        cmp ax,3276    ;if boilertemp>=80 deg C then switch pump
        jnc ponboff    ;on and boiler off
        mov dx,1b1h    ;else pump on and boiler on
        mov al,3
        out dx,al
```

```
        jmp again        ;read temperatures again
poffboff:
        mov dx,1b1h      ;switch pump off and boiler off
        mov al,0
        out dx,al
        jmp again        ;read temperatures again
ponboff:
        mov dx,1b1h      ;switch pump on and boiler off
        mov al,1
        out dx,al
        jmp again        ;read temperatures again

AtoD:                    ;A/D converter subroutine
        shl al,4
        add al,2
        out dx,al
        add al,1
        out dx,al
        call delay
        mov dx,700h
        in ax,dx
        and ax,0fffh
        ret
delay:
        mov cx,0ffh
more:
        loop more
        ret
```

Producing delay routines in a program Software generated delays in the form of 'waste time' loops can be incorporated into control programs as necessary. The basic procedure is as follows:

```
        Load register or memory location with a counter
        REPEAT
                waste time instructions
        UNTIL counter=0
```

A conditional jump instruction can be used to terminate the decrementing of the counter or alternatively a 'LOOP' instruction can be used. This operates on the basis that if the value held in the CX register is not zero then the automatic decrementing of this value is continued for each loop in the program. It takes the form

```
        MOV CX,counter  ;load number of required loops into CX register
    delay:
        NOP             ;No OPeration—takes 3 clock cycles
        LOOP delay      ;decrement CX register for each loop
```

The LOOP instruction is useful for executing a sequence for a specified number of times as loaded into the CX register.

With single loops, even with 16-bit counter values, the magnitude of the delays produced are actually quite small and for delays of the order of seconds a double loop must be used. For example, say an inner loop with a counter of FFFF hex is to be activated 5 times. The routine is as follows:

```
delay:                          ;delay routine
        MOV w[200H],5           ;counter=5 loaded into address 200
again:
        MOV w[300H],0FFFFH      ;store inner counter at address 300
repeat:
        DEC w[300H]             ;decrement the data held at 300
        JNZ repeat              ;wait until zero reached
        DEC w[200H]             ;decrement the data held at 200
        JNZ again              ;if not zero then load inner counter again
        RET                     ;return from delay routine to main program
```

The time taken to execute the delay routines can be theoretically evaluated since it is known that each instruction takes a precise number of clock cycles. The clock frequency then decides the actual execution time. However, there are slight differences in the clock cycle values for the 8086, 80286, 80386 and 80486 processors. Additionally, the clock frequencies for different makes of PC may vary substantially. For this reason, the outer counter value is best obtained by using a trial and error solution to obtain the delay required. For the double loop shown, with the inner counter held at FFFF hex and an outer counter of 5, a delay of approximately 2 s is produced when executed on an 8086 machine running at 8 MHz. The corresponding outer loop counter for an 80386 running at 20 MHz is 32 decimal. It should be noted that if the outer counter is also set to FFFF hex then the resulting delay can run into hours. Examples of counting and timing are illustrated in Programs 9.34 and 9.35.

Program 9.34 Driving a stepper motor.

```
;program to drive a stepper motor CW or ACW
        porta   equ     01b0h
        portb   equ     01b1h
        conreg  equ     01b3h

        mov dx,conreg           ;set up ports-A input, B-output
        mov al,90h
        out dx,al

start:
        mov dx,porta            ;check for CW rotation
        in al,dx
        and al,1
        jz cw
        mov dx,porta            ;check for ACW rotation
        in al,dx
        and al,2
        jz acw
        jmp start

cw:                             ;cw driving routine
        mov dx,porta            ;check for stop condition
```

```
          in al,dx
          and al,128
          jz fin1
          mov dx,portb        ;pulse motor for cw rotation
          mov al,0
          out dx,al
          call delay
          mov al,1
          out dx,al
          jmp cw
fin1:
          jmp start
acw:                          ;acw driving routine
          mov dx,porta        ;check for stop condition
          in al,dx
          and al,128
          jz fin2
          mov dx,portb        ;pulse motor for acw rotation
          mov al,2
          out dx,al
          call delay
          mov al,3
          out dx,al
          jmp acw
fin2:
          jmp start
delay:                        ;delay subroutine
          mov w[200h],2       ;store counters at specified locations
more:
          mov w[300h],0fffh
repeat:
          dec w[300h]
          jnz repeat
          dec w[200h]
          jnz more
          ret
```

Program 9.35 Sequencing of a pneumatic cylinder.

```
; program to sequence a pneumatic cylinder from the retracted position
          dseg    segment
          org     0200h

          porta   equ     01b0h
          portb   equ     01b1h
          conreg  equ     01b3h

          count1  dw      ?       ;counters for the delay routine
          count2  dw      ?

          dseg    ends
```

```
        cseg    segment
        org     0100h

        mov dx,conreg           ;set up ports-A input and B output
        mov al,90h
        out dx,al
        call off                ;switch all outputs off
        mov cx,10               ;counter for number of cycles
start:
        mov dx,porta            ;check for start switch sw1 on
        in al,dx
        and al,1
        jnz start
more:
        mov dx,portb            ;extend cylinder
        mov al,252
        out dx,al
sw3:
        mov dx,porta            ;wait for end of stroke
        in al,dx
        and al,4
        jnz sw3
        call delay              ;call delay routine
        mov dx,portb            ;retract cylinder
        mov al,250
        out dx,al
sw2:
        mov dx,porta            ;wait for start of stroke
        in al,dx
        and al,2
        jnz sw2
        loop more               ;repeat cycle for counter in cx reg
        call off                ;switch everything off
        int 21h                 ;return to system

off:
        mov dx,portb            ;routine to switch everthing off
        mov al,255
        out dx,al
        ret
delay:
        mov count1,20h          ;delay subroutine
again:
        mov count2,0ffffh
repeat:
        dec count2
        jnz repeat
        dec count1
        jnz again
        ret
```

Indexed addressing All of the previous programs are illustrative of register, immediate, direct and relative addressing but there is another mode which is useful for accessing blocks of data in memory with only a single instruction. An index register such as the 'source index' (SI) can be used to hold a displacement which is automatically added to a base value when forming an effective address. The base address of the block of memory being accessed can be stored in the base register BX and by this means a block of data can be referenced by two variables—BX and SI.

Example Suppose that a table of ASCII codes for the 16 hexadecimal digits 0–9 and A–F are stored at addresses 380–38F. The corresponding codes being 30–39 and 41–46.

The problem is to take any hexadecimal digit which is placed at 400, convert it into its ASCII equivalent and then store the result at 401.

Suppose, for example, the value of 0D (with its ASCII equivalent in the table address of 38D) is placed in 400 then the answer of 44 can be obtained by adding the table's base address of 380 to the 0D in order to evaluate the address of the code required. The following program performs this algorithm:

```
MOV BL,b[400H]      ;read hexadecimal digit value
SUB BH,BH           ;clear BH register
MOV AL,[BH+380H]    ;get ASCII code from table
MOV [401H],AL       ;store result
INT 21H             ;return to DOS
```

Both the BX and SI registers can be used for indexing and an alternative program using SI is

```
SUB SI,SI           ;clear the SI register
MOV AL,00           ;clear address 401
MOV [401H],AL
MOV SI,[400H]       ;read hexadecimal digit value
MOV AL,[SI+380H]    ;get ASCII code from table
MOV [401H],AL       ;store result
INT 21H             ;return to DOS
```

There are a number of 8086 mnemonic codes and addressing modes available in addition to those covered. However, the limited instructions included within this section are quite sufficient for a large variety of control applications and give the reader an insight into the fascinating subject of assembly language programming.

FURTHER READING

Bennett, S. (1988) *Real-Time Computer Control: An Introduction*, Prentice-Hall, Englewood Cliffs, NJ.

Bennett, S. and D. A. Linkens (eds) (1986) *Real-Time Computer Control*, Peter Peregrinus, London.

Brey, B. B. (1991) *The Intel Microprocessors—8086/8088, 80186, 80286, 80386 and 80486*, 2nd edn, Merrill/Macmillan, New York.

Cassell, D. A. (1983) *Microcomputers and Modern Control Engineering*, Reston Publishing, Reston, Virginia.

Coffron, J. W. (1983) *Programming the 8086/8088*, Sybex, Paris.

Fraser, C. J. and J. S. Milne (1990) *Microcomputer Applications in Measurement Systems*, Macmillan, London.

Gardner, J. (1989) *From C to C: An Introduction to ANSI Standard C*, HBJ Publishers, San Diego, CA.

Gosling, P. (1990) *Mastering Computer Programming*, 3rd edn, Macmillan, London.

Hahn, B. D. (1988) *PC BASIC for Beginners*, Arnold, London.

Kernighan, B. and D. Ritchie (1978) *The C Programming Language*, Prentice-Hall, Englewood Cliffs, NJ.

Krishnamoorthy, V. and K. R. Radhakrishnan (1988) *Programming in C*, Tata McGraw-Hill, New York.
Lane, M. G. and J. D. Mooney (1988) *A Practical Approach to Operating Systems*, Boyd and Fraser, Boston, Mass.
Leventhal, L. A. (1988) *Microcomputer Experimentation with the IBM PC*, Holt Rinehard and Winston, New York.
Lomuto, A. N. and N. Lomuto (1983) *A Unix* Primer*, Prentice-Hall, Englewood Cliffs, NJ.
Peterson, J. and A. Silberschatz (1983) *Operating System Concepts*, Addison-Wesley, Reading, Mass.

EXERCISES

9.1   Develop programs in QUICKBASIC and C to evaluate the integral of a specified function between limits, using the Simpson's Rule numerical integration technique. The number of ordinates chosen (N) should be input interactively into the program and the result printed to the screen.
Take the function to be integrated as:

$$f(x) = 3x^2 + 2x + 1$$

and the limits as $x = 1$ to $x = 2$.
It should be noted that the number of ordinates should be odd and the integral according to Simpson's Rule is given as:

[(sum of the first and last ordinates) + (twice the sum of the odd ordinates)

+ (four times the sum of the even ordinates)] multiplied by $dx/3$.

where dx is the increment in x which will be related to the number of ordinates and the limits of the integration. The result for various values of N should be compared with the analytical answer.

9.2   For the pump question illustrated in Program 9.5 and Program 9.20 develop graphics routines in both QUICKBASIC and C which could be added to these programs to plot a graph of efficiency and pressure rise through the pump on a base of flow rate. The axes should be titled appropriately.

9.3   Using appropriate hardware and software as illustrated in Programs 9.12/9.13 and 9.27/9.28 create a disk file of temperature/time data. Retrieve the data from the file and process as a graphical display. If no hardware is available then create suitable artificial data for say a heating process from a low temperature to a steady state value. The temperature data should be in the form of 12-bit A/D converter output values within the range of 0–4095 representative of 0–100°C.

9.4   An On/Off control strategy with a deadband for the heating of a room is as follows:
If the room temperature is less than 20°C, then the heater is ON and it stays ON until a temperature of 21°C is reached. Thereafter the heater is switched OFF and the room is allowed to cool until the 20°C is reached when the heater is again switched ON.
(*a*) Draw a flow diagram for the control algorithm and develop programs in QUICKBASIC and C by inputting the room temperature value from the keyboard in response to a screen prompt and output the corresponding ON/OFF state each time to the middle of the screen.
(*b*) Repeat with a built-in simulated temperature rise of 0.2°C every second and a temperature drop of 0.2°C every 2 s from an initial temperature of 18°C. Display the appropriate ON/OFF state to the centre of the screen.
(*c*) Repeat with actual hardware for a water heating application and in addition to using QUICKBASIC and C include an 8086 assembly language program.

9.5   A 'burglar alarm' control strategy using a microprocessor based controller with digital I/O ports is as follows:
A sensor, when activated, causes bit 5 on the input port to experience a high to low transition. When this occurs bit 7 on the output port goes from the low state (OFF) to the high state (ON) and latches ON even if the sensor is deactivated. Draw the flow diagram for the strategy and develop suitable programs in QUICKBASIC, C and 8086 assembly language.
Verify that they function correctly by using appropriate hardware.

9.6   Two stepper motors A and B are to be operated as follows:
Once a start switch has been activated the sequence is
     (i)   motor A rotates clockwise at 60 rev/min for 2 revolutions;
    (ii)   motor B rotates anticlockwise at 60 rev/min for 3 revolutions;
   (iii)   4 s delay;
   (iv)   motor A rotates anticlockwise at 180 rev/min for 2 rev;
    (v)   motor B rotates clockwise at 180 rev/min for 3 rev;
   (vi)   cycle ends.
Each stepper motor requires 48 pulses/rev and an SAA1027 interface is used as detailed in Program 9.10.
Clearly indicate the I/O connections chosen and develop suitable programs in QUICKBASIC, C and 8086 assembly language.

9.7 A sequencing operation with two pneumatic cylinders is as follows:

(i) The cycle commences once a normally-open, spring-return start switch is activated to allow compressed air from the supply manifold into the system via a 2/2-way ON/OFF valve which is solenoid operated with a spring return.

(ii) The sequence is then

$$A+;\ B+;\ 2\,s\ delay;\ B-;\ A-$$

repeating 5 times then stops.

At the end of the sequence the air supply should be switched off. Sensors are used to indicate the end-of-stroke condition and both of the direction control valves are 4/2-way with solenoid/spring return operation.

Develop suitable control programs in QUICKBASIC, C and 8086 assembly language. Clearly illustrate the I/O connection chosen and use the same digital I/O addresses as in Programs 9.11 and 9.26.

CHAPTER
TEN

DIGITAL AND ANALOGUE INTERFACING

10.1 DIGITAL INTERFACING

Power Switching with Transistors and Relays

Generally, a system includes everything required to perform a specific task and it encompasses various subsystems which take in all of the computer-related hardware. In a mechatronic-type system a suitable connection between the microprocessor-based controller and the mechanical devices being controlled is required. This involves appropriate electronic circuitry, generally referred to as the interface, which makes the computer and the controlled devices compatible.

An integral part of the interface subsystem is the interface adapter, such as the 6522 VIA or 8255 PPI, as outlined in Sec. 8.3. These ICs give access to parallel ports which can be used under software control for the switching of power loads such as lamps, heaters, solenoids or motors. However, typical interface adaptor ICs are only capable of delivering an output current of about 0.4 to a few milliamps at a voltage level of 2.5 to 4.5 V DC. This means that even a light-emitting diode (LED), used for indicating purposes, cannot be directly wired into an output port bit since it requires typically 20 to 80 mA. A current driver interface must therefore interpose the port and the LED. A switching mechanism must be employed such that the small output current available from the port switches in a larger current to the load from an external power source. A transistor-based load switching interface may be suitable and the general configuration is illustrated in Fig. 10.1.

In order to activate the load, sufficient current must flow from the computer port into the base of the transistor to turn it on completely. Care should be taken not to allow too much current to flow otherwise it will start to turn off again. Fortunately, most computer ports will not supply sufficient current to damage the transistor. The precise amount of current which should flow is difficult to determine unless the complete manufacturer's specification for the transistor is available. A 1 kΩ resistor in the base connection limits the current to about 5 mA and this allows a BC 107 type of transistor to turn on fully and switch power to the load.

To produce a larger current gain, two transistors can be connected together. This arrangement is referred to as a Darlington pair. It is important to note that if the load being

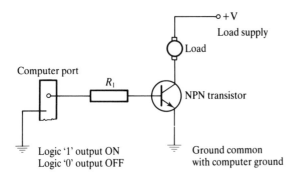

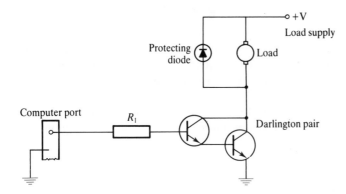

Figure 10.1 Load switching using a transistor.

Figure 10.2 Darlington pair with diode protection of the load.

switched is coil based, such as in a motor, solenoid or relay, then a diode is required in parallel with the load. This protects the transistor from high voltage spikes which may cause damage. A typical circuit for the switching of a DC motor from a computer port is shown in Fig. 10.2.

The concept of transistor switching is relatively simple but the correct transistor and the accompanying resistors must be chosen. Darlington Driver ICs are available, such as the ULN 2801A (RS 303–438), which can handle up to eight outputs. Each output has a maximum current sink capability of 500 mA at 50 V DC maximum operating voltage. The IC requires no input resistors and has its own internal diode protection circuit.

Many computer control applications require precise and abrupt switching of the control circuitry and a Schmitt trigger can provide this. They are available in IC form within the 74 series of TTL semiconductor family, such as the 7414 (RS 306–358). This is a hex Schmitt inverter, which as well as providing six precise switching elements, also gives a degree of buffering where a small input current switches in a larger output current source. The symbol for such a switching device is shown in Fig. 10.3.

When interfacing large loads, a transistor-based driving device can be used to switch in an electro-mechanical relay (EMR) which in turn brings in the main load. With more than 150 years of development behind it, the relay has evolved into a switching device of considerable sophistication. It is available in many variations and can be used in some demanding applications. The basic structure of the EMR is a coil wound on a soft iron core. When current is passed through the coil, the core is magnetized and the armature of the relay is attracted by the magnetic force acting towards the core. Consequently the resulting lever action operates the

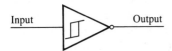

Figure 10.3 A Schmitt triger inverter.

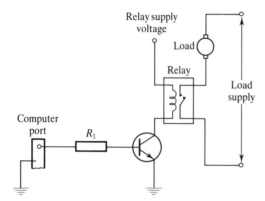

Figure 10.4 Interfacing a large load.

electrical contacts. Only a relatively small input power is necessary to switch a large power load. The economic value of a relay is decided mainly for its quality, its power consumption, its purchase price, its size and its operating time. One of its most important characteristics is that the input circuit supplying the coil current is electrically isolated from the output circuit in which the contacts operate. The ground associated with the load should not be made common with the controlling computer ground or the relay input power source ground. Figure 10.4 shows an interfacing circuit for a large load.

Thyristor Devices and Firing Methods

The features that are generally expected of a modern interface circuit environment are basically:

Microprocessor compatibility
High operating speeds
Long life
Vibration and shock resistant
Low electrical noise generation
Small size
Silent operation
Positional insensitivity
Magnetic insensitivity

A convenient solution to meeting these requirements is the solid state relay (SSR). They are quiet and switch much faster than EMRs. However, their initial cost is greater although they may be cheaper in the long run because of a longer life expectancy. They are generally compatible with TTL level signals and can be switched by an input voltage level in the range 3–32 V. It should be noted that SSRs are susceptible to being turned on by extraneous transient signals and usually fail in the 'on' state which may be dangerous.

The generic name for a semiconductor switch is 'thyristor'. This forms a large family which includes the diode thyristor, the triode thyristor and the tetrode thyristor. The simplest thryistor structure, and the most common, is the reverse blocking triode thyristor which is usually referred to as a 'thyristor' or 'silicon controlled rectifier' (SCR). Its circuit symbol is shown in Fig. 3.18. The most complex structure is the bi-directional triode thyristor which is usually referred to as a 'triac'. This device is able to pass current bi-directionally and is used in AC power control. It consists of two thyristors connected in parallel but in opposition and controlled by the same gate. A 50 mA gate current can handle up to 100 A load current and it is a useful device for motor speed control applications. The connections are the main terminals (MT1 and MT2) and the gate (G).

The triac configuration can be used to control the amount of power supplied to a heater load by varying the proportions of 'on' time to 'off' time. The thermal mass of the system assists in smoothing any cycling effects. The method is particularly suited for full-wave AC power heating applications and various firing methods can be used such as static switching, burst firing and phase control.

The static switching (or on–off triggering) technique is used extensively and is the simplest and most economical method of controlling power. The ratio of on-time to off-time defines the average power supplied to the load. In temperature control applications the controller can be tuned to optimize the cycle time and amplitude of oscillation to ensure the best control performance. In a high-power AC circuit where the switch may connect or disconnect the load at any point during the mains cycle then radio frequency interference (RFI) is likely to occur at the instants of switching. Radio frequency interference occurs at any time that there is a step change in current caused by a switch operation and this is usually unacceptable. However, if the switch is closed at the moment that the load supply AC voltage passes through the zero condition then there is no step rise in current and thus no interference is generated. A thyristor or triac device naturally switches off at the zero-crossing points of the AC mains supply and no RFI occurs.

The burst firing method is a technique of controlling power by triggering the thryistor in bursts for a number of cycles rather than on an individual cycle basis as in static switching. This might involve switching on for say one cycle in five for 20 per cent power or five cycles in five for 100 per cent power (Fig. 10.5). All that is required from the microcomputer is a logic 1 pulse that varies in width over a defined time. The burst cycle is usually only applicable for loads which have a relatively slow response time compared with the total number of AC supply cycles which occur during the control period.

Phase angle firing by varying the phase of the trigger pulses relative to the load AC supply controls the power by altering the conduction angle. For 100 per cent power the thyristor would conduct for the whole cycle and 50 per cent power means that the thyristor conducts for only half the cycle. The method is particularly suited for fast-acting loads such as AC motors. Dedicated integrated circuits are generally used to generate the trigger pulse which is delayed behind the time when the instantaneous supply voltage passes through the zero condition. These units contain all the circuitry necessary to provide control from near 0° to near 180° conduction angles with a 0–5 V input (RS 301–678). For such devices an analogue output signal is required from the controller. The relationship between the control voltage and the thyristor firing angle is linear but as this angle is referred to the control of a sine wave the effective power supplied to the load is nonlinearly related to the phase angle. The basic load switching circuit and power/phase angle relationship is shown in Fig. 10.6. Phase angle firing allows such features as a soft start by applying a gradual increase in firing angle, and current limiting to avoid current surges into loads with a low cold resistance.

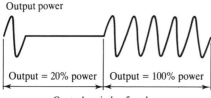

Output power

Output = 20% power | Output = 100% power

Control period = 5 cycles

Figure 10.5 Burst cycle for 20% and 100% power.

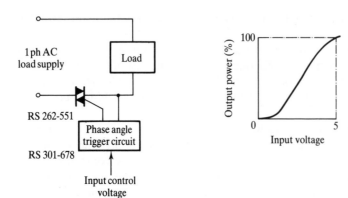

Figure 10.6 Phase angle control of thyristor.

Opto-isolation

Opto-isolators or photo-couplers are solid-state devices which provide protection for microprocessor-based controllers from circuit failures which may occur in the interface that activates the load power switching. There is no physical connection inside the device between the input and the output. The logic switching signal is transmitted by optical means. Infra-red light energy is generated by a light-emitting diode within the fully enclosed opto-isolator IC once a logic signal is received from the port. LEDs are special diodes which emit infra-red light when they are forward biased. The LED is then optically coupled to a phototransistor, which is also contained within the package, and this in turn controls the input to the high voltage part of the circuit. The phototransistor is similar to a bipolar transistor except that the current flowing between the emitter and collector is controlled by the amount of light received rather than the base current. Thus there is no hardwired electrical connection between the logic level part and the power switching part of the circuit. The isolation between the output and the input can be in excess of 4 kV. The arrangement for a single control channel is illustrated in Fig. 10.7. Integrated circuit packages are available which contain a number of opto-isolator circuits on the one chip, and this facilitates the construction of interfaces where a number of loads are to be switched (e.g. quad opto-islator RS 307-064).

Opto-isolation can also be applied to the switching signals from limit switches and other sensing devices which are received at input ports in order to detect when events have occurred in a system that is under computer control. These signals are often obtained from sources which have a zero volt reference condition that differs from that of the digital controller. For large voltage differences the connection between the digital sensor and the computer port must be in a

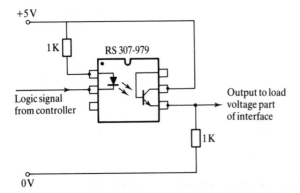

Figure 10.7 Opto-isolator circuit.

form which ensures that the input voltage is electrically isolated from the logic signal handling part of the interface. This is achieved by using opto-isolators in the circuit.

Switch Inputs

A wide variety of switches are used as input sensors to microcomputer controllers to indicate the occurrence of an event. The usual method of connecting a normally open (NO) switch to an input port is to use a resistor to source current from the 5 V logic supply and connect the switch between the port bit and the 0 V. Thus the occurrence of an event can be detected by examining within the control software for a high to low transition indicative of when the switch is closed. When the switch is operated the contacts do not generally make cleanly and they bounce for 10–20 ms before coming to rest. This is illustrated in Fig. 10.8.

The switch 'contact bounce' may produce amplitudes which change logic levels and this must be avoided since it can give rise to an incorrect or erratic behaviour in the system being controlled. Debouncing can be achieved by using either a suitable hardware interface such as given in Fig. 10.9 or alternatively a routine can be incorporated into the control software. The interface consists of two NAND gates and when the single-pole double-throw (SPDT) switch is in position A then the output to the computer input port is a logic 1. When the switch is moved to position B then the output is a logic 0 and will remain latched at this condition even if the switch bounces. A clean transition from logic 1 to logic 0 and vice versa therefore occurs. The software debouncing routine should incorporate a delay of approximately 20 ms to allow for the effects of switch bounce to stabilize. The sequence is:

1. Read switch state.
2. If not closed then read switch at step 1 again.
3. Read switch state again.
4. If not closed read switch at step 1 again else take action related to the closed state.

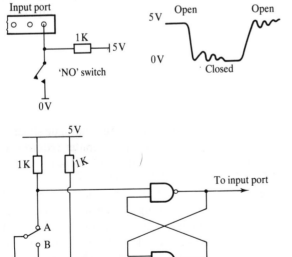

Figure 10.8 Switch operation.

Figure 10.9 Hardware circuit for switch debouncing.

Input/Output Modules

A variety of standard self-contained encapsulated modules designed specifically for industrial control applications are available from a number of suppliers. These units are basically high performance microprocessor-compatible switches which provide an electrically clean noise-free input/output interface between the controller and electro-mechanical devices such as limit switches and motors. A colour code is used to define the function of the module and this assists assembly and field maintenance. For example, an input module capable of handling say 90 V– 140 V AC may be yellow and an output module for say switching 24–280 V AC loads may be black. The modules can be plugged, on a mix and match basis, into a fuse protected mounting board which typically holds 4, 8 or 16 units. All field and control connections to the board are usually through a screw terminal block and/or an edge connector.

DC and AC input modules are used for sensing a wide range of on/off voltage levels from sensors, switches, push buttons and relay contacts. They are converted into opto-isolated logic level signals via filtering and debounce circuitry to eliminate noise. The output can then be fed directly to TTL and CMOS circuits in the microprocessor-based controller. Some manufacturers also fit a built-in LED status indicator which gives a helpful indication of the current state of a system during a controlled sequence.

The function of the self-contained output module is to accept a logic control signal from the microcomputer controller and convert it into a voltage and current large enough to drive the load. They are available for a range of both DC and AC voltages and typical applications include the switching of relays, solenoids, motor starters, heaters and lamps. The units usually provide opto-isolation and transient protection devices, which are useful when switching inductive loads.

Interfacing modules mounted on standard racks are also available for interconnecting a wide variety of real-world analogue signals to computer-based systems for industrial measurement and control applications. These units accept inputs directly from thermo-couples, platinum resistance thermometers, strain gauges and 4–20 mA output devices. They then condition the signals into a form which is directly suitable for the analogue-to-digital conversion process which is necessary immediately prior to inputting to the microcomputer.

With the large variety of solid state interfacing hardware now available, the precise theory of their operation is really of little concern to a person who is using the device as opposed to one who is designing the device. The behaviour of the device within the system is the important issue.

10.2 ANALOGUE INTERFACING

The basic role of the analogue interface is one of conversion of the continuous analogue signals, from process measuring transducers, to the digital representation that the computer requires to operate on. In all practical applications, the monitoring and acquisition of the data is the necessary precursor to the subsequent control functions which might be actioned.

The process variables are ultimately represented as voltages. Using the appropriate signal conditioning circuits, these voltages would ideally be processed to range between zero and some reference value. The final task is the digitization of the analogue signal, which is accomplished through an analogue-to-digital converter, ADC. The ADC samples the analogue signal, performs the conversion and outputs a digitally encoded binary number which is directly proportional to the magnitude of the input voltage. The essential elements in the signal train are shown in Fig. 10.10.

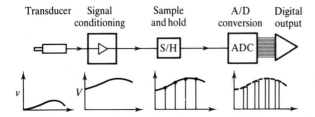

Figure 10.10 Analogue-to-digital conversion.

Figure 10.10 indicates a sample and hold (S/H) element between the signal conditioner and the ADC. Since the analogue input may be varying while the conversion is taking place, there is a degree of uncertainty in deciding the instant in time to which the output code represents. The sample and hold element removes this uncertainty by capturing an instantaneous 'snapshot' of the input for the ADC to convert before moving on to the next sample. The S/H element is only essential if the input signal is varying very rapidly. The ADC and S/H functions are often packaged within a composite integrated circuit. Some ADCs also feature a digital-to-analogue converter (DAC) as a necessary subsystem within the ADC. The DAC generates a discretely increasing reference voltage for comparison with the analogue input voltage. It is appropriate therefore that we consider first of all the general operation of a DAC.

Digital-to-Analogue Converters

Adder converter The adder converter is shown schematically in Fig. 10.11. In essence, the digital pattern to be converted into an analogue output voltage is loaded into a binary register. The outputs from the register are used to switch in a reference voltage through a series of input resistors connected to a summing operational amplifier (see also Sec. 3.6). The input resistors are weighted in binary proportion with the MSB input resistor having the smallest value and each consecutively lower bit having an input resistor with twice the value of the adjacent higher bit. For the 4-bit DAC shown, the output voltage with all the resistors connected is given as

$$V_o = -V \times (R/2)[1/8R + 1/4R + 1/2R + 1/R] = -(V/2)[1/8 + 1/4 + 1/2 + 1/1] \quad (10.1)$$

$$\text{LSB} \quad \text{---} \quad \text{---} \quad \text{MSB} \qquad \text{LSB} \quad \text{---} \quad \text{---} \quad \text{MSB}$$

The output voltage is therefore determined by the bit pattern presented from the register and is incremented proportionally by $(-1/16)$ V for each consecutive increase in the binary input pattern. The output voltage therefore ranges between 0 and $(-15/16)$ V, with 16 discrete voltage levels, for a binary input in the range 0000 to 1111. The further addition of a unity gain inverting amplifier produces a positive output voltage range.

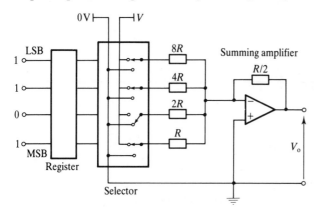

Figure 10.11 Adder type, 4-bit DAC.

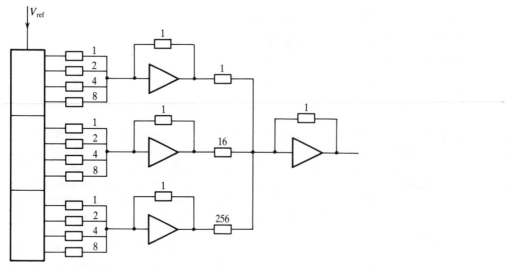

Figure 10.12 12-bit, adder-type DAC.

A practical difficulty exists for adder networks, however, in that for higher resolution binary inputs, say 16 bits, the size of the LSB input resistor becomes prohibitively large. If for example the MSB input resistor was $10 \, \text{k}\Omega$, then the LSB input resistor would have to be $10^4 \times 2^{15} = 327.68 \, \text{M}\Omega$. This may be overcome by separating the binary inputs into groups of say four and then feeding the outputs from the groups to a final summing amplifier. Figure 10.12 shows a possible arrangement for a 12-bit adder-type DAC.

Ladder-type converter A more efficient method of obtaining binary division in a resistive network is to use a ladder type network as shown in Fig. 10.13. Analysis of the circuit using Thevenin's theorem shows that the output voltage with all the bits connected is given by

$$V_o = -(V_{ref}/2)[1/8 + 1/4 + 1/2 + 1] = (-15/16)V_{ref} \tag{10.2}$$

$$\text{LSB} \qquad\qquad \text{MSB}$$

The circuit behaves in a similar manner to the adder circuit, producing 16 discrete and proportional voltage levels for each of the 16 possible binary inputs. The ladder type DAC is preferred to the adder type and they are normally available in integrated circuit form, with an inverted output, to give a positive voltage range.

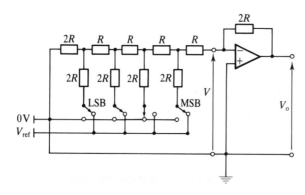

Figure 10.13 4-bit, ladder type DAC.

Analogue to Digital Converters

ADCs are available in a number of different varieties.

Up-counter type ADC The up-counter type is the simplest form of ADC, Fig. 10.14. The device incorporates a signal generator, usually a DAC, which produces a voltage increasing in small steps under the control of a synchronized clock signal. At each step the ramp input is compared with the analogue input. When the discrete ramp voltage is approximately equal to the input, the process is halted and a binary count is made òf the number of steps taken during the process. The binary count from zero represents the coded digital output.

The up-counter type ADC has relatively slow conversion times, typically 20 ms. They are cheap, however, and are essentially immune to electronic noise.

Integrating type ADC (or dual slope) The major elements comprising a dual slope ADC are illustrated in Fig. 10.15.

At the start of conversion a voltage-to-current converter is switched to the integrator causing it to ramp up a slope which is proportional to V_{in}. This occurs over a fixed period of time at the end of which the input is switched over to the reference current source. At the instant of switching the integrator output voltage is proportional to V_{in}, a counter is enabled and counting begins at a rate set by the internal clock. In the meantime, the reference current causes the integrator to ramp down at a slope which is proportional to V_{ref}, i.e. a constant slope. When the integrator output again reaches ground the zero-crossing detection comparator switches the counter off and the counter then contains a digitally encoded value proportional to V_{in}. Figure 10.16 shows the voltage variation at the integrator output.

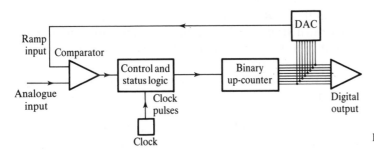

Figure 10.14 Up-counter type ADC.

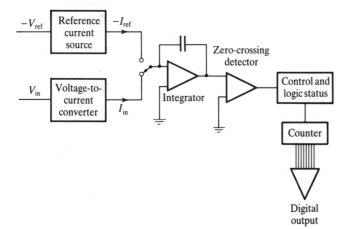

Figure 10.15 Dual slope ADC.

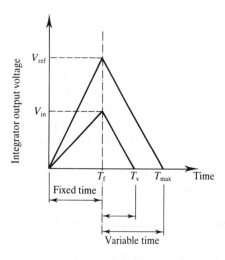

Figure 10.16 Integrator voltage variation.

From Fig. 10.16 it can be seen that there are two similar triangles such that

$$V_{in} = V_{ref}(T_v - T_f)/(T_{max} - T_f) \tag{10.3}$$

T_v is directly proportional to the counter output and with T_{max}, T_v and V_{ref} all known, the input voltage, V_{in}, can be determined by proportion.

The integrating type of ADC has similar operating characteristics and conversion times to that of the up-counter types. For faster analogue-to-digital conversion, the 'successive approximation' ADC is generally employed.

Successive approximation type ADC In this ADC, the input signal is compared with a number of standard reference voltages, generated from a DAC, until the combination of standard voltages required to make up the input value has been determined. The main components of the converter are a clock, a counter, a comparator and a DAC.

When an analogue signal is input to the converter the counter starts a count and passes a digital value to the DAC. The DAC generates a voltage to represent the most significant bit and the comparator assesses this against the analogue input. If the analogue signal is greater than the voltage from the DAC then the logic 1 in the MSB is retained. If the analogue signal is smaller, then a logic 0 is assigned to the MSB. This process is then repeated on the next most significant bit and so on for all the other bits down to the LSB. The conversion is completed in n clock cycles, where n is the number of bits in the digitally encoded output. The conversion time for these type of converters may be of the order of 10–25 µs, but this will depend upon the hardware design. Figure 10.17 outlines the essential features of a successive approximation ADC.

Parallel conversion type ADC The parallel type ADC has by far the fastest conversion time, at about 1 µs, but it is also the most expensive. With parallel conversion, the analogue input is fed simultaneously to a number of comparator circuits, each having a different reference voltage. The resulting comparator outputs are fed to a logical coding network which generates the appropriate digital values to represent the state of the comparator outputs.

Regardless of the type of ADC used, the pin functions on the integrated circuit are basically similar and generally comprise the power supply, the data bits, the start conversion pin ($\overline{SC}$ or $\overline{CONVERT}$), and the end of conversion pin (ECO or $\overline{STATUS}$). The $^-$ signifies that the pin is active low.

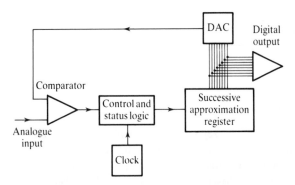

Figure 10.17 Successive approximation ADC.

The conversion is software initiated, typically by sending a 'pulse' (logic 0, followed by logic 1) to the $\overline{\text{CONVERT}}$ pin. On the negative edge of this pulse the counter in the successive approximation ADC is set to zero and on the positive edge the counter starts incrementing. At the start of conversion the $\overline{\text{STATUS}}$ pin goes from low to high and when it again goes low, the conversion is complete (Fig. 10.18).

The end of conversion signal may be readily detected using suitable software. Alternatively it is possible to include a software generated time delay, following the start conversion pulse, to allow adequate conversion time before reading the digitally encoded output. The length of the delay can generally be found by trial and error.

In choosing the appropriate ADC for a particular application, the four main features to be considered are:

1. *Conversion time.* The conversion time is a measure of the operating speed of the converter and is the time taken for the complete translation of an analogue signal to digital form. The conversion time in many of the up-counter and the integrating types of ADC are dependent on the level of the analogue input signal. Faster conversion times are obtained with low-level inputs due to the manner in which the conversion is completed. A 12-bit up-counter ADC, for example, will require $2^{12} = 4096$ clock cycles to generate the complete discrete ramp voltage. Successive approximation and parallel conversion types of ADC have a fixed conversion time. This is because they use the exact same conversion process regardless of the analogue input level. A 12-bit successive approximation ADC will require only 12 clock cycles to complete the conversion process.
2. *Resolution.* The resolution of an ADC is the number employed to represent the digital output in binary form. The resolution, for example, of an 8-bit ADC is limited to one part in 256 of the maximum voltage corresponding to the full-scale setting. An improvement in resolution can be obtained with a 12-bit converter, with one part in 4096. Table 10.1 summarises the relation between the number of bits and the resolution.

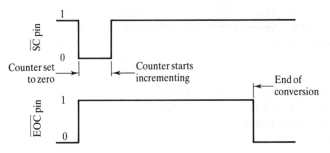

Figure 10.18 Start conversion and end of conversion pin signals.

Table 10.1 ADC resolution.

Number of bits	2^n	Resolution (%)
8	256	0.4
10	1024	0.1
12	4096	0.025
16	65536	0.0015

3. *Accuracy*. The accuracy is related to linearity defects, zero error and calibration deficiencies in the electronics of the converter and should not be confused with the resolution.
4. *Cost*. Cost will depend on the quality required in the three areas previously described and on the means of conversion employed. The cost is closely associated with the speed of the conversion and with the resolution and accuracy. Cost generally increasing with increases in all, or either of the three other variables.

Example Two 4-bit ADCs have an output voltage range of 0 to 10 V. One ADC is an up-counter type while the other is a successive approximation type. Both ADCs operate on a clock signal of 10 kHz. Determine the conversion times for both ADCs when the analogue input signal is 7.5 V.

Regardless of the size of the analogue input signal, the successive approximation type ADC will require only 4 clock cycles to complete the conversion.
Time for one clock cycle $= 1/10^4 = 0.1$ ms.
Conversion time for the successive approximation type ADC $= 4 \times 0.1 = 0.4$ ms.
The up-counter type ADC will generate a ramp voltage with 15 discrete voltage levels. The discrete increment in voltage $= 10/15 = 0.666\,667$ V. The number of clock cycles required $= 7.5/0.666\,667 = 11.25 = 12$.
It is assumed here that the DAC will have to generate a discrete voltage which exceeds the analogue input level.
Conversion time for the up-counter type ADC $= 12 \times 0.1 = 1.2$ ms.
NB. If the analogue input was equal to the maximum value, then 15 clock cycles would be required to generate the full range of discrete voltages, giving a maximum conversion time of 1.5 ms.

Quantization Error

Figure 10.19 shows a discretely increasing voltage level generated from a DAC. Superimposed on the figure is an analogue voltage level which is to be compared against the discrete voltage.
    It can be seen that the analogue voltage does not match exactly with any of the two nearest discrete voltage levels. If the circuitry is designed to take the nearest and lower discrete voltage as the approximation to the analogue input then the maximum possible error is $+1$ bit in the digital representation of the analogue input. This is the so-called quantization error which is closely related to the resolution of the ADC. Many ADCs are designed to round up or round down, depending on whether the analogue signal is above or below the mid-point between two discrete levels. The quantization error in this type of ADC is $+/-$ half of one bit.

Example An ADC has a resolution of 8 bits and a quantization error of $+/-$ half of one bit. The output voltage level ranges from 0 to 10 V. Determine the quantization error in volts and as a percentage of the full-scale output.
The binary number output represents $2^8 - 1 = 255$ discrete levels.

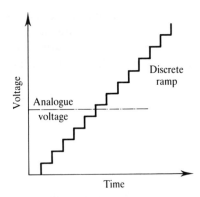

Figure 10.19 Comparison of analogue voltage against a discretely varying ramp input.

A 1-bit change is equal to $(1/255) \times 10 = 0.0392 \, \text{V}$.
Quantization error is given by

$$+/-(1/2)\text{-bit} = 0.0392/2 = 0.0196 \, \text{V}$$

Alternatively, quantization error is

$$(0.0196/10) \times 100\% = +/-0.196\% = +/-0.2\%$$

Input Interface

The analogue input interface will consist of all the electronic circuitry required to condition the primary signal from a measuring transducer, typically of the order of a few millivolts, to something compatible with that required for an ADC. ADCs usually incorporate switch selectable input ranges, typically 0 to 10 V, 0 to 5 V, or 0 to 2.5 V for unipolar inputs and -10 to $+10$ V, -5 to $+5$ V, or -2.5 to $+2.5$ V for bipolar inputs. The signal conditioning interface is therefore geared to producing a variable analogue voltage to make the best use of the full range of the ADC input channel.

10.3 MULTIPLEXING

In applications where a number of transducers are to be sampled, a multiplexer (MUX) can be used to switch in various channels as and when required to a single ADC. The switching is software controlled from the computer and Fig. 10.20 illustrates the basic principle.

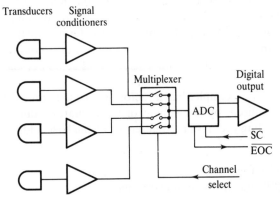

Figure 10.20 Multiplexer for multiple inputs.

The multiplexer and ADC often form part of a composite integrated circuit. Stand-alone multiplexers, or analogue switches as they are sometimes called, are also available with various numbers of input channels. Minimum cost conditions usually dictate whether multiplexing will be implemented or not, but the reduced cost must be balanced against an inevitable reduction in sampling rate.

10.4 DATA ACQUISITION PRINCIPLES

Digital Sampling

Digital sampling should ideally be carried out as fast as possible in order to reduce the time between samples during which there is a gap in the information being logged. While the sampling rate must be fast enough to capture an authentic representation of the input signal, it cannot be as fast, and certainly not faster than the analogue-to-digital conversion rate. The integrating and up-counter types of ADC have slow conversion time and this limits their application in terms of sampling rate. For faster data acquisition applications the successive approximation type of ADC must be used. Modern versions of the successive approximation type of ADC can operate down to the order of one microsecond conversion time, i.e. a 1 MHz conversion speed. It is never possible to achieve the same sampling speed however, since there must always be some 'overhead' time allowance for storing the acquired data and updating the storage byte locations. The typical conversion process is

$$\begin{matrix} \text{initiate the} \\ \text{A/D converter} \end{matrix} \rightarrow \begin{matrix} \text{wait for} \\ \text{conversion} \end{matrix} \rightarrow \begin{matrix} \text{digital output} \\ \text{from converter} \end{matrix} \rightarrow \begin{matrix} \text{store data and} \\ \text{update counter} \end{matrix}$$

The last function is a characteristic of the microcomputer and depends on the type of processor and how the wait for conversion time may be utilized. To maximize the sampling rate, assembly language data acquisition routines must be used.

Data Acquisition using an IBM-PC or Compatible Machine

The dominance of the International Business Machines (IBM) company in the 16-bit microcomputer market has let to the establishment of an industry standard machine in the form of the IBM-PC. Predominantly a business machine, however, the IBM-PC, and numerous other compatible machines, have limited input/output facilities. They generally come supplied solely with an RS232 serial port and a parallel printer port. To function as the workhorse in a data-acquisition/control context, the machine must be extended through the addition of appropriate expansion boards. Fortunely, there exists a large selection of these boards which can plug directly into any one of the PC's option slots. A typical composite board might include 16 analogue input lines, 4 analogue output lines, 24 programmable I/O lines and 3 counter timers. Many other similar A/D expansion cards are available and a selection of some popular makes are given in Table 10.2.

The Blue Chip Technology ACM-42 card, for example, has a factory-set base address of &H300. This may be altered by the user, if required, by adjustment of the miniature jumper switches on the card. All ports used by a controlling program are referenced to the base address as follows:

Base + 0   ADC bit 7 going high registers an end of conversion signal.
Base + 1   ADC result, high byte with four most significant bits set to zero.

Table 10-2 A/D, D/A expansion cards for IBM-PCs and compatibles.

Card name	Manufacturer	Specification
ACM-42	Blue Chip Technology Deeside, CLYWD, CH5 3PP	24 digital I/O lines 2 D/A output lines 16 single-ended A/D input channels, or 8 differential A/D inputs channels. 1 timer for interrupt generation 12-bit resolution 12 µs conversion time link selectable input range
PC-26A	Amplicon Liveline Ltd Brighton BN2 4AW	16 A/D input channels 12-bit resolution 25 µs conversion time unipolar or bi-polar input ranges
PC-30A	Amplicon Liveline Ltd Brighton, BN2 4AW	Similar to the PC-26A but additionally including: 24 digital I/O lines two 12-bit D/A output lines two 8-bit D/A output lines one counter/timer 35 µs conversion time
PC SUPER ADDA-8	Flight Electronics Ltd	64 A/D input channels 8-bit resolution 25 µs conversion time bipolar input only, −5 V to +5 V 24 digital I/O lines three 16-bit ripple counters

Base + 2   ADC result, low byte and automatic start conversion signal.
Base + 3   DAC update output.
Base + 4   DAC 'A', low byte load register.
Base + 5   DAC 'A', high byte load register.
Base + 6   DAC 'B', low byte load register.
Base + 7   DAC 'B', high byte load register.
Base + 8   Digital I/O port 'A'.
Base + 9   Digital I/O port 'B'.
Base + 10 Digital I/O port 'C'.
Base + 11 Digital I/O control register.
Base + 12 Analogue multiplexer channel select.
Base + 13 Programmable interrupt source control.

If the analogue, ADC, or output, DAC, facilities are used then these can be accessed using the relevant base offsets given above. The analogue input is set for bipolar inputs in the range −2.5 V to +2.5 V, but this can be changed, if necessary, by adjusting the jumper connections on the card. If the digital I/O ports are to be used in any application however, then the control register, Base+11, must be set up as required by writing the appropriate control word to the control register as outlined in Sec. 9.3. The instruction OUT BASE+11,&H93 for example configures the 8255 PPI with port A, port B and the upper four bits of port C set for input. The lower four bits of port C are set for output.

A suitable BASIC program to continuously monitor analogue input channel 6 is shown in Program 10.1.

Program 10.1 Single-channel analogue input.

```
PORT=&H300                   :REM set base address
OUT PORT+12,6                :REM select channel 6
S=INP(PORT+1)                :REM start conversion by reading low byte
FOR J=1 TO 10:NEXT J         :REM small time delay to allow for A/D conversion
cycle:
HIGH=INP(PORT+2)             :REM read high byte
LOW=INP(PORT+1)              :REM read low byte
RESULT=LOW+256*HIGH          :REM Calculate the 12-bit result
PRINT RESULT
VOLTS=(RESULT-2048)*5/4095   :REM convert digital RESULT to voltage level
PRINT VOLTS
GOTO cycle
```

A start conversion pulse is generated by reading the low byte result at BASE + 1. This is first done in line three of the program, followed by a small delay. Since this is also done in line seven of the program then after the variables RESULT and VOLTS are calculated and printed to the screen the GOTO statement directs control to the label 'cycle' as opposed to line three. The two calculation and print statements take up enough time to allow for the next A/D conversion.

To continuously scan through the 16 analogue input channels consecutively, the coding could be altered as shown in Program 10.2.

Program 10.2 16-channel, multiplexed analogue input.

```
PORT=&H300                   :REM set base address
start:
FOR K=0 TO 15
OUT PORT+12,K                :REM select channel K
S=INP(PORT+1)                :REM start conversion by reading low byte
FOR J=1 TO 10:NEXT J         :REM small time delay to allow for A/D conversion
HIGH=INP(PORT+2)             :REM read high byte
LOW=INP(PORT+1)              :REM read low byte
RESULT=LOW+256*HIGH          :REM Calculate the 12-bit result
PRINT" Value on channel ";K;" = ";RESULT
NEXT K
PRINT:PRINT
GOTO start
```

In the first line of both sample programs, the base address is set to the corresponding addres selected on the jumper switches. The form of the instructions may differ from one A/D expansion card to another, but the formal 'procedure' will remain variant. The general data acquisition procedure is therefore:

1. Define the card base address with a suitable variable.
2. Select an input channel.
3. Send out a start conversion signal.
4. Check for end of conversion.
5. Read the A/D converter.
6. Store data in memory.

Various looping routines can then be devised, as illustrated in the examples, to monitor continuously, or to scan through the channels. For slow to moderate speed data acquisition applications the routines given in BASIC may be perfectly adequate. The capture of fast transient states however will require the data acquisition routines to be written in assembly language.

Microcomputers based on the 8086 and 8088 microprocessor use the same instruction set (see Chapter 8). An assembly language routine written for an IBM-PC, with the 8088 processor, would run equally well on any other machine using the 8086 processor. The converse is also true, and from an assembly language programmer's point of view, the two machines are identical. The 16-bit technology which features in these two microprocessors, nonetheless, makes the assembly language routines slightly more complicated than the equivalent instructions for an 8-bit microprocessor.

Programming the 8086/8088 for fast data acquisition The essential elements of assembly language programming for the 8086 microprocessor are covered in Chapter 9. In any data acquisition application however there is a general requirement to store the captured data in an ordered form into the computer's memory. Access to the stored data can then be performed later and any specific post processing functions carried out as necessary.

Storing data in memory may be done one or two bytes at a time. If the AX register contained 4AF2H and the instructions MOV [20H],AX were executed, offset location 20H would be assigned the number F2H and offset location 21H would contain 4AH. Sixteen-bit data is stored with the lower byte first, followed by the higher byte. If the data is moved in the other direction, from a memory location to a register, then the order is reversed such that a self consistency is maintained. In the majority of cases, programmers need not concern themselves with this aspect.

Using the CX register as a counter, Program 10.3 will store, in consecutive locations from 3000H to 3064H inclusive, the integer numbers ranging between 1 and 100.

Program 10.3 Data storage to memory in assembly language.

```
TABLE:                  ; name of assembly language routine
MOV AL,1                ; assign an initial value of unity to AL
MOV BX,3000H            ; set the base address for the data storage
MOV CX,64H              ; set the counter to 100 decimal
DAT:                    ; program label
MOV [BX],AL             ; store the current value contained in AL to
                        ; the current offset given by BX
INC AL                  ; increment the contents of AL by one
INC BX                  ; increment the contents of BX by one
LOOP DAT                ;  return to label DAT and repeat
RETF                    ; return to the CALLing program
```

The loop instruction returns the program to the DAT label, where the process repeats. A LOOP instruction, in addition, automatically decrements the CX register such that the process will be continued until CX becomes equal to zero. In the above case, the loop will repeat 100 times since the initial value in CX was 100 decimal.

The assembly language routine may be CALLed from a QUICKBASIC program and the procedures for embedding assembly language inserts into QUICKBASIC programs involves creating .OBJ files for both programs which are then linked together.

In the above program, the data is stored at an offset location, given by the current value in BX, relative to the data segment address, DS. Since the operating system manipulates DS, external control of memory addressing may be better actioned through the extra segment, ES, register which can be handled independently of the operating system. It must be remembered, however, that when data is stored to, or fetched from memory relative to ES, an override prompt must always be included in the instruction, e.g.

```
MOV ES:[BX],AL   ;store the current value in the AL register at
                 ;the offset location given by BX, relative to ES
```

In the previous section, a BASIC program was given for a data acquisition application, using the ACM-42 expansion board. The equivalent coding in 8086 assembly language, to read and store 2^{15}, or 32K of data from the 12-bit A/D converter might take the form shown in Program 10.4.

Program 10.4 Fast data acquisition and mass data storage to memory.

```
data:              ; assembly language routine label
MOV AX,3000H       ; load 3000 hex into AX then into the extra segment, ES
MOV ES,AX          ; ie. starting address for data = 3000 hex
MOV DX,302H        ; load DX with low byte address
MOV BX,00H         ; set BX to zero, used to address the data relative to ES
MOV CX,08000H      ; load 8000 hex into CX, ie. 8000 hex = 32768 = 32k
DATA_CONV:         ; start of data acquisition loop
IN AL,DX           ; start conversion, equivalent to INP(PORT+2) in BASIC
PUSH CX            ; push current value of CX to the stack
MOV CX,0FH         ; load a new value of CX to time a delay loop
DELAY:             ; delay loop to allow for A/D conversion
NOP                ; No OPeration
LOOP DELAY         ; LOOP instruction causes CX to decrement until CX = 0
POP CX             ; retrieve original value of CX from the stack for the main loop
MOV DX,301H        ; load DX with high byte address
IN AL,DX           ; read high byte into AL, equivalent to INP(PORT+1) in BASIC
MOV ES:[BX],AL     ; store high byte at relative address held in BX
INC BX             ; increment BX  to next address datum
MOV DX,302H        ; load DX with low byte address
IN AL,DX           ; read low byte into AL, equivalent to INP(PORT+2) in BASIC
MOV ES:[BX],AL     ; store low byte at relative address held in BX
INC BX             ; increment BX to next datum
LOOP DATA_CONV     ; repeat until CX = 0
RETF               ; return to the calling program
```

In the program given, the CX register is used primarily to count down the 32K of data. Note that since the data is generated as 12-bit numbers then two bytes are used for their storage. The CX register is also used in the main listing to time a wait for end of conversion delay. While the delay loop is executed the current value of CX must be temporarily stored on the stack and then retrieved following the delay loop. This is done using the PUSH and POP instructions as shown.

The delay routine consists of two instructions and can be timed by referring to the number of clock cycles required for each instruction.

```
                        cycles
        DELAY:          0
        NOP             3
        LOOP DELAY      17 with branch, 5 without branch
```

Thus one trip round the delay routine, with a branch at the end, involves 20 clock cycles. The 8086 microprocessor operates at 8 MHz. If this particular microprocessor is used, then the single trip is completed in 2.5 μs. The last trip, through the loop, with no branch at the end, takes 8 clock cycles.

The LOOP instruction also decrements the CX register by one on each execution. The instruction immediately before the delay cycle assigns a temporary value of 0F hex, i.e. 15 decimal, to CX, such that the delay routine will be executed 16 times. In other words, the actual delay, in real time, is 38.5 μs. Since the conversion time of the ADC is quoted at 12 μs, then the delay is more than adequate. The delay can be adjusted by resetting the value assigned to CX. The timing for the rest of the data acquisition routine is:

```
            cycles
DATA_CONV:            0
IN AL,DX              8
PUSH CX              11
MOV CX,0FH            4
Delay routine       308
POP CX               8
MOV DX,301H          4
IN AL,DX             8
MOV ES:[BX],AL      19
INC BX               2
MOV DX,302H          4
IN AL,DX             8
MOV ES:[BX],AL      19
INC BX               2
LOOP DATA_CONV      17
            Total   422
```

A 8 MHz operating speed, 422 clock cycles represents about 52.75 μs. The corresponding data acquisition rate is therefore approximately 18.96 kHz. As with any microprocessor-based system, the biggest restriction on the sampling rate is associated with the delay routine required to allow for the completion of the A/D conversion. If a very fast A/D converter can be used, with say a 1 μs conversion time, the delay cycle need only be executed once. The total processing time would then take about 16.75 μs and a sampling rate of about 60 kHz could be realized. Still faster sampling rates can be achieved if the microprocessor operates with a faster clock signal. Modern 80486 machines may operate with a clock signal of 50 MHz and data acquisition rates of about 300 kHz are possible with these machines.

The ACM-42 has an onboard end of conversion checking facility. A better alternative therefore is to use the facility to check for the end of conversion signal which is generated on bit 7 of the ADC at Base + 0. The appropriate coding to replace the lines between and including the PUSH and POP instructions would be

```
busy:
MOV DX,0330H ;load DX with the base address 300H
IN AL,DX     ;read the status of the base address
AND AL,080H  ;perform a logical AND with 080H, i.e. mask all bits except bit 7
JZ busy
```

The last instruction, 'JZ—jump if zero', will return control to the 'busy' label until the end of conversion signal is set on bit 7 of the base address. When this happens the logical AND will set the zero flag in the flags register to 1, and the JZ command will not be executed. The program will then continue on to the next sequential instruction. The coding thus provides a suitable delay which is implemented until an end of conversion signal is generated by the ADC.

The section of the program preceding the data acquisition loop is concerned with the initialization of the various registers, i.e.

MOV AX,3000H
MOV ES,AX

The above effectively sets the starting address for the storage of data at the location 30000 hex. This is assured by the manner in which the machine calculates actual addresses.

The two remaining instructions in the initialization process are

MOV DX,302H
MOV CX,08000H

The first assigns the numerical value of (BASE + 2) to the DX register. DX is subsequently used in the 'start conversion' and in the 'read port' instructions within the data acquisition loop. The CX register is set to 8000 hex, or 32768 decimal, and on every LOOP instruction, the CX register will be decremented by one. This ensures that the data acquisition cycle will be performed 32K times and 32K individual 12-bit data elements will be committed to storage. Note that this will require the full segment memory capacity of 64K.

If more than 32K of data are required, then the program would have to be extended. This would involve resetting the registers as follows:

ES to 4000H
CX to 08000H
BX to 00H

The exact same data acquisition loop could then be executed again and this would fill 32K of additional 12-bit data between locations 40000H and 4FFFFH inclusive. A less cumbersome method is to make further use of the CX register in a third mode to count down the two 64K memory segments.

The total RAM available is 640K of which a small amount is required by the operating system (0–500 hex). Uncertainty of the exact location of the code segment may prevent maximum use of memory for data storage. However, allowing three complete segments for the operating system and the program, i.e. setting the data starting address at 30000 hex, will still leave up to 7 segments, or 448K of memory for data storage. This would accommodate for example, an 11 s sampling interval, at 20 kHz sampling rate, using 12-bit accuracy with the data stored in two consecutive bytes.

The program listing given is not the only means of performing the same operations. For example, repetitive loops may be devised using the extensive variety of compare (CMP) and jump (JMP) instructions available. It is beyond the scope of the present text to outline the range of alternatives possible and the reader is directed to the texts for further reading at the end of the chapter and invited to experiment with variations to the coding given.

Access to the stored data following its capture may be done in BASIC, if speed is not essential. The assembly language routine is CALLed from a compiled BASIC program and a suitable program to be run in conjunction with the routine given might be as shown in Program 10.5.

Program 10.5 Data retrieval in BASIC.

```
REM data retrieval
DECLARE SUB data
CALL data
DEF SEG=&H3000
FOR I=0 to 32768 STEP 2
HIGH=PEEK(I)
LOW=PEEK(I+1)
RESULT=LOW+256*HIGH
PRINT RESULT
NEXT I
END
```

The program listing provides access to the data. The DEF SEG statement defines the address assigned to the appropriate segment register. Any subsequent command which accesses a memory location will access the location relative to the segment register. Thus by setting DEG SEG = &H3000, the data will be fetched from the same memory locations where it was stored in the assembly language routine, high byte first followed by the low byte.

An Example in Engine Monitoring

In measuring the performance of an internal combustion engine one of the many requirements is to record the variation of the pressure within the cylinders as a function of time. This has ramifications on the combustion efficiency and the internal losses associated with the engine. In the four-stroke engine, one complete cylinder cycle of suction, compression, expansion and exhaust is completed in two revolutions of the crankshaft. For a single-cylinder engine then, running at say 3000 rev/min, an engine cycle is completed in about 0.04 s. Any data acquisition system therefore has to be reasonably fast in order to capture the cylinder pressure history over a 40 ms interval. The data acquisition system described below was developed for experimental performance studies on a single-cylinder, variable compression petrol engine.

The cylinder pressure was monitored using a piezoelectric pressure transducer in conjunction with a charge amplifier. The output signal from the charge amplifier however was unsuitable for direct interfacing to the analogue input expansion card, the ACM-42, and an additional conditioning interface was added to provide further signal amplification and inversion to be compatible with the -2.5 to $+2.5$ V input range of the ACM-42. Figure 10.21 shows the pressure transducer signal conditioning interface.

The variable resistor in the balance circuit is used to adjust the offset of the signal to best fit the analogue input range of the ADC.

The timing reference points were provided by a magnetic pick-up sensor which responds to a single machined groove on the engine flywheel at the position of top dead centre (TDC). The passage of the TDC flywheel mark generates a short positive then negative pulse from the magnetic pick-up circuit. The amplitude of this signal was somewhat variable, depending on the engine speed, and might change between $+1$ and $+2.5$ V. This signal was further conditioned therefore to output a logic level pulse which could be input directly to a digital I/O port. The TDC signal conditioning circuit is depicted in Fig. 10.22.

If the input voltage at pin 3 ever exceeds that at pin 2, then the output from the comparator flips low. The voltage at pin 2 is set by a potentiometer to be above any noise resident at the input. This effectively negates the possibility of incorrect triggering. In operation, the output

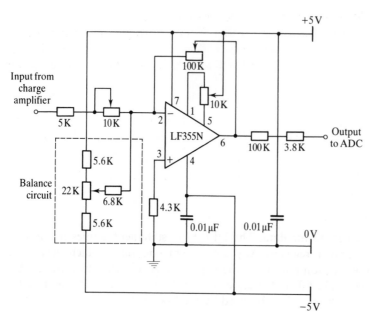

Figure 10.21 Pressure transducer signal conditioning interface.

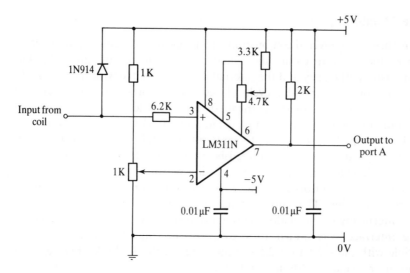

Figure 10.22 TDC signal conditioning interface.

from the comparator goes low whenever a TDC pulse is detected. The typical duration of the 0 logic level pulse was found to be about 5–10 μs, depending on the engine speed.

The comparator output was fed to bit 0 of the digital I/O port A on the ACM-42. To measure the engine speed, bit 0 of port A was constantly monitored. When a TDC pulse was detected a 16-bit register was continually incremented until a second TDC pulse was registered. This corresponds to one revolution of the crankshaft. The value contained in the register is directly proportional to the engine speed and the speed could then be computed from a calibration constant. It was found that the count did not vary significantly between one consecutive revolution and another, typically better than half of one per cent. This indicates that the engine speed was reasonably uniform over a complete engine cycle and the count between consecutive TDC pulses was therefore an effective method of measuring the mean engine speed.

The output signal from the pressure transducer conditioning interface was fed to channel 0 of the analogue input section of the ACM-42. Particular memory offset addresses were allocated to store data as follows:

FFEB   low byte, total of count between two consecutive TDC pulses for speed measurment
FFEC   high byte, total of count between two consecutive TDC pulses for speed measurement

FFED   low byte, total number of pressure measurements over four TDC pulses
FFEE   high byte, total number of pressure measurements over four TDC pulses
FFE0   total number of TDC pulses counted

FFE6   low byte, total number of data points per rev
FFE8   high byte, total number of data points per rev

FFF2   low byte, total number of pressure measurements in first rev
FFF3   high byte, total number of pressure measurements in first rev

FFF4   low byte, total number of pressure measurements in second rev
FFF5   high byte, total number of pressure measurements in second rev

Program 10.6 and the associated assembly language subroutines captures and stores the cylinder pressure history over one complete engine cycle.

Program 10.6 Engine cylinder pressure monitoring program.

```
REM Engine monitoring program
DECLARE SUB speed
DECLARE SUB dat
REM Set up the ACM-42 ADC card
PORT=&H300
REM Set the digital I/O with port A and port B for input
OUT PORT+11,&H93
REM Select analogue input channel 0
OUT PORT+12,0
CALL speed
LOW=PEEK(&HFFEB)
HIGH=PEEK(&HFFEC)
X%=LOW+256*HIGH
REVS=INT(5393333.3/X%)
PRINT"Engine speed = ";REVS;" RPM"
REM Data acquisition routine
CALL dat
DAT1=PEEK(&HFFF2)+256*(PEEK(&HFFF3))
DAT2=PEEK(&HFFF4)+256*(PEEK(&HFFF5))
TOTAL=(PEEK(&HFFED)+256*PEEK(&HFFEE))/2
PRINT"Samples captured in first rev = ";DAT1
PRINT"Samples captured in second rev = ";DAT2
PRINT"Total number of samples captured = ";TOTAL
END
```

```
speed:
MOV AX,03000H
MOV ES,AX              ; set ES to 3000 hex
MOV ES:[0FFEBH],00H    ; set memory location FFEB to zero
start:
MOV DX,0308H           ; set DX to 308 hex, ie. digital port A
IN AL,DX               ; read port A
AND AL,01H             ; logical AND with bit 0 of port A
JNZ start              ; delay until a TDC pulse is detected
tdc:
MOV DX,0308H
IN AL,DX
AND AL,01H
JZ tdc                 ; delay until end of TDC pulse is detected
tot:
ADD ES:[0FFEBH],01H    ; increment memory location FFEB by one
MOV DX,0308H
IN AL,DX
AND AL,01H
JNZ tot                ; increment FFEB until next TDC pulse detected
RETF                   ; end of speed measurement subroutine

dat:
MOV AX,03000H
MOV ES,AX              ; set ES to 3000 hex
MOV ES:[0FFE0H],00H    ; set memory location FFE0 to zero
MOV ES:[0FFE6H],00H    ; set memory location FFE6 to zero
mov bx,00H             ; set BX to zero

notre:
MOV DX,0308H
IN AL,DX
AND AL,01H
JNZ notre              ; delay until a TDC pulse is detected

pulse:
MOV DX,0308H
IN AL,DX
AND AL,01H
JZ pulse               ; delay until end of TDC pulse is detected

press:
MOV DX,0302H           ; set DX to 302 hex, ie. ADC low byte
IN AL,DX               ; read ADC low byte, ie. start conversion

busy:
MOV DX,0300H           ; set DX to 300 hex, ie. ADC base address
IN AL,DX               ; read ADC base address
AND AL,080H            ; logical AND with bit 7 of base address
JZ busy                ; delay until end of conversion signal detected
```

```
MOV DX,0301H              ; set DX to 301 hex, ie. ADC high byte
IN AL,DX                  ; read ADC high byte
MOV ES:[0FFE8H],AL        ; store ADC high byte at location FFE8
MOV DX,0302H              ; set DX to 302 hex, ie. ADC low byte
IN AL,DX                  ; read ADC low byte and place in AL
MOV AH,ES:[0FFE8H]        ; store high byte of ADC in AH
MOV ES:[BX],AX            ; store data, ie. AX, in location BX relative to ES
INC BX                    ; increment BX
INC BX                    ; increment BX again
ADD ES:[0FFE6H],01H

delay:
MOV DX,0308H
IN AL,DX
AND AL,01H
JZ totdc                  ; jump to "totdc" if a TDC pulse is detected

JMP press                 ; jump back to "press" if no TDC pulse is detected

totdc:
ADD ES:[0FFE0H],01H       ; increment memory location FFE0 by one
PUSH BX                   ; save current value of BX to the stack
MOV BX,ES:[0FFE0H]        ; move data in memory location FFE0 into BX
SHL BX,1                  ; shift left data in BX, equivalent to
                          ; mulyiplying by two.
                          ; This is necessary since FFE0 only counts one TDC
                          ; pulse per rev.  There are always two TDC pulses
                          ; in one complete revolution.

ADD BX,0FFF0H             ; add FFF0 hex to BX
MOV AX,ES:[0FFE6H]        ; move current value stored in location FFE6 into AX
MOV ES:[BX],AX            ; store current value in AX to location given by BX
MOV ES:[0FFE6H],00H       ; reset memory location FFE6 to zero
POP BX                    ; retrieve original value of BX from the stack
CMP ES:[0FFE0H],02H       ; compare the value held in location FFE0 with 2
JAE finish                ; if current value in FFE0 = 2 then goto "finish"

waiting:
MOV DX,0308H
IN AL,DX
AND AL,01H
JZ waiting                ; delay until end of TDC pulse is detected

JMP press                 ; unconditional jump to "press"

finish:
MOV ES:[0FFEDH],BX        ; store current value of BX to location FFED

RETF                      ; end of data capture subroutine
```

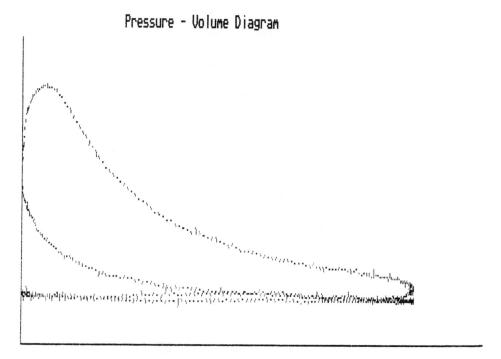

Figure 10.23 Pressure–volume trace for a four-stroke engine cycle.

The program continuously monitors and stores the pressure signal over two consecutive revolutions of the engine crankshaft. The pressure data are stored consecutively, as 16-bit numbers, from memory location 3000 hex upwards. In addition the number of data samples taken over the first and second revolutions, and the total number of samples taken are totalized and stored in specially allocated memory locations.

Once stored in memory, the data can be accessed later and processed according to the requirements. The data is captured at approximately 23 kHz and, since the engine runs at constant speed, this knowledge enables the pressure readings to be related to the corresponding cylinder volume during the cycle. Figure 10.23 shows a typical pressure–volume trace for one engine cycle.

Additional data processing reveals the effective area enclosed by the pressure–volume diagram which relates to the indicated power and the combustion performance of the engine. The example described is too specific to go into any further detail but the data acquisition techniques used are quite general and may be equally well applied to the capture of any other fast transient phenomena.

FURTHER READING

Brighouse, B. and G. Loveday (1987) *Microprocessors in Engineering Systems*, Pitman, London.
Derenzo, S. I. (1990) *Interfacing—A Laboratory Approach Using the Microcomputer for Instrumentation, Data Analysis and Control*, Prentice-Hall, Englewood Cliffs, NJ.
Liu, Y. and G. A. Gibson (1984) *Microcomputer Systems: The 8086/8088 Family*, Prentice-Hall, Englewood Cliffs, NJ.
Parr, E. A. (1987) *Industrial Control Handbook, Vol. 2, Techniques*, BSP Professional Books, Oxford.
Pessen, D. W. (1989) *Industrial Automation—Circuit Design & Components*, Wiley, New York.

Rector, R. and G. Alexy (1980) *The 8086 Book*, Osbourne/McGraw-Hill, New York.
Sauer, H. (1986) *Modern Relay Technology*, Dr. Alfred Heuthig Verlag GmbH, Heidelberg.
Thorne, M. (1986) *Programming the 8086/8088 for the IBM and Compatibles*, Addison-Wesley, Reading, Mass.

EXERCISES

10.1 Investigate the operation and characteristics of a Schmitt trigger and sketch a detailed wiring diagram of the package device within an interface circuit.

10.2 Draw a block diagram of a power switching interface for the operation of a 24 V DC, 5 W solenoid on a pneumatic control valve. The complete circuit should comprise a 7404 hex inverter IC, an opto-isolator IC and a Darlington Driver IC. Show a detailed pin to pin connection diagram and include all power connections along with the input from the microcomputer output port. Explain the function of the inverter.

10.3 Specify a suitable interface for controlling the amount of heating power supplied to a 3 kW 1 Ph 240 V AC load. Sketch a detailed wiring diagram for the interface chosen clearly specifying the components used and the supplier.

10.4 Describe, using sketches as appropriate, the principle of operation of the encapsulated solid-state input/output modules which are available for the interfacing of a variety of I/O devices to a microcomputer in a data acquisition and control application.

10.5 A 4-bit ladder type DAC has a full range output of 0–5 V. Determine the output voltage for each of the following binary inputs:
(i) 0101; (ii) 1000; (iii) 1011; (iv) 0111.

$$[1.5625, 2.5, 3.4375, 2.1875]$$

10.6 Two 8-bit ADCs have a full range output of 0–10 V and operate on clock cycles of 20 kHz. Determine the conversion times for an input signal of 8 V when:
  (i) The ADC is an up-counter type.
  (ii) The ADC is a successive approximation type.

$$[10.2\,\text{ms}, 0.4\,\text{ms}]$$

10.7 Determine the quantization error in volts and percentage of full-scale range for each of the following ADCs. The output voltage range, in all cases, is 0–10 V.
  (i)   Resolution = 4 bits   :error $= +/-(1/2)$ bit
  (ii) Resolution = 8 bits   :error $= +/- 1$ bit
  (iii) Resolution = 12 bits   :error $= +/-(1/2)$ bit
  (iv) Resolution = 16 bits   :error $= +/- 1$ bit

$$[(\text{i}) +/-0.3333\text{V}, +/-3.333\%; (\text{ii}) +/-0.0392\,\text{V}, +/-0.39\%;$$
$$(\text{iii}) +/-0.0012\,\text{V}, +/-0.012\%; (\text{iv}) +/-0.000076\,\text{V}, +/-0.00076\%]$$

10.8 Using an assembly language insert, store the consecutive decimal numbers from 1 to 2000 in consecutive memory offset locations starting at &H3000. Read the numbers back and print them to the screen using a BASIC program.
Note: Numbers greater than 255 require to be stored as a 16-bit binary equivalent. For simplicity, it is easier to store all the numbers as 16-bit, in a high-byte/low-byte form.

10.9 Write a program to calculate the average value of the data stored in exercise 10.8:
  (i) in BASIC;
  (ii) in an assembly language insert.
Compare the run times for each program.

$$[\text{about } 60 \text{ to } 1]$$

10.10 Using any appropriate D/A expansion card for an IBM-PC, or compatible machine, write a program in BASIC to generate:
  (i) a square wave output signal; (ii) a sinusoidal output signal.

10.11 Using example 10.10 as a basis, write assembly language routines to generate the output functions. Compare the maximum output signal frequencies in each case.

10.12 Using any proprietry A/D expansion card for an IBM-PC, or compatible machine, write a program in BASIC to sample data from a single channel. The data should be stored as elements in a one-dimensional array. Limiting the number of samples to 1000, use the TIMER function to determine the data acquisition rate. If the software is available, compare the data acquisition rate of a compiled version of the program.

10.13 Using an appropriate A/D expansion card for an IBM-PC, or compatible, write an assembly language insert to capture 64K of 8-bit data, or 32K of 12-bit data, at the maximum rate that the conversion speed of the card will allow. If a waveform generator is available with control on input amplitude and frequency, test the data acquisition routine for input frequencies up to the maximum sampling frequency.

Note: If the input signal is periodic, then as the input signal frequency approaches the maximum sampling frequency, the digitized data will tend towards a constant value. This is a good illustration of the aliasing problem.

ELEVEN

PRINCIPLES OF CONTINUOUS CONTROL

11.1 BASIC CONTROL SYSTEMS

Control engineering is based on the linear systems analysis associated with the development of feedback theory. A control system is constituted as an interconnection between the components which make up the system. These individual components may be electrical, mechanical, hydraulic, pneumatic, thermal or chemical in nature and the well designed control system will provide the 'best' response of the complete system to external, time-dependent disturbances operating on the system. In quantifying what is meant by the adjective 'best', the basic functions of the control system are:

1. to minimize the error between the actual and the desired output;
2. to minimize the time response to load changes in the system.

Paradoxically, however, these two functions are interrelated in an incompatible manner. For example the steady-state output error can be reduced in a proportional action controller by increasing the controller gain. Increased gain, however, has a detrimental effect on the time response of the system which becomes increasingly oscillatory and takes much longer to settle down. An optimized controller is one in which the influencing parameters are adjusted to make the best compromise between the two conflicting attributes. Invariably, the system to be controlled can be represented as a block diagram, as in Fig. 11.1.

The system is a group of physical components combined to perform a specific function. The variable controlled may be temperature, pressure, flow rate, liquid level, speed, voltage, position, or perhaps some combination of these. Analogue or digital techniques may be individually or simultaneously employed to implement the desired control action. In more

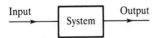

Figure 11.1 System to be controlled.

recent times the advances made in microelectronics have resulted in an emphasis towards digital techniques and the majority of modern control systems are now microprocessor based. A detailed study of analogue, or continuous, control systems is still required, however, in order to establish the fundamental principles and concepts. Note that this is not wasted effort since these principles and concepts have direct relevance and application to the more modern digital control systems which are considered in Chapter 13.

Classification of Control Systems

Engineering control systems are classified according to their application and these include the following:

Servomechanisms Servomechanisms are feedback control systems in which the controlled variable, or output, is a position or a speed. Direct current motors, stepper motor position control systems and some linear actuators, are the most commonly encountered examples of servomechanisms. These are especially prevalent in robotic arms and similar manipulators. In general, servomechanisms are associated with fast-acting devices having typical time constants in the milliseconds range.

Sequential control A system operating with sequential control is one where a set of prescribed operations are performed in sequence. The control may be implemented as 'event-based', where the next action cannot be performed until the previous action is completed. An alternative mode of sequential control is termed 'time-based', where the series of operations are sequenced with respect to time. Event-based sequential control is intrinsically a more reliable 'fail-safe' mode than time based. Consider, for example, an industrial process in which a tank is to be filled with a liquid and the liquid subsequently heated. The two control systems are depicted in Fig. 11.2.

The time-based sequential control system (a) is the simplest. The pump is switched on for an interval which would discharge enough liquid into the tank to fill it to approximately the correct level. Following this, the pump is switched off and the heater is switched on. Heating is similarly allowed to continue for a preset time, after which the liquid temperature would approximately have reached the desired value. Note that the control function is inexact and there are no fail-safe features. If the drive shaft between the motor and the pump becomes disengaged, or broken, then the heater will still come on at the prescribed time, irrespective of whether there is liquid in the tank or not. The event-based sequential control system has fail-safe features built in and is much more exact. In operation the pump is switched on until the liquid-level sensor indicates that the tank is filled. Then, and only then, is the pump switched off and the heater switched on. The temperature of the liquid is also monitored with a sensor and heating is applied until such time that the temperature reaches the desired value. Obviously, with two additional sensors, the event-based system is the more expensive. The advantages it offers over the time-based system, however, far outweighs the disadvantages, and event-based sequentially

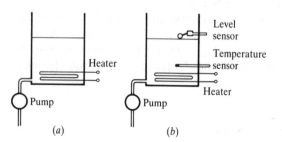

Figure 11.2 Simple sequential control systems: (a) time-based; (b) event-based.

controlled systems are by far the most common. Time-based systems do exist, nonetheless, and they are found in applications where the results of malfunction would be far less potentially catastrophic than those occurring in the example described. The essential difference between the two systems is that event-based sequential control incorporates a check that any operation has been completed before the next is allowed to proceed.

Numerical control In a system using numerical control the numerical information, in the form of digital codes, are stored on a control medium which may be a paper tape, a magnetic sensitive tape, or a magnetic sensitive disk. This information is used to operate the system in order to control such variables as position, direction, velocity and speed. There are a large variety of manufacturing operations involving machine tools which utilize this versatile method of control.

Process control In this type of control the variables associated with any process are monitored and subsequent control actions are implemented to maintain the variables within the predetermined process constraints. The word 'process' is all-encompassing and might include, for example, electrical power generation. The generation of 'electricity' can be considered as a manufacturing process where the 'product' is kilowatt hours. In the control of power generation, some of the variables which are measured include temperature, pressure, liquid level, speed, flow rate, voltage, current and a range of various gas concentrations. This is further complicated by the need to satisfy the power demand and it is apparent that the control of such a system is necessarily complex. Similarly complex examples exist in the oil and paper making industries, and in the automotive assembly industries.

11.2 LINEAR CONTROL THEORY

Open- and Closed-Loop Control

The basic open-loop system is shown in Fig. 11.1 and is extended in Fig. 11.3 to illustrate a more complete picture.

The input element supplies information regarding the desired value of the controlled variable X. This information is then acted on by the controller to alter the output Y, to the load. External disturbances are fed in as shown and cause the output to vary from the desired value. The open-loop system may be likened to the driving of a vehicle where two variables, the speed and the direction of motion, are controlled. The actuator, in the case of speed, is the engine throttle valve, and in the case of direction, is the steering system.

In order that the system becomes closed-loop, two further elements must be added. These are:

1. a monitoring element to measure the output Y;
2. a comparing element, to measure the difference between the actual output and the desired value X.

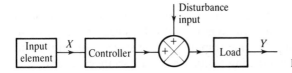

Figure 11.3 Open-loop control system.

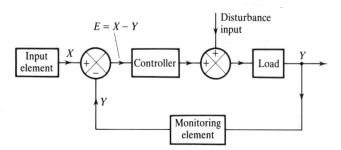

Figure 11.4 Closed-loop feedback control system.

The monitoring and comparing elements are connected through the 'feedback' link as shown in Fig. 11.4.

The vehicle driver in the previous example also performs the functions of monitoring and comparing. The driver therefore, if considered to be part of the complete system, closes the feedback loop. For the purpose of rigorous definition, however, any system which incorporates some form of feedback is termed a closed-loop system. With no feedback mechanism, the system is categorized as open-loop. For most practical engineering purposes, control systems are of the closed-loop variety to take advantage of the benefits of feedback, which may be either 'positive' or 'negative'. A positive feedback signal, however, aids the input signal and it is possible to have an output with no input when using positive feedback. Since this is detrimental to the control function, then positive feedback systems are very rarely encountered.

Linear and Nonlinear Control Systems

For a control system to be linear it must satisfy both the amplitude proportionality criteria and the principle of superposition. If a system output at a given time is $Y(t)$ for a given input $X(t)$, then an input of $kX(t)$ must produce an output of $kY(t)$ if amplitude proportionality is satisfied. In similar manner, if an input of $X_1(t)$ produces an output of $Y_1(t)$, while an input of $X_2(t)$ produces an output of $Y_2(t)$, then if an input of $[X_1(t) + X_2(t)]$ produces an output of $[Y_1(t) + Y_2(t)]$ then the superposition principle is satisfied. Nonlinear systems do not necessarily satisfy both of these criteria and generally these systems are 'compensated' such that their behaviour approaches that of an equivalent linear system.

Characteristics of Control Systems

The characteristics of a control system are related to the output behaviour of the system in response to any given input. The parameters used to define control system characteristics are stability, accuracy, speed of response and sensitivity. The system is said to be 'stable' if the output attains a certain value in a finite interval after the input has undergone a change. When the output reaches a constant value the system is said to be in steady state. The system is unstable if the output increases with time. In any practical control system, stability is absolutely essential. Systems involving a 'time delay', or a 'dead time' may tend to be unstable and extra care must be taken in the design of such systems to ensure stability. The stability of control systems can be analysed using various analytical and graphical techniques (see Secs 11.7, 11.8, 11.9 and 11.10).

The accuracy of a system is a measure of the deviation of the actual controlled value in relation to its desired value. Accuracy is therefore synonymous with the steady-state error. In like manner, stability is closely associated with the time response of the system. Accuracy and stability are therefore interactive in the same conflicting manner as steady-state error and time response. The accuracy of a system might be improved, but this will be at the expense of reduced stability. The converse also applies.

The speed of response is a measure of how quickly the output attains a steady-state value after the input has been altered. The speed of the response is also constrained by stability limitations.

Sensitivity is another important factor and is a measure of how the system output responds to external environmental conditions. Ideally the output should be a function only of the input and should not be influenced by undesirable extraneous signals.

Dynamic Performance of Systems

The dynamic performance of a control system is assessed by mathematical modelling, or by experimentally measuring the output of the system in response to a particular set of test input conditions. The step input is perhaps the most important test input since a system which is stable to a step input will also be stable under any of the other forms of input. The step input is applied to gauge the transient response of the system and gives a measure of how the system can cope with a sudden change in the input. A ramp input is used to indicate the steady-state error in a system attempting to follow a linearly increasing input. Finally, the sinusoidal input over a varying range of input frequencies, is the standard test used to determine the frequency dependent characteristics of the system. Although the three standard test inputs may not be strict representations of the actual inputs to which the system will be subject, they do cover a comprehensive range. A system which performs satisfactorily under these idealized test inputs will, in general, perform well under a more natural range of inputs.

11.3 MATHEMATICAL MODELS OF SYSTEMS—TIME DOMAIN ANALYSIS

The time domain model of a system results in an output $Y(t)$ with respect to time, for an input $X(t)$. The time domain system model is expressed as a differential equation, the solution of which is displayed as a function of output against time. In the context of instrumentation and measurement, the time domain solutions for first- and second-order systems are considered in some detail in Sec. 4.3.

In contrast, a frequency domain model describes the system in terms of the effect that the system has on the amplitude and phase of sinusoidal inputs. Typically the system performance is displayed in plots of amplitude ratio ($[Y(t)/X(t)]$ or $20\log_{10}[Y(t)/X(t)]$) and phase angle, against input signal frequency. Neither system model has overriding advantage over the other and both are used to good effect in describing system performance and behaviour.

11.4 LAPLACE NOTATION FOR DIFFERENTIAL EQUATIONS—FREQUENCY DOMAIN ANALYSIS

For analysis in the frequency domain it is customary to write the differential equation in terms of the Laplace operator 's'. This gives rise to the system 'transfer function' which is formed by replacing the input and output, X and Y, respectively, with their corresponding Laplace transforms $X(s)$ and $Y(s)$. The method applies only to linear differential equations. In practice, many systems would contain some degree of nonlinearity and various assumptions would have to be made to simplify and approximately linearize the governing equations. The advantage in using the Laplace transform method is that it allows the differential equation to be expressed as an equivalent algebraic relation in s. Differentiation is represented by multiplication with the

Table 11.1 Laplace transforms for some common time functions.

Time domain $f(t),\ t > 0$	Frequency domain $f(s)$
K	K/s
Kt	K/s^2
Ke^{-at}	$K/(s+a)$
Kte^{-at}	$K/(s+a)^2$
$K\sin(\omega t)$	$K\omega/(s^2+\omega^2)$
$K\cos(\omega t)$	$Ks/(s^2+\omega^2)$
$Ke^{-at}\sin(\omega t)$	$K\omega/[(s+a)^2+\omega^2]$
$Ke^{-at}\cos(\omega t)$	$K(s+a)/[(s+a)^2+\omega^2]$
$K[1-(e^{-t/\tau})]$	$K/s(\tau s+1)$

Laplace variable s; thus dY/dt becomes $s\,Y(s)$ and d^2Y/dt^2 is replaced with $s^2\,Y(s)$. Table 11.1 lists the Laplace transforms for the more common time functions.

First-order Systems

The differential relation which describes a first-order system was given as Eq. (4.2), i.e.

$$\tau(dY/dt) + Y = kX$$

The equation is re-written with the appropriate Laplace transforms replacing the differential operators:

$$\tau s Y(s) + Y(s) = kX(s) \tag{11.1}$$

Thus

$$Y(s)[1 + \tau s] = kX(s) \tag{11.2}$$

The system transfer function is defined as the ratio of the output to the input and is

$$[Y(s)/X(s)] = k/(1 + \tau s) \tag{11.3}$$

Equation (11.3) enables the convenient facility of incorporating the transfer function within the usual block structure representation of a control system. Thus a first-order, open-loop control system can be systematically depicted as shown in Fig. 11.5.

In the frequency domain model we are predominantly concerned with the system response to sinusoidal inputs. Differentiation, or integration, of a sinusoidal function does not alter the shape or frequency, there is simply a change in amplitude and phase, e.g.

$$\text{input} = A\sin(\omega t) \tag{11.4}$$

$$d/dt[A\sin(\omega t)] = \omega A\cos(\omega t)$$
$$= \omega A\sin(\omega t + \pi/2) \tag{11.5}$$

On comparison of Eqs. (11.4) and (11.5), it can be seen that differentiation has changed the amplitude A to ωA and that there is a phase shift of 90° associated with the process. Equation (11.5), in fact, describes the steady-state output from a first-order, open-loop control system.

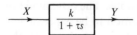

Figure 11.5 First-order, open-loop control system.

The transient part of the output, which the time domain solution illustrates in Fig. 4.4, is not apparent in the frequency domain solution. The Laplace operator s may be replaced with '$j\omega$', where j is the complex operator $\sqrt{-1}$. Equation (11.3) then becomes

$$Y/X = k/(1 + j\omega\tau)$$

Using the complex conjugate it may be shown that the amplitude ratio is given by

$$Y/X = \frac{k}{(1 + j\omega\tau)} \cdot \frac{(1 - j\omega\tau)}{(1 - j\omega\tau)} = \frac{k(1 - j\omega\tau)}{(1 + \omega^2\tau^2)}$$

$$Y/X = \frac{k}{(1 + \omega^2\tau^2)} - \frac{jk\omega\tau}{(1 + \omega^2\tau^2)}$$

(11.6)

The transfer function invariably reduces to a single complex number of the form given by Eq. (11.6). The magnitude, or modulus of the complex number represents the amplitude ratio, or gain. The angle of the complex number represents the phase angle.

The modulus of the amplitude ratio is given as

$$| Y/X | = \sqrt{(\text{real part})^2 + (\text{imaginary part})^2}$$

$$= \sqrt{\frac{k^2}{(1 + \omega^2\tau^2)^2} + \frac{k^2(\omega t)^2}{(1 + \omega^2\tau^2)^2}}$$

$$= \sqrt{\frac{k^2}{(1 + \omega^2\tau^2)^2} + \frac{k^2\omega^2\tau^2}{(1 + \omega^2\tau^2)^2}}$$

$$= \sqrt{\frac{k^2(1 + \omega^2\tau^2)}{(1 + \omega^2\tau^2)^2}} = \sqrt{\frac{k^2}{(1 + \omega^2\tau^2)}}$$

Hence

$$| Y/X | = k/\sqrt{(1 + \omega^2\tau^2)}$$

(11.7)

Equation (11.7) shows how the output amplitude will be influenced by the input signal frequency ω. Note that this agrees with the time domain solution, Eq. 4.5, for large values of time t, after which the steady state is achieved.

The phase angle lag is given by

$$\phi = \tan^{-1}(\text{imaginary part/real part})$$

For the first order system considered

$$\phi = -\tan^{-1}(\omega\tau)$$

(11.8)

Figure 11.6(a) shows the variation in the amplitude ratio for increasing input signal frequencies and a gain $k = 1$. The plot depicts the complete frequency characteristics of the system. If the vertical ordinate is plotted in decibels, i.e. $20 \log_{10}(Y/X)$, then the resulting graph is termed a Bode diagram. The horizontal axis is plotted in a logarithmic scale and is made non-dimensional by presenting the data in terms of the product $(\omega\tau)$. The behaviour of the phase angle with increasing signal frequency is shown in Fig. 11.6(b).

An alternative representation of the frequency response, shown in Fig. 11.7, is given as a polar plot of the amplitude ratio and the phase angle. This is also referred to as a Nyquist plot (see Sec. 11.7). The real and imaginary axes correspond to the complex form of the amplitude ratio given in Eq. (11.6). For the first-order system, the frequency response in polar coordinates

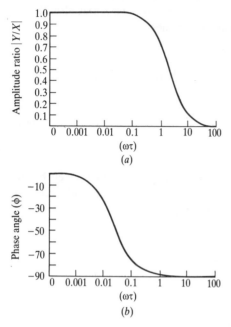

Figure 11.6 Frequency response of a first-order system.

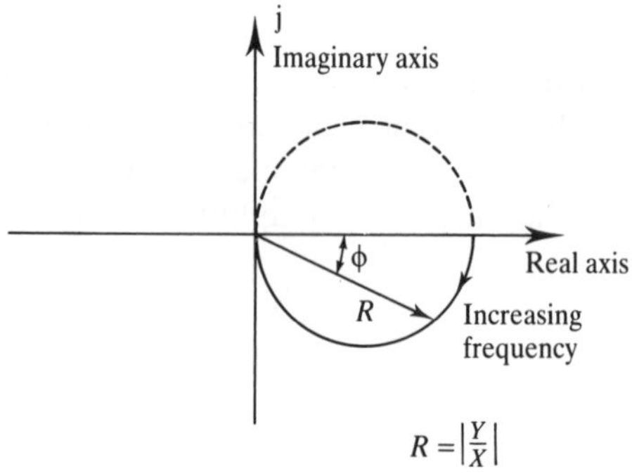

Figure 11.7 Frequency response of a first-order system in polar coordinates.

describes a perfect semicircle. The section of the response shown as a broken line is obtained for negative values of ω. This part of the response therefore has no physical significance.

The method of analysis outlined above is quite general and may be applied to determine the frequency response of any second-, or higher-order system.

Second-order Systems

The second-order system is defined by the differential relation given as Eq. (4.6), i.e.

$$(d^2Y/dt^2) + 2\zeta\omega_n(dY/dt) + \omega_n^2 Y = \omega_n^2 K$$

Denoting the input forcing function as X and using the Laplace operator, the governing equation may be re-written in the form:

$$s^2 Y(s) + 2\zeta\omega_n s Y(s) + \omega_n^2 Y(s) = \omega_n^2 X(s) \tag{11.9}$$

Thus

$$Y(s)[s^2 + 2\zeta\omega_n s + \omega_n^2] = \omega_n^2 X(s)$$

The system transfer function is

$$Y(s)/X(s) = \omega_n^2/[s^2 + 2\zeta\omega_n s + \omega_n^2] \tag{11.10}$$

Thus a second-order, open-loop control system can be represented schematically as in Fig. 11.8.

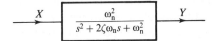

Figure 11.8 Second-order, open-loop control system.

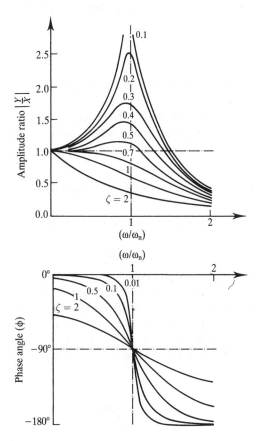

Figure 11.9 Second-order, open-loop control system frequency response.

For a sinusoidal input of the form $X = X_o \sin(\omega t)$, manipulation of the complex conjugate in the frequency domain analysis gives the following steady-state solutions for the amplitude ratio and the phase angle:

$$| Y/X | = \frac{1}{\sqrt{(1 - r^2)^2 + (2\zeta r)^2}} \tag{11.11}$$

$$\phi = -\tan^{-1}[(2\zeta r)/(1 - r^2)] \tag{11.12}$$

where $r = [\omega/\omega_n]$. The frequency response characteristics are shown in Fig. 11.9.

When the input signal frequency is equal to the system's natural frequency the amplitude ratio has the value $(1/2\zeta)$ and the phase angle is $-90°$. Note that if the damping ratio is zero, then the amplitude ratio theoretically approaches infinity under this special resonance condition. In practice, if the damping ratio is moderately low, then very large output amplitudes can be expected if the input frequency is in the vicinity of the system natural frequency.

Thus far we have considered the open-loop system response for first- and second-order systems. Such systems are unconditionally stable. The addition of a controller, with an associated transfer function, and a feedback loop, however, increases the possibility that the second-order system with feedback may become unstable. Furthermore, if any system, first or second order, incorporates a 'time-delay', also known as a 'deadtime' or a 'transportation lag', then unstable operation is more likely to occur (see also Sec 11.7).

11.5 DETERMINATION OF THE CLOSED-LOOP TRANSFER FUNCTION

In a closed-loop system the transfer function becomes modified by the feedback loop. The first task therefore is to determine the overall transfer function for the complete system. For simple open-loop systems the transfer functions are combined according to the following rules:

1. For elements in series, the overall transfer function is given by the product of the individual transfer functions (Fig. 11.10).
2. For elements in parallel, the overall transfer function is given by the sum of the individual transfer functions (Fig. 11.11).

For a system with feedback, the overall transfer function can be evaluated using a consistent step-by-step procedure. Series and parallel control elements are combined in the manner shown to reduce the system to a single block, which then represents the overall transfer function. Consider the simple control system depicted in Fig. 11.12. The open loop transfer function is $G(s)$. Since the feedback line does not include any transfer function it is termed a 'unity feedback' system, i.e. the output is compared directly with the input to produce the error signal. The closed loop transfer function is obtained as follows:

$$Y = G(s)E$$

The output from the comparator is $E = (X - Y)$, thus

$$Y = G(s)[X - Y] = G(s)X - G(s)Y$$

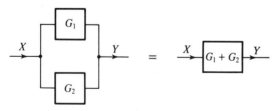

Figure 11.10 Transfer functions in series.

Figure 11.11 Transfer functions in parallel.

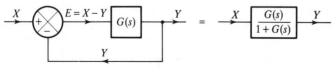

Figure 11.12 Control system with unity feedback.

i.e.

$$Y + G(s)Y = Y[1 + G(s)] = G(s)X$$

Hence

$$Y/X = G(s)/[1 + G(s)] \tag{11.13}$$

The analysis reduces the control system with feedback to an open-loop system with a single equivalent transfer function. If the element whose open-loop transfer function $G(s)$ is a first order subsystem, then $G(s)$ may be replaced with the expression given in Eq. (11.3). The closed-loop transfer function may then be written as

$$\frac{Y}{X} = \frac{(k/[1 + \tau s])}{(1 + k/[1 + \tau s])} \tag{11.14}$$
$$Y/X = k/(1 + k + \tau s)$$

Dividing top and bottom by $(1 + k)$ results in

$$\frac{Y}{X} = \frac{(k/[1 + k])}{(1 + \tau s/[1 + k])}$$

Defining the following terms

$$k_c = k/(1 + k) \tag{11.15}$$

$$\tau_c s = \tau s/(1 + k) \tag{11.16}$$

then k_c is the closed-loop gain and τ_c is the closed-loop system time constant.

Equations (11.15) and (11.16) show, respectively, that the closed-loop system gain and time constant are less than those associated with the open-loop system. This means that the closed-loop response is faster than the open-loop response. At the same time, however, the closed-loop gain is reduced. The final closed-loop transfer function may be expressed as

$$Y/X = k_c/(1 + \tau_c s) \tag{11.17}$$

Note that the closed-loop transfer function takes the same form as the open-loop transfer function, i.e. Eq. (11.3). The closed-loop transfer function, however, incorporates the reduced gain k_c and reduced time constant τ_c. The method presented in Sec. 11.4 may now be used to determine the modulus of the amplitude ratio and the phase angle with the resultant frequency domain solution given as

$$|Y/X| = k_c/\sqrt{(1 + \tau_c^2 \omega^2)} \text{ and } \phi = -\tan^{-1}(\omega \tau_c)$$

More complex control systems are analysed in much the same manner.

Example Determine the overall transfer function for the control system depicted schematically in Fig. 11.13.

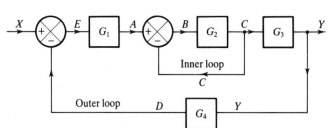

Figure 11.13 Schematic representation of a multiple loop control system.

If is often helpful to label the various signals in the system as shown. Considering the inner feedback loop first of all:

$$C = BG_2 = [A - C]G_2$$

$$C/A = G_2/[1 + G_2] \tag{11.18}$$

Equation (11.18) constitutes an equivalent transfer function which performs the operation associated with the inner loop. The control system can therefore be modified as shown in Fig. 11.14(a).

In the forward path shown in Fig. 11.14(a) there are three transfer functions appearing in series. These can be multiplied together to form a single equivalent transfer function, $G_1G_2G_3/[1 + G_2]$, giving a further simplification as shown in Fig. 11.14(b). The equivalent system now consists of a single feedback loop. Hence

$$Y = EG_1G_2G_3/[1 + G_2] = (X - D)G_1G_2G_3/[1 + G_2]$$

$$Y = (X - YG_4)G_1G_2G_3/[1 + G_2]$$

$$Y(1 + G_2) = XG_1G_2G_3 - YG_1G_2G_3G_4$$

thus

$$Y/X = [G_1G_2G_3]/[1 + G_2 + G_1G_2G_3G_4] \tag{11.19}$$

Equation (11.19) gives the closed-loop transfer function for the complete system. The Laplace transforms of the various components which make up the transfer function can be substituted and the amplitude ratio and phase angle determined as before.

Using the general procedures outlined, any other complex control system may be similarly analysed to determine the closed-loop transfer function. Thus knowing the gain constants and other characteristics of the elements which make up the system, the frequency response may be obtained. The stability of the system may then be assessed and any corrective measures taken as necessary.

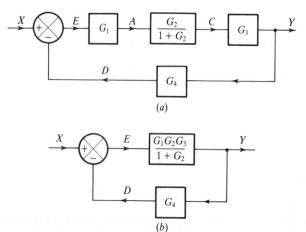

Figure 11.14 Simplification of the block diagram of a control system.

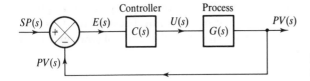

Figure 11.15 Basic unity feedback closed-loop process control system.

11.6 CONTROL STRATEGIES

The basic closed-loop process control system with common symbol representation is shown in Fig. 11.15, where the nomenclature used is defined as follows:

$SP(s)$ is the set point (required value, $r(t)$ is sometimes used)
$PV(s)$ is the process value (corrected value, $c(t)$ is sometimes used)
$E(s)$ is the error signal, which is the difference between SP and PV
$U(s)$ is the control effort output from the controller to the process
$C(s)$ is the controller transfer function
$G(s)$ is the process transfer function

The transfer function for the closed loop system is obtained as before:

$$PV(s) = C(s)G(s)E(s) = C(s)G(s)[SP(s) - PV(s)]$$

i.e.

$$\frac{PV(s)}{SP(s)} = \frac{C(s)G(s)}{1 + C(s)G(s)} \tag{11.20}$$

ON/OFF Control

In many applications, a simple ON/OFF strategy is perfectly adequate to control the output variable within preset limits. The ON/OFF control action results in either full power or zero power being applied to the process under control. A mechanical type of thermostat provides a good example of an ON/OFF-based controller. The ON/OFF control strategy results in an output which fluctuates about the set point as illustrated in Fig. 11.16.

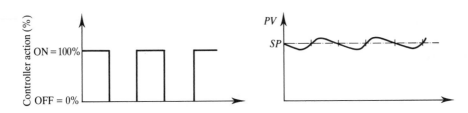

Figure 11.16 Output variation with ON/OFF control.

ON/OFF controllers usually incorporate a 'deadband' over which no control action is applied. The deadband is necessary to limit the frequency of switching between the ON and OFF states. For example in a temperature control system, the ON/OFF control strategy would be

$$\text{if temperature} < T_{\min}, \text{then heater is to be switched ON}$$

$$\text{if temperature} > T_{\max}, \text{then heater is to be switched OFF}$$

The deadband in the above case is $(T_{\max} - T_{\min})$ and while the temperature remains within the deadband no switching will occur. A large deadband will result in a correspondingly large fluctuation of the process value about the set point. Reducing the deadband will reduce the level of fluctuation but will increase the frequency of switching. The simple ON/OFF control strategy is mostly applicable to processes and systems which have long time constants and in consequence have relatively slow response times, for example, temperature and level control systems. ON/OFF control with rapid switching using thyristor circuits are used, however, in faster acting systems, for example, motor speed control.

While being simple in concept, ON/OFF control systems are, in fact, highly nonlinear and they require complex nonlinear techniques to investigate their stability characteristics.

Three Term, or PID Control

Since complicated transfer functions can be very difficult to model, the most common strategy used to define the controller transfer function is the so-called 'three term', or PID controller. PID is the popular shortform for proportional, integral and derivative. The three elements of the controller action U based on the evaluated error E are:

Proportional action

$$\text{controller output} = KE \tag{11.21}$$

where K is the controller gain.

Manufacturers of three-term controllers tend to favour the parameter 'proportional band' PB in preference to gain K. The proportional band represents the range of input over which the output is proportional to the input. The PB is usually expressed as a percentage of the input normalized between 0 and 100 per cent (Fig. 11.17).

To illustrate the concept of proportional band, a temperature control application can be considered where the set point is 80°C and the proportional band is set to 5 per cent over a measured temperature span of 0°C to 100°C. The actual proportional band is therefore 5 Centigrade degrees and proportional action will apply over the temperature range between 75°C and 80°C. If the temperature is below 75°C then 100 per cent of the available power will be supplied to the heating device. Between 75°C and 80°C, a proportion of the available power will

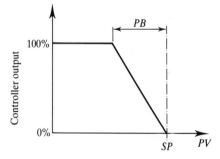

Figure 11.17 Illustration of the proportional band.

be applied to the heating device as shown in Fig. 11.17. For temperatures in excess of 80°C, 0 per cent of the available power is supplied. It should be apparent that proportional band is a much more meaningful term than controller gain. The two parameters, however, are very simply related:

$$PB\% = 100/K \tag{11.22}$$

It is also apparent from Fig. 11.17 that as the proportional band is decreased then the control action is tending towards an ON/OFF strategy. A very large proportional band will result in a somewhat sluggish response. It must also be noted that for proportional control only, there must always be an error in order to produce a control action. From Eq. (11.20), proportional control gives a transfer function of the form:

$$\frac{PV(s)}{SP(s)} = \frac{KG(s)}{1 + KG(s)} = \frac{1}{[1/\{KG(s)\} + 1]} \tag{11.23}$$

For steady-state conditions, s tends to 0 and $G(s)$ tends to a constant value. Equation (11.23) shows therefore that the gain must theoretically tend to infinity if $PV = SP$ and the steady-state error is to approach zero. With a very high gain, i.e. low proportional band, the steady-state error can be very much reduced. A low proportional band, however, tends to ON/OFF control action and in a time-sensitive system, a violent unstable oscillation may result.

Note, however, that many industrial PID controllers are designed to operate with 50 per cent of the available power output at the set point. That is the set point is located at the mid-point of the proportional band.

Integral action The limitations of proportional control can be partly alleviated by adding a controller action which gives an output contribution which is related to the integral of the error value with respect to time, i.e.

$$\text{controller action} = K_i \int E \, dt \tag{11.24}$$

where K_i is the controller integral gain $= K/T_i$, and T_i is the controller 'integral time', or 'reset'.

The nature of integral action, Eq. (11.24), suggests that the controller output will increase monotonically as long as an error exists. As the error tends to zero the controller output tends towards a steady value. The general behaviour of the controller output with integral action is shown in Fig. 11.18.

If T_i is very large, the integral contribution will be low and the error may persist for a considerable time. If, on the other hand T_i is too small, then the response time of the integrator may be faster than that of the process being controlled. Under these circumstances the magnitude of the integral term may cause excessive overshoot in the output response, or may even result in unstable operation. This is referred to as integral saturation and modern industrial controllers avoid this situation by inhibiting the integral contribution when the measured process variable is outwith the proportional band.

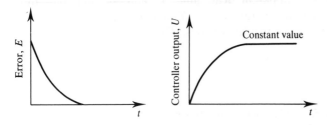

Figure 11.18 Controller output with integral action.

Derivative action The stability of a system can be improved and any tendency to overshoot can be reduced by adding derivative action. Derivative action is based on the rate of change of the error and implements a contribution to the controller ouput based on the assumption that the process variable will continue to change at the rate currently measured. In this manner derivative action acts as a process lead function, predicting the effects of process changes and compensating to a certain extent for lags in the process dynamics, i.e.

$$\text{controller output} = K_d(dE/dt) \tag{11.25}$$

where K_d is the controller derivative gain $= KT_d$, and T_d is the controller 'derivative time', or 'rate'.

Equation (11.25) indicates that the derivative action is dependent on how quickly, or otherwise, the error is changing. Derivative action tends therefore to come into operation during the early transient part of a system's response when there is a large and rapidly changing error.

The full three term control strategy may be written as

$$U = K[E + (1/T_i)\int E\,dt + T_d(dE/dt)] \tag{11.26}$$

To summarize, the proportional action governs the speed of the response, the integral action improves the accuracy of the final steady state and the derivative action improves the stability. Note that derivative action may result in poor performance of the system if the error signal is particularly noisy. A noisy signal results in an erratic derivative term which can adversely affect the overall performance of the system. In Laplace notation, the three term controller transfer function is as shown in Fig. 11.19.

Empirical Rules for PID Controller Settings

A simple and still popular technique for obtaining the controller settings to produce a stable control condition is due to Ziegler and Nichols. The technique is purely empirical and is based on existing, or measurable operating records of the system to be controlled.

Open loop 'reaction curve' method The process to be controlled is subjected to a step input excitation and the system open-loop response is measured. A typical open-loop response curve is shown in Fig. 11.20. Any system which has a response similar to that given in Fig. 11.20 has a transfer function which approximates to a first-order system with a time delay, i.e.

$$G(s) = k\,e^{-sT_1}/(1 + T_2 s) \tag{11.27}$$

In general industrial applications, oscillatory open-loop responses are extremely rare and Fig. 11.20 is in fact representative of quite a large number of real practical processes. N is the process steady-state value for a controller step input of P. The system steady state gain is

$$k = N/P \tag{11.28}$$

From the process response curve the 'apparent dead time' T_1 and the 'apparent time constant' T_2 can be measured directly. The three parameters, k, T_1 and T_2 are then used in a set of empirical rules to estimate the optimum controller settings. The recommended controller settings are given in Table 11.2.

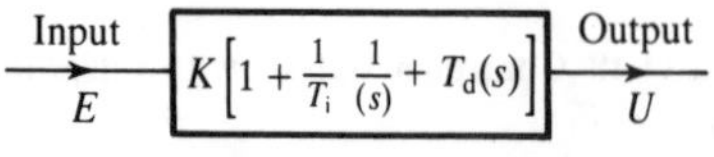

Input $\longrightarrow$ $\boxed{K\left[1 + \frac{1}{T_i}\frac{1}{(s)} + T_d(s)\right]}$ $\longrightarrow$ Output
E $\qquad\qquad\qquad\qquad\qquad\qquad U$

Figure 11.19 Three-term, or PID control.

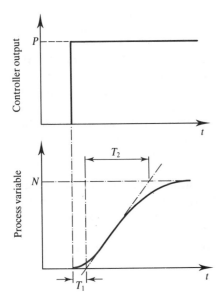

Figure 11.20 Open-loop system response to a step input.

Table 11.2 Optimum controller settings according to Ziegler and Nichols.

Control action	K	T_i	T_d
P	$T_2/(T_1 k)$	—	—
$P + I$	$(0.9 T_2)/(T_1 k)$	$T_1/0.3$	—
$P + I + D$	$(1.2 T_2)/(T_1 k)$	$2 T_1$	$0.5 T_1$

In fast acting servomechanisms, where T_1 may be very small, the method is none too successful. For moderate response systems, however, the method will yield very reasonable first approximation controller settings.

Example During startup, the control valve of a process was maintained constant until the controlled variable reached a steady state near to the normal operating value. The control valve position was then changed by 10 per cent. An output response similar to Fig. 11.20 was obtained where the output changed from 38 to 46 per cent. Measurements of the output response gave an apparent dead time of 2 min and an apparent time constant of 6 min. Determine the appropriate settings for an industrial controller using a full PID control strategy.

System steady-state gain $= k = \Delta N / \Delta P = (46 - 38)/10 = 0.8$. $T_1 = 2 \, \text{min}$; $T_2 = 6 \, \text{min}$.
From Table 11.2

$$K = 1.2 \times T_2/(T_1 \times k) = 1.2 \times 6/(2 \times 0.8) = 4.5$$

$$T_i = 2 T_1 = 2 \times 2 = 4 \, \text{min} = 240 \, \text{s}$$

Thus

$$T_d = 0.5 \times T_1 = 0.5 \times 2 = 1 \, \text{min} = 60 \, \text{s}$$

Closed-loop 'continuous cycling' method The process to be controlled is connected to the PID controller and the integral and derivative terms are eliminated by setting $T_d = 0$ and $T_i = \infty$. In some industrial controllers the integral term is eliminated with $T_i = 0$. A step change is introduced and the system run with a small controller gain value K. The gain is gradually increased for a step input until constant amplitude oscillations are obtained as illustrated in Fig. 11.21. The gain, K_u which produces the constant amplitude condition is noted and the period of the oscillation T_u is measured. These two values are then used to estimate the optimum controller settings according to the empirical rules listed in Table 11.3.

For a temperature control system, typical values of T_u are about 10 s for a tungsten filament lamp, 2 min for a 25 W soldering iron and from 10 to 30 min for a 3 kW heat treatment furnace.

Example A process control system, incorporating an industrial PID controller was tested at startup. The derivative mode was turned off by setting $T_d = 0$ and the integral mode was disabled by setting $T_i = 100$. The gain was then gradually increased until the output response to a step input exhibited a steady oscillation. The particular gain setting was 2.2 and the period of the oscillation was 8 min. Determine the most appropriate controller PID settings.

$$K_u = 2.2 : T_u = 8 \text{ min}$$

From Table 11.3

$$K = 0.6 \times K_u = 0.6 \times 2.2 = 1.32$$
$$T_i = T_u/2 = 6/2 = 3 \text{ min} = 180 \text{ s}$$
$$T_d = T_u/8 = 6/8 = 0.75 \text{ min} = 45 \text{ s}$$

The PID settings obtained according to the Ziegler & Nichols methods are approximate only and some 'fine tuning' would almost certainly be required in practice.

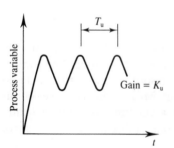

Figure 11.21 Continuous cycling method.

Table 11.3 Optimum controller settings according to Ziegler and Nichols.

Control action	K	T_i	T_d
P	$0.5K_u$	—	—
P + I	$0.45K_u$	$T_u/1.2$	—
P + I + D	$0.6K_u$	$T_u/2$	$T_u/8$

Three-term Controller with a First-order System

The block diagram of the system is depicted in Fig. 11.15 and Eq. (11.20) defines the closed-loop transfer function. If a $P + I$ controller is to be used, i.e. no derivative action, then the controller transfer function is

$$C(s) = K[1 + 1/(T_i s)] \qquad (11.29)$$

The process is modelled as a first-order system and its open-loop transfer function is given by Eq. (11.3). Substituting Eqs (11.3) and (11.29) into Eq. (11.20) results, after some manipulation, in

$$\frac{PV(s)}{SP(s)} = \frac{(kK/T_i\tau)[1 + sT_i]}{s^2 + [(1/\tau) + (kK/\tau)]s + (kK/T_i\tau)} \qquad (11.30)$$

Comparing the denominator with that for the generalized second-order system, i.e. Eq. (11.10), it can be shown that

$$2\zeta\omega_n = [1/\tau + kK/\tau]$$

and

$$\omega_n^2 = (kK/T_i\tau)$$

Note that since the integral time T_i is a constant, then sT_i represents $T_i d(SP)/dt$ which is zero following a step input. The numerator of Eq. (11.30) therefore reverts to the standard form given by Eq. (11.10).

For the system being controlled, both k and τ are known either via a mathematical model, or an open-loop test. The controller settings K and T_i can then be calculated for a chosen damping ratio ζ and natural frequency ω_n. Alternatively a controller gain can be imposed and the corresponding natural frequency evaluated. For full PID control an initial value of $T_d = T_i/4$ can be used. Other systems can be similarly handled to obtained the approximate PID controller settings. In all cases some fine adjustment would probably be necessary to obtain the optimum output response.

11.7 STABILITY CRITERIA

The possibility of sustained oscillations always exist in a closed-loop control system. The reason for this tendency is related to the feedback loop and the particular instance when the open-loop phase angle is $-180°$. If the closed-loop control system depicted in Fig. 11.22 has an open-loop gain of unity and an open-loop phase angle of $-180°$, then the output response to a single step pulse is a self-sustaining oscillation at the output (Fig. 11.22). The input signal is a single square pulse as shown. Since there is no feedback signal at this time then the same signal will appear at the output, but delayed by a phase lag equivalent to $-180°$. This output signal is also fed back to the comparator where it will become inverted and fed directly into the system since there is now no longer a signal at the input. After another time delay of half of one period, i.e. another phase lag of $-180°$, the inverted signal will again appear at the output and again be simultaneously fed back to the comparator where the process will repeat indefinitely. In this manner, even if there is no input signal, the output is self-sustaining and will appear as a square-wave oscillation. If the system gain k was greater than unity then the output oscillation will not only be self-sustaining, but will exhibit an increasing amplitude. On the other hand if the gain is less than unity then, even though the oscillation is self-sustaining, it will exhibit a decreasing amplitude and eventually reduce to zero. This behaviour epitomizes the difference between a stable and an

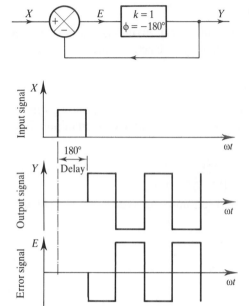

Figure 11.22 Self-sustained closed-loop response.

unstable system and allows us to make some definitive statements related to the criterion for stability:

1. A system is stable if the open-loop gain is less than unity when the open-loop phase angle is −180°.
2. A system is unstable if the open-loop gain is greater than unity when the open-loop phase angle is −180°.
3. A system is marginally stable if the open-loop gain is equal to unity when the open-loop phase angle is −180°.

The important point to realize is that it is the open-loop gain and phase angle characteristics which determines the stability of the closed-loop control system. This is further reinforced by consideration of Eq. (11.13) which defines the closed-loop transfer function for a unity feedback control system. Clearly the system is unstable if the denominator of the transfer function is equal to zero. This condition is satisfied when the open-loop transfer function is equal to −1 and this occurs when the open-loop gain is unity and the open-loop phase angle is −180°. This latter condition, however, is essentially that for marginal stability. A more general statement is:

4. A control system is unstable if the open-loop gain is greater or equal to unity when the open-loop phase angle is −180°.

Various standard graphical methods are used to assess the stability of a control system and these include the Bode and the Nyquist plots. The Bode plot is a graph of amplitude ratio in decibels and phase angle variation with input signal frequency. The resulting normalized plot for an open-loop first-order system is shown in Fig. 11.23. Note that when the input signal frequency is equal to the inverse of the system time constant, also known as the 'break-point', the output amplitude has been decreased, or attenuated, by −3 dB. The phase lag at this point is −45°. This is a general characteristic of first-order systems.

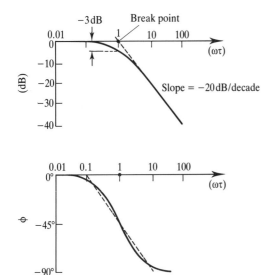

Figure 11.23 Bode plot for an open-loop, first-order system.

The Nyquist plot represents the same information in an alternative form. The plot is in polar coordinates and combines the modulus of the amplitude ratio and the phase angle in a single diagram. Figure 11.7, shown earlier, illustrates the Nyquist plot for the open-loop, first-order system.

Bode and Nyquist Stability Criteria

The Bode criteria for stability are:

1. The system is stable if the amplitude ratio is less than unity, or 0 dB, when the phase angle is −180°.
2. The system is stable if when the amplitude ratio is 0 dB, the phase angle is greater than −180°.

This two-way stability criteria are illustrated graphically in Fig. 11.24, which represents a stable system since Bode's criteria are satisfied. The 'gain margin' (*GM*) and 'phase margin' (*PM*) are used as measures of how close the frequency response curves are to the stability limits of the system. Note that if one of the criteria is satisfied then the other criteria is also automatically satisfied. Standard practice is to use a gain margin of −6 dB and a phase margin of 40°. The Nyquist criterion for stability is:

> The system is stable if the amplitude ratio is greater than −1 at a phase angle of −180°. In effect this means that the locus of the plot of the amplitude ratio and phase angle must not enclose the point −1 on the real axis.

A stable response curve is shown plotted in Fig. 11.25, which also indicates the gain margin and phase margin in the context of the Nyquist plot.

In practice it is often found that the gain of some of the system elements require to be reduced in order to ensure stable operation. Another commonly applied corrective measure is to add a phase lead circuit into the system. In purely simplistic terms, the phase lead circuit swings the response plot in the anticlockwise direction about the origin to shift the curve away from the

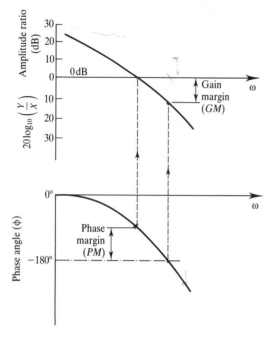

Figure 11.24 Bode's stability criteria.

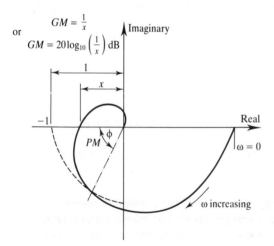

Figure 11.25 Nyquist's stability criteria.

critical point. The phase lead circuit however will also distort the response curve to a certain extent.

Example A control system has an open loop transfer function given as

$$C(s)G(s) = 10/[s(1 + 0.1s)(1 + 0.05s)]$$

Construct Bode and Nyquist diagrams for the open-loop transfer function and determine, using both diagrams, the gain margin and the phase margin for the system.
Replacing the Laplace variable s with $j\omega$ results in

$$C(s)G(s) = 10/[\{j\omega\}\{1 + 0.1(j\omega)\}\{1 + 0.05(j\omega)\}]$$

The amplitude modulus and corresponding phase angle can be written generally as

$$M' e^{j\phi'} = 10 \times M_1 e^{j\phi_1} \times M_2 e^{j\phi_2} \times M_3 e^{j\phi_3} \tag{11.31}$$

where

$$
\begin{aligned}
M' &= 10 \times M_1 \times M_2 \times M_3 \\
&= [10] \times [1/\{\omega\}] \times [1/\sqrt{\{1 + (0.1\omega)^2\}}] \times [1/\sqrt{\{1 + (0.05\omega)^2\}}]
\end{aligned}
\tag{11.32}
$$

and

$$
\begin{aligned}
\phi' &= \phi_1 + \phi_2 + \phi_3 \\
&= -90° + \tan^{-1}(-0.1\omega/1) + \tan^{-1}(-0.05\omega/1) \\
&= -90° - \tan^{-1}(0.1\omega/1) - \tan^{-1}(0.05\omega/1)
\end{aligned}
\tag{11.33}
$$

The solution is shown for a range of appropriate frequencies in Table 11.4.
The Bode diagram is shown in Fig. 11.26, where the gain margin is 9 dB and the phase margin is 30°.
The Nyquist plot is shown in Fig. 11.27, where the amplitude ratio corresponding to marginal stability is $(1/0.34) = 2.94$. This gives a corresponding gain margin of $20 \log_{10}(2.94) - 9.4$ dB. The phase margin from the diagram is 34°.

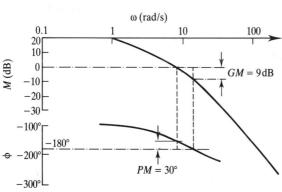

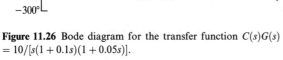

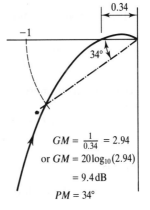

Figure 11.26 Bode diagram for the transfer function $C(s)G(s)$ $= 10/[s(1 + 0.1s)(1 + 0.05s)]$.

Figure 11.27 Nyquist plot for the transfer function $C(s)G(s) = 10/[s(1 + 0.1s)(1 + 0.05s)]$.

Table 11.4 Solution to the example.

ω	M_1 $1/\omega$	M_2 $1/\sqrt{\{1 + (0.1\omega)^2\}}$	M_3 $1/\sqrt{\{1 + (0.05\omega)^2\}}$	M'	$20 \log_{10}(M')$	ϕ_2	ϕ_3	ϕ'
1	1	0.995	0.994	9.89	19.9	−5.71	−2.86	−98.6
2	0.5	0.98	0.995	4.88	13.77	−11.3	−5.7	−107
4	0.25	0.928	0.98	2.27	7.12	−21.8	−11.3	−123.1
5	0.2	0.894	0.97	1.735	4.79	−26.6	−14.04	−130.6
6	0.167	0.858	0.957	1.37	2.73	−31.0	−16.7	−137.7
8	0.125	0.781	0.928	0.906	−0.858	−38.6	−21.8	−150.4
10	0.1	0.707	0.894	0.632	−4.01	−45.0	−26.6	−161.6
15	0.0667	0.555	0.8	0.296	−10.57	−56.31	−36.87	−183.2
20	0.05	0.447	0.707	0.158	−16.02	−63.43	−45	−198.4
30	0.033	0.316	0.555	0.056	−25.04	−71.56	−56.31	−217.9

Both methods give similar results with the minor deviations being due to the inaccuracies associated with any graphical technique. The Nyquist diagram, in addition, shows that if the gain were to be increased by the factor $(1/0.34)$ then the amplitude ratio when $\phi = -180°$ would become -1. This is indicative of marginal stability and the limiting value of the gain is therefore $(1/0.34) \times 10 = 29.4$.

Example The open-loop transfer function of a control system is given as

$$C(s)G(s) = K/[s(1 + 0.05s)(1 + 0.05s + 0.002s^2)]$$

Determine:
(i) the value of the gain corresponding to marginal stability;
(ii) the value of the gain to give a gain margin of at least 6 dB and a phase margin of at least 40°.

The previous example shows how to deal with first-order terms. The second-order term may be written as

$$\frac{500}{(500 + 25s + s^2)}$$

Comparison with Eq. (11.10) shows that

$$\omega_n^2 = 500 \quad \text{and} \quad 2\zeta\omega_n = 25$$

Equation (11.11) gives the modulus of the amplitude ratio for a second-order term as

$$M = \frac{1}{\sqrt{(1 - (\omega/\omega_n)^2)^2 + (2\zeta\omega/\omega_n)^2}}$$

Substituting the relevant numerical values gives

$$M = \frac{1}{\sqrt{(1 - 0.02\omega^2)^2 + (0.05\omega^2)}}$$

The phase angle is

$$\phi = -\tan^{-1}[(2\zeta\omega/\omega_n)/(1 - (\omega/\omega_n)^2)]$$

Thus the modulus of the amplitude ratio for the complete transfer function is

$$M' = K \times \frac{1}{\omega} \times \frac{1}{\sqrt{1 + (0.05\omega)^2}} \times \frac{1}{\sqrt{(1 - 0.02\omega^2)^2 + (0.05\omega^2)}}$$

The relationship for the phase angle is

$$\phi' = -90° - \tan^{-1}(0.05\omega) - \tan^{-1}[0.05\omega/(1 - 0.002\omega^2)]$$

Assuming for the purpose of calculation a value of gain of $K = 50$, the frequency response can be calculated over an appropriate frequency range as shown in Table 11.5.
From the tabulated data it can be seen that when the phase angle is $-180.7°$, i.e. approximately $-180°$, the amplitude ratio is 2.87. The system with a gain of 50 is therefore clearly unstable. Note that there is no real requirement to plot the Nyquist diagram in order to determine this fact. For marginal stability, the required gain is $K = 50/2.87 = 17.4$.
For a gain margin of 6 dB, the ratio $1/x = 10^{-6/20} = 0.5$. The means that the amplitude ratio must be 0.5 when $\phi = -180°$. The required gain is therefore $K = 17.4 \times 0.5 = 8.7$.

Table 11.5 Frequency response for a gain $K = 50$.

ω (rad/s)	M_1 $\dfrac{1}{\omega}$	M_2 $\dfrac{1}{\sqrt{(1+(0.05\omega)^2}}$	M_3 $\dfrac{1}{\sqrt{(1-0.002\omega^2)^2+(0.05\omega)^2}}$	M'	ϕ_2	ϕ_2	ϕ'
1	1	0.9987	1.007	50.28	−2.86	−2.87	−95.7
3	0.33	0.9889	1.007	16.58	−8.53	−8.68	−107.2
5	0.2	0.997	1.018	9.88	−14.0	−14.7	−118.8
10	0.1	0.894	1.06	4.74	−26.6	−32.0	−148.6
15	0.067	0.8	1.075	2.87	−36.9	−53.8	−180.7
20	0.050	0.707	0.98	1.732	−45.0	−78.7	−213.7
30	0.033	0.555	0.588	0.543	−56.3	−118.1	−264.4
40	0.025	0.447	0.336	0.188	−63.4	−137.7	−291.1
50	0.020	0.371	0.212	0.079	−68.2	−148.0	−306.2

Table 11.6 Results for the Bode plot at gain $K = 8.7$.

ω (rad/s)	M'	$20\log_{10}(M')$	ϕ
1	8.75	18.84	−95.7
3	2.89	9.2	−107.2
5	1.72	4.7	−118.8
10	0.825	−1.673	−148.6
15	0.500	−6.03	−180.7
20	0.300	−10.4	−213.7
30	0.095	−20.5	−264.4
40	0.033	−29.7	−291.1
50	0.014	−37.2	−306.2

The analysis shows that for a gain margin of 6 dB, the maximum controller gain is 8.7. To determine the corresponding phase margin, we must plot the frequency response as a Bode or Nyquist diagram. Choosing the Bode plot, and keeping the gain equal to 8.7, we obtain the results shown in Table 11.6 and plotted in Fig. 11.28.

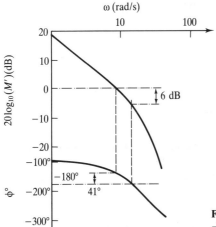

Figure 11.28 Bode diagram for the transfer function $C(s)G(s)$ $= 8.7/[s(1+0.05s)(1+0.05s+0.002s^2)]$.

From the plot it can be seen that for a gain margin of 6 dB, the phase margin is 41°. Thus both of the stated stability criteria are satisfied.

Effect of Transport Delay

Time delays are virtually impossible to handle mathematically when they occur in differential equations. For this reason solutions in the time domain become extremely difficult and frequency domain methods are almost exclusively used to assess the behaviour of the more complex control systems involving time delays.

The influence of a transport, or time delay on the response of an underdamped second-order system to a step input is displayed in Fig. 11.29.

Although a time delay cannot be handled in a differential equation it is simply accommodated in the frequency domain model as an additional element in the system block diagram. In the frequency domain model, the time delay effects a phase shift of $-\omega T$ radians and can be expressed in Laplace notation as

$$\text{time delay} = e^{-sT} \tag{11.34}$$

The open-loop first-order system incorporating a time delay is illustrated in Fig. 11.30.

The open-loop transfer function becomes

$$Y/X = Y(s)/X(s) = G(s) = k\,e^{-sT}/(1 + \tau s) \tag{11.35}$$

The effect of the time delay is to shift the output response without influencing the actual magnitude of the amplitude ratio. The amplitude ratio is therefore given as before:

$$\text{amplitude ratio} = \left|\frac{Y}{X}\right| = \frac{k}{\sqrt{(1 + \omega^2 \tau^2)}} \tag{11.36}$$

The response, however, incorporates an additional lag and the phase angle is now

$$\text{phase angle} = \phi = -[(\omega T) + \tan^{-1}(\omega \tau)] \quad \text{radians} \tag{11.37}$$

The first-order, open-loop system response with a time delay is shown in Fig. 11.31.

In a similar manner, a time delay in a system with feedback does not alter the amplitude ratio but implements an additional phase shift to the frequency response. Systems involving additional time delays therefore become less stable and in some cases it may be necessary to reduce the closed-loop gain in order to obtain a stable response.

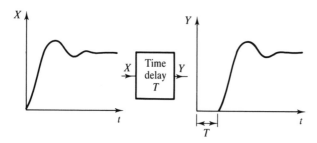

Figure 11.29 Effect of transport delay.

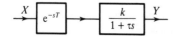

Figure 11.30 First-order system with a time delay.

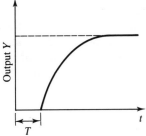

Figure 11.31 First-order, open-loop system response with a time delay

Example An industrial process is modelled as a first-order system with a time delay. An open-loop test gives the apparent time delay as 2 s and the apparent time constant as 80 s. The process is controlled using an industrial PID controller using proportional mode only and a gain of 50. Investigate the stability of the system and determine the maximum controller gain for marginal stability.

The frequency response of the system and the resultant stability characteristics can be assessed using a Nyquist diagram. Writing the open-loop transfer function as

$$C(s)G(s) = K e^{-sT}/(1 + \tau s) = 50 e^{-2s}/(1 + 80s)$$

from Eq. (11.36) the amplitude ratio is

$$M = 50/\sqrt{[1 + (80\omega)^2]}$$

and from Eq. (11.37) the phase angle is

$$\phi = -[(2\omega) + \tan^{-1}(80\omega)] \quad \text{radians}$$

For ω ranging between 0.001 rad/s and 2 rad/s, the amplitude ratio and phase angles are given in Table 11.7.

For stability considerations we are only interested in the magnitude of the amplitude ratio when the phase angle is $-180°$. The tabulated values show that the amplitude ratio is approximately 0.786 when $\phi = -180°$. The system is therefore stable as the Nyquist criterion is satisfied.

If the gain were to be increased to $K(1/0.786) = 50/0.786 = 63.6$, then the system would become marginally stable. For gain in excess of 63.6, the system is unstable.

Table 11.7 Amplitude ratio and phase angle for the example.

ω(rad/s)	M	$\phi°$
0.001	49.8	−4.7
0.010	39	−39.8
0.100	6.2	−94.3
0.500	1.25	−145.9
0.625	0.9998	−160.55
0.780	0.801	−178.5
0.790	0.791	−179.6
0.795	0.786	−180.2
0.800	0.780	−180.8
1.000	0.625	−203.9
2.000	0.312	−318.8

Also of interest is the point on the Nyquist diagram where the amplitude ratio is approximately unity. From the table this occurs when $\omega = 0.625$ rad/s. The corresponding phase angle is $-160.55°$. This means that the system could tolerate a second time delay and still remain marginally stable. The additional time delay would given an additional phase lag of $(180 - 160.55) = 19.45°$. The additional time delay, T_2 in seconds would be given by

$$(T_2\omega)(180/\pi) = 19.45$$

i.e.

$$T_2 = 19.45\pi/(0.625 \times 180) = 0.54\,\text{s}$$

Another way of looking at this situation is that the original time delay of 2 s could have been 2.54 s and the system would still have remained marginally stable.

The Passive Phase Lead Circuit

If a particular control system gives a frequency response which is marginally stable then the gain and phase margins can always be improved by reducing the controller gain K. Reduction of the gain, however, is undesirable since this will reduce the amplification characteristics of the controller. A phase lead circuit often presents a viable alternative to give improved stability without an attendant reduction in gain. The passive element phase lead circuit is shown in Fig. 11.32.

Using the complex notation (see Sec. 2.10) the reactive capacitance $X_c = 1/j\omega C$. For the circuit shown in Fig. 11.32, the capacitor C and the resistance R_1 in parallel have an equivalent impedance given by

$$1/Z = [1/R_1 + j\omega C] \text{ or } Z = R_1/[1 + j\omega CR_1]$$

Using Ohm's law, it can be shown that $V_o/V_i = R_2/[Z + R_2]$, i.e.

$$V_o/V_i = \frac{R_2[1 + j\omega CR_1]}{R_1 + R_2[1 + j\omega CR_1]}$$

Denoting CR_1 as τ, and substituting the Laplace variable s for $j\omega$ we obtain

$$V_o/V_i = \frac{R_2[1 + \tau s]}{R_2[1 + \tau s] + R_1} = \frac{R_2[1 + \tau s]}{(R_2 + R_1)[1 + R_2\tau s/(R_2 + R_1)]}$$

Denoting $R_2/(R_2 + R_1)$ as α, then

$$V_o/V_i = \frac{\alpha[1 + \tau s]}{[1 + \alpha\tau s]}$$

Furthermore, if α is small, i.e. $R_1 \gg R_2$, then

$$V_o/V_i = \alpha[1 + \tau s]$$

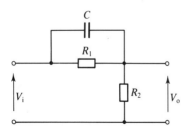

Figure 11.32 The passive element phase lead circuit.

It can be seen that the circuit implements both proportional and derivative action. Typical values for α, however, are of the order of 0.1, which means that the output voltage is considerably attenuated. To counteract this effect the circuit is normally gain compensated using a wideband amplifier with a gain of $1/\alpha$. The gain compensated phase lead circuit then has an overall transfer function given as

$$V_o/V_i = [1 + \tau s] \tag{11.38}$$

The amplitude ratio and corresponding phase angle for the circuit are then

$$|V_o/V_i| = \sqrt{1 + \omega^2 \tau^2} \quad \text{and} \quad \phi = \tan^{-1}(\omega \tau)$$

The frequency response of such a circuit, having $\tau = 1$ s, is shown in Table 11.8.

At low frequencies the overall gain is approximately 1. At the higher frequencies, the gain increases essentially in direct proportion with the frequency. More importantly, however, the phase angle is always positive. This means that the circuit will always incorporate a phase lead at all frequencies, with a maximum value of $+90°$. The addition of a phase lead circuit will therefore tend to improve the stability characteristics of a control system.

The value of the phase lead time constant τ to give the optimum improvement in stability is normally found by trial and error. A tentative rule of thumb however is to arrange $\omega \tau = 1$ at the original gain cross-over point. This corresponds to a frequency ω at which the original gain was unity.

Example A control system, with unity feedback, has an open-loop transfer function given as $C(s)G(s) = 7.5/[s(1 + 0.2s)(1 + 0.3s)]$
(i) Construct the Nyquist diagram and comment on the gain and phase margins.
(ii) If a gain compensated phase lead circuit is introduced in the forward path, with a transfer function of $(1 + 0.1s)$, plot the modified Nyquist diagram and determine the resultant gain and phase margins.
The amplitude ratio and phase angles for the original control system are given in Table 11.9. The frequency response curve is plotted in Fig. 11.33. The gain and phase margins are, respectively, 1.14 dB and 3.5°. Although the system is stable, the response curve is rather too

Table 11.8 Frequency response of phase lead circuit, $\tau = 1$ s.

ω (rad/s)	$|V_o/V_i|$	$\phi°$
0.001	1	0.057
0.01	1	0.57
0.1	1.005	6.27
1.0	1.414	45
10.0	10.05	84.3
100.0	100.005	89.4

Table 11.9 Amplitude ratio and phase angle for the example.

ω	$1/\omega$	$1/\sqrt{1 + (0.2\omega)^2}$	$1/\sqrt{1 + (0.3\omega)^2}$	M'	$-90° - \tan^{-1}(0.2\omega) - \tan^{-1}(0.3\omega)$
3	0.33	0.857	0.743	1.58	−162.95
4	0.25	0.781	0.640	0.94	−178.85
5	0.20	0.707	0.555	0.59	−191.31
6	0.167	0.640	0.486	0.39	−201.14
10	0.10	0.447	0.316	0.106	−225.00

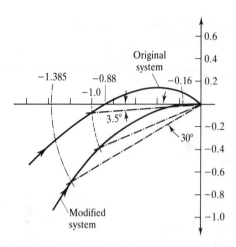

Figure 11.33 Nyquist diagram for the transfer function $C(s)G(s) = 7.5/[s(1 + 0.2s)(1 + 0.3s)]$.

Table 11.10 Frequency response of phase lead and modified system response.

ω	$\sqrt{1 + \omega^2\tau^2}$	$\tan^{-1}(0.1\omega)$	$M_{modified}$	$\phi_{modified}$
3	1.04	16.7	1.64	−146.25
4	1.08	21.8	1.02	−157.0
5	1.12	26.57	0.66	−164.74
6	1.17	30.96	0.46	−170.18
10	1.41	45	0.16	−180.0

close to the stability limits and the output response would be too oscillatory for most practical purposes.

The phase lead circuit with $\tau = 0.1$ gives the frequency response shown in Table 11.10. The resultant effect on the system is also tabulated.

The frequency response curve for the modified system is also shown in Fig. 11.33, where the modified gain and phase margins are $1/0.16 = 6.25$ or $20\log_{10}(6.25) = 15.9\,\text{dB}$ and $22.5°$, respectively.

The modified gain margin is acceptable but the modified phase margin might still be regarded as rather low. If the minimum phase margin was say 30°, then this could be achieved by now reducing the gain by the factor $1/1.385$, i.e.

$$\text{reduced gain} = 7.5/1.385 = 5.42$$

The corresponding gain margin is now $1.385/0.16 = 8.66$ or $20\log_{10}(8.66) = 18.75\,\text{dB}$.

11.8 ROOT LOCUS METHOD FOR STABILITY ANALYSIS

The root locus method was devised in 1948 by Evans (see further reading list) and still remains a popular and useful technique for the analysis of control system stability. The method is basically a graphical technique in which all the possible roots of the denominator term in the closed loop transfer function are plotted as the controller gain K is varied from zero to infinity.

It is assumed that the open-loop transfer function can be represented as a polynomial with the general form

$$C(s)G(s) = \frac{A_0 + A_1 s + A_2 s^2 + A_3 s^3 + \ldots + A_m S^m}{B_0 + B_1 s + B_2 s^2 + B_3 s^3 + \ldots + B_n s^n} \tag{11.39}$$

To be completely general the process transfer function $G(s)$ can include any transfer function associated with a measuring transducer in the feedback loop. To remain an open-loop system, however, the feedback line is not connected to the input comparator.

For any real physical system, $n > m$, otherwise there would be a non-zero gain when the input signal frequency tends to infinity. The condition $n = m$ is possible however. The denominator of the closed-loop transfer function is

$$1 + C(s)G(s) = 1 + \frac{A_0 + A_1 s + A_2 s^2 + A_3 s^3 + \ldots + A_m S^m}{B_0 + B_1 s + B_2 s^2 + B_3 s^3 + \ldots + B_n s^n} \tag{11.40}$$

$$= \frac{(A_0 + B_0) + (A_1 + B_1)s + (A_2 + B_3)s^2 + \ldots}{B_0 + B_1 s + B_2 s^2 + \ldots}$$

The closed loop transfer function then becomes

$$\frac{C(s)G(s)}{1 + C(s)G(s)} = \frac{A_0 + A_1 s + A_2 s^2 + A_3 s^3 + \ldots + A_m S^m}{(A_0 + B_0) + (A_1 + B_1)s + (A_2 + B_3)s^2 + \ldots}$$

If we now assume that the roots of the denominator are a, b, c, etc., while the roots of the numerator are p, q, r, etc., then the closed-loop transfer function can be written as

$$\frac{PV(s)}{SP(s)} = \frac{(s-p)(s-q)(s-r)\ldots}{(s-a)(s-b)(s-c)\ldots}$$

The simplest form of input function is a step impulse $SP(s) = 1$. For this input the output $PV(s)$ becomes

$$PV(s) = \frac{(s-p)(s-q)(s-r)\ldots}{(s-a)(s-b)(s-c)\ldots} \tag{11.41}$$

Expanding Eq. (11.41) in terms of the equivalent partial fractions gives

$$PV(s) = \frac{K_1}{(s-a)} + \frac{K_2}{(s-b)} + \frac{K_3}{(s-c)} + \ldots \tag{11.42}$$

where K_1, K_2, K_3, etc., are arbitrary constants depending on the initial conditions and the control system parameters.

Finally using the inverse Laplace transform we obtain

$$PV(t) = K_1 e^{at} + K_2 e^{bt} + K_3 e^{ct} + \ldots \tag{11.43}$$

Equation (11.43) gives the time domain solution for the output $PV(t)$. The important factor to be aware of is that if any one of the roots a, b, c, etc., are real and positive, then the output will increase exponentially with time. This is indicative of an unstable system and establishes a further criteria for system stability as follows:

A control system is stable only if **all** the roots of the denominator of the closed-loop transfer function are negative and real.

The above statement forms the basis of the root locus method as a tool for stability analysis.

Example Examine the stability of a control system whose open-loop transfer function is given as

$$C(s)G(s) = K[(s+6)/(s+2)]$$

For stability considerations we are examining the roots of

$$1 + C(s)G(s) = 1 + K[(s+6)/(s+2)] = 0 \qquad (11.44)$$

$$(s+2) + K(s+6) = 0 \qquad (11.45)$$

Equation 11.45 is referred to as the characteristic equation for the system under consideration, and can be re-written

$$s(K+1) + 6K + 2 = 0$$

Solving for s gives

$$s = -(6K+2)/(K+1) \qquad (11.46)$$

As K tends to 0, s tends to -2. Re-writing Eq. (11.45) as

$$s = -[6 + 2/K]/[1 + 1/K] \qquad (11.47)$$

in this form, as K tends to infinity, s tends to -6.

The analysis shows that the roots of the equation change from -2 to -6 as the controller gain varies from zero to infinity. As the roots are always real and negative then this control system is always stable, irrespective of the value of the gain K.

Example Use the root locus technique to investigate the stability of a control system whose open-loop transfer function is given as

$$C(s)G(s) = K/s(s+10) \qquad (11.48)$$

The denominator of the closed-loop transfer function is $1 + K/s(s+10)$, i.e.

$$s(s+10) + K = 0$$
$$s^2 + 10s + K = 0$$

The characteristic equation for this example is in the general form of a quadratic equation with the roots given as

$$s = \{-10 +/- \sqrt{10^2 - 4K}\}/2$$
$$= -5 +/- \sqrt{25 - K}$$

The variation of the two roots as K is increased from zero to 125 is shown in Table 11.11. It can be seen that the roots are all real and negative until the gain K has a value of 25. For higher gains, the real component remains at -5 while the imaginary component increases. When the roots of the characteristic equation have imaginary components, they always exist as a complex conjugate pair. The root locus is plotted on an Argand diagram, or complex plane, as shown in Fig. 11.34.

Since an unstable system is denoted by one of the roots having a positive real component then the root locus of a stable system will never cross into the positive real half of the Argand diagram. An unstable system, on the other hand, will indicate a cross-over of the root locus into the positive real half of the diagram. The system considered therefore is always stable, but the significance of the increasing imaginary components have limiting implications on the performance of the system for increasing controller gain. If the imaginary component is large

Table 11.11 Root locus of the system with the open-loop transfer function given by Eq. (11.48).

K	s_1	s_2
0	0	−10
9	−1	−9
16	−2	−8
24	−4	−6
25	−5	−5
50	−5 + j5	−5 − j5
125	−5 + j10	−5 − j10

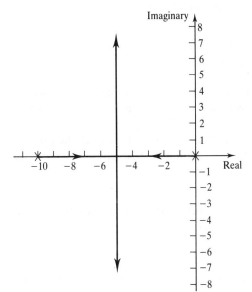

Figure 11.34 Root locus plot for the open-loop transfer function given by Eq. (11.48).

then the system will exhibit a large oscillatory response. It is desirable therefore in any real control system that the controller gain is of such a value that the real component of the roots of the characteristic equation are large, in the negative sense, to ensure a reasonably fast response. The imaginary, or complex, part of the roots should ideally be small to minimize the oscillatory period.

The Root Locus Method for Higher-order Systems

Assume, for example, that the characteristic equation is third order and can be written in the form:

$$(s - r_1)(s - r_2)(s - r_3) = 0$$

where r_1, r_2 and r_3 are the roots of the characteristic equation.

Note that the number of roots is always equal to the order of the characteristic equation. Factorizing the equation out gives

$$s^3 - (r_1 + r_2 + r_3)s^2 + (r_1r_2 + r_1r_3 + r_2r_3)s - r_1r_2r_3 = 0$$

If we denote $r_1 = -\delta$; $r_2 = -\alpha + j\beta$; $r_3 = -\alpha - j\beta$, then the characteristic equation becomes

$$s^3 + (\delta + 2\alpha)s^2 + (2\alpha\delta + \alpha^2 + \beta^2)s + \delta(\alpha^2 + \beta^2) = 0 \qquad (11.49)$$

It can be seen that if any of the equation coefficients are zero, or negative, then either α or δ must be negative. This would mean that there would then be a root with a positive real part and the system would be unstable. Note also that the term β does not appear on its own but as β^2. This simply means that β does not affect the polarity of any of the coefficients.

Construction of the root locus requires some skill which can only come with practice. It is possible, however, to apply a set of general construction rules which greatly facilitate the plotting of the root locus. Rigorous proofs of the construction rules are quite complex and essentially beyond the scope of this text. The construction rules will therefore simply be stated and their use illustrated in the solution of some practical examples.

The open-loop transfer function, in factorized form for the generalized system can be written as

$$C(s)G(s) = \frac{K(s - Z_1)(s - Z_2)(s - Z_3)\ldots}{(s - P_1)(s - P_2)(s - P_3)\ldots} \qquad (11.50)$$

Z_n, the open-loop 'zeros', are those values in the numerator function which make the numerator equal to zero. P_n, the open loop 'poles', are those values in the denominator function which make the denominator equal to zero.

The highest power of the Laplace variable s in the numerator function denotes the order of the numerator m. Similarly, the highest power of s in the denominator function n denotes the order of the denominator.

Example Plot the root locus and investigate the stability characteristics for the control system which has the following open-loop transfer function:

$$C(s)G(s) = K/[s(s + 3)(s + 9)] \qquad (11.51)$$

Note that there are no terms involving s in the numerator. In consequence $m = 0$ and there are no open-loop zeros in the root locus plot.

The denominator function, when multiplied out, will have one term in s^3. The order of the denominator is $n = 3$ and there will therefore be three open-loop poles in the root locus. Examination of the denominator function shows that these three open-loop poles will occur at 0, -3 and -9, i.e.

$$P_1 = 0; \; P_2 = -3; \; P_3 = -9$$

The location of the open-loop poles are marked X on the root locus shown in Fig. 11.35.

Rule 1 Each locus segment starts at an open-loop pole when $K = 0$, and ends when $K = $ infinity, at an open loop zero or at infinity. If there are more poles than zeros, as is normally the case, then the remaining segments finish at infinity. The number of segments going to infinity is therefore the excess of poles over zeros.

For the example considered, $n = 3$ and $m = 0$. Thus there are $(n - m)$, i.e. three segments going to infinity.

Rule 2a The locii are symmetrical about the real axis since complex roots always appear in conjugate pairs. In the example given there are no complex roots and therefore no complex conjugate open-loop poles.

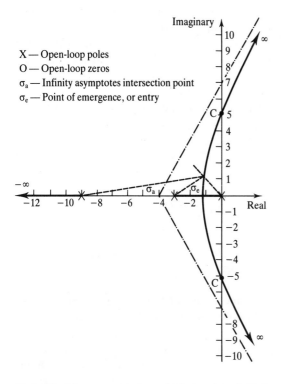

X — Open-loop poles
O — Open-loop zeros
σ_a — Infinity asymptotes intersection point
σ_e — Point of emergence, or entry

Figure 11.35 Root locus for the transfer function $C(s)G(s) = K/[s(s+3)(s+9)]$.

Rule 2b The asymptotes which tend to infinity are equally spaced such that the angle between adjacent asymptotes is given by $360/(n-m)$. In addition, when the numerical value of $(n-m)$ is an odd number, then one of the infinity asymptotes is coincident with the real axis.

In our example, since $(n-m) = 3$, then the angle between the infinity asymptotes is $360/3 = 120°$, with one asymptote coincident with the real axis.

Rule 3 The infinity asymptotes meet at a point σ_a on the negative real axis where

$$\sigma_a = \frac{\text{sum of the real parts of the poles} - \text{sum of the real parts of the zeros}}{(n-m)} \qquad (11.52)$$

For the example considered, $\sigma_a = [(0) + (-3) + (-9) - (0)]/3 = -4$.

Using rules 2b and 3, the infinity asymptotes can now be drawn on the diagram. These are shown as chain dotted lines in Fig. 11.35.

Rule 4 The parts of the negative axis which are segments of the root locus can be determined by starting at the origin and progressing out to −infinity. All points which have an odd number of open-loop poles and open-loop zeros to the right form part of the root locus. Multiple roots must be allowed for, but complex roots have no effect since they appear as conjugate pairs.

Any section which joins two open-loop poles must be parts of two segments. These segments will meet at a common point on the real axis and then diverge to follow complex conjugate paths. Similarly, any section joining two zeros comprises the end of two converging complex conjugate paths.

A section joining an open-loop pole and an open-loop zero is often a complete segment, but may incorporate two sets of complex conjugate paths between the pole and the zero.

Using rule 4, two sections of the root locus can be drawn from 0 to -3 and from -9 to $-$infinity. Since the section from 0 to -3 joins two open-loop poles then these sections will meet at a common point and then diverge out along complex conjugate paths. These conjugate paths will then asymptote to the two chain dotted lines at $60°$ and $-60°$. The last section must therefore start at -9 and asymptotes at $-$infinity.

Rule 5 The point σ_e on the negative real axis at which a conjugate pair of segments breaks away or re-enters is given by

$$0 = \frac{1}{P_1 - \sigma_e} + \frac{1}{P_2 - \sigma_e} + \qquad + \frac{2(a_1 - \sigma_e)}{(a_1 - \sigma_e)^2 + b_1^2} + \cdots \tag{11.53}$$

or

$$0 = \frac{1}{Z_1 - \sigma_e} + \frac{1}{Z_2 - \sigma_e} + \qquad + \frac{2(c_1 - \sigma_e)}{(c_1 - \sigma_e)^2 + d_1^2} + \cdots \tag{11.54}$$

where P_n are the open-loop poles, Z_n are the open-loop zeros and $a_n +/- jb_n$ and $c_n +/- jd_n$ are the complex open-loop poles and open-loop zeros, respectively.

Equations (11.53) and (11.54) give the 'point of emergence' of the conjugate poles, or the 'point of entry' of the conjugate zeros, respectively. In both cases the symbol σ_e is used to denote these points.

In either case the evaluation of σ_e is done by trial and error. A suitable value is assumed and then inserted into Eq. (11.53) or (11.54). The correct value is the one in which the right-hand side of the equation equates to zero.

For the example considered there are no zeros but we do know that there must be a point of emergence somewhere between 0 and -3 on the real axis. These conjugate paths then asymptote to infinity at $60°$ and $-60°$ as was determined from rule 4. Using Eq. (11.53), the right-hand side may be written as

$$0 = \frac{1}{0 - \sigma_e} + \frac{1}{-3 - \sigma_e} + \frac{1}{-9 - \sigma_e}$$

Multiplying through by -1 gives

$$\frac{1}{\sigma_e} + \frac{1}{3 + \sigma_e} + \frac{1}{9 + \sigma_e}$$

Using a trial value

$\sigma_e = -2$	gives	$-(1/2) + (1/1) + (1/7)$	$= 0.643$
$= -1$	gives	$-(1) + (0.5) + (0.125)$	$= -0.375$
$= -1.5$	gives	$-(0.666) + (0.666) + (0.133)$	$= 0.133$
$= -1.3$	gives	$-(0.769) + (0.588) + (0.130)$	$= -0.05$
$= -1.35$	gives	$-(0.7407) + (0.606) + (0.131)$	$= -0.004$
$= -1.355$	gives	$-(0.738) + (0.6079) + (0.1308)$	$= +0.0007$

The latter value is sufficiently accurate for a graphical approximation and the information obtained so far enables a reasonable sketch of the complete root locus to be drawn. This is shown in Fig. 11.35.

The most significant observation from the root locus is that the conjugate paths cross over into the positive real axis. This denotes that the system can become unstable. On the imaginary axis, the cross-over point, indicated by C, cuts the axis at $j\omega = 5.2$. The cross-over point corresponds therefore to a circular frequency of 5.2 rad/s.

The critical value of the gain K which corresponds to this frequency is given by

$$K_{\text{crit}} = \frac{\text{summation of the pole modulus vectors}}{\text{summation of the zero modulus vectors, or unity, whichever is larger}} \quad (11.55)$$

The modulus vector is defined as the distance between the poles or zeros and the cross-over point. In the example, there are three pole modulus vectors these being

$$\sqrt{9^2 + 5.2^2} = 11.377 \qquad \sqrt{3^2 + 5.2^2} = 6.003 \qquad \text{and} \qquad 5.2$$

Thus

$$K_{\text{crit}} = [11.377 \times 6.003 \times 5.2]/1 = 355$$

A more precise method gives $K_{\text{crit}} = 324$. The error in the graphical method is therefore of the order of $+/-$ 10 per cent.

Although not used in this example there is one further rule which cannot be neglected, particularly when the root locus involves conjugate open-loop poles or zeros.

Rule 6 The angle at which a locus leaves a complex open-loop pole or approaches a complex zero is

$$\begin{aligned} \alpha_{\text{d}} = 180^\circ &- (\text{summation of the angles of the vectors from all other poles}) \\ &+ (\text{summation of the angles of the vectors from all other zeros}) \end{aligned} \quad (11.56)$$

Rules 5 and 6 are virtually essential in determining which segment associates with each asymptote. The phase angle criterion, however, has much more generality and can indeed be applied to any arbitrary point on the root locus. The phase angle criterion can, for example, be used as a check that the cross-over point has been reasonably estimated. For the example given, the angles subtended by the three open-loop poles and the cross-over point are

$$\tan^{-1}(5.2/9) = 30.02^\circ \qquad \tan^{-1}(5.2/3) = 60.02^\circ \qquad \tan^{-1}(5.2/0) = 90^\circ$$

The summation of these angles is $(30.02 + 60.02 + 90) = 180.04^\circ$. Since the summation of the angles is approximately 180°, then this provides confirmation that the cross-over point is reasonably accurately located.

The value of gain at the point of emergence is that value which will ensure that the two dominant complex roots are critically damped. This value of gain can be calculated using the same method for K_{crit}, shown previously, i.e.

$$K' = 1.355 \times (3 - 1.355) \times (9 - 1.355) = 17$$

Thus with a gain $K = 17$, the system is critically damped with no oscillation. If the gain is increased above 17, then the output signal will exhibit an oscillatory response. Gain values below 17 correspond to an overdamped system.

Lastly, if the two complex roots are to have a damping factor of $\zeta = 0.7$, then this corresponds to an angle of $-180 - \cos^{-1}(\zeta)$ in the complex plane. The angle is therefore $-180 - \cos^{-1}(0.7) = -225^\circ$. The appropriate gain to give this damping factor can be obtained from the position where the -225° line cuts the root locus, evaluating the gain in the usual manner, i.e.

$$K_{(\zeta=0.7)} = 1.626 \times 2.178 \times 7.93 = 28.1$$

Checking the point using the 180° rule gives $(360 - 225) + 31.87 + 8.33 = 175.2^\circ$. This value is sufficiently close to 180° for an approximate graphical method.

Example Investigate the stability of the control system which has an open-loop transfer function given by the relation

$$C(s)G(s) = K/[s(s+1.5)(s+3)(s^2+2s+2)]$$

There are no open-loop zeros, therefore $m = 0$. The open-loop poles are real poles at $0, -1.5$ and -3, and complex poles from $s^2 + 2s + 2$, with roots of $0.5(-2 +/- \sqrt{2^2 - 4 \times 2})$, i.e. complex roots at $(-1 + j)$ and $(-1-j)$.

Rule 1: $n = 5$ and $m = 0$. Thus $(n - m) = 5$, giving five segments tending to infinity.

Rule 2: infinity asymptotes equally spaced at $360/5 = 72°$, with one asymptote coincident with the real axis.

Rule 3: $\sigma_a = [(0) + (-1.5) + (-3) + (-1) + (-1)]/(5 - 0) = -1.3$.

Rule 4: gives those parts of the root locus on the real axis.

Rule 5: gives

$$0 = \frac{1}{\sigma_e} + \frac{1}{1.5 + \sigma_e} + \frac{1}{3 + \sigma_e} + \frac{2(-1 - \sigma_e)}{(1 + \sigma_e)^2 + 1}$$

$\sigma_e = -1$	gives	$-1 + 2 + 0.5 + 0$	$= 1.5$
-0.5	gives	$-2 + 1 + 0.4 + 0.8$	$= 0.2$
-0.4	gives	$-2.5 + 0.91 + 0.38 + 0.8$	$= -0.33$
-0.45	gives	$-2.22 + 0.95 + 0.39 + 0.85$	$= -0.03$
-0.46	gives	$-2.174 + 0.962 + 0.394 + 0.836$	$= 0.018$

Take $\sigma_e = -0.46$ as sufficiently accurate.

Rule 6: $\alpha_d = 180 - [90 + 135 + 63.5 + 26.5] = -135°$.

Using the information obtained from application of the construction rules, the root locus can be sketched as shown in Fig. 11.36.

From the root locus plot, the limit of stability occurs when $j\omega = 0.8$, i.e. when $\omega = 0.8$ rad/s. Thus

$$K_{crit} = 0.8 \times 1.02 \times 1.7 \times 2.06 \times 3.1 = 8.86$$

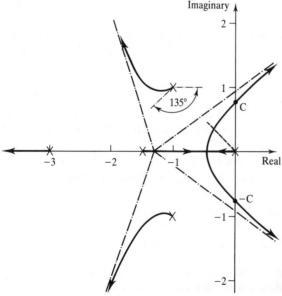

Figure 11.36 Root locus for the transfer function $C(s)G(s) = K/[s(s+1.5)(s+3)(s^2+2s+2)]$.

i.e. to remain stable, the gain must not exceed 8.86.

At the point of emergence, the value of the gain is that for critical damping. Thus for critical damping

$$K' = 0.46 \times (1.5 - 0.46) \times (3 - 0.46) \times (1.136)^2 = 1.57$$

No oscillatory response is exhibited when the gain is less than, or equal to 1.57. For a damping factor of $\zeta = 0.7$, the corresponding gain is

$$K_{(\zeta=0.7)} = 0.5 \times 0.92 \times 1.15 \times 2.65 \times 1.5 = 2.1$$

It should be apparent that the root locus method can be used to give much more information than just simply the limiting value of gain for the onset of instability. Some modern self-tuning controllers are in fact based on the root locus method. These controllers seek to locate the conjugate open-loop poles at particular positions in the complex plane by adjustment of the gain. In this manner the system dynamic behaviour is generally kept constant for varying influential parameters which would otherwise alter the form of the output response.

11.9 APPROXIMATE BODE DIAGRAMS FROM THE OPEN-LOOP TRANSFER FUNCTION

In the construction of Bode diagrams (Sec. 11.7) the calculation of the amplitude ratio over a range of frequencies is a laborious procedure. In a great many instances, however, the Bode diagram follows asymptotic lines over considerable ranges of signal frequency. It is possible therefore to make use of this property in the construction of approximate Bode plots from a knowledge of the open-loop transfer function. Only four types of function need be considered and these are listed in Table 11.12.

Constant terms. These type of terms are independent of frequency and the amplitude ratio in decibels is also a constant, i.e. $N = 20 \log_{10}(K)$. The phase angle associated with a constant term is zero.

$(j\omega)^n$ *terms.* The index n may be either positive or negative. For $n = +1$, the term denotes a differentiation process. Integration is implied when $n = -1$. The amplitude ratio, in decibels, is $N = n20 \log_{10}(\omega)$. Since the frequency axis is logarithmic, then $(j\omega)^n$ terms produce an amplitude ratio characteristic which appears as a straight line on the Bode plot. The slope is $n20\,\text{dB/decade}$ and may be either positive, or negative, depending on the sign of the index n. Note that when $\omega = 1$, the amplitude ratio is $0\,\text{dB}$ irrespective of the value of n. Terms involving $(j\omega)^n$ therefore have an amplitude ratio which appears as a constant slope on a Bode diagram, always passing through $0\,\text{dB}$ at $\omega = 1$.

Table 11.12 Transfer function terms.

Function type	Laplace form	Complex form
Constant term	K	K
Differentiation or integration	s^n	$(j\omega)^n$
First-order term	$[1 + s\tau]^n$	$[1 + j\omega\tau]^n$
Second-order term	$[1 + bs + as^2]^n$	$[1 + bj\omega + a(j\omega)^2]^n$

$(1 + j\omega t)^n$ *terms.* In most practical instances, the index will be either $+1$ or -1. When $n = -1$, the term represents a simple first-order lag. The amplitude ratio is given by Eq. (11.7) in Sec. 11.4. For unity gain with $k = 1$, the amplitude ratio, in decibels, is

$$N = 20 \log_{10}(\sqrt{1 + \omega^2 \tau^2})$$

$$\text{For } \omega \ll 1, \ N = +/- 20 \log_{10}(1) = 0 \, \text{dB}$$

$$\text{For } \omega \gg 1, \ N = +/- 20 \log_{10}(\omega \tau) = +/- 20 \, \text{dB/decade}$$

The above two asymptotes meet at the break point when $\omega = 1/\tau$ (see Sec. 11.4). The actual amplitude ratio at the break point is $+/- 3 \, \text{dB}$ and this represents the error between the actual amplitude ratio and the asymptotic approximation at the break point. The phase angle for $(1 + j\omega\tau)^n$ terms is $\phi = +/- \tan^{-1}(\omega\tau)$.

$[1 + b(j\omega) + a(j\omega)^2]^n$ *terms.* Normally the index is either $+1$ or -1. For second-order terms the amplitude ratio and phase angle are given in Sec. 11.4 by Eqs (11.11) and (11.12), respectively. The amplitude ratio, in decibels, is

$$N = +/- 20 \log_{10}[\sqrt{\{1 - (\omega/\omega_n)^2\}^2 + \{2\zeta\omega/\omega_n\}^2}] \tag{11.57}$$

Phase angle is given by

$$\phi = +/- \tan^{-1}[\{2\zeta\omega/\omega_n\}/\{1 - (\omega/\omega_n)^2\}] \tag{11.58}$$

The asymptotic approximations of N are only of limited use since the amplitude ratio is highly dependent on the value of ζ (see, for example, Fig. 11.9). However, at frequencies far enough removed from ω_n, the asymptotic approximations are quite reasonable.

$$\text{For } \omega \ll \omega_n, \ N = +/- 20 \log_{10}(1) = 0 \, \text{dB} \qquad \text{phase angle } \phi = 0°`$$

$$\text{For } \omega \gg \omega_n, \ N = +/- 20 \log_{10}[(\omega/\omega_n)^2] = +/- 40 \, \text{dB/decade} \quad \text{and} \quad \text{phase angle } \phi = +/- 180°$$

The above two conditions represent the low and high frequency asymptotes for second-order terms. These asymptotes meet when $\omega = \omega_n$ and the actual amplitude ratio at this point is

$$+/- 20 \log_{10}(2\zeta) \tag{11.59}$$

The corresponding phase angle when $\omega = \omega_n$ is $+/- 90°$.

It can be concluded that the asymptotic approximations may be considerably in error at any break points. However, it is known that the actual amplitude ratio, for a first-order term, is $+/- 3 \, \text{dB}$ at a break point. For a second-order term the error in the amplitude ratio at a break point is given by Eq. (11.59). These facts allow suitable corrections to be made at any break points and a fairly representative Bode diagram can then be constructed for the four types of term considered.

The main advantage in representing a frequency response in terms of the Bode diagram coordinates is that because the amplitude ratio is in decibels, then the separate effects of different types of terms are additive. This also applies to the phase angles. A complex transfer function can therefore be split up into groups of the four terms described, and the separate effects of individual terms added together in the Bode representation.

Example A control system has an open-loop transfer function as given below. Plot the Bode diagram for input frequencies in the ragne 0.1 to 10 rad/s and hence determine the gain and phase margins.

$$C(s)G(s) = 2/[s(1+s)(1+0.25s)]$$
$$= 2/[(j\omega)(1+j\omega)(1+0.25j\omega)]$$

Constant term, $N = 20\log_{10}(2) = 6\,dB$. The constant term may be plotted by subtracting 6 dB with the other terms. Alternatively the constant can be accounted for by simply shifting the base line down by 6 dB at the end, after all the other terms have been taken into consideration.

The derivative term $(j\omega)$ has a slope of $-20\,dB/decade$ and passes through $\omega = 1$.
The first-order lag $(1 + j\omega)$ has a break point at $\omega = 1/\tau = 1/1 = 1\,rad/s$.
The first-order lag $(1 + 0.25j\omega)$ has its break point at $\omega = 1/\tau = 1/0.25 = 4\,rad/s$.
The phase lags are shown in Table 11.13.
The resulting Bode diagram for the system is shown in Fig. 11.37.
Making allowance for the amplitude ratio to be $-3\,dB$ down at the break points results in the response shown as the full line in Fig. 11.37.
The gain and phase margins obtained from the diagram are

$$GM = 8\,dB \quad \text{and} \quad PM = 20°$$

The phase margin is somewhat low, but the system is still stable. If the gain were to be increased to 5 however, i.e. $20\log_{10}(5) = 14\,dB$, then the system would become marginally stable. For gains in excess of 5, the system is unstable.

Table 11.13 Phase lags for the example.

Term ω	$(j\omega)$ $-90°$	$(1+j\omega)$ $-\tan^{-1}(\omega)$	$(1+0.25j\omega)$ $-\tan^{-1}(0.25\omega)$	Total $\phi°$
0.1	$-90°$	-5.7	-1.43	-97.13
0.5	$-90°$	-26.6	-7.13	-123.7
1.0	$-90°$	-45	-14	-149
2	$-90°$	-63.4	-26.6	-180
4	$-90°$	-76	-45	-211
10	$-90°$	-84.3	-68.2	-242.5

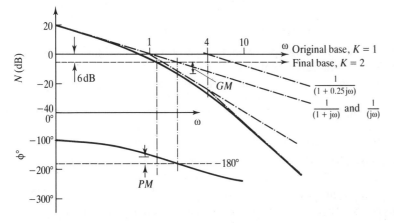

Figure 11.37 Bode diagram for the transfer function $C(s)G(s) = 2/[s(1+s)(1+0.25s)]$.

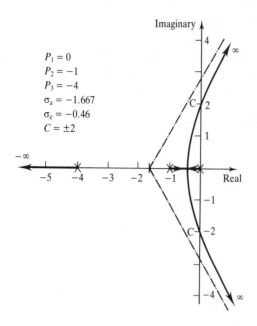

$P_1 = 0$
$P_2 = -1$
$P_3 = -4$
$\sigma_a = -1.667$
$\sigma_e = -0.46$
$C = \pm 2$

Figure 11.38 Root locus for the transfer function $C(s)G(s) = (4K)/[s(s+1)(s+4)]$.

The open-loop transfer function may alternatively be expressed as

$$C(s)G(s) = (4K)/[s(s+1)(s+4)]$$

In this form, the gain K is left as an arbitrary constant to be determined for marginal stability. Using the root locus methods presented in Sec. 11.8, the following data are obtained:

Three real poles at 0, -1 and -4, respectively. Three infinity asymptotes with 120° spacing and one infinity asymptote coincident with the real axis; intersection point of the infinity asymptotes at $\sigma_a = 1.667$. Point of emergence of the complex conjugate poles at $\sigma_e = -0.46$. This information allows the approximate root locus to be drawn as shown in Fig. 11.38.

The cross-over point occurs at a numerical value of 2 on the imaginary axis. The resultant critical value of $4K$ for marginal stability is therefore 20. This results in a critical value of $K = 5$ which, as might be expected, is in agreement with the critical value of gain obtained from the Bode diagram.

Example A unity feedback control system has an open-loop transfer function given as

$$C(s)G(s) = K/[s(1+0.2s)(1+1.4s+s^2)]$$

Construct a Bode diagram and making approximate asymptotic corrections determine:
(i) The gain corresponding to marginal stability.
(ii) The gain which would give a gain margin of 10 dB, and the corresponding phase margin.

Rewriting the transfer function as

$$C(s)G(s) = K/[(j\omega)(1+0.2j\omega)(1+1.4j\omega+(j\omega)^2)]$$

The constant term is independent of ω, with an amplitude ratio $N = 20\log_{10}(K)$.
The $(j\omega)$ term gives a slope of -20 dB/decade, passing through $\omega = 1$.
The $(1+0.2j\omega)$ has a break point at $\omega = 1/0.2 = 5$ rad/s, with phase angle $= -\tan^{-1}(0.2\omega)$. and slope of -20 dB/decade after the break point. Maximum error at the break point is -3 dB.

The $(1 + 1.4j\omega + (j\omega)^2)$ term has a break point at ω_n, and a slope of -40 dB/decade after the break point.

$$\text{phase angle} = -\tan^{-1}[\{2\zeta\omega/\omega_n\}/\{1 - (\omega/\omega_n)^2\}]$$

From Eq. (11.9) and by comparison with the second-order term, it can be shown that

$$2\zeta/\omega_n = 1.4 \quad \text{and} \quad 1/\omega_n^2 = 1$$

Thus

$$\omega_n = 1 \text{ rad/s} \quad \text{and} \quad \zeta = 1.4/2 = 0.7$$

Error at the break point $= -20\log_{10}(2\zeta) = -2.92$ dB.
The total system phase angle is

$$-90° - \tan^{-1}(0.2\omega) - \tan^{-1}[1.4\omega/(1 - \omega^2)]$$

The phase angle associated with each term is shown in Table 11.14 over a range of suitable frequencies.
The Bode diagram is shown in Fig. 11.39.
From the diagram, the maximum value of gain is given by $20\log_{10}(K) = 3$ dB, i.e.

$$K_{max} = 1.41$$

Table 11.14 Phase angles for each term of the example.

ω	$(j\omega)$	$(1 + 0.2j\omega)$	$(1 + 1.4j\omega + (j\omega)^2)$	Total $\phi°$
0.1	-90	-1.15	-8.05	-99.2
0.5	-90	-5.71	-43.03	-138.7
1.0	-90	-11.31	-90	-191.31
4.0	-90	-38.7	-159.53	-288.2
10.0	-90	-63.4	-171.95	-325.4

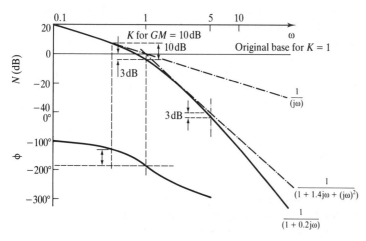

Figure 11.39 Bode diagram for the transfer function $C(s)G(s) = K/[s(1 + 0.2s)(1 + 1.4s + s^2)]$.

If the gain margin was to be 10 dB, then the corresponding gain would have to be less than unity, i.e.

$$20 \log_{10}(K) = -7 \qquad K = 10^{-(7/20)} = 0.447$$

The corresponding phase margin is $PM = 55°$.

In theory the procedure as outlined could be operated in reverse and a transfer function estimated from a measured frequency response presented as a Bode diagram. This would involve fitting tangents to the frequency response and interpreting the intersections of these tangents either as time constants, or as natural frequencies in a second-order term. The procedure becomes very difficult if similar terms exist both in the numerator and the denominator, or if a second-order term has a particularly high damping factor. In general there are too many unknown factors, and the method is too imprecise, to enable a truly representative transfer function to be obtained from a Bode plot.

11.10 DISTURBANCE SENSITIVITY

The main problem with the classical single-loop control system is that it is not truly representative of the natural environment in which the system operates. In an ideal single-loop control system the controlled output is a function only of the input. In most practical systems, however, the control loop is but a part of a larger system and it is therefore subject to the constraints and vagaries of the larger system. This larger system, which includes the local ambient, can be a major source of disturbing influences on the controlled variable. The disturbance may be regarded as an additional input signal to the control system. Any technique therefore which is designed to counter the effect of the disturbance must be based on a knowledge of the time-dependent nature of the disturbance and also its point of entry into the control system. Two methods commonly used to reduce the effect of external disturbances are 'feedforward' and 'cascade' control.

Feedforward control The principle of a feedback loop is that the output is compared with the desired input and a resultant error signal acted upon by the controller to alter the output as required. This is a control action which is implemented 'after the fact'. In other words the corrective measures are taken after the external disturbance has influenced the output. An alternative control strategy is to use a feedforward system where the disturbance is measured. If the effect of the disturbance on the output is known, then theoretically the corrective action can be taken before the disturbance can significantly influence the output. Feedforward can be a practical solution if the external disturbances are few and can be quantified and measured. The block diagram illustrating the feedforward concept is shown in Fig. 11.40.

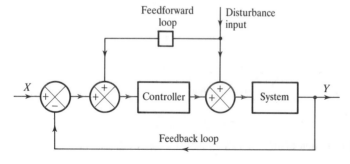

Figure 11.40 Feedforward control system.

Feedforward control can be difficult to implement if there are too many, or perhaps unexpected external disturbances. In Fig. 11.40, the path which provides the corrective signal appears to go back. The strategy is still feedforward, however, since it is the disturbance which is measured and the corrective action which is taken is based on the disturbance and not the output signal. Some control systems can be optimized by using a combination of feedforward and feedback control.

Cascade control Cascade control is implemented with the inclusion of a second feedback loop and a second controller embodied within a main feedback loop in a control system (Fig. 11.41).

The second feedback loop is only possible in practice if there is an intermediate variable which is capable of being measured within the overall process. Cascade control generally gives an improvement over single-loop control in coping with disturbance inputs. The time constant for the inner loop is less than that for the component it encloses and the undamped natural frequency of the system is increased. The overall effects of cascade control are an increase in the system bandwidth and a reduction in the sensitivity to disturbances entering the inner loop. Disturbances entering the outer loop are unaffected. Cascade control works best when the inner loop has a smaller time constant than the outer loop.

11.11 STATE-VARIABLE TECHNIQUES

State-Variable Representation of Systems

The state-variable approach to system modelling involves the use of matrix and vector methods which provide a consistent solution procedure for the analysis of complex control problems. While state-variable methods can be applied to any single-input–single-output control system, the real power in the method lies in its application to multiple-input–multiple-output systems. The state-variable representation also finds application to the analysis of nonlinear control systems where the nonlinear elements of a system are accounted for in a self-consistent manner.

In order to generate a system of state-variable equations, the system must be adequately defined in terms of the governing differential equations in a continuous system, or in terms of the difference equations in a discrete system (Sec. 13.3). A convenient method of representing the mathematical operations and equations is by means of a block diagram made up of the appropriate sequence of operators. In a continuous control system, the most common operators are shown in Fig. 11.42.

The simple damped spring and mass system serves as a useful illustrative example (Fig. 11.43). The relation which governs the motion of the mass is obtained by considering the forces acting on the mass and the resultant acceleration caused by these forces. There are basically

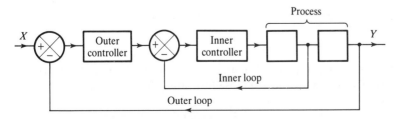

Figure 11.41 Cascade control system.

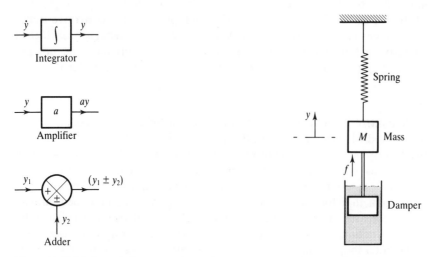

Figure 11.42 Mathematical operators in continuous control systems.

Figure 11.43 Simple damped spring and mass system.

three forces, which arise from the deflection of the spring, the viscous resistance in the dashpot and the external forcing function f. The net effect of these forces is to accelerate the mass M, i.e.

$$M \frac{d^2 y}{dt^2} = -Sy - C \frac{dy}{dt} + f$$

where S is the spring stiffness in $N\,m^{-1}$ and C is the viscous damping factor in $N s\,m^{-1}$. Note that the forces associated with the spring and the damper are both negative since they always act in opposition to the direction of motion. Dividing through by the mass M gives

$$\frac{d^2 y}{dt^2} + (C/M) \frac{dy}{dt} + (S/M)y = (f/M) = u \tag{11.60}$$

where u is the external forcing function per unit mass. Comparing Eq. (11.60) with the generalized equation for second-order systems (Eq. (4.6)) shows that

$$\omega_n^2 = (S/M) \quad \text{and} \quad 2\zeta\omega_n = (C/M)$$

Equation (11.60) may therefore be written generally as

$$\frac{d^2 y}{dt^2} + 2\zeta\omega_n \frac{dy}{dt} + \omega_n^2 y = u \tag{11.61}$$

or

$$\ddot{y} + 2\zeta\omega_n \dot{y} + \omega_n^2 y = u \tag{11.62}$$

Solving for the highest derivative gives

$$\ddot{y} = u - 2\zeta\omega_n \dot{y} - \omega_n^2 y \tag{11.63}$$

The block diagram representation of Eq. (11.63) may be developed by first of all integrating $\ddot{y}$ twice as shown in Fig. 11.44. The loop may then be closed by satisfying the requirement of Eq. (11.63) as shown in Fig. 11.45.

State variables are not unique and there is an endless range of possible combinations which may be chosen. It is normal, however, to select as state variables those quantities which are

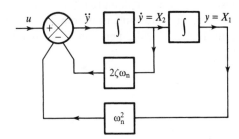

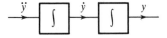

Figure 11.44 Double integration process.

Figure 11.45 Block diagram representation of Eq. (11.63).

significant to the problem under consideration. In this respect the output, the first derivative of the output and any higher-order derivatives of the output would make the most suitable choice of state variables. In choosing the set of state variables it should be recognized that the state variables must be related through a differential equation in a continuous control system, or a difference equation in a digital control system. In a continuous control system the normal practice is to select the output from any integrator as an appropriate state variable.

For the damped spring mass system, the following state variables are selected:

$$X_1 = y : X_2 = \dot{y}$$

Consideration of the block diagram of Fig. 11.45 shows that

$$\dot{X}_1 = X_2 \tag{11.64}$$

$$\dot{X}_2 = -\omega_n^2 X_1 - 2\zeta\omega_n X_2 + u \tag{11.65}$$

It transpires therefore that the state-variable representation reduces the original second-order differential equation to two simultaneous first-order differential equations. In like manner a third, or higher-order differential equation could be represented as a set of three, or higher number of first-order differential equations.

Writing Eqs (11.64) and (11.65) in matrix notation gives

$$\begin{bmatrix} \dot{X}_1 \\ \dot{X}_2 \end{bmatrix} = \begin{bmatrix} 0 & 1 \\ -\omega_n^2 & -2\zeta\omega_n \end{bmatrix} \begin{bmatrix} X_1 \\ X_2 \end{bmatrix} + u \begin{bmatrix} 0 \\ 1 \end{bmatrix} \tag{11.66}$$

$$y = \begin{bmatrix} 1 & 0 \end{bmatrix} \begin{bmatrix} X_1 \\ X_2 \end{bmatrix} + u[0] \tag{11.67}$$

Any suitable matrix method can be used to solve for X_1, which is equivalent to the system output, i.e. the position of the mass as a function of time, for any given input u. Alternatively Eqs (11.64) and (11.65) may be written as simple finite difference approximations and solved simultaneously over an appropriate time increment. For free vibration following a step disturbance to the system, $u = 0$. The finite difference approximation may be written as

$$(\Delta X_2)_i = \Delta t[-2\zeta\omega_n (X_2)_{i-1} - \omega_n^2 (X_1)_{i-1}] \tag{11.68}$$

$$(X_2)_i = (X_2)_{i-1} + (\Delta X_2)_i \tag{11.69}$$

$$(\Delta X_1)_i = \Delta t (X_2)_i \tag{11.70}$$

$$(X_1)_i = (X_1)_{i-1} + (\Delta X_1)_i \tag{11.71}$$

With suitable values calculated for ζ and ω_n and initial values designated to X_1 and X_2 at time $=$ zero, the solution can march forward in time using a suitably small time increment Δt. Program 11.1 in BASIC performs the calculations and generates a suitable graphical output.

Program 11.1 Step response of a damped spring/mass system.

```
SCREEN 9: COLOR 4, 7
start:
CLS
LOCATE 2, 6: PRINT "   Step response of a damped spring/mass system"
LOCATE 4, 6: INPUT "Spring stiffness in N/m = "; SPR
LOCATE 6, 6: INPUT "Damping ratio in Ns/m, max is 20 = "; RD
LOCATE 8, 6: INPUT "System mass in kg = "; M
LOCATE 4, 52: INPUT " Xo in metres, = "; XO
LOCATE 6, 52: INPUT " (dX/dt)o in m/s = "; DXO
CLS
LOCATE 2, 6: PRINT "   Step response of a damped spring/mass system"
LOCATE 6, 6: PRINT "   Time Domain                              Phase Plane"
DIM X1(250), X2(250)
X1(1) = XO: X2(1) = DXO
X1MAX = ABS(XO): X2MAX = ABS(DXO)
WN = SQR(SPR / M)
ZETA = RD / (2 * SQR(SPR * M))
IF ZETA > 1 THEN GOTO start    'zeta must be <=1
WD = WN * SQR(1 - ZETA * ZETA)
PI = 4 * ATN(1)
PER = 2 * PI / WD
DT = PER / 50
IF DT > .01 THEN DT = .01
FOR K = 2 TO 200
DX2 = DT * (-(2 * ZETA * WN / M) * X2(K - 1) - WN * WN * X1(K - 1) / M)
X2(K) = X2(K - 1) + DX2
DX1 = DT * X2(K)
X1(K) = X1(K - 1) + DX1
IF ABS(X1(K)) > X1MAX THEN X1MAX = ABS(X1(K))
IF ABS(X2(K)) > X2MAX THEN X2MAX = ABS(X2(K))
NEXT K
LINE (40, 300)-(40, 100), 1
LINE (40, 200)-(280, 200), 1
T = 0
FOR K = 2 TO 200
T = T + DT
A1 = (40 + T * 100)
B1 = 200 - X1(K - 1) * 60 / X1MAX
A2 = 40 + (T + DT) * 100
B2 = 200 - X1(K) * 60 / X1MAX
LINE (A1, B1)-(A2, B2)
NEXT K
LINE (300, 200)-(600, 200), 1
LINE (450, 300)-(450, 100), 1
```

```
FOR K = 2 TO 200
A1 = 450 + X1(K - 1) * 80 / X1MAX
B1 = 200 - X2(K - 1) * 40 / X2MAX
A2 = 450 + X1(K) * 80 / X1MAX
B2 = 200 - X2(K) * 40 / X2MAX
LINE (A1, B1)-(A2, B2)
NEXT K
LOCATE 23, 1
END
```

A plot of the displacement X_1, which is the system output, against time gives the solution to the equation in the time domain. The more usual state-variable representation, however, is shown as a plot of the state variables X_2 against X_1. For the damped spring mass system considered, this state-space plot is a record of the instantaneous values of the velocity of the mass against its position with time as parameter. Figure 11.46 shows a set of results for a spring stiffness of $100\,\mathrm{N\,m^{-1}}$, a damping factor of $10\,\mathrm{Ns\,m^{-1}}$, a system mass of $1\,\mathrm{kg}$ and with initial conditions $X_1(0) = -0.25\,\mathrm{m}$ and $X_2(0) = 0\,\mathrm{m\,s^{-1}}$.

The curve which results from the solution of the state variable equations is referred to as the trajectory in the state space. For a second-order system, the plot is more generally called the phase plane. The values of the state variables are said to represent the state of the system. With a knowledge of future inputs and the governing state-space equations, the phase plane trajectory can be predicted and hence also the behaviour of the system in general. Figure 11.47 shows another set of phase plane trajectories for the damped spring mass system. In these plots the system is critically damped and the trajectories start from a range of different $X_1(0)$ conditions with $X_2(0) = 0$. Plots such as these are referred to as phase plane portraits.

One further example is included where a negative damping factor of -1 has been imposed and the computation started from $X_1(0) = -0.10$ and $X_2(0) = 0$. The resultant time domain and phase plane plots are shown in Fig. 11.48. Negative damping renders the system unstable and the amplitude of the oscillation increases with time as shown in the time domain plot. The phase

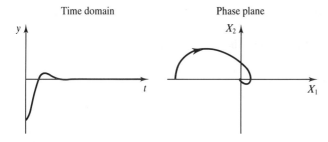

Figure 11.46 Time domain and state space representation of the damped spring mass system.

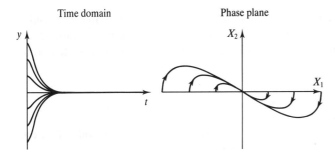

Figure 11.47 Time domain and phase plane portrait for the critically damped spring mass system.

Time domain   Phase plane

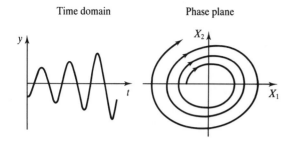

Figure 11.48 Time domain and phase plane trajectory for the spring mass system with negative damping.

plane plot indicates a trajectory which is spiralling outwards and this is the general state-space representation of an unstable system.

Other information which may be easily gleaned from the phase plane trajectory are an indication of whether the system response is over or under-damped and the extent of any system overshoots.

Application to a First-order System with a P+I Controller

Figure 11.49 shows the control block diagram for a process which has an open-loop transfer function which can be modelled as a first-order differential equation. The control effort U, is determined through a controller which utilizes a combination of proportional and integral action as shown.

The closed-loop transfer function, Eq. (11.30), is written as

$$\frac{PV(s)}{SP(s)} = \frac{(kK/T_i\tau)[1 + sT_i]}{s^2 + [(1/\tau) + (kK/\tau)]s + (kK/T_i\tau)} \tag{11.30}$$

Cross-multiplication gives

$$\frac{d^2(PV)}{dt^2} + \left[\frac{1}{\tau} + \frac{kK}{\tau}\right]\frac{d(PV)}{dt} + \frac{kK}{\tau T_i}(PV) = \frac{kK}{\tau}\left[\frac{d(SP)}{dt} + \frac{(SP)}{T_i}\right] \tag{11.72}$$

The differential equation, Eq. (11.72), may be represented in block diagram form as shown in Fig. 11.50.

Choosing the state variables as the outputs from the two integrators gives

$$X_1 = (PV) : X_2 = (\dot{PV})$$

Thus

$$\dot{X}_1 = X_2$$
$$\dot{X}_2 = \frac{-kK}{\tau T_i}X_1 - \left[\frac{1 + kK}{\tau}\right]X_2 + \frac{kK}{\tau}\left[\dot{SP} + \frac{SP}{T_i}\right] \tag{11.73}$$

The state variable equations can be written again as finite difference approximations and a solution marched forward in time from specified initial conditions. The step response of the system for various settings of system gain, controller gain, integral time and system time constant are illustrated in Fig. 11.51.

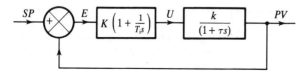

Figure 11.49 First-order system with a P+I controller.

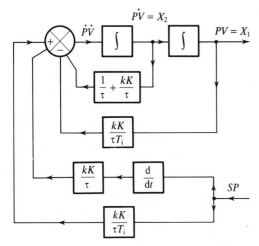

Figure 11.50 Block diagram representation of Eq. (11.72).

First order system with a P + I controller

System time constant, $\tau = 1$ Controller integral time, $T_i = 10$
System gain, $k = 1$ Controller gain, $K = 4$

First order system with a P + I controller

System time constant, $\tau = 1$ Controller integral time, $T_i = 0.1$
System gain, $k = 1$ Controller gain, $K = 4$

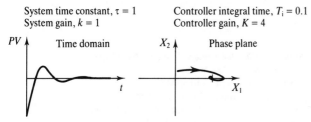

First order system with a P + I controller

System time constant, $\tau = 1$ Controller integral time, $T_i = 0.01$
System gain, $k = 1$ Controller gain, $K = 4$

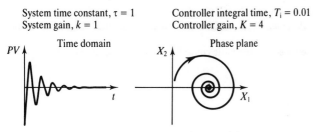

Figure 11.51 System response to step input.

11.12 CONTROL SYSTEM SIMULATION

The state-variable technique represents one particular method of control system simulation. Any such simulation constitutes a mathematical model of the system, usually with a suitable graphical output, and they have useful applications to the analysis of the behaviour of the control systems which they are intended to represent. The computer-based model can be used to quickly assess the effects of varying any one of the control parameters on the systems output response and stability. The set of responses given in Fig. 11.51, for example, show the effect of varying the integral time on the response of a first-order system with a P + I controller. In recent times general software packages have become readily available which allow the user to study the behaviour of control system models of varying complexity (see further reading). These packages usually include graphical outputs showing the open- and closed-loop response in the time domain and the usual Bode and Nyquist plots of the frequency response. Other packages allow the user to construct a customized control system using basic first- and second-order elements and a PID-based control strategy. Full flexibility is usually allowed on any of the system parameters and the frequency response of the modelled system is displayed in the usual graphical terms. In point of fact, however, a truly representative model of a real control system transfer function is perhaps the most difficult part of the procedure involved in the construction of the model. Once the system transfer functions have been determined it is relatively easy to calculate the frequency response and assess the stability of the system. The constants appearing in the transfer function, however, are dependent on the physics of the process being controlled and this is where the variety and challenge of the modelling problem is centred. Control system modelling is further considered in the following chapter.

FURTHER READING

Bateson, R. N. (1989) *Introduction to Control System Technology*, 3rd edn, Merrill Publishing, Columbus, Ohio.

Bode, H. W. (1974) 'Relations between attenuation and phase in feedback amplifier design', *Automatic Control: Classical Linear Theory*, ed. G. J. Thaler, Dowden, Hutchison and Ross, Stroudsburg, Penn, pp. 145–178.

Burghes, D. and A. Graham (1980) *Introduction to Control Theory, Including Optimal Control*, Ellis Horwood series—Mathematics and its Applications, Chichester.

Cambridge Control Ltd (1988) *Simbol 2—Control System Design and Simulation on IBM-PC or PS/2*, Cambridge Control Ltd, Cambridge.

DeRusso, M. P., R. J. Roy and C. M. Close (1965) *State Variables for Engineers*, Wiley, New York.

Doebelin, E. O. (1985) *Control System Principles and Design*, Wiley, New York.

Dorf, R. C. (1989) *Modern Control Systems*, 5th edn, Addison-Wesley, Reading, Mass.

Evans, W. R. (1950) 'Control system synthesis by the root locus method', *Trans. AIEE*, **69**, 66–69.

Gayakwad, R. and L. Sokoloff (1988) *Analog and Digital Control Systems*, Prentice-Hall, Englewood Cliffs, NJ.

Golten, J. and A. Verwer (1991) *Control System Design and Simulation*, McGraw-Hill, London.

Kuo, B. C. (1991) *Automatic Control Systems*, 6th edn, Prentice-Hall, Englewood Cliffs, NJ.

Nyquist, H. (1974) 'Regeneration theory', *Automatic Control: Classical Linear Theory*, ed. G. J. Thaler, Dowden, Hutchison and Ross, Stroudsburg, Penn., pp. 105–126.

Raven, F. H. (1987) *Automatic Control Engineering*, 4th edn, McGraw-Hill, New York.

Saunders, A. F. (1989) *Laplace Systems Analysis Programs*, Laplace Systems – Arthur F Saunders, Woolavington, Bridgewater.

Zeigler, J. G. and N. B. Nichols (1942) 'Optimum settings for automatic controllers', *Trans. ASME*, **64**, 759.

EXERCISES

11.1 Starting with the transfer function for a second-order system, i.e. Eq. (11.10), and using the complex conjugate, derive the expressions (11.11) and (11.12) for the amplitude ratio and the phase angle.

11.2 A control system is represented schematically as shown in Fig. Q11.2. Determine the overall open-loop transfer function.

$$[G_1G_2/(1 + G_2G_3 + G_1G_2G_4G_5)]$$

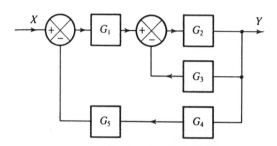

Figure Q11.2

11.3 An idealized control system is shown in block diagram form in Fig. Q11.3. Determine the overall open-loop transfer function.

$$\left[\frac{G_1G_2 + G_2G_5 + G_1G_2G_4G_5}{1 + G_1G_4 + G_1G_2G_3}\right]$$

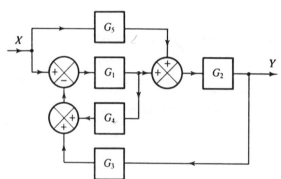

Figure Q11.3

11.4 A control system on open loop was subjected to a step input when a control valve position was altered by 20 per cent. The output variable changed from 60 to 75 per cent, with a response curve similar to Fig. 11.20. The apparent dead time and apparent time constant for the system was found to be 7 s and 20 s, respectively. Determine appropriate values for a PID controller.

[4.75, 14 s, 3.5 s]

11.5 A process control system incorporating an industrial PID controller was tested using the continuous cycling method. A steady-state oscillation in the output variable was observed when the controller gain was 3.6. The period of the oscillation was approximately 35 s. Determine appropriate values for the PID variables.

[2.16, 17.5 s, 4.375 s]

11.6 A remote position controller employs an amplifier and an electric motor with an inertial load. The open-loop transfer function is given as

$$C(s)G(s) = 92/[s(1 + 0.01s)(1 + 0.02s)]$$

Plot the Nyquist diagram for the open loop transfer function and determine:
   (a) the gain margin;
   (b) the phase margin;
   (c) the value of the gain for marginal stability.

[1.6, 14°, 147]

11.7 (a) The open-loop transfer function for a unity feedback control system is

$$C(s)G(s) = 10/[1 + 0.3s]^3$$

Plot the open loop frequency response as a Nyquist diagram and comment on the stability of the system.

(b) (i) Determine the value of the gain which will result in the system being marginally stable.

(ii) Determine the value of the gain which will gain margin of 6 dB and the corresponding phase margin.

[(a) system is unstable, (b) 8, 4, 90°]

11.8 An industrial process is modelled as a first-order system with a time delay. An open-loop test gave the apparent dead time and the apparent time constant as 5 s and 25 s, respectively. Determine the maximum gain of a proportional controller for marginal stability.

[8.62]

11.9 (a) An industrial blending process is modelled as a first-order system with a time delay. A reaction curve test gave the apparent dead time as 20 s and the apparent system time constant as 700 s. A PID controller with proportional action only is used to control the system and the controller gain is set to 20. Determine the gain margin and the phase margin of the system.

[9.1 dB, 63°]

(b) It is proposed to modify the above process to include additional mixing before the blending is carried out. This will involve an additional time delay in the process transfer function. Determine the maximum length of the additional time delay which will still give marginal stability when the system is operated with the same controller gain.

[36.9 s]

11.10 The open loop response of a servo system is given as

ω(rad/s)	4	8	10	15	40
M'	1.95	0.92	0.58	0.3	0.1
$\phi°$	-144	-164	-177	-204	-244

(a) Plot the Nyquist diagram and determine the gain and phase margins.

(b) If a gain compensated phase advance circuit having a transfer function of $(1 + 0.03s)$ is inserted into the system, determine the new gain and phase margins.

[5.2 dB, 27.4°, 9.9 dB, 30°]

11.11 Using the root locus graphical method show that the control system which has an open-loop transfer function given by $C(s)G(s) = K/[s(s+4)]$ is critically damped when the gain is 4.

11.12 Sketch the root locus for a control system which has an open-loop transfer function in the form:

$$C(s)G(s) = K/[s(s+2)(s+5)]$$

Hence determine:

(a) The value of the gain for the system to be critically damped.

(b) The value of the gain and the oscillation frequency for the onset of instability.

(c) The value of the gain and the oscillation frequency which gives an underdamped response with a damping factor of 0.5.

[4.05, 72, 3.2 rad/s, 12.12, 1.25 rad/s]

11.13 Using the root locus graphical method, investigate the stability of a control system which has the open-loop transfer function

$$C(s)G(s) = K(s+2)/[(s+0.5)(s+1.5)(s+4)]$$

Hence determine:

(a) The value of the gain for the system to be critically damped.

(b) The value of the gain and the oscillation frequency which will give an underdamped response with a damping factor of 0.707.

[System is always stable, 0.72, 5.2, 1.55 rad/s]

11.14 Using the root locus graphical method, investigate the stability of a control system which has an open-loop transfer function given by

$$C(s)G(s) = K/[s(s+3)(s^2 + 2s + 2)]$$

Hence determine:

(a) The value of the gain and the oscillation frequency which gives marginal stability.

(b) The value of the gain and the oscillation frequency which results in an underdamped response with an amplitude reduction ratio of 0.1 over each complete cycle.

Hint: Section 4.3 indicates how the damping factor can be obtained from the amplitude ratio.

[8.24, 1.1 rad/s, 2.22, 0.675 rad/s]

11.15 (*a*) A control system has an open-loop transfer function which is given as

$$C(s)G(s) = K/[(s+1)(s^2 + 4s + 5)]$$

Using the root locus graphical method investigate the stability of the system and determine:
  (i) The value of the gain which corresponds to marginal stability.
  (ii) The value of the gain which results in an underdamped response with a damping factor of 0.7.

[36, 2.26]

  (*b*) Investigate the effect of the addition of an open-loop zero, at -1.5 along the real axis, in the above transfer function, i.e.

$$C(s)G(s) = K(s+1.5)/[(s+1)(s^2 + 4s + 5)]$$

[The addition of a zero basically makes the system stable for all values of gain.]

11.16 The open-loop transfer function for a control system is given as

$$C(s)G(s) = K/[s(1 + 0.5s)(1 + 0.2s)]$$

Construct a Bode diagram and estimate the value of the gain K for marginal stability.

[6.9 approximately]

11.17 The open-loop transfer function for a unity feedback control system is given as

$$C(s)G(s) = K/[s(1 + 0.1s)(1 + 0.2s)(1 + s)]$$

Construct a Bode diagram over the frequency range 0.1 rad/s to 50 rad/s and determine:
  (*a*) The required value of the gain for a gain margin of 8 dB and the corresponding phase margin.
  (*b*) The value of the gain which would result in marginal stability.

[1.41, 25°, 3.6]

CHAPTER

TWELVE

CONTROL SYSTEM MODELLING

12.1 SYSTEM TRANSFER FUNCTION FROM A STEP INPUT TEST

In any real control system the transfer function will not be known beforehand and it must therefore be deduced, or approximated in some way, before any meaningful predictive analysis of the system frequency response can be carried out. The characteristics of a process will depend on the basic elements which constitute the system. The elements which make up the system may be mechanical, electrical, thermal, pneumatic, hydraulic, or chemical in nature and the system may also incorporate some complicated combination of any of these. The most effective method of deriving the system transfer function is to subject the open-loop system to a step input and to then measure the resulting output response. Many industrial processes will exhibit an open-loop output response similar to that shown in Fig. 11.20. Processes which follow this response can be modelled as a first-order system with a transport delay and Eq. (11.27) can then be used as a first approximation to the system transfer function. The system parameters, i.e. dead time and time constant, can be easily estimated from the output response. A word of caution, however, is appropriate here, since if the process is actually an overdamped second-order system, then the output response will be very similar to that shown in Fig. 11.20. Under these circumstances, the simple first-order system with a transport delay is an inadequate representation of the actual system dynamics.

If the open-loop response to a step input exhibits a decaying oscillation, then the system can be adequately represented in the form of an underdamped second-order differential equation. The damping ratio and the damped frequency can be measured and the transfer function constants determined using the general form of differential equation given as Eq. (4.6). Note that the relationship between the damped frequency and the natural frequency is given as

$$\omega_d = \omega_n \sqrt{1 - \zeta^2} \qquad (12.1)$$

The above technique represents a basic experimental method to determine the system open-loop transfer function. Once the differential form of the transfer function has been obtained, then it can be re-written in terms of the Laplace variable and combined with standard controller transfer functions to establish the closed-loop frequency characteristics of the system.

Example A position control system was subjected to a step input in order to establish the open-loop transfer function. The measured output showed an oscillatory response with a damping factor of 0.316 and a damped frequency of 9 rad/s. The system gain was $k = 5/9$.
(a) Determine the form and the value of the constants which define the open-loop transfer function.
(b) The system is to be controlled using a PID controller which incorporates a proportional gain $K = 4$ and a derivative term. Integral action is to be eliminated by setting $T_i = \infty$. Determine the value of T_d, which will result in a closed-loop response with a damping factor of 0.7.
Using Eq. (12.1)

$$\omega_n = \omega_d/\sqrt{1 - \zeta^2} = 9/\sqrt{1 - 0.316^2} = 9.486 \, \text{rad/s}$$

The standard form for the open loop transfer function is given by Eq. (11.10):

$$Y(s)/X(s) = G(s) = \frac{k\omega_n^2}{s^2 + 2\zeta\omega_n s + \omega_n^2}$$

Hence

$$k\omega_n^2 = (5/9) \times (9.486)^2 = 50$$

$$2\zeta\omega_n = 2 \times 0.316 \times 9.486 = 6 \quad \text{and} \quad \omega_n^2 = 90$$

The resulting open loop transfer function becomes

$$G(s) = 50/(s^2 + 6s + 90)$$

The controller transfer function is $C(s) = K(1 + T_d s)$ where $K = 4$ and T_d remains an undetermined variable. The closed-loop transfer function is given by Eq. (11.20). For this particular system we obtain

$$\frac{PV(s)}{SP(s)} = \frac{50K(1 + T_d s)}{(s^2 + 6s + 90) + 50K(1 + T_d s)}$$

Substituting the numerical values and grouping like terms gives

$$\frac{PV(s)}{SP(s)} = \frac{200(1 + T_d s)}{s^2 + (6 + 200T_d)s + 290}$$

For the closed-loop transfer function, $\omega_n^2 = 290$, which gives $\omega_n = \sqrt{290} = 17.03 \, \text{rad/s}$. Also

$$2\zeta\omega_n = 2 \times 0.7 \times 17.03 = (6 + 200T_d)$$

Thus

$$T_d = [(2 \times 0.7 \times 17.03) - 6]/200 = 0.089 \, \text{s}$$

The analysis shows that to obtain a closed-loop response with a damping factor of 0.7, the derivative time constant is $T_d = 0.089 \, \text{s}$.

The alternative approach to system modelling is to break down the system into subsets, each having a well defined governing equation with known physical constants. These governing equations can then be manipulated to derive the overall relationship between the output and the input of the complete system. This method requires a good understanding of the actual physical processes occurring within the system being controlled.

12.2 SYSTEM TRANSFER FUNCTION FROM A PHYSICAL MODEL

First-order Lag Processes

Hydraulic system A simple hydraulic system is depicted in schematic form in Fig. 12.1

A difference between the incoming flow Q_i and the outgoing flow Q_o will be manifested as a change in the level of the liquid stored in the tank. This relation may be written as

$$Q_i - Q_o = A \, dh/dt \tag{12.2}$$

where A is the cross-sectional area of the tank.

If the flow in the outlet pipe is laminar and the kinetic energy of the fluid at exit from the system can be neglected, then Q_o is directly proportional to the 'head' of liquid above the outlet nozzle, i.e.

$$Q_o = kh \tag{12.3}$$

The constant k is a system-dependent parameter related to the density and viscosity of the liquid in the tank, the acceleration due to gravity and the physical dimensions of the outflow pipe. A more detailed consideration of Eq. (12.3) is usually covered in most standard texts on fluid mechanics.

Differentiating Eq. (12.3) gives $dQ_o/dh = \text{constant} = k$. We may write the term (dh/dt) in the form $(dh/dQ_o)(dQ_o/dt)$, or $dh/dt = (1/k)(dQ_o/dt)$. Substitution into Eq. (12.2) gives

$$Q_i - Q_o = A(1/k)(dQ_o/dt) = (A/k) \, dQ_o/dt \tag{12.4}$$

In Laplace notation Eq. (12.4) becomes

$$Q_i(s) - Q_o(s) = \tau_L s Q_o(s) \tag{12.5}$$

where $\tau_L = (A/k)$ is a characteristic time constant for the hydraulic system.

Rearranging Eq. (12.5) results in

$$\frac{Q_o(s)}{Q_i(s)} = \frac{1}{1 + \tau_L s} \tag{12.6}$$

Equation (12.6) defines the open-loop transfer function for the hydraulic system. The form is similar to Eq. (11.3) which is the characteristic equation for any arbitrary first-order system. Step changes in the input flow rate Q_i will result in a liquid level response which will adjust itself to restore a balance between the inlet and outlet flow rates. A plot of the outlet flow rate response will take the general form typified by that shown in Fig. 4.4. Note, however, that if the flow is turbulent then the relationship between outlet flow rate and level height becomes nonlinear with $Q_o \propto (h)^{1/2}$. In such cases Eq. (12.3) no longer applies.

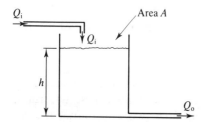

Figure 12.1 Simple hydraulic system.

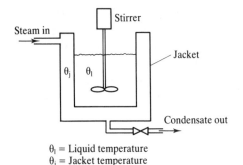

θ_l = Liquid temperature
θ_j = Jacket temperature

Figure 12.2 Simple thermal system.

Thermal system A simplified thermal system is shown in Fig. 12.2.

The stirrer maintains a uniform temperature throughout the liquid in the vessel, θ_l, which is the system output variable. The input to the system is the jacket temperature θ_j, which is determined by the temperature of the steam entering the jacket. For a step change in jacket temperature, the heat transferred between the jacket and the liquid is equal to the product of the temperature change of the liquid, $\Delta\theta_l$, and the thermal capacity C of the liquid in the vessel. The heat transferred may alternatively be expressed as the difference between the jacket and liquid temperatures, multiplied by an appropriate heat transfer coefficient h. A more detailed theoretical development is usually presented in most standard texts on heat transfer or thermodynamics. For an incremental increase in the heat transfer rate over an increment in time, Δt, the heat transfer equations may be written in the form:

$$\Delta Q = C \, \Delta\theta_l = h(\theta_j - \theta_l) \, \Delta t \tag{12.7}$$

where ΔQ is the incremental change in heat transfer rate over the time interval Δt.

In the limit, as $\Delta t \to 0$, Eq. (12.7) can be written as

$$C \, d\theta_l = h(\theta_j - \theta_l) \, dt$$

or

$$d\theta_l/dt = (h/C)(\theta_j - \theta_l) \tag{12.8}$$

In Laplace notation Eq. (12.8) becomes

$$s[\theta_l(s)] = (h/C)[\theta_j(s) - \theta_l(s)]$$

Some rearranging gives

$$\frac{\theta_l(s)}{\theta_j(s)} = \frac{1}{1 + (C/h)s} = \frac{1}{1 + \tau_\theta s} \tag{12.9}$$

where τ_θ is a thermal time constant appropriate to the system.

Equation (12.9) gives the open loop transfer function for the thermal system which again shows that the output will conform with the standard first-order response. Other simple systems which reduce to a first-order transfer function include pressure vessels, blending processes and the simple resistive–capacitive and resistive–inductive electrical circuits which were considered in Sec. 2.10.

Dead Time Processes

A dead time process is one in which the mass, or energy, is transported from one point to another in the system. The output signal is identical to the input, but is delayed by the time it takes for the input to be transported through to the output. In any practical dead time process the output is monitored and the input adjusted to suit the requirements of the process. The effect of the adjustment made at the input, however, will not be noticed at the measuring point until the dead time has elapsed. If the dead time is excessively long, then, the control system may 'overadjust' because it is not immediately seeing the effects of the adjustments being made. In the real control system, some allowance must be made for the dead time, perhaps by ensuring that the samping interval is greater, or at least equal to the dead time. Figure 12.3 shows two simple dead time processes. In both cases, the dead time is given as

$$T = d/v \qquad (12.10)$$

where v is the velocity of the transported signal and d is the distance travelled. In either case, the open loop transfer function is

$$Y(s)/X(s) = G(s) = \mathrm{e}^{-sT} \qquad (12.11)$$

First-order Lag Process plus a Dead Time

Figure 12.4 depicts a simple blending process in which the hydraulic aspect constitutes a first-order lag process and the supply of material, via a conveyor belt, constitutes a dead time process. The complete system open-loop transfer function consists of the two separate systems in series and would take the form:

$$G(s) = \mathrm{e}^{-sT}/(1 + \tau s) \qquad (12.12)$$

where T is the dead time and τ is the first-order time constant.

Example A blending process is shown schematically in Fig. 12.4. Determine the open-loop transfer function for the system given the following data:
Belt speed $= 1.1\,\mathrm{m\,s^{-1}}$: Distance travelled by belt $= 7.6\,\mathrm{m}$
Tank volume $= 12.2\,\mathrm{m^3}$: Inlet water flow rate $= 0.01\,\mathrm{m^3\,s^{-1}}$.
Dead time $= d/v = 7.6/1.1 = 6.91\,\mathrm{s}$.
In steady state, the outlet flow rate will be equal to the inlet flow rate, i.e. $Q_i = Q_o$. Assuming that the outflow can be considered to be laminar, then $Q_o = kh$. The hydraulic

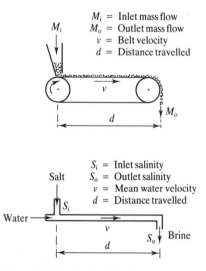

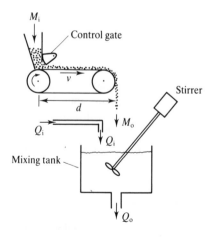

Figure 12.3 Simple dead time processes.

Figure 12.4 First-order lag, plus dead time blending process.

system time constant is $\tau_1 = A/k$, where A is the cross-sectional area of the tank. The volume, or capacity of the tank is Ah. Thus

$$Ah = 12.2 \quad \text{or } h = 12.2/A$$

Hence

$$Q_o = kh = (k/A)12.2 = 0.01 \, \text{m}^3 \, \text{s}^{-1}$$

i.e.

$$(A/k) = \tau_1 = 12.2/0.01 = 1220 \, \text{s}$$

From Eq. (12.12) the open-loop transfer function is

$$G(s) = e^{-s6.91}/(1 + 1220s)$$

Second-order Lag Processes

Series coupled hydraulic systems Figure 12.5 shows two hydraulic systems which are coupled in a series arrangement. The process input is the flow rate into the first tank and the process output is the flow rate at exit from the second tank. The open-loop transfer functions for each tank consist of simple first-order lags, with appropriate time constants τ_1 and τ_2. Since the complete system is in series then the overall transfer function for the system will consist of the product of the two first-order lags, i.e.

$$G(s) = \frac{1}{1 + \tau_1 s} \times \frac{1}{1 + \tau_2 s}$$

Thus

$$G(s) = 1/[1 + (\tau_1 + \tau_2)s + (\tau_1\tau_2)s^2] \tag{12.13}$$

The complete system then takes the form of a second-order lag process.

DC-motor-driven load A schematic representation of an inertial load, with viscous damping, driven by a voltage-controlled DC motor is shown in Fig. 12.6. The electrical equation for the armature winding is:

$$V = E + L\,di/dt + iR \tag{12.14}$$

where E = back e.m.f. generated by the winding, V
  L = inductance of the armature coil, H
  R = armature resistance, Ω
  i = armature current, A

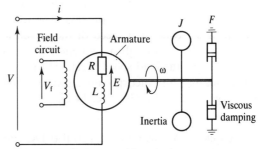

Figure 12.5 Coupled hydraulic systems. Figure 12.6 DC motor driven load.

The back e.m.f. will depend on the motor speed and can be written in the form:

$$E = K_e\omega \tag{12.15}$$

where K_e is the e.m.f. constant in V s/rad and ω is the motor speed in rad/s.
The motor torque is proportional to the armature current (see also Sec. 5.3), thus

$$T = K_t i \tag{12.16}$$

where K_t is the torque constant of the motor in $Nm\,A^{-1}$

Lastly, the torque required to drive the load must be able to overcome both the inertia of the mechanical system and also the viscous damping. The load torque is generally expressed in terms of the two components as

$$T = J(d\omega/dt) + F\omega \tag{12.17}$$

where $\quad J$ = moment of inertia of the load, $kg\,m^2$
$(d\omega/dt)$ = the angular acceleration of the load, rad/s^2
F = damping resistance in Nms/rad
Since the torque generated by the motor drives the mechanical load directly then

$$K_t i = J(d\omega/dt) + F\omega$$

Thus

$$i = (J/K_t)(d\omega/dt) + (F/K_t)\omega \tag{12.18}$$

Differentiating Eq. (12.18) with respect to time gives

$$di/dt = (J/K_t)(d^2\omega/dt^2) + (F/K_t)(d\omega/dt) \tag{12.19}$$

Substituting Eqs. (12.15), (12.18) and (12.19) into Eq. (12.14) gives

$$V = K_e\omega + (LJ/K_t)(d^2\omega/dt^2) + (LF/K_t)(d\omega/dt) + (RJ/K_t)(d\omega/dt) + (RF/K_t)\omega$$

Some rearranging gives

$$V(K_t/LJ) = (d^2\omega/dt^2) + (F/J + R/L)(d\omega/dt) + (K_t K_e/LJ + RF/LJ)\omega \tag{12.20}$$

Equation (12.20) may be expressed in the general form:

$$V(k_s\omega_n^2) = (d^2\omega/dt^2) + 2\zeta\omega_n(d\omega/dt) + \omega_n^2\,\omega \tag{12.21}$$

where k_s = overall system gain
ζ = system damping factor
ω_n = system natural frequency
In Laplace notation, the open-loop transfer function can be written as

$$\omega(s)/V(s) = G(s) = k_s\omega_n^2/[s^2 + 2\zeta\omega_n s + \omega_n^2] \tag{12.22}$$

It can be seen therefore that the DC motor driving an inertial load with viscous damping behaves as a second-order process. The input to the system is the armature voltage and the output is the rotational speed of the driven load. In some rotational drive systems the motor drives the load through a reduction gearbox. In these cases the gearbox acts as a torque amplifier and the load speed is related to the motor speed through the gearing ratio. The basic equations may also incorporate a gearbox transmission efficiency to account for frictional losses in the gear train (see also Sec. 14.2).

Example An armature-controlled DC motor provides a direct line drive to a mechanical load and the system has the following measured characteristics:

$$F = 0.002\,\text{Nms/rad} : J = 0.0032\,\text{kg m}^2 : K_e = 0.22\,\text{Vs/rad}$$

$$K_t = 0.22\,\text{Nm A}^{-1} : L = 0.075\,\text{H} : \text{R} = 1.2\,\Omega$$

(a) Determine the natural frequency and the damping ratio of the system. Hence define the open-loop transfer function.

(b) If the armature resistance is doubled, determine the general effect on the system.

By comparing Eqs (12.20) and (12.21) we obtain

$$\omega_n^2 = (RF/LJ) + (K_eK_t/LJ) = [(1.2 \times 0.002) + (0.22 \times 0.22)]/(0.075 \times 0.0032) = 211.67$$

i.e.

$$\omega_n = \sqrt{211.67} = 14.55\,\text{rad/s}$$

Also

$$2\zeta\omega_n = (F/J + R/L) = (0.002/0.0032) + (1.2/0.075) = 16.625$$

Therefore

$$\zeta = 16.625/(2 \times 14.55) = 0.57$$

Also, since $k_s\omega_n^2 = K_t/(LJ)$, then

$$k_s = K_t/(LJ\omega_n^2) = 0.22/(0.075 \times 0.0032 \times 211.67) = 4.33$$

The complete open-loop transfer function has the final form:

$$G(s) = 916.5/[s^2 + 15.625s + 211.67]$$

The system is basically stable and for a step increase in motor voltage, the load speed would oscillate with decreasing amplitude and settling to the adjusted value in a reasonable time. If the armature resistance becomes equal to $2.4\,\Omega$, then

$$\omega_n^2 = [(2.4 \times 0.002) + (0.22 \times 0.22)]/(0.075 \times 0.0032) = 221.67$$

i.e.

$$\omega_n = \sqrt{221.67} = 14.0\,\text{rad/s}$$

Also

$$2\zeta\omega_n = (F/J + R/L) = (0.002/0.0032) + (2.4/0.075) = 32.625$$

Therefore

$$\zeta = 32.625/(2 \times 14.9) = 1.094$$

With an armature resistance of $2.4\,\Omega$, the system is slightly overdamped.

In the example considered, doubling the value of the armature resistance has had little effect on the system natural frequency but has considerable influence on the damping factor. In a similar manner, a reduced armature resistance will not have much effect on the natural frequency but will considerably reduce the damping factor. Reduced armature resistance therefore will have serious implications for the transient response of the system and could lead to an unacceptably long transient oscillation of the output load speed.

In many real practical applications we are basically concerned with some motor-driven system for speed, or position control. The dynamic load in such systems can usually be accounted for by including an inertial component and a friction dependent component. If the output is a position, then the inertial component is associated with the second derivative of the position, i.e. the acceleration. The frictional term in a position control system is associated with the first derivative of the position, i.e. the speed.

If the controlled output variable is speed, however, then the inertial component is associated with the first derivative of the output and the frictional component is associated with the output itself. Note that this is a consistent treatment since the output, being a speed, is already a first time-derivative of position.

This simple system model can be used in a great many applications and can provide reasonable results even in cases where the real system is much more complicated. Denoting the inertial term as J and the frictional term as F, the open-loop transfer functions for a position control system and a speed control system are as depicted in Fig. 12.7.

12.3 SYSTEM CLOSED-LOOP TRANSFER FUNCTIONS

With the inclusion of a controller in the forward path and a feedback system, the closed-loop control system offers many more opportunities for parameter adjustment to obtain a desired response. In the attempt to predictively fine tune a control system, an adequate model of the closed-loop transfer function must first of all be obtained.

> **Example** In a remote position control system, the driven load has an inertia of $0.0016 \, \text{kg} \, \text{m}^2$ and the viscous damping is measured as $72 \times 10^{-6} \, \text{Nms/rad}$. A proportional controller gives an output torque of K times the position error and the damping ratio of the system is 0.4. The transient response of the system is satisfactory but it has twice the acceptable error for a ramp, i.e. velocity input. If this error is to be brought within the required limits while the transient response is maintained, investigate the possibilities of achieving this end by modifying the system to incorporate:
> (*a*) positive acceleration feedback;
> (*b*) positive feedforward of velocity input.
> Determine the forms of the original and the modified transfer functions, and calculate the amount of compensation required, if appropriate, in each case.
> The original control system with unity feedback is shown in Fig. 12.8. Analysis of the system gives the closed-loop transfer function as
>
> $$PV(s)/SP(s) = (K/J)/[s^2 + (F/J)s + (K/J)] \qquad (12.23)$$
>
> Comparison with the general second-order transfer function then gives
>
> $$\omega_n^2 = (K/J) \quad \text{and} \quad 2\zeta\omega_n = (F/J)$$
>
> i.e.
>
> $$\zeta = (F/J)/[2\sqrt{(K/J)}] = F/[2\sqrt{JK}] = 0.4$$

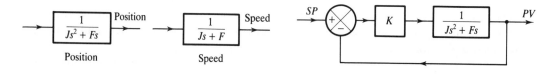

Figure 12.7 Open-loop transfer functions for position and speed control systems.

Figure 12.8 Original closed-loop control system.

Hence

$$K = [(F/0.8)^2]/J = [(72 \times 10^{-6}/0.8)^2]/(1.6 \times 10^{-3}) = 5.0625 \times 10^{-6} \, \text{Nms/rad}$$

$$\omega_n = \sqrt{(K/J)} = \sqrt{(5.0625 \times 10^{-6})/(72 \times 10^{-6})} = 0.265 \, \text{rad/s}$$

Also

$$\omega_d = \omega_n \sqrt{1 - \zeta^2} = 0.265 \times \sqrt{1 - 0.4^2} = 0.243 \, \text{rad/s}$$

For a velocity step, $SP = \Omega t$, where Ω is the input velocity.
The steady-state solution, after the transient part has decayed, is given by the particular integral, i.e.

$$PV_{ss} = \omega_n^2/[s^2 + 2\zeta\omega_n s + \omega_n^2] SP = \omega_n^2/[s^2 + 2\zeta\omega_n s + \omega_n^2](\Omega t)$$

where PV_{ss} denotes the system steady-state output, or

$$PV_{ss} = [1 + \{(s^2/\omega_n^2) + (s2\zeta/\omega_n)\}]^{-1}(\Omega t)$$

Expanding the square bracketed term binominally gives

$$PV_{ss} = [1 - \{(s^2/\omega_n^2) + (s2\zeta/\omega_n)\} + \{(s^2/\omega_n^2) + (s2\zeta/\omega_n)\}^2 \ldots + \ldots](\Omega t) \qquad (12.24)$$

The first derivative of (Ωt) is Ω and any higher-order derivatives are zero; thus

$$PV_{ss} = \Omega t - 2\zeta\Omega/\omega_n$$

The steady state error is

$$E_{ss} = SP - PV_{ss} = \Omega t - [\Omega t - 2\zeta\Omega/\omega_n] = 2\zeta\Omega/\omega_n$$

Since $2\zeta\omega_n = F/J$, then

$$E_{ss} = F\Omega/(J\omega_n^2) = F\Omega J/(JK) = F\Omega/K \qquad (12.25)$$

i.e.

$$E_{ss} = (72 \times 10^{-6} \times \Omega)/(5.0625 \times 10^{-6}) = 14.2\Omega \, \text{rad/s}$$

The performance parameters of the original system are summarized as

$$\omega_n = 0.265 \, \text{rad/s} : \omega_d = 0.243 \, \text{rad/s} : \zeta = 0.4 : K = 5.0625 \times 10^{-6} : E_{ss} = 14.2\Omega \, \text{rad/s}$$

If the system is now modified to include positive acceleration feedback, then the modified control block diagram takes the form shown in Fig. 12.9. Note that K_a is the gain of the acceleration transducer, or accelerometer.
Analysis of the modified control system gives the closed-loop transfer function as

$$\frac{PV(s)}{SP(s)} = \frac{K/(J - KK_a)}{[s^2 + \{F/(J - KK_a)\}s + \{K/(J - KK_a)\}]} \qquad (12.26)$$

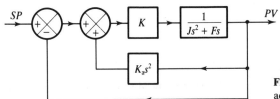

Figure 12.9 Modified control system with positive acceleration feedback.

Comparison with the original transfer function shows that the system inertia J has been effectively reduced to $J' = J - KK_a$. The system damping factor and natural frequency are also effectively modified, with

$$\omega_n' = \sqrt{K/(J - KK_a)} \quad \text{and} \quad \zeta' = F/2(\sqrt{KJ - K^2 K_a})$$

The original steady state error was $E_{ss} = 2\zeta\Omega/\omega_n$. The modified steady state error becomes $E_{ss}' = 2\zeta'\Omega/\omega_n'$, i.e.

$$E_{ss}' = \frac{2F\Omega}{2\sqrt{(KJ - K^2 K_a)}} \times \frac{\sqrt{(J - KK_a)}}{\sqrt{K}}$$

or

$$E_{ss}' = F\Omega/K \tag{12.27}$$

Comparison with Eq. (2.25) shows that the addition of positive acceleration feedback has had no effect on the steady-state error for a velocity input. If the steady-state error is to be reduced by one half, then the only system parameter which can be adjusted is the controller gain K. This, however, could just have easily have been done in the original system without acceleration feedback. In either system, an increase in the controller gain by a factor of two will reduce the steady-state error by one half. This action in each case will increase the system natural frequency and decrease the system damping factor. The magnitude of these changes however will be different in each case.

The second possible alternative strategy for consideration, was to incorporate a positive velocity feedforward loop in the forward path. This modification is shown in Fig. 12.10. Consideration of the control system gives

$$PV(s) = [SP(s) - PV(s) + K_v s SP(s)]K/[Js^2 + Fs]$$

where K_v is the velocity feedforward gain. Thus

$$PV(s)[Js^2 + Fs + K] = SP(s)[K(1 + K_v s)]$$

Hence

$$\frac{PV(s)}{SP(s)} = \frac{(K/J)[1 + K_v s]}{[s^2 + (F/J)s + (K/J)]} \tag{12.28}$$

On comparing the modified closed-loop transfer function with the original system, i.e. Eq. (12.23), it can be seen that the denominator term is exactly the same. This means that the modified system, with positive velocity feedforward, will have the same transient response as the original system.

To obtain the steady-state error for a velocity input, we must again calculate the value of the particular integral, i.e.

$$PV_{ss} = [1 + \{(s^2/\omega_n^2) + (s2\zeta/\omega_n)\}]^{-1}(\Omega t)[1 + K_v s]$$

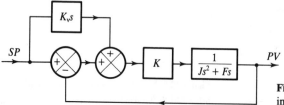

Figure 12.10 Modified control system with positive input velocity feedforward.

$$PV_{ss} = [1 - \{(s^2/\omega_n^2) + (s2\zeta/\omega_n)\} + \{(s^2/\omega_n^2) + (s2\zeta/\omega_n)\}^2 \dots](\Omega t)[1 + K_v s]$$

Hence

$$PV_{ss} = \Omega t + K_v \Omega - 2\zeta\Omega/\omega_n$$

$$E_{ss} = SP - PV_{ss} = \Omega t - \Omega t - K_v \Omega + 2\zeta\Omega/\omega_n = -K_v \Omega + 2\zeta\Omega/\omega_n$$

Since $2\zeta\omega_n = (F/J)$ and $\omega_n^2 = (K/J)$, then $E_{ss} = F\Omega/K - K_v\Omega$. The original system has a steady state error of $F\Omega/K$. If this error is to be reduced by one half, then

$$(F\Omega)/(2K) = F\Omega/K - K_v\Omega$$

thus

$$K_v = F/(2K) = (72 \times 10^{-6})/(2 \times 5.0625 \times 10^{-6}) = 7.1$$

The analysis shows that a positive velocity feedforward loop, with a gain of $K_v = 7.1$, will reduce the steady-state error to a velocity step by one half. The feedforward loop, in addition, will not alter the transient response of the original system.

The example considered, although quite lengthy, serves to illustrate how the system model can be used to good effect in quantifying the effects of major system modifications.

Example An automatic radar tracker consists of a motor of inertia $2 \times 10^{-6}\,\text{kg m}^2$. The motor turns an ariel of inertia $0.2\,\text{kg m}^2$ through a 100/1 step-down gear box. The ariel signal passes into a receiver which generates a 1 V/degree error in positioning the ariel on target. This voltage is amplified and used to drive the motor. The motor torque is directly proportional to the applied voltage and at 100 V, the measured torque is 0.04 Nm. Viscous friction measured at the motor shaft is $50 \times 10^{-6}\,\text{Nms/rad}$ and the damping ratio is 0.25. If the ambient wind exerts a static torque of 0.28 Nm on the ariel, determine the resultant error, in degrees, relative to a stationary target and the motor voltage under these conditions.

The control system can be represented in the form shown in Fig. 12.11.
Receiver gain $K_R = 360$ V per $360° = 360$ V per 2π rad, i.e. $K_R = (180/\pi)$ V/rad.
The amplifier gain K_A is unspecified.
The motor produces an output torque in response to an input voltage. Expressing this as a proportional gain, $K_M = 0.04/100 = 4 \times 10^{-4}\,\text{Nm/V}$.
The gearbox operates as a torque amplifier which may also be expressed in terms of a gain K_G. The input torque to the gearbox is magnified by 100, such that $K_G = 100$.

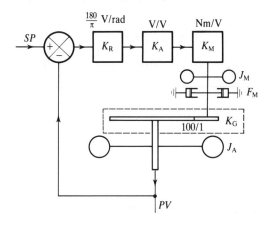

Figure 12.11 Idealized radar tracking control system.

These four system elements are in series and their combined effect results in a total system gain K where

$$K = K_R \times K_A \times K_M \times K_G = (180/\pi) \times K_A \times 4 \times 10^{-4} \times 100$$

i.e.

$$K = 2.29 K_A \, \text{Nm/rad}$$

When dealing with a geared system, the inertia and friction components on the driver side can be referred to the driven side by scaling the equivalent values by the square of the gearing ratio. Thus the inertia of the motor, J_M, has an equivalent inertia on the driven side of $J_M \times K_G^2$. The friction components can be similarly scaled by the square of the gearing ratio. Thus the total equivalent inertia on the driven shaft side is $J = J_A + J_M \times K_G^2$ where J_A is the inertia of the ariel. Thus

$$J = 0.2 + 2 \times 10^{-6} \times 100^2 = 0.22 \, \text{kg m}^2$$

Similarly

$$F = 50 \times 10^{-6} \times 100^2 = 0.5 \, \text{Nms/rad}$$

where F is the equivalent friction component, measured at the motor and referred to the driven side.

These simplifications allow us to represent a dynamically equivalent control system as shown in Fig. 12.12.

Consideration of the closed-loop system gives a closed-loop transfer function as

$$PV(s)/SP(s) = (K/J)/[s^2 + (F/J)s + (K/J)]$$

Comparison with the standard form for a second-order system gives

$$\omega_n^2 = (K/J) = 2.29 K_A/0.22 = 10.41 K_A$$

$$2\zeta\omega_n = (F/J) = 0.5/0.22 = 2.273$$

Since ζ was given as 0.25, then $\omega_n = 2.273/(2 \times 0.25) = 4.55 \, \text{rad/s}$. Hence

$$K_A = \omega_n^2/10.41 = (4.55)^2/10.41 = 1.985 \, \text{V/V}$$

Also, the overall system gain, $K = 2.29 \times K_A = 2.29 \times 1.985 = 4.546 \, \text{Nm/rad}$. The static torque due to ambient wind conditions is 0.28 Nm. This torque will result in a static error of 0.28/4.546 rad, i.e.

$$\text{static error} = 0.28/4.546 = 0.0616 \, \text{rad or } (0.28/4.546)(180/\pi) = 3.53°$$

The corresponding motor voltage is $0.0616 \times K_R \times K_A = 0.0616 \times (180/\pi) \times 1.985 = 7 \, \text{V}$.

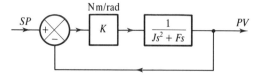

$K = K_R \times K_A \times K_M \times K_G$
$J = J_A + J_M (K_G)^2$
$F = F_M (K_G)^2$

Figure 12.12 Simplified radar tracking control system.

One final example is included to illustrate the use of a system model in the quantitative assessment of a commonly applied practical measure to modify the response of a closed-loop feedback control system. This concerns the addition of a phase advance compensator in the forward path, which is designed to improve the overall stability of the system.

Example A simple proportional position control system, when subjected to a step input, is found to give a decaying oscillatory response with a damped frequency of 2 cycles/s and a first overshoot of 60 per cent. In order to improve the transient response, a compensation unit is to be added in the forward path having a transfer function of $k(1 + \tau s)$.

(a) Derive expressions for the velocity lag, with and without compensation, and thus ascertain the general effect of the compensation unit gain k.

(b) It is desired to reduce the first overshoot from 60 to 5 per cent without altering the time response of the system. Determine suitable values for k and τ.

The basic control system is shown in Fig. 12.13. The closed-loop transfer function without the compensation unit can be determined by inspection as

$$PV(s)/SP(s) = (K/J)/[s^2 + (F/J)s + (K/J)]$$

From Eq. (4.14), the percentage overshoot is given by

$$PO = 100 \times \exp(-\pi\zeta/\sqrt{1 - \zeta^2})$$

i.e.

$$60 = 100\exp(-\pi\zeta/\sqrt{1 - \zeta^2})$$

Thus

$$\ln(0.6) = -\pi\zeta/\sqrt{1 - \zeta^2}$$

or

$$(1 - \zeta^2) = \pi^2\zeta^2/[\ln(0.6)]^2 = 37.82\zeta^2$$

Hence

$$\zeta = \sqrt{1/38.82} = 0.163$$

Also

$$\omega_d = 2 \text{ cycles/s} = 4\pi \text{ rad/s}$$

Thus

$$\omega_n = \omega_d/\sqrt{1 - \zeta^2} = 4\pi/\sqrt{[1 - (0.163)^2]} = 12.74 \text{ rad/s}$$

For a step velocity input, i.e. $SP(s) = (\Omega t)$, the steady-state output is

$$PV_{ss} = [1 - (s^2/\omega_n^2 + 2\zeta s/\omega_n)](\Omega t) = \Omega t - 2\zeta\Omega/\omega_n$$

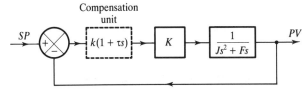

Compensation unit

SP → $k(1 + \tau s)$ → K → $\dfrac{1}{Js^2 + Fs}$ → PV

Figure 12.13 Basic proportional position control system.

The steady-state, or velocity lag is

$$SP - PV_{ss} = E_{ss} = 2\zeta\Omega/\omega_n$$

Now $\omega_n^2 = (K/J)$ and $2\zeta\omega_n = (F/J)$, thus

$$E_{ss} = \Omega(2\zeta\omega_n/\omega_n^2) = \Omega(F/J)(J/K) = F\Omega/K \tag{12.29}$$

Consideration of the compensated system gives the closed-loop transfer function

$$PV(s)/SP(s) = (kK/J)(1 + \tau s)/[s^2 + (F/J + kK\tau/J)s + (kK/J)]$$

The modified transfer function incorporates a modified natural frequency and a modified damping factor, i.e.

$$\omega_n'^2 = kK/J \quad \text{and} \quad \zeta' = [F/J + kK\tau/J]/(2\omega_n')$$

For the step velocity input to the modified system, the steady state output is

$$\begin{aligned} PV_{ss} &= [1 - (s^2/\omega_n'^2 + 2\zeta's/\omega_n')]SP(s)(1 + \tau s) \\ &= [1 - (s^2/\omega_n'^2 + 2\zeta's/\omega_n')](\Omega t + \tau\Omega) \\ &= \Omega t + \tau\Omega - 2\zeta'\Omega/\omega_n' \end{aligned}$$

Thus

$$E_{ss} = SP(s) - PV_{ss} = \Omega t - \Omega t - \tau\Omega + 2\zeta'\Omega/\omega_n' = -\tau\Omega + 2\zeta'\Omega/\omega_n'$$

Substituting the expressions obtained for $\omega_n'^2$ and ζ' gives

$$E_{ss} = -\tau\Omega + \Omega(2\zeta'\omega_n'/\omega_n'^2) = -\tau\Omega + \Omega(F/J + kK\tau/J)/(kK/J)$$

Hence

$$E_{ss} = -\tau\Omega + (\Omega F)/(kK) + \tau\Omega = F\Omega/(kK) \tag{12.30}$$

Equations (12.29) and (12.30) give the steady-state error for a step velocity input for the original and the compensated systems, respectively.

It is clear that the compensated system incorporates the additional compensation unit gain k in the denominator. If therefore $k > 1$, then the steady-state error will be reduced. A compensation unit gain of less than 1, however, will increase the steady state error. It is required to have a first overshoot of 5% in the compensated system. Thus

$$5 = 100\exp(-\pi\zeta'/\sqrt{1 - \zeta'^2})$$

Solving for the modified damping factor gives $\zeta' = 0.69$.

For the modified system to have the same time response, the modified damped frequency must have the same value as the original system, i.e. $\omega_d' = \omega_d = 4\pi\,\text{rad/s}$. Thus

$$\omega_n' = \omega_d'/\sqrt{1 - \zeta'^2} = 4\pi/\sqrt{1 - (0.69)^2} = 17.36\,\text{rad/s}$$

Now $\omega_n'^2 = kK/J$ and $\omega_n^2 = (K/J)$, therefore $(\omega_n'^2)/(\omega_n^2) = (17.36/12.74)^2 = 1.86 = k$, i.e. the compensation unit gain $k = 1.86$. Also

$$\zeta' = (F + kK\tau)/(2J\omega_n') \quad \text{and} \quad \zeta = F/(2J\omega_n)$$

Thus

$$F = \zeta 2J\omega_n$$

Hence

$$\zeta' = (\zeta 2J\omega_n + kK\tau)/(2J\omega_n')$$

Since $\omega_n' = (17.36/12.74)\omega_n = 1.363\omega_n$, then

$$\zeta' = (\zeta 2J\omega_n + kK\tau)/(2 \times J \times 1.363\omega_n) = (\zeta/1.363) + (kK\tau)/(2.725 \times J \times \omega_n)$$

Now $(K/J) = \omega_n^2$, thus

$$\zeta' = (\zeta/1.363) + (k\tau\omega_n)/2.725$$

Substituting numerical values gives

$$0.69 = (0.163/1.363) + (1.86 \times \tau \times 12.74)/2.725$$

therefore

$$\tau = (0.69 - 0.12)[2.725/(1.86 \times 12.74)] = 0.0655\,\text{s}$$

The analysis shows that a compensation transfer function of the form $1.86(1 + 0.0655s)$, will give a system transient response with a first overshoot of 5 per cent in the same time as the original system.

In this chapter we have addressed the problem of system modelling and have considered some applications related to the fine tuning of particular control systems. If the control system is based on a digital computer then these techniques can still be applied provided that the sampling time for the digital system is correctly chosen. Under these circumstances the digital control system is a close approximation to its continuous analogue counterpart. If, however, the sampling time becomes significant, then the digital system incorporates what is effectively an additional time delay. These control systems then become characteristically discrete in operation and alternative mathematical techniques are used for the analysis of the system performance. Discrete control systems are considered in the following chapter.

FURTHER READING

Bateson, R. N. (1989) *Introduction to Control System Technology*, 3rd edn, Merrill Publishing Co., Columbus, Ohio.
Doebelin, E. O. (1985) *Control System Principles and Design*, Wiley, New York.
Dorf, R. C. (1989) *Modern Control Systems*, 5th edn, Addison-Wesley, Reading, Mass.
Kuo, B. C. (1987) *Automatic Control Systems*, 5th edn, Prentice-Hall, Englewood Cliffs, NJ.
Raven, F. H. (1987) *Automatic Control Engineering*, 4th edn, McGraw-Hill, New York.

EXERCISES

12.1 A liquid filled thermometer is illustrated in Fig. Q12.1. The amount of heat ΔQ transferred from the fluid surrounding the bulb to the liquid inside the bulb is related to the product of the heat transfer coefficient h, the temperature difference between the two fluids and the time interval Δt. The heat transferred is also given by the product of the temperature change and the thermal capacity C of the fluid inside the bulb. Denoting the bulb fluid temperature as θ_b and the tank fluid temperature as θ_f, derive from first principles, an equation to describe the temperature variation with time of the bulb fluid in terms of the relevant parameters.

$$[(C/h)\,\mathrm{d}\theta_b/\mathrm{d}t + \theta_b = \theta_f]$$

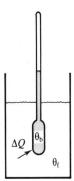

12.2 A process blending tank has a volume of $3\,\text{m}^3$ and in normal operation, the inlet water flow rate is $0.15\,\text{m}^3\,\text{min}^{-1}$. Granular material is fed to the process by means of a motor driven conveyor belt. The driving pulley is 200 mm in diameter and the motor runs at

200 rev/min. The effective length of the conveyor 1.2 m. Assuming that the flow through the process is laminar, derive the open-loop transfer function for the process.

$$[G(s) = e^{-0.573s}/(1 + 1200s)]$$

12.3 An armature-controlled DC motor provides a direct line drive to an inertial load with some inherent viscous damping. The system has the following measured parameters.

$$J = 5 \times 10^{-4} \, \text{kg m}^2 : F = 10^{-4} \, \text{Nms/rad} : L = 0.03 \, \text{H} : R = 2.4 \, \Omega$$

$$K_e = 0.2 \, \text{Vs/rad} : K_t = 0.2 \, \text{Nm/A}$$

Determine the natural frequency of oscillation, the damping factor and hence deduce the open-loop transfer function.

$$[5.18 \, \text{rad/s}, \, 0.77, \, G(s) = 1.33 \times 10^4/\{s^2 + 80s + 2683\}]$$

12.4 In a remote position controller, the inertia of the driven load is $15.5 \times 10^{-6} \, \text{kg m}^2$ and the damping factor is 0.6. The driving motor gives an output torque of $1.6 \times 10^{-4} \, \text{Nm}$ per radian of error signal. Determine the frequency of the output signal, and the maximum overshoot for a step input.

$$[2.57 \, \text{rad/s}, \, 9.26\%]$$

12.5 A position control system consists of a proportional controller which supplies a torque of K times the error signal and drives a rotational load. The load inertia is $1 \, \text{kg m}^2$ and it is found that a torque of $20 \, \text{Nm}$ applied to the output shaft gives a steady state error of 0.2 rad. A further test shows that for a constant velocity input of 0.1 rad/s, the steady-state error is 0.1 rad. Determine the form, and numerical value of the constants, for the closed-loop transfer function.

$$[PV(s)/SP(s) = 100/(s^2 + 10s + 100)]$$

12.6 A simple proportional position control system drives an inertial load with some inherent viscous damping. The transient response to a step input shows a decaying oscillation with a first overshoot of 50 per cent and a damped frequency of 1.2 cycles/s. In order to improve the system performance a compensating network, with the transfer function $C(s) = (k_1 + k_2s)$, is to be added in the forward path.

(a) Derive an expression for the velocity lag of the compensated system.

(b) If it is desired to achieve a 60 per cent reduction in velocity lag by the addition of the compensating network and also to provide a step response with a first overshoot of 10 per cent determine suitable values for k_1 and k_2 to satisfy these conditions.

$$[k_1 = 2.5, \, k_2 = 0.19]$$

12.7 A rotary proportional position control system, with relatively little inherent viscous damping, is to have its transient response improved by a combination of positive acceleration feedback and negative velocity feedback. Figure Q12.7 shows the block diagram representation of the modified system.

(a) Establish the closed loop transfer function and derive an expression for the steady-state error in response to a ramp input.

$$[PV(s)/SP(s) = \omega_n'^2/\{s^2 + 2\zeta'\omega_n' + \omega_n'^2\} \text{ with } \omega_n'^2 = K/J' \text{ and } \zeta' = F'/2J'\omega_n']$$
$$[\text{also } F' = F + KK_V : J' = J - KK_A : E_{ss} = 2\zeta'\Omega/\omega_n']$$

(b) In response to a step input, the original system shows a damped output oscillation with the amplitude reducing by one-half of its original value over two complete cycles. This corresponds to a time of 0.4 s. Furthermore, the steady-state position error in response to a constant input velocity of 15 rev/min was found to be 1 degree. In attempting to improve the step response, by the means indicated, it is required to ensure that an effective damping factor of 0.65 will prevail. In addition, the minimum amount of acceleration feedback is to be utilized, consistent with it being permissable for the steady-state position error to be doubled. Under these circumstances, determine suitable values for the feedback coefficients K_A and K_V.

$$[K_V = 0.011, \, K_A = 0.001]$$

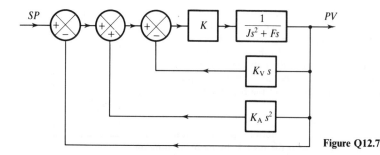

Figure Q12.7

THIRTEEN

DIGITAL CONTROL TECHNIQUES

13.1 DIRECT DIGITAL CONTROL

Control system modelling has been considered in the previous chapter where the main objective was to develop an adequate dynamical model of the system in terms of a differential equation with the appropriate physical constants. For many real processes, however, an adequate system model can be difficult, if not impossible to obtain. The modern emphasis therefore is towards an application of computer-based control strategies that can be made to work with real systems. The recent developments in microelectronics, particularly microprocessors, has made microcomputer devices the natural choice as the controller for many systems. The microcomputer provides the ability to implement such functions as arithmetic and logic manipulation, timing and counting, and with many analogue input/output modules available to interface to the microcomputer, the overall 'intelligence' of the system is greatly enhanced.

The basic elements of the computer-based control system includes the microprocessor, memory, an input interface to measure the process variable and an output interface to supply power to the controlled process. The control effort output to the process is determined by the

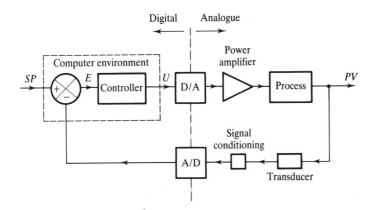

Figure 13.1 Fundamental digital-based control system.

control strategy which takes the form of an algorithm incorporated within the computer software. The fundamental digital-based control system is depicted in Fig. 13.1.

In the generalized layout given in Fig. 13.1, the microcomputer performs a number of tasks which would require separate elements in an equivalent analogue system. The two inputs to the microcomputer are the desired set point and a signal from the process via a feedback loop. The term 'process' is being used in a quite arbitrary sense in this context. The microcomputer first performs the function of comparing the process value with the set point to establish the error. The control strategy is then applied to the error value to determine the corrective action necessary. The microcomputer subsequently outputs the appropriate signal to the process via other additional elements in the system. These are basically the same functions performed by any analogue control system. The major difference between a digital control system and the analogue counterpart, however, is the fact that the digital system functions in a discrete manner.

13.2 SAMPLED DATA SYSTEMS, THE z-TRANSFORM

In a sampled data system the computer acts as the compensator in the control loop and the analogue-to-digital and digital-to-analogue interfaces provide the link between the digital-based computer and the otherwise analogue-based controlled system. Being digitally based, the computer operates in discrete time intervals and indeed the control strategy, which exists in the software, must also take a finite time for its evaluation and implementation. Time delays are also inevitable in the analogue-to-digital conversion process and these cummulative time delays result in what is called a 'sampled-data system'. The difference between a sampled data, or discrete signal and its continuous counterpart is displayed in Fig. 13.2. The closure time q is the time taken to complete the digitization of the instantaneous signal. Generally $q \ll T$.

It is apparent that much less information is available in the sampled data signal as it exists only as a pulse train, interspaced with gaps in the information between the sampled points. If the sampling frequency is high enough then this need not be troublesome (see also Sec. 10.4). The inevitable additional time delays in a sampled data system, however, has implications regarding the overall stability of the system. Digital control systems are therefore inherently less stable than their analogue counterparts.

In a sampled data system the z-transform is used to provide an algebraic technique for representing a sequence of digital data with respect to time. The symbol z for the digital system is analogous to the symbol s in the continuous system. The z-transform is associated with the time shifting in a difference equation as the Laplace operator s is associated with differentiation in a differential equation. The operators may be mathematically defined as follows:

$$s = \mathrm{d}/\mathrm{d}t = \mathrm{j}\omega$$
$$z = \mathrm{e}^{sT}$$

(13.1)

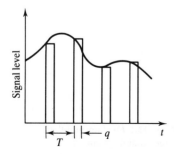

Figure 13.2 Discretization of a continuous signal.

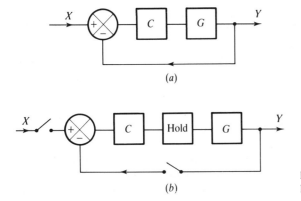

Figure 13.3 Continuous (*a*) and discrete (*b*) closed-loop control systems.

where T is the discrete time sampling interval. The operator z^{-1} represents a delay of one sampling interval.

On comparison with Eq. (11.34), it can be seen that the operator z^{-1}, i.e. e^{-sT}, is associated with a time delay. Equation (13.1) then gives a basic conformal mapping from the s-plane to the z-plane and provides the means for the analysis of discrete time control systems. The general method of solution involves the derivation of the closed-loop transfer function in terms of the Laplace variable. The equivalent discrete time system is then represented by introducing a 'zero-order hold' to account for the additional time delay in the discrete system (Fig. 13.3).

In Fig. 13.3, the output signal Y is continuous in nature. The data capture and analogue-to-digital conversion processes, however, means that the signal which is fed back to the controller exists as a pulse train. This is indicated in the figure by inserting a fictitious 'sampler' in the feedback line. Similarly, the input signal X may also be continuous, but when being processed within the computer environment it too exists as a discrete pulse train. The input line also therefore incorporates a fictitious sampler before entry into the computer environment. This in some ways is fortuitous since, for the purpose of analysis, all of the signals within the system are discrete. This eliminates the need to deal with a hybrid system involving both continuous and discrete signals.

The transfer function for a zero-order hold in terms of the Laplace variable is

$$[1 - e^{-sT}]/s \tag{13.2}$$

The zero-order hold is simply included in the evaluation of the closed-loop transfer function for the discrete time system. The next step in the solution procedure is to replace the Laplace transforms with their equivalent z-transforms. The resulting transfer function, in terms of z-transforms, can then be analysed for stability in much the same manner as the root locus method is used for continuous systems.

Representation of Discretely Sampled Data

The characteristics of a digital control loop are related to the sampling process associated with the conversion of transducer analogue data into a digital format and the converse between the controller output and the system being controlled. The sequence of events is as follows:

1. The process variable is measured and the corresponding analogue signal is converted into a digital value using an A/D converter.

2. This value is compared with the declared set point to give an error value upon which the controller transfer function operates to produce a control effort as a numerical value, preferably in the range 0–100 per cent.
3. The control effort derived is then converted by means of a final control element into the actual power supplied to the plant or process. This final control element involves a D/A converter which holds the value of the impulse received until the next value arrives in a staircase fashion, that is a 'zero-order hold' device.

The overall time for the sequencing cycle is the sampling frequency $f_s = 1/T$, where T is the sampling time interval.

It is most important to appreciate the physical nature of the variables at each stage in the loop and this is illustrated in Fig. 13.4. The discretely sampled data associated with the process variable and its derived values of error and control effort are displayed at time intervals of T. These are suffixed by an asterisk * to indicate that they are snapshots of the plant state at a particular time. The z-transform provides an algebraic way of mathematically presenting such sequences of digital information.

Consider the variation of the derived error signal E as shown in Fig. 13.5. Numerical values, quoted as percentages of the span of the measuring transducer, are inserted to illustrate the mathematical form of the z-transform equation in representing the variation of E with time. The sequence is shown as

$$E(n) = 80, 60, 40, 25, 12, 6, 0, 0, \ldots$$

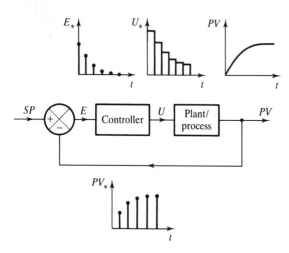

Figure 13.4 Nature of variables in a digital control loop.

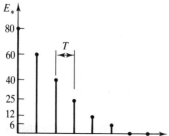

t **Figure 13.5** Variation of discrete error values with time.

and the corresponding z-transform of the sequence is defined by the sum:

$$E(z) = 80 + 60z^{-1} + 40z^{-2} + 25z^{-3} + 12z^{-4} + 6z^{-5}$$

This method of representation is particularly useful for handling time delays. For example, if the sequence was delayed by one sampling interval then it transposes to

$$0, 80, 60, 40, 25, 12, 6, 0, 0, \ldots$$

The corresponding z-transform is

$$E(z) = 80z^{-1} + 60z^{-2} + 40z^{-3} + \ldots$$

Notice that this is simply the first sequence multiplied by z^{-1}. Thus multiplication by z^{-1} denotes a one sampling interval delay. Similarly, multiplication by z^{-2} would denote a delay of two sampling intervals.

Generally, z-transform models of digitally sampled data, or it derivatives, can be obtained provided that the relationship between the continuous variation of the data with time is known in some mathematical form. For example, say that the error value can be expressed in the particular form:

$$E(t) = 100\,e^{-t} \tag{13.3}$$

which for the data sampled at intervals of T would yield

$$E(z) = 100[1 + e^{-T}\,z^{-1} + e^{-2T}\,z^{-2} + e^{-3T}\,z^{-3} + \ldots] \tag{13.4}$$

This relation is equivalent to the sum of a geometric series which is given as

$$\begin{aligned} \text{SUM} &= 100/[1 - e^{-T}\,z^{-1}] \\ &= 100z/[z - e^{-T}] \end{aligned} \tag{13.5}$$

which is the z-transform of $E(z)$. If the data was sampled at say a frequency of $10\,\text{Hz}$, i.e. $T = 0.1\,\text{s}$, then

$$E(z) = 100z/[z - 0.905] \tag{13.6}$$

In order to aid the design process associated with digital techniques, z-transforms of common sampled functions have been tabulated in a similar way to Laplace transforms. Examples of some of the more common Laplace transforms and their corresponding z-transforms are given in Table 13.1.

When applying digital techniques, the z-transform $G(z)$ must usually be derived from the corresponding transfer function for the operation expressed in terms of the Laplace variable s, i.e. $G(s)$. It should be noted that it is not simply a case of substituting z for s in the function. One basic approach is to obtain the partial fraction expansion of $G(s)$ to yield individual components which can then translate into z-transforms using a standard table such as that shown. Consider, for example, the transfer function given by $G(s) = 1/s(1 + 2s)$, or equivalently $G(s) = 0.5/s(s + 0.5)$. Although this form appears explicitly in the table is can be used to illustrate the technique.

Using partial fractions, the function can be rewritten as

$$G(s) = A/s + B/(1 + 2s) \tag{13.7}$$

from which $A = 1$ and $B = -2$. Hence

$$G(s) = (1/s) - 2/(1 + 2s) \tag{13.8}$$

Table 13.1 Common Laplace transforms and their corresponding z-transforms.

Laplace transform	z-transform
$1/s$	$z/(z-1)$
$1/s^2$	$Tz/(z-1)^2$
$1/s^3$	$\dfrac{T^2z(z+1)}{2(z-1)^3}$
$1/(s+a)$	$z/(z-e^{-aT})$
$1/(s+a)^2$	$\dfrac{Tze^{-aT}}{(z-e^{-aT})^2}$
$a/s(s+a)$	$\dfrac{z(1-e^{-aT})}{(z-1)(z-e^{-aT})}$
$s/(s+a)^2$	$\dfrac{z[z-e^{-aT}(1+aT)]}{(z-e^{-aT})^2}$

Rearranging the second term to conform to the appropriate Laplace transform given in the table gives

$$G(s) = 1/s - 1/(s+0.5)$$

The constituent parts result in the z-transform

$$G(z) = z/(z-1) - z/(z-e^{-0.5T})$$

After a little manipulation this resolves to

$$G(z) = z(1-e^{-0.5T})/[(z-1)(z-e^{-0.5T})] \tag{13.9}$$

This is as expected from the Laplace transform $a/s(s+a)$ as given in the table.

Example Obtain the corresponding z-transform of the Laplace transform given by $a/s^2(s+a)$.

Expanding the function into partial fractions gives

$$A/s^2 + B/(s+a) = a/s^2(s+a)$$

This results in $A = 1$ and $B = -1/s$, i.e.

$$\frac{1}{s^2} - \frac{1}{s(s+a)}$$

Expanding the second term gives

$$\frac{1}{s^2} - \left[\frac{C}{s} + \frac{D}{(s+a)} \right]$$

Consideration of the partial fraction expansion of the bracketed term gives $C = 1/a$ and $D = -1/a$. Thus the complete partial fraction expansion is

$$\frac{1}{s^2} - \frac{1/a}{s} + \frac{1/a}{(s+a)} = \frac{1}{s^2} - \frac{1}{a}\left[\frac{1}{s} - \frac{1}{(s+a)}\right]$$

The z-transform equivalent functions can now be read off from Table 13.1 and substituted to give

$$G(z) = \frac{Tz}{(z-1)^2} - \frac{1}{a}\left[\frac{z}{(z-1)} - \frac{z}{(z-e^{-aT})}\right]$$

$$= \frac{Tz}{(z-1)^2} - \frac{1}{a}\left[\frac{z[1 - e^{-aT}]}{(z-1)(z - e^{-aT})}\right]$$

Another method which can be used is to express $G(s)$ in the form $G(s) = N(s)/D(s)$, where $D(s)$ has a finite number of distinct roots. The corresponding z-transform, given without proof, is

$$G(z) = \sum_1^n \frac{N(x_n)}{D'(x_n)}\frac{1}{(1 - e^{x_n T}z^{-1})} \tag{13.10}$$

where $D' = \partial D/\partial s$, and x_n are the roots of the equation $D(s) = 0$.

Example Obtain the corresponding z-transform of the Laplace transform given as

$$G(s) = 1/[(s+a)(s+b)]$$

$N(s) = 1$ and $D(s) = (s+a)(s+b) = s^2 + (a+b)s + ab$, hence $D' = 2s + a + b$. The roots of $D(s)$ are $x_1 = -a$ and $x_2 = -b$. Inserting these into Eq. (13.10) gives

$$G(z) = \frac{1}{(-a+b)}\frac{1}{(1 - e^{-aT}z^{-1})} + \frac{1}{(a-b)}\frac{1}{(1 - e^{-bT}z^{-1})}$$

$$= \frac{1}{a-b}\left[\frac{z}{z - e^{-bT}} - \frac{z}{z - e^{-aT}}\right]$$

$$= \frac{1}{a-b}\left[\frac{z[e^{-bT} - e^{-aT}]}{(z - e^{-bT})(z - e^{-aT})}\right]$$

The method using the partial fraction expansion may be used to check the validity of the resulting z-transform.

The z-transform for a Closed-loop System

Before z-transforms for the digital control loop illustrated in Fig. 13.1 can be derived, it is necessary to consider the nature of the input and the output to the plant/process. The input, associated with the digital-to-analogue conversion hardware, is basically a zero-order hold element which effectively supplies a control effort to the process in a pulsed form. The nature of the output from the controller relates to the analogue-to-digital conversion which is indicative of the discrete sampling process. Thus the input is a step and the output sets the sampling characteristics of the loop on the basis of the sample time T. This arrangement, with the nature of the appropriate signals, is shown in Fig. 13.6.

What is required is the z-transform for this complete arrangement, $G'(z)$, and not simply the equivalence of $G(s)$ alone. This is usually referred to as the 'pulse transfer function'. The total

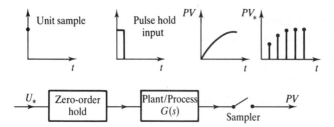

Figure 13.6 Discrete digital sampling in a digital control loop.

sampled response consists of the difference between the positive stepped input to the process and the same value delayed by one sampling period. This will give the required pulse transfer function and it can be written as

$$G'(z) = (1/s)G(s) - (e^{-sT})(1/s)G(s)$$
$$= \text{product of } (1 - z^{-1}) \text{ and the } z\text{-transform of } [(1/s)G(s)] \tag{13.11}$$
$$= \text{product of } [(z-1)/z] \text{ and the } z\text{-transform of } [(1/s)G(s)]$$

This gives the z-transform equivalent of all the elements shown in Fig. 13.6.

The closed-loop transfer function in terms of the z-transform is derived in a similar way to that for a continuous system with $G'(z)$ representing the pulse transfer function associated with the hold, plant/process and the sampling routine.

Consider the basic loop as shown in Fig. 13.7. The forward path transfer function is

$$PV(z) = G'(z)\,U(z)$$
$$= G'(z)\,C(z)\,E(z)$$

and the closed-loop transfer function is

$$\frac{PV(z)}{SP(z)} = \frac{C(z)\,G'(z)}{1 + C(z)\,G'(z)} \tag{13.12}$$

Note that this is similar in form to the transfer function for a system with a continuous feedback loop.

The procedure for evaluating the response of a plant/process to a step input with digital control using a sample time of T is as follows:

1. Obtain the pulse transfer function $G'(z)$ from the known form for $G(s)$.
2. Express the controller transfer function $C(s)$ in z-transform format.
3. Evaluate the closed-loop transfer function for $PV(z)/SP(z)$.
4. Algebraically manipulate this expression to yield a discrete time ordered equation which formulates the current value of PV, say PV_i, in terms of the past values of PV and SP. This is obtained using the relationships:

$$PV(z)z^{-1} = PV_{i-1}$$

where the subscript $i - 1$ denotes one sampling period back in time. Similarly, $PV(z)z^{-2} = PV_{i-2}$, etc.

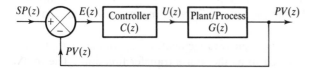

Figure 13.7 Closed-loop control system in terms of z-transforms.

Proportional Control Using Digital Techniques

For a proportional control strategy, the controller transfer function $C(s)$ and the corresponding z-transform is simply the controller gain K. Taking as an example the plant transfer function to be that for a first-order system with a system gain $k = 1$, the required pulse transfer function is

$$G'(z) = \text{the product of } (z - 1)/z \text{ and the } z\text{-transform of } [1/s(1 + \tau s)]$$

$$= \frac{(z - 1)}{z} \frac{z}{(z - 1)} \frac{(1 - e^{-T/\tau})}{(z - e^{-T/\tau})}$$

$$= C_1/(z - C_2)$$

where $C_1 = 1 - e^{-T/\tau}$ and $C_2 = e^{-T/\tau}$. Hence the z-transform for the closed loop is

$$\frac{PV(z)}{SP(z)} = \frac{C(z)G'(z)}{1 + C(z)G'(z)} = \frac{[KC_1/(z - C_2)]}{1 + [KC_1/(z - C_2)]}$$

$$= \frac{KC_1}{z - C_2 + KC_1} = \frac{a}{z + b} \tag{13.13}$$

where $a = KC_1$ and $b = (KC_1 - C_2)$.

It is now necessary to transform this equation into a discrete time stepped form which expresses the current value of the process variable PV_i, as a function of previous values. This can be obtained by dividing the numerator and denominator by z raised to the power corresponding to the maximum value in the denominator. In this example, the dividing factor is simply z, i.e.

$$PV(z)/SP(z) = az^{-1}/(1 + bz^{-1})$$

or

$$PV(z) = a\,SP(z)z^{-1} - b\,PV(z)z^{-1}$$

Writing this as a finite time difference equation gives

$$PV_i = a\,SP_{i-1} - b\,PV_{i-1} \tag{13.14}$$

For a step input, $SP = 1$ for $i > 1$. The starting values are $i = 1$, $SP = 1$ and $PV = 0$.

Equations of this form are easily programmed for a computer to produce a graphical time response of PV to a step input for declared values of system time constant τ, controller gain K and sample time T.

Figures 13.8 and 13.9 illustrate the effect of the sample time on the predicted response of the system using the z-transform technique outlined with $\tau = 1$ and $K = 10$. These figures clearly illustrate the effect of a long time delay on the system due to the insufficiently rapid sampling of the process variable. Increasing the sample time leads to an execssively oscillatory response, and eventually to instability. The choice of a satisfactory sampling interval is considered in Sec. 4.14

Figure 13.8 Proportional control of a first-order system with $K = 10$ and $T = 0.01$ s.

Figure 13.9 Proportional control of a first-order system with $K = 10$ and $T = 0.15$ s.

and Sec. 10.4. It should be noted, however, that in a closed-loop control system, the sampling interval is also dependent on the system time constant and the controller settings.

The z-transform for a PID Controller

The PID control law for a continuous control system, as outlined in Sec. 11.6, is

$$U = K[E + (1/T_i)\int E \, dt + T_d(dE/dt)]$$

The integral term can be approximated numerically as a summation of rectangular elements which at any time t can be expressed as

$$I_i = I_{i-1} + E_i T \qquad (13.15)$$

where I_{i-1} is the value of the integral term up to the instant $t - T$.

Alternatively, in z-transform notation:

$$I(z) = I(z)z^{-1} + E(z)T$$

From which

$$I(z) = [Tz/(z-1)]E(z) \qquad (13.16)$$

Similarly, the derivative term can be approximated as the slope of the line joining the current E value and the previous E value, i.e. a backwards difference approximation.

$$D_i = [E_i - E_{i-1}]/T \qquad (13.17)$$

or

$$D(z) = [E(z) - E(z)z^{-1}]T$$
$$= [(z-1)/Tz]E(z) \qquad (13.18)$$

The integral and derivative terms in z-transform notation can now be substituted into the full three-term expression to give $C(z)$:

$$C(z) = U(z)/E(z) = K[1 + (1/T_i)\{Tz/(z-1)\} + T_d\{(z-1)/Tz\}] \qquad (13.19)$$

A P+I Strategy Using Digital Techniques

For a P + I strategy

$$C(z) = U(z)/E(z) = K[1 + (1/T_i)\{Tz/(z-1)\}]$$

Application of this strategy to a first-order system with unity gain gave the following pulse transfer function

$$G'(z) = C_1/(z - C_2)$$

where $C_1 = (1 - e^{-T/\tau})$ and $C_2 = e^{-T/\tau}$ as shown before. Substituting for $C(z)$ and $G'(z)$ in the closed-loop transfer function, i.e. Eq. (13.12), gives

$$\frac{PV(z)}{SP(z)} = \frac{K[1 + (1/T_i)\{Tz/(z-1)\}]\,[C_1/(z-C_2)]}{1 + K[1 + (1/T_i)\{Tz/(z-1)\}]\,[C_1/(z-C_2)]}$$

Multiplying top and bottom by $(z - C_2)$ and $(z - 1)$ gives

$$\frac{PV(z)}{SP(z)} = \frac{KC_1[z - 1 + Tz/T_i]}{(z - C_2)(z - 1) + KC_1[z - 1 + Tz/T_i]}$$

Multiplying top and bottom by z^{-2} gives

$$\frac{PV(z)}{SP(z)} = \frac{KC_1[z^{-1} - z^{-2} + z^{-1}(T/T_i)]}{1 - (1 + C_2)z^{-1} + C_2 z^{-2} + KC_1[z^{-1} - z^{-2} + z^{-1}(T/T_i)]}$$

$$= \frac{KC_1(1 + T/T_i)z^{-1} - KC_1 z^{-2}}{1 + [KC_1(1 + T/T_i) - (1 + C_2)]z^{-1} + [C_2 - KC_1]z^{-2}}$$

Defining the following terms:

$$a = KC_1[1 + T/T_i] = K[1 - e^{-T/\tau}][1 + T/T_i]$$
$$b = KC_1 = K[1 - e^{-T/\tau}]$$
$$c = [1 + C_2] - KC_1[1 + T/T_i] = [1 + e^{-T/\tau}] - K[1 - e^{-T/\tau}][1 + T/T_i]$$
$$d = KC_1 - C_2 = K[1 - e^{-T/\tau}] - e^{-T/\tau}$$

then

$$\frac{PV(z)}{SP(z)} = \frac{az^{-1} - bz^{-2}}{1 - cz^{-1} - dz^{-2}} \qquad (13.20)$$

Thus

$$PV(z)[1 - cz^{-1} - dz^{-2}] = SP(z)[az^{-1} - bz^{-2}]$$

or

$$PV(z) = a\,SP(z)z^{-1} - b\,SP(z)z^{-2} + c\,PV(z)z^{-1} + d\,PV(z)z^{-2}$$

Writing this as a finite time difference equation, we obtain

$$PV_i = a\,SP_{i-1} - b\,SP_{i-2} + c\,PV_{i-1} + d\,PV_{i-2} \qquad (13.21)$$

For a step input, at time $t = 0$, $PV = 0$ and $SP = 1$.

The solution of Eq. (13.21) is computed in BASIC Program 13.1, which includes a graphical display of the response.

Figure 13.10 illustrates the response of the first-order system with $\tau = 1$ and $k = 1$ when a P + I control strategy is applied using a controller gain $K = 2$ and an integral time $T_i = 0.1$. When the discrete time sample T is sufficiently small, i.e. taken as 0.01 s, the output response compares favourably with that obtained for continuous control.

If, however, the time step is increased to 0.36 s then the simulated plant responds in a much more oscillatory manner for the same controller settings. This is illustrated in Fig. 13.11.

When the sampling time is increased beyond the value of 0.36 s, the simulated system behaves in an unstable manner. With digital control, the sampling time which would cause the system to go unstable depends on the values of the system time constant and also the particular controller settings.

Program 13.1 Digital control of a first-order system with a P + I controller.

```
SCREEN 9: COLOR 4, 7: KEY OFF: CLS
DIM PV(300)
PV(0) = 0: PV(1) = 0
CLS
LOCATE 4, 6: INPUT "Controller gain, K = "; KS
LOCATE 6, 6: INPUT "Integral time const, Ti = "; TI
LOCATE 8, 6: INPUT "System gain, k = "; KP
LOCATE 10, 6: INPUT "System time constant, tau = "; TAU
LOCATE 12, 6: INPUT "Sampling Time, T = "; DT
A = KS * (1 - EXP(-DT / TAU)) * (1 + DT / TI)
B = KS * (1 - EXP(-DT / TAU))
C = (1 + EXP(-DT / TAU)) - KS * (1 - EXP(-DT / TAU)) * (1 + DT / TI)
D = KS * (1 - EXP(-DT / TAU)) - EXP(-DT / TAU)
PV(0) = 0: PV(1) = 0
FOR I = 2 TO 300
IF I >= 2 THEN SP1 = 1 ELSE SP1 = 0
IF I >= 3 THEN SP2 = 1 ELSE SP2 = 0
PV(I) = A * SP1 - B * SP2 + C * PV(I - 1) + D * PV(I - 2)
NEXT I
CLS
LOCATE 2, 6: PRINT "                    First order system with a P + I Controller"
LOCATE 5, 6: PRINT "PV"
LOCATE 16, 60: PRINT "time"
LINE (40, 300)-(40, 100)
LINE (40, 200)-(500, 200)
T = 0 - DT
FOR K = 1 TO 300
T = T + DT
IF T > 5 THEN GOTO 100
A1 = 40 + T * 50
B1 = 300 - PV(K - 1) * 100
A2 = 40 + (T + DT) * 50
B2 = 300 - PV(K) * 100
LINE (A1, B1)-(A2, B2), 1
NEXT K
100
LOCATE 22, 2
END
```

Stability in Discrete Time Systems

As seen in the previous sections, an incorrectly chosen sample time can result in a system becoming unstable due to the imposed time delay associated with the sampling process. The critical value of T can be obtained by considering the representation of the poles and zeros of the closed-loop transfer function, $PV(z)/SP(z)$, in the z-plane. Analysis of the poles and zeros in the transfer function is analogous to the root locus method for continuous systems, described in Sec. 11.8.

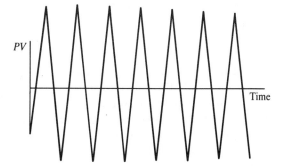

Figure 13.10 System response with $K = 2$, $T_i = 0.1$ s and $T = 0.01$ s.

Figure 13.11 System response with $K = 2$, $T_i = 0.1$ s and $T = 0.36$ s.

If the closed-loop transfer function is written in terms of a numerator $N(z)$ and a denominator $D(z)$ then the poles and zeros are defined as the roots of the equations $D(z) = 0$ and $N(z) = 0$, respectively. These roots may contain both real and complex components and the resulting plot is termed the 'z-plane'.

When using the z-transform method of analysis for the digital control of a system, the position of the poles in the z-plane are dependent on the magnitude of the sample time chosen. For example, consider a process having a transfer function $G(s) = 1/s$ and controlled using a proportional control strategy. Using the method outlined previously, the corresponding pulse transfer function, and closed-loop z-transform function, are respectively:

$$G'(z) = T/(z-1)$$
$$PV(z)/SP(z) = KT/[z - (1 - KT)]$$

(13.22)

i.e.

$$D(z) = z - (1 - KT)$$

(13.23)

The transfer function has a single pole at $(1 - KT)$, and no zeros. For the system to be stable, the single pole on the real axis should lie in the range $(-1 < z < +1)$. Thus for a pole location at -1, the value of KT must be no more than 2 to remain within the limit of stability. If (say), $K = 5$, then the sample time must be no greater than 0.4 for the system to remain stable. The locus of the pole for KT ranging between 0 and 3 is shown as a z-plane plot in Fig. 13.12.

Multiplying the numerator and denominator of Eq. (13.22) by z^{-1}, and rearranging, gives the finite time difference equation:

$$PV_i = KTSP_{i-1} + (1 - KT)PV_{i-1}$$

(13.24)

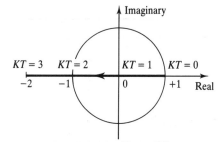

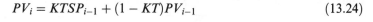

Figure 13.12 z-plane plot of the pole locus of Eq. (13.23).

For a step input at time $t = 0$, $SP = 1$ and $PV = 0$. Equation (13.24) may therefore be written for time $t > 0$ in the form:

$$PV_i = KT + (1 - KT)PV_{i-1} \qquad (13.25)$$

Solving Eq. (13.25) for various values of KT generates the results given in Table 13.2.

At $KT = 0.5$, the pole location is at $+0.5$ on the real axis of the z-plane and the output response is similar to an overdamped system. With $KT = 1$, the pole is located at zero on the real axis and the output response is essentially critically damped. When $KT = 1.5$, the pole is located at -0.5 on the real axis of the z-plane and the output response is oscillatory. A value of $KT = 2$, with the pole located at -1, corresponds to marginal stability and the output is a self-sustaining oscillation. However when $KT = 3$, an unstable response is exhibited.

A general observation can be made at this point to the effect that when the single real pole is located in the positive half of the z-plane, the output response is non-oscillatory. Similarly, when the single real pole is located in the negative half of the z-plane, the output is oscillatory with marginal stability indicated when the pole is located at -1 on the real axis.

Example Determine the poles and zero locations of the closed-loop transfer function given as

$$PV(z)/SP(z) = (z + 1)/[(z - 0.8)(z - 0.6)]$$

and comment on the system response.

The transfer function has one zero at -1 and two poles at 0.8 and 0.6. Since both poles lie within the unit circle, then the system is stable. The pole at 0.8 is associated with the output response which takes the longer time to die away and this therefore is the dominant pole.

Example Determine the poles and zero locations of the closed-loop transfer function given as

$$PV(z)/SP(z) = z/(z + 2z + 5)$$

and comment on the system response.

The function has one zero at 0 and two complex poles given by

$$[-2 +/- j\sqrt{2^2 - 4 \times 5}]/2 = -1 +/- j2$$

Since the complex poles lie outside of the unit circle, then the system is unstable. The output response would be oscillatory with increasing amplitude.

Table 13.2 Results for PV, with KT ranging from 0.5 to 3.0.

Time			PV at KT value		
	0.5	1.0	1.5	2.0	3.0
0	0	0	0	0	0
T	0.5	1	1.5	2	3
$2T$	0.75	1	0.75	0	−3
$3T$	0.875	1	1.125	2	9
$4T$	0.9375	1	0.9375	0	−15
$5T$	0.96875	1	1.03125	2	33
$6T$	0.984375	1	0.993375	0	−63

Example A simple process is effectively modelled by an open loop transfer function in the form $G(s) = 1/s(s + 1)$. A proportional control strategy is then used in a digital control loop with unity feedback, to control the process. The sampling time is 0.1 s. By consideration of the locus of the closed-loop poles, assess the stability of the system for variable gain K increasing from a minimum value of 0.5

The pulse transfer function is given as

$$G'(z) = (z - 1)/z \times \text{the } z\text{-transform of } [(1/s)G(s)]$$

It is required to determine the z-transform of $1/s^2(s + 1)$. This particular function was considered earlier in the general form $a/s^2(s + a)$. The particular z-transform, with the constant $a = 1$ is

$$G(z) = \frac{Tz}{(z - 1)^2} - \frac{z[1 - e^{-T}]}{(z - 1)(z - e^{-T})}$$

Thus the pulse transfer function is

$$G'(z) = \frac{(z - 1)}{z}\left[\frac{Tz}{(z - 1)^2} - \frac{z[1 - e^{-T}]}{(z - 1)(z - e^{-T})}\right] = \frac{T}{(z - 1)} - \frac{(1 - e^{-T})}{(z - e^{-T})}$$

The closed-loop transfer function is

$$\frac{PV(z)}{SP(z)} = \frac{KG'(z)}{1 + KG'(z)}$$

Some algebraic manipulation results in

$$\frac{PV(z)}{SP(z)} = \frac{K[T(z - e^{-T}) - (z - 1)(1 - e^{-T})]}{(z - 1)(z - e^{-T}) + K[T(z - e^{-T}) - (z - 1)(1 - e^{-T})]}$$

For a sampling time $T = 0.1$ s, the closed-loop transfer function becomes

$$\frac{PV(z)}{SP(z)} = \frac{K[0.1(z - 0.905) - (z - 1)0.905]}{(z - 1)(z - 0.905) + K[0.1(z - 905) - (z - 1)0.905]}$$

Grouping terms gives

$$\frac{PV(z)}{SP(z)} = \frac{0.005Kz}{z^2 - (1.905 - 0.005K)z + 0.905} \tag{13.26}$$

The transfer function has one zero at 0, and two complex roots given by

$$[(1.905 - 0.005K) +/- j\sqrt{(1.905 - 0.005K)^2 - 4 \times 0.905}]/2$$

For K varying from 0.5 to 761, the complex roots describe a circle of centre zero and radius 0.9513. For higher values of gain, the roots follow asymptotic paths where one root asymptotes to the single zero in the transfer function and the other root asymptotes to $-$infinity along the real axis. The root locus is shown in Fig. 13.13.

The critical value of K, where the locus crosses the point -1 is given by evaluating the real part of the roots to -1, i.e. $(1.905 - 0.005K)/2 = -1$, from which $K = 3.905/0.005 = 781$. Thus, provided that the gain is less than 781, then the system will remain stable for a sampling period of 0.1 s. If the sampling time were to be increased, then the maximum gain for marginal stability would be correspondingly reduced.

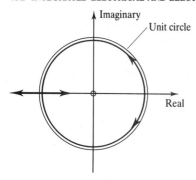

Figure 13.13 Root locus for the transfer function given as Eq. (13.26).

From Eq. (13.26) in the last example, the closed-loop transfer function can be written in the form:

$$\frac{PV(z)}{SP(z)} = \frac{az}{z^2 - bz + c} \tag{13.27}$$

where $a = 0.005K$, $b = (1.905 - 0.005K)$ and $c = 0.905$.
Multiplying the numerator and denominator of Eq. (13.27) by (z^{-2}) gives

$$\frac{PV(z)}{SP(z)} = \frac{az^{-1}}{1 - bz^{-1} + cz^{-2}}$$

or

$$PV(z) - b\,PV(z)z^{-1} + c\,PV(z)z^{-2} = a\,SP(z)z^{-1}$$

Writing this as a finite time sequence gives

$$PV_i = a\,SP_{i-1} + b\,PV_{i-1} - c\,PV_{i-2} \tag{13.28}$$

Solving Eq. (13.28) for a limited range of values of gain gives the output responses shown in Fig. 13.14. Also shown in the figure are the corresponding locations of the complex poles in the z-plane for the stated values of gain K.

It can be seen that when the poles are complex and contained within the unit circle, then the output response is stable and oscillatory. The frequency of the oscillation increases as the poles move from the positive real half of the z-plane into the negative half.

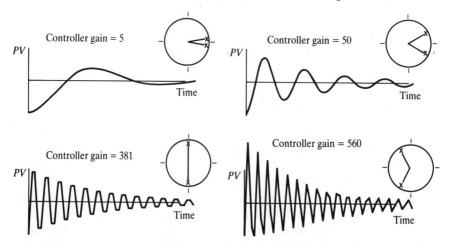

Figure 13.14 Output responses and complex root locations for Eq. (13.27).

At this juncture some general observations can be made regarding the pole locations in a z-plane.

1. Poles located within the unit circle correspond to output sequences which die away with time. The closer the poles are to the origin, the faster the decay rate for a given sampling time.
2. Poles on the positive real axis correspond to non-oscillatory responses when $0 < z < 1$. A decaying oscillatory response occurs when the poles lie on the real axis in the range $-1 < z < 0$.
3. Complex conjugate pairs of poles within the unit circle correspond to a decaying oscillatory response. An unstable oscillation occurs when the complex poles lie outside the unit circle.

The previous example gives some insight on the effect that increasing gain has on the stability of a digital control system. Increasing the sampling time has a similar effect but we must return to the basic closed-loop transfer function in order to assess the influence of increasing the sample time. In most instances this involves a more complicated analysis since the sampling time T can appear in a transfer function in a number of various ways. In general it is impossible to predict the effect of increasing the sampling time on the closed-loop pole position without a detailed analysis of the particular case.

Example A process is modelled by the open-loop transfer function $G(s) = 1/(1 + s)$. A proportional digital control strategy with unity feedback is to be used in the forward path, with a fixed gain of $K = 10$. Investigate the effect on increasing the sampling time on the stability of the system.

The pulse transfer function is $G'(z) = [(z - 1)/z] \times z$-transform of $[1/s(1 + s)]$
From Table 13.1, this gives $G'(z) = [(z - 1)/z] \times [z(1 - e^{-T})/\{(z - 1)(z - e^{-T})\}]$, i.e.

$$G'(z) = (1 - e^{-T})/(z - e^{-T})$$

The closed-loop transfer function is $KG'(z)/[1 + KG'(z)]$, i.e.

$$\frac{PV(z)}{SP(z)} = \frac{K(1 - e^{-T})}{(z - e^{-T}) + K(1 - e^{-T})}$$

For $K = 10$, the transfer function becomes

$$\frac{PV(z)}{SP(z)} = \frac{10(1 - e^{-T})}{z + 10 - 11 e^{-T}}$$

The transfer function has no zeros and a single pole at $(11 e^{-T} - 10)$.
For marginal stability

$$(11 e^{-T} - 10) = -1$$

Solving for T gives

$$T = -\ln(9/11) = 0.2\,\text{s}$$

The maximum sampling time for stable operation therefore is 0.2 s. For a very low sampling time, say 0.000 001 s, the pole is located at $11\,e^{-0.000\,001} - 10 = +0.9999$. The locus of the pole, as the sampling time increases from 0 to 0.2 s, therefore follows the real axis from $+1$ to -1. Note that the digital control system with a very low sampling time equates to an equivalent continuous system.

By locating the z-plane poles we can immediately test whether a sampled data system is stable or not. The mathematics becomes rather laborious, however, as the order of the characteristic equation in z increases. For most practical systems, pole locus plotting is best actioned using one of the various commercial software packages which are currently available for the purpose.

One further useful property, however, related to the location of the poles in the z-plane, is worthy of some consideration. The location of a pole, or pair of complex poles, within the unit circle can be represented in the form:

$$z = M e^{+/-j\theta} = M, +/- \underline{/\theta} \tag{13.29}$$

where M is the length of the radius from the centre of the unit circle to the pole location, and θ is the angle subtended by the radius relative to the positive real axis.

If the sampling frequency is known, i.e. $f_s = 1/T$, then the transient frequency of the output oscillation is given by

$$f = f_s(\theta/2\pi) \tag{13.30}$$

Furthermore, the amplitude decay rate between successive peaks in the output response is given directly by the numerical value of M.

Example A closed-loop transfer function has a pair of poles at $z = 0.6 +/- 60°$. If the sampling times was 0.1 s, determine the frequency of oscillation of the output response.
The sampling frequency $= f_s = 1/T = 1/0.1 = 10$ Hz.
Thus the frequency of the output response $= f = 10/(60/360) = 1.67$ Hz.

Another way of viewing this result is that for one cycle of the output response, six samples are measured. If the angle subtended had been, say 30°, then the transient output would have been at 0.83 Hz, and there would then have been 12 samples measured over one cycle of the output response.

If the poles lie in the negative half of the unit circle, and particularly if the angle subtended approaches 180°, then the transient oscillation frequency of the output is very close to half of the sampling frequency. That is there are only two samples measured over one cycle of the output. Under these conditions, while the system is nominally stable, there is a greater likelihood of problems occurring due to aliasing errors. For poles which lie in the negative half of the unit circle it is desirable therefore that the value of M is small such that the transient period of the output oscillation dies away more rapidly.

When the poles lie on the positive axis, the angle $\theta = 0°$ and the output response is non-oscillatory. It can be concluded therefore that complex poles should ideally lie either in the positive half of the z-plane, or close to the centre in the negative half. Note also how the dynamic response parameters given by the location of the poles in the z-plane has to be interpreted in relation to a known sampling frequency. If the sampling frequency is not known, then no real time significance can be attached to the pole locations.

13.3 STATE-VARIABLE TECHNIQUE FOR SAMPLED DATA SYSTEMS

In a discretely sampled system the relationship between the output and the input can be represented in terms of z-transforms, or as a time difference equation as shown previously. In any system described by linear difference equations, however, a block diagram can be constructed using the basic building elements of the adder, the amplifier and the unit time delay.

The unit time delay, which is analagous to the integrator in continuous systems, is depicted in Fig. 13.15.

The input to the unit time delay appears at the output one period later, or delayed by a time T. If the difference equation has, for example, the form given in Eq. (13.31), then the block diagram for the system is as shown in Fig. 13.16, and

$$y_i = X_i - ay_{i-1} - by_{i-2} \tag{13.31}$$

The system may also be handled in z-transform notation and a block diagram constructed to represent the system in terms of the appropriate operators.

Following the procedures outlined in Sec. 13.2 a closed-loop digital control system can be represented by the appropriate z-transform operators. The closed-loop transfer operator may subsequently be manipulated and reduced to a finite difference, or time sequence equation. For the P+I control strategy used in conjunction with a process which can be represented as a first-order differential equation (see Sec. 13.2), the resulting time sequence equation was shown to be

$$PV_i = a\,SP_{i-1} - b\,SP_{i-2} + c\,PV_{i-1} + d\,PV_{i-2} \tag{13.21}$$

where a, b, c and d are as defined in Sec. 13.2 and i is an integer variable used to denote the time periods. The block diagram to represent the difference equation is shown in Fig. 13.17.

The appropriate state variables are chosen as

$$X_1 = PV_{i-2} : X_2 = PV_{i-1}$$

The state-variable equations can be written in the forms:

$$(X_1)_{k+1} = (X_2)_k \tag{13.32}$$

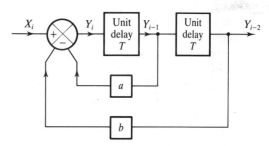

Figure 13.16 Block representation of Eq. (13.31).

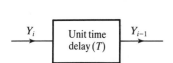

Figure 13.15 The unit time delay.

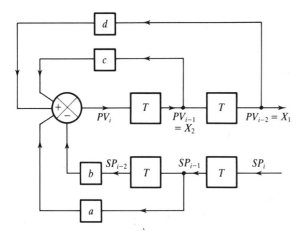

Figure 13.17 Block representation of Eq. (13.21).

$$(X_2)_{k+1} = a\,SP_k - b\,SP_{k-1} + c\,(X_2)_k + d\,(X_1)_k \tag{13.33}$$

where k is an integer variable used to denote the time periods.

In matrix notation the state-variable representation is

$$\begin{bmatrix} (X_1)_{k+1} \\ (X_2)_{k+1} \end{bmatrix} = \begin{bmatrix} 0 & 1 \\ d & c \end{bmatrix} \begin{bmatrix} (X_1)_k \\ (X_2)_k \end{bmatrix} + (a\,SP_k - b\,SP_{k-1}) \begin{bmatrix} 0 \\ 1 \end{bmatrix} \tag{13.34}$$

$$PV_i = \begin{bmatrix} 0 & 1 \end{bmatrix} \begin{bmatrix} (X_1)_{k+1} \\ (X_2)_{k+1} \end{bmatrix} + (a\,SP_k - b\,SP_{k-1})[0] \tag{13.35}$$

With any given initial conditions, Eqs (13.32) and (13.33) may be solved simultaneously for discrete time steps in T. A suitable program in BASIC is given at Program 13.2. Figure 13.18 shows the response to a step input when $K = 2$, $T_i = 0.05$ and T is set at 0.1 s.

Program 13.2 State variable solution for a digital P + I controller and a first-order system.

```
SCREEN 9: COLOR 4, 7: KEY OFF: CLS
DIM X2(300), X1(300)
X2(1) = 0: X1(1) = 0
CLS
LOCATE 4, 6: INPUT "Controller gain, K = "; KS
LOCATE 6, 6: INPUT "Integral time const, Ti = "; TI
KP = 1
LOCATE 10, 6: INPUT "System time constant, tau = "; TAU
LOCATE 12, 6: INPUT "Sampling Time, T = "; DT
A = KS * (1 - EXP(-DT / TAU)) * (1 + DT / TI)
B = KS * (1 - EXP(-DT / TAU))
C = (1 + EXP(-DT / TAU)) - KS * (1 - EXP(-DT / TAU)) * (1 + DT / TI)
D = KS * (1 - EXP(-DT / TAU)) - EXP(-DT / TAU)
X2(0) = 0
FOR I = 2 TO 300
IF I >= 2 THEN SP1 = 1 ELSE SP1 = 0
IF I >= 3 THEN SP2 = 1 ELSE SP2 = 0
X1(I) = X2(I - 1)
X2(I) = A * SP1 - B * SP2 + C * X1(I) + D * X2(I - 2)
NEXT I
CLS
LOCATE 2, 6: PRINT "                 First order system with a P + I Controller"
LOCATE 4, 6: PRINT "System time constant, Tau = "; TAU
LOCATE 4, 40: PRINT "Controller integral time, Ti = "; TI
LOCATE 6, 6: PRINT "System gain, k = "; KP
LOCATE 6, 40: PRINT "Controller gain, K = "; KS
LOCATE 8, 6: PRINT "  Time Domain                      Phase Plane"
LOCATE 20, 10: PRINT "Sampling interval = "; DT
LINE (40, 300)-(40, 100)
LINE (40, 200)-(300, 200)
T = 0 - DT
```

```
FOR K = 2 TO 300
T = T + DT
IF T > 5 THEN GOTO 100
A1 = 40 + T * 50
B1 = 300 - X2(K - 1) * 100
A2 = 40 + (T + DT) * 50
B2 = 300 - X2(K) * 100
LINE (A1, B1)-(A2, B2), 1
NEXT K
100
LINE (440, 300)-(440, 100)
LINE (320, 200)-(600, 200)
LINE (540, 210)-(540, 190)
FOR K = 2 TO 300
A1 = 440 + X2(K - 1) * 100
B1 = 200 - (X2(K - 1) - X1(K - 1)) / DT * 10
A2 = 440 + X2(K) * 100
B2 = 200 - (X2(K) - X1(K)) / DT * 10
LINE (A1, B1)-(A2, B2), 1
NEXT K
LOCATE 22, 2
```

First order system with a P + I controller

System time constant, $\tau = 1$ Controller integral time, $T_i = 0.05$
System gain, $k = 1$ Controller gain, $K = 2$

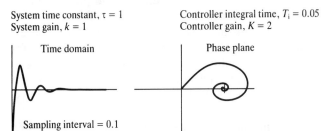

Time domain   Phase plane

Sampling interval = 0.1

Figure 13.18 System response to a step input.

The phase plane trajectory is shown where the parameter $(X_2 - X_1)/T$ is plotted against X_2. In terms of the actual control system, this plot is equivalent to a graph of the discrete time rate of change of the process variable against the process variable itself. This gives a direct comparison with the equivalent continuous system outlined in Sec. 11.11. The technique outlined, in some respects, simply constitutes an alternative numerical method for solving the finite time sequence equations. While this may be true, the method does present another useful means of assessing the system stability in the form of the phase plane trajectory. In general terms, the phase plane trajectories which converge on a single point, or on a limit cycle, denote stable systems. Diverging trajectories denote unstable systems.

13.4 MICROPROCESSOR-BASED INDUSTRIAL CONTROLLERS

Following the inception of the microprocessor in the mid-1970s, the logical progression was to increase component density and to incorporate memory and input/output interface facilities onto the one device. These so-called single-chip microcomputers, or SCMs, are usually referred to as microcontrollers and they provide the intelligence required for such applications as measuring equipment and industrial control.

The architecture of a typical SCM is similar to that of a traditional 'single card computer', and comprises:

1. CPU
2. Memory—RAM and ROM
3. Parallel and serial ports
4. Timers
5. Hardware interrupt lines
6. Analogue-to-digital converters

There are a large number of SCMs currently available and some display all of the above features. This greatly simplifies the designer's task since many of the functions that previously necessitated separate chips in a microprocessor system, are included on a single integrated circuit. Examples of some of the popular devices currently available include:

The Mitsubishi Series 740 of 8-bit CMOS Microcontrollers

These are ultra-low-cost devices which are available in a variety of different forms. For example, a Mitsubishi designer's kit based on the M50734 SCM includes a user's manual and software manual along with designer's notes, and comes complete with such facilities as four 8-bit I/O ports, a four-channel multiplexed 8-bit A/D converter, timers and counters, a pulse width modulation output and a single-channel full duplex UART with a built-in baud rate generator.

There is, unfortunately, no internal memory and external RAM and EPROM must be memory mapped through appropriate decoding chips into the system. With a 16-bit address bus, however, 64K bytes of memory can be accessed although a specific area is designated for special function registers associated with the I/O availability, system stack and interrupt vectors. A typical arrangement for the memory map in a control application would be 2K bytes of RAM at the bottom end of memory, i.e. 0000–07FF, and an 8K EPROM at the top end of memory, i.e. C000–FFFF.

The additional hardware required to make the microcontroller functional is a 5 V, +/– 10% power supply, a crystal clock oscillator running at 8 MHz and a RESET control. The architecture is based on six main registers similar to those used in the popular 6502 microprocessor and the instruction set is upwards compatible but includes additional mnemonic coding.

An alternative to the Mitsubishi M50734 is the M50747-PGYS which has an 8K EPROM, mounted piggy-back fashion onto the top of the SCM. Since 192 bytes of internal RAM are available, no external memory with associated decoding is necessary. This particular model has a number of bi-directional 8-bit I/O ports and timers, but has no A/D conversion facilities.

The Motorola MC 68705R3 Microcontroller

This is a powerful SCM which comprises an 8-bit CPU with 112 bytes of RAM, about 4K bytes of EPROM, four 8-bit I/O ports, a timer and a four-channel A/D converter. The integrated circuit which makes this possible requires more on board transistors than the 16-bit microprocessor used in the Apple Mackintosh microcomputer.

The EPROM facility for the user software is not of the piggy-back variety, but is embedded into the package. This has the distinct disadvantage of requiring a specialized software development system. The inherent A/D converter, however, is extremely useful in control sytems which involve analogue inputs. The A/D converter uses the successive approximation technique with an internal sample and hold circuit and the conversion time is 30 μs with a 4 MHz crystal clock. The external reference voltage which corresponds to the full 8-bit resolution is connected directly onto the SCM package.

The Rockwell R6500/1 One-Chip Microcomputer

This is an easy-to-use SCM which contains 64 bytes of RAM and 2K (R6500/1EB1), or 3K (RS6500/1EB3) of addressable EPROM fixed piggy-back fashion onto the package. This allows a standard EPROM, such as a 2716, or 2732, to be easily removed, programmed, or re-programmed, then re-inserted as often as required.

The four ports have 32 bi-directional TTL compatible I/O lines available, with a 16-bit timer/counter that can operate in four different modes. This makes a useful and versatile sequential controller which can be used with pneumatic or hydraulic systems. To make the package functional, a power supply, clock and reset switch are connected as shown in Fig. 13.19.

The EPROM contains the reset vectors which directs the program counter to the start address of the code which is to be executed in sequence to carry out the specified control function. The reset vectors are also held within the same EPROM. The RAM available must also be used for stack operation and the stack pointer must be set up at the start of the application software.

Some emphasis has been placed here on the hardware and off-the-shelf availability which is relatively inexpensive. The applications software, however, is rarely obtainable in a ready-made form, and the software development requires the user to be knowledgeable in both low-level programming languages and in the use of the software development tools. The most convenient software development systems which are available are those which are PC based.

PC-based Software Development Systems for SCMs

A SCM may be chosen on the basis of its external I/O facilities and/or the ease of use of its instruction set. The problem of software development nonetheless must also be faced. This requires the writing of a program into the system memory when no keyboard, display monitor or operating software exists. The inexpensive approach is to choose a SCM which supports an external EPROM in piggy-back fashion. The software code for the specific fask may then be developed using an appropriate assembler program which operates on an IBM-PC, or other suitably compatible machine. The resulting code is then used to 'blow', or 'burn', the EPROM. This method can, however, be very time consuming since the debugging process will require the

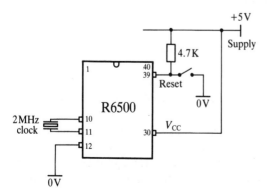

Figure 13.19 SCM with necessary external connections.

continual updating of the EPROM data as the program is edited to achieve the specified requirements.

An alternative is to use an EPROM emulator inserted into the target system to temporarily hold the program which is transmitted from the host computer memory. This enables the user to easily alter the program as required and then to finally blow the EPROM for permanent use. EPROM emulation should not be confused with the technique of 'in-circuit emulation', which involves the removal of the microprocessor from the target system. The in-circuit emulator then takes complete control by emulating, in real time, all the functions of the removed microprocessor it replaces.

A software development system should therefore comprise the following:

Hardware
• A host microcomputer with keyboard and display monitor
• A printer for hardcopy listings and disassemblies
• Disk drives for the permanent storage of data and programs
• An EPROM emulator
• An EPROM programmer

Software
• An editor
• Translation tools such as an assembler, or cross-assembler, disassembler, debugger and linker.

Traditional cross-assemblers will only assemble for one microprocessor and it can be very expensive if a number of upgrades, or different types, are to be accommodated. These very sophisticated and dedicated development systems are generally too expensive and complicated for producing the operational programs to control a fairly basic and ordered sequence of events as usually occurs in mechanical systems. An alternative is to employ an IBM-PC, or compatible, with an assembler which can handle multiple instruction sets. The processor to be used is specified in the source code and the assembler adapts automatically to the correct format. Tailoring a general purpose and readily available machine, such as the IBM-PC, to a semi-dedicated role requires a relatively low investment and low software production costs. For one-off applications, this is the only viable proposition. Just such an entity is the METAi development system which allows the designer to:

• write programs in assembly language for any one of over 50 microprocessors of both the 8-bit and the 16-bit variety;
• assemble to produce an object code;
• link to other modules and various library routines;
• test and debug as quickly as possible, using an EPROM emulator.

The METAi system can also recreate source code from object code using a labelling disassembler.

The emulator, which can handle EPROMs in the range 2K to 64K and can emulate up to four EPROMs at one time, is connected to an interface card inserted into one of the PC bus expansion slots.

An execllent editor is included in the package for preparing the source code and the first line of the program must specify the microprocessor name on which the code is to be executed. The address at which the code is to be placed in the target system memory must also be indicated by means of the 'segment' directive. If this code is to be executed via the reset switch in the system, then the start address must be placed in the appropriate vectors. This is easily accomplished by specifying the segment as a 16-bit word at the named low byte of the vectors. This is a·powerful facility which makes software development for devices such as SCMs with piggy-back EPROMs relatively simple.

As an illustrative example consider a demonstration program, in 6502 assembly language, for use with an RS6500/1 SCM which would make port A mimic the state of port B. The code is to run from an EPROM at address 800 hex and is to be initiated by the reset vectors held at FFC and FFD.

```
6502/
;read port B and write to port A
porta    equ       $080
portb    equ       $081
;now set up the stack
         segment byte at 800 'eprom'
start    cld
         ldx       #$3F    ;stack at top of
         txs               ;available ram
;now read/write indefinitely

again    lda       portb  ;read portb
         sta       porta  ;write to porta
         jmp       again  ;repeat

;put start address of code in reset vectors
         segment word at ffc 'vectors'
         word      start

         end
```

This source code is assembled to include a printer listing of the program and a symbol table, if required. The resulting OBJ file is then linked to any specified library or other files to produce the resulting machine code routine as a disk file. Software is provided to transport this final code to various specified devices such as an EPROM emulator, or an RS232 serial port in a straight binary, INTEL hex, or ASCII-space-hex format.

Being able to send the code to an EPROM emulator in the target system greatly enhances the debugging procedures and the correct form of the required program can then be blown into the actual EPROM.

A number of EPROM programmers, which provide flexible and economic ways to blow EPROMs, are available for use with IBM-PCs or compatibles. These connect directly into the RS232 serial port. User-friendly software is also usually supplied which allows:

- the selection of the EPROM type;
- the loading of memory from disk file;
- saving of memory to disk file;
- displaying of memory;
- blowing an EPROM from memory;
- reading an EPROM into memory;
- comparing the contents of an EPROM with memory.

13.5 PROGRAMMABLE LOGIC CONTROLLERS, PLCs

The PLC in Automated Systems

Automatic control has become an important consideration in most industrial processes where certain repetitive operations are performed. This applies to situations such as the automatic assembly of modules and products where a cycle of events are conducted in a consistent and uniform manner. Applications generally include a combination of feeding, handling, drilling, cutting, assembling, discharging, inspecting, packaging and transporting by conveyor.

Prior to the introduction of computer-based control systems the automation of such events was achieved by using either electrical relay logic circuits or pneumatic logic circuits. Although these are conceptionally simple and easy to maintain they are somewhat bulky and can be expensive. More important is the fact that the resulting control circuits are inflexible and do not lend themselves to easy system control alterations.

The late 1960s saw the introduction of the programmable logic controller (PLC) as a direct replacement for the relay sequence controllers. In essence the PLC replaces the hardwired relay or pneumatic logic with a more flexible programmable logic. It offers a simple, flexible and low-cost means of implementing a sequence control strategy where outputs for switching devices on and off are set according to input conditions as read from digital sensor states. It should be noted that, particularly in the USA, the PLC is often referred to as a 'programmable controller' with the abbreviation of PC. It should not be confused with the personal computer 'PC' or IBM-PC.

The PLC is composed of the same ingredients as a microcomputer such as a microprocessor, memory and input/output facilities. The processor executes the instructions held in memory by operating on inputs derived from the controlled process and providing outputs in accordance with the logic sequence defined in the control program. Its basic principle of operation during the execution of the program is that the program is scanned very fast, typically 1 to 20 μs per step, to record all input states. The outputs are then set according to the logic specified in the program. The sequence is continually repeated for each scan period of the controller.

Small PLCs dedicated to sequential control have typically 12 inputs and 8 outputs with the possibility of expansion up to 128 I/O lines. They come complete with an input interface to accommodate a range of input signals from the controlled process which are then converted to an appropriate form for the processor. Similarly, provision is made at the output of the PLC to interface with a variety of process hardware such as lamps, motors, relays and solenoids. The typical handling voltages are 24 V DC and 110 V AC.

Program instructions can be input into the battery backup RAM of a PLC by means of either a hand-held programming keypad or a connected PC with an appropriate software development package. Some LCD programming consoles incorporate a limited graphical display which illustrates the program in ladder logic format as the programmer builds it up using symbolic keys. This is also the principle of the PC-based development system where additionally the programmer has access to a larger visual display and the PC's disk operating system for data storage and retrieval. Once the program has been debugged and the control strategy verified by simulation, the codes can be loaded into an erasable and programmable read only memory chip (EPROM) which can then be installed in the PLC.

There are a large number of manufacturers of PLCs. Although some use their own particular software language the majority are based on the ladder logic diagram. Historically this was introduced in order to gain the acceptance of customers who were interested in moving from hardwired relay control systems to the PLC. In addition to the basic input/output facilities the PLC also contains timers, counters and other special functions.

Communicating with a variety of other control devices has not been a strength of traditional PLC networks. Many industrial controllers are equipped with an RS232 serial port for the transfer of data to and from other digital control devices in a system. Many PLCs designed on a modular construction have this facility with appropriate software for communicating with say the IBM-PC *de facto* standard to allow a wide ranging interconnection and interchange of data. The successful distributed control system vendors are those who offer applications know-how based on software applications packages with local support provision rather than simply the hardware technology that they provide. This involves incorporating standards into products in order that PLCs can be connected to PCs, other computers, instruments and other control systems. The hardware buzzwords are *standards*, *connectivity* and *open systems*.

Ladder Logic Programming

As mentioned previously the most common method of programming PLCs is by drawing a ladder diagram of the logic to be used for a sequence of operations in a control cycle. The corresponding program can be entered into the PLCs battery back-up RAM by either keying in assembly like mnemonic codes using a hand-held programmer, or by building up a graphical representation of the ladder diagram using a PC-based software development package. Some hand-held programmers can actually operate in a graphics mode and show the ladder diagram on an LCD display. The various methods obviously differ vastly in cost.

The ladder logic language is different from PC-related high- and low-level languages. It is basically related to the components used in industrial control systems such as switches, relays, solenoids, contactors, timers and counters. The ladder diagram concept has been used extensively for the documentation of electrical control circuits. When PLCs were first introduced to replace relay logic control hardware it was natural to adopt a similar format for the programming language. The ladder structure refers directly to physical inputs, outputs and functions within the PLC itself. The mnemonic programming technique is not really too user friendly and it can be extremely time consuming to check and relate a coded program to the actual circuit function. The graphic programming methods are preferable in this respect.

Ladder diagrams consist basically of two vertical lines which represent the power supply rails with horizontal rungs that incorporate the input contacts and the dependent output load. Typical inputs are digital sensors such as limit switches, optical switches and push-button switches. Outputs are usually solenoids, relays, contactors, timers and counters. It should be noted that the outputs can also be inputs on any ladder rung. Figure 13.20 illustrates some of the symbols used in electrical ladder diagrams.

The input/output symbols used in PLC ladder logic diagrams which are representative of those in electrical diagrams are shown in Fig. 13.21.

Each rung of the ladder logic diagram must start with an input or series of inputs and end with only one output. Following the notation for the Mitsubishi F series PLCs the input elements are preceded with an X and the outputs by a Y. Auxiliary relays which are internal to the PLC are preceded by an M, counters by a C and timers by a T. For example, the F2-20M has 12 inputs, 8 outputs, 128 general purpose auxiliary relays, 8 counters and 8 timers. These are numbered using an octal numbering system (base 8) as follows:

Inputs	X400–X413	(12)
Outputs	Y430–Y437	(8)
Auxiliary relays	M100–M277	(128)
Counters	C460–C467	(8)
Timers	T450–T457	(8)

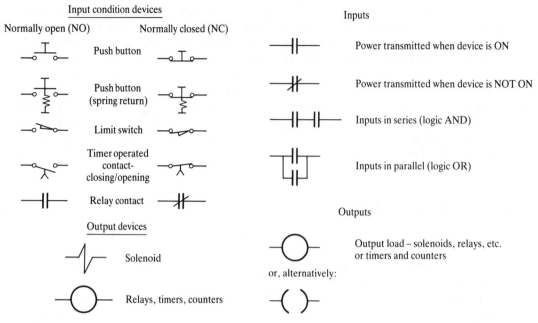

Figure 13.20 Electrical ladder diagram symbols.

Figure 13.21 Instruction set ladder logic symbols.

Consider an electrical ladder diagram with a solenoid output dependent upon a number of input condition devices as shown in Fig. 13.22. The figure also includes the corresponding PLC ladder logic diagram.

In order to energize the output solenoid (Y430) the normally open start switch (X400) must be activated and either of the microswitches (X402 or X403) must be on. The normally closed stop switch (X401) must then be opened to break the circuit and switch off the solenoid. It can be seen from both diagrams that they do in fact correspond directly to a digital logic circuit (Chapter 7) and this is illustrated in Fig. 13.23.

The PLC itself can really be regarded as a black box with inputs and outputs. The inputs in the above case are the push-button switches and the limit switches. The output is the solenoid. The program executed within the black box will set the output on or off according to the input

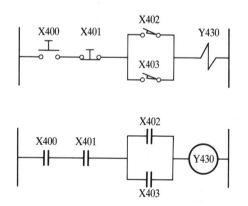

Figure 13.22 Electrical ladder diagram and corresponding PLC ladder logic diagram.

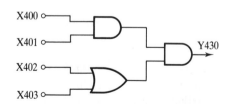

Figure 13.23 Logic gate circuit corresponding to the ladder diagrams.

states. The logic implemented is identical to the hardwired logic circuit except that alterations can be made by changing software rather than digital logic hardware. All necessary power switching interfacing is incorporated into the PLC and the advantage of using such flexible controllers in preference to relay logic circuits is evident.

Example Draw the ladder logic diagram for a machine start/stop arrangement where a contactor switching power to a drive motor comes on by pressing a nomally open spring return push-button switch. The motor remains on until a normally open spring return stop switch is pressed. Take the I/O requirements for the PLC as:

$$
\begin{array}{ll}
\text{start switch} & \text{X400} \\
\text{stop switch} & \text{X401} \\
\text{contactor} & \text{Y430}
\end{array}
$$

With the start switch being spring return it is necessary to latch the load on with itself and switch it off with the normally open spring return stop switch. The appropriate ladder rung to execute this requirement is shown in Fig. 13.24.

The corresponding digital logic circuit is shown in Fig. 13.25 and the Boolean equation defining the process is

$$Y430 = (X400 \text{ OR } Y430) \text{ AND NOT } X401$$

In practice it is usual to have a normally closed stop switch but the example is illustrative of the passing of power along a rung when a switch is not on.

Auxiliary relays These are basically output devices which are completely internal to the PLC and no external physical connections to a load can be identified with them. They are programmed in exactly the same way as output contacts and can be incorporated into the ladder logic program in the same way as other I/O elements. They are really useful devices for the programmer to use appropriately for developing good structured ladder diagrams. For example, consider the electrical wiring diagram for an electro-mechanical relay which can have two outputs—one which is on (normally closed) when the relay coil is not activated and one which is off (normally open) for the same input condition. When the relay coil is energized the condition of the outputs reverse. Use can be made of auxiliary internal control relays to implement this switching strategy by a PLC ladder logic diagram. This is illustrated in Fig. 13.26(*a*) and (*b*).

A ladder rung must start with inputs and terminate with one output. Usually an output can only appear once in a ladder logic program. If a situation occurs where an output is dependent upon say two different input arrangements, then appropriate use can be made of auxiliary control relays. This is demonstrated in Fig. 13.27. Output Y430 will come on if either auxiliary relays M100 or M101 are on.

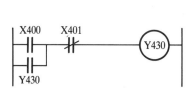

Figure 13.24 Machine start/stop control.

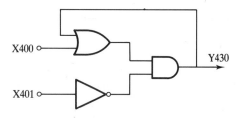

Figure 13.25 Corresponding digital logic circuit.

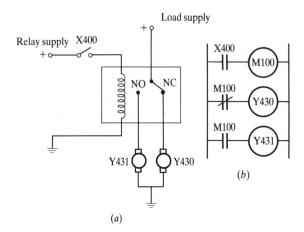

(a)

(b)

Figure 13.26 Use of an auxiliary relay: (a) electrical connections; (b) ladder logic diagram.

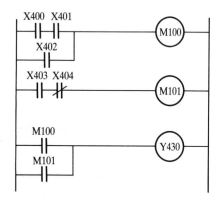

Figure 13.27 Switching an output from two different conditional inputs.

Translating ladder logic diagrams into mnemonics Once a ladder diagram has been drawn up to satisfy a particular sequence control then it must be entered into the PLCs memory for testing. Most manufacturers have adopted the use of a PC as a development tool which provides enhanced facilities in ladder logic graph programming which is menu driven. This PC environment allows the generation, editing and storage of PLC programs. However, a common method of programming small PLCs is by keying mnemonic codes corresponding to the ladder diagram into a programming unit directly attached to the controller. Care should be taken during this transfer stage in order to get a true implementation of the control program. For example, consider the ladder rungs illustrated in Fig. 13.28(a), (b), (c) and (d).

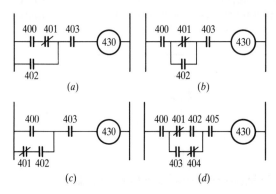

(a)

(b)

(c)

(d)

Figure 13.28 Ladder rungs for translating into mnemonics.

The corresponding mnemonics are:

(a)
LD 400
ANI 401
OR 402
AND 403
OUT 430

(b)
LD 400   alternatively
LDI 401   LDI 401
OR 402   OR 402
ANB   AND 400
AND 403   AND 403
OUT 430   OUT 430

(c)
LD 400   alternatively
LDI 401   LDI 401
AND 402   AND 402
ORB   OR 400
AND 403   AND 403
OUT 430   OUT 430

(d)
LD 400   alternatively
LDI 401   LDI 401
AND 402   AND 402
LD 403   LD 403
ANI 404   ANI 404
ORB   ORB
ANB   AND 400
AND 405   AND 405
OUT 430   OUT 430

Note the use of the AND BLOCK (ANB) and the OR BLOCK (ORB) for combining two prior consecutive load or load inverse statements (LD or LDI).

Timers Time delays are commonly used in control applications and timers in a PLC are incremented by an internally generated clock signal. The time resolution is usually either 1 s or 0.1 s. Although manufacturers may adopt different ways of specifying timer activities in a ladder diagram, the same basic principles of operation apply. This involves the enabling of the timer from some specified input condition and at the end of the timed period the timer switches on. The timer condition can then be used as an input to other ladder rungs which define outputs that are dependent upon an elapsed time. In order to be used again the timer must first be reset by disenabling the input. For the Mitsubishi PLC the timer is enabled and reset by the same input condition.

The principles involved are best illustrated by means of examples.

Example Develop a ladder logic diagram with timers which would cause an output to cycle on and off at a frequency of 1 Hz.

User time T450 to hold the output Y430 ON for 0.5 s and timer T451 to hold it OFF. The ladder diagram with the corresponding mnemonics is shown in Fig. 13.29.

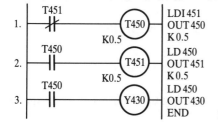

Figure 13.29 Output cycling ON/OFF at 1 Hz frequency.

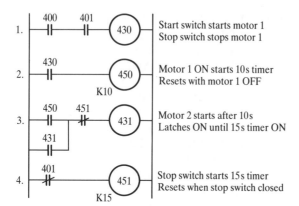

Figure 13.30 Start/stop control of two motors.

Example Develop a ladder logic diagram to operate two motors as follows:
1. A normally open start button starts motor 1 immediately and 10 s later motor 2 starts.
2. A normally closed stop button stops motor 1 immediately and 15 s later motor 2 stops.
Use the following I/O connections:

start switch (NO)	X400
stop switch (NC)	X401
motor 1	Y430
motor 2	Y431
10 s timer	T450
15 s timer	T451

The ladder diagram with appropriate comments is shown in Fig. 13.30.

Example In a *time-driven* sequential control strategy a pump is to be switched on for 2 min in order to achieve a specified water level in a tank. The pump is then switched off and a heater is switched on for 1 min so that the water can reach a required temperature. At this point the heater is switched off and another pump is started to empty the tank. This takes 2 min.
Details of the PLC I/O are:

supply pump	Y430
discharge pump	Y431
heater	Y432
supply pump timer	T450
heater timer	T451
discharge pump timer	T452

The PLC ladder diagram which controls the sequence as described is shown in Fig. 13.31. A description of the ladder is as follows:
(It should be noted that if any one of the load outputs are to be ON then the other two must be OFF.)

Rung 1   The supply pump switches ON immediately and goes OFF after 2 min when heater Y432 comes ON.

Rung 2   Timer T450 starts with the supply pump coming ON and resets when the pump goes OFF.

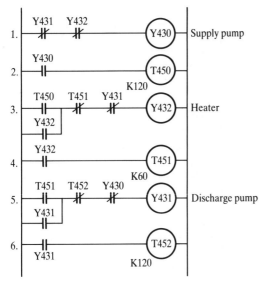

Figure 13.31 Control of a time-driven sequence.

Rung 3 The heater switches ON when timer T450 comes ON. It is latched ON and is switched OFF when timer T451 comes ON.

Rung 4 Timer T451 starts when the heater comes ON and resets when the heater goes OFF.

Rung 5 The discharge pump starts when timer T451 comes ON. It is latched ON and is switched OFF when timer T452 comes ON.

Rung 6 Timer T452 starts when the discharge pump comes ON and resets when the pump switches OFF.

Example A conveyor driven by an electric motor (Y430) can be started by a normally open start switch (X400) and stopped at any time by a normally closed stop switch (X401).

A component is placed onto the conveyor and transported to a printing station which is indicated by an optical sensor (X402) consisting of a transmitter and a receiver. When the component interrupts the light beam the sensor signal fed to the PLC controller switches to the OFF state and the conveyor stops for 5 s to allow the printing process to be conducted. At the end of this delay period the motor is restarted. An additional photoelectric sensor (X403) is incorporated into the transport system further along the conveyor in order to ensure that a component has surely cleared the work area prior to the next component triggering the first sensor. A diagram of the system is shown at Fig. 13.32.

The ladder logic diagram for the control of the system is shown in Fig. 13.33.

A description of the ladder logic follows:

First note the use of the two control relays M100 and M101 which are used in the motor control rung of the ladder. M101 depends upon sensor X403 and it is included in the motor control logic in preference to T450 in order to remove the uncertainty of M100 being ON before the timer resets. This is quite common in problems of this nature where two outputs switch simultaneously and there is no guarantee of the order of switching. Additional sensors, such as X403, must be added to ensure the correct operation of the sequence.

Rung 1 The power to the motor is initially via the start switch X400 and a latch is produced by the motor ON and sensor X402 ON. The motor restart is produced

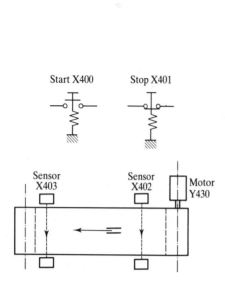

Figure 13.32 Conveyor system.

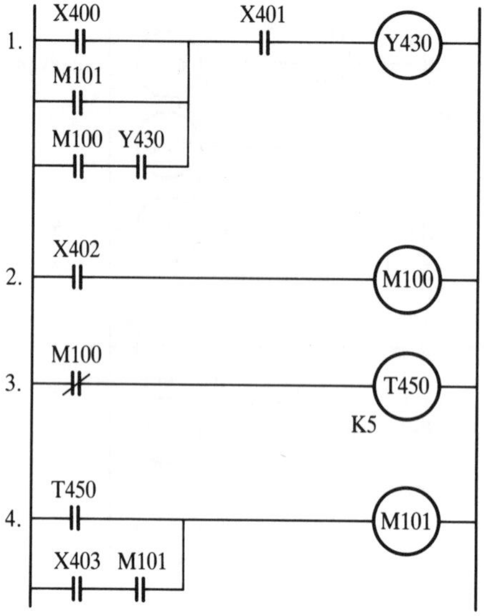

Figure 13.33 Ladder logic diagram for the control of the conveyor system.

by the control relay M101 which will come ON at the end of the 5 s timing operation. The stop switch X401 will stop the motor at any time.

Rung 2   Once sensor X402 is activated (OFF) the timer starts and it will reset when the motor restarts.

Rung 3   Once M100 goes OFF the timer starts and it resets when the motor restarts.

Rung 4   Once the timer comes ON the control relay M101 comes ON to restart the motor. Note that M101 will remain ON until switch X403 is activated. The use of sensor X403 ensures the correct operation of the system.

Counters   Counting operations can also be performed in ladder logic format by activating an output counter after a specified number of counts have been completed. A counter operates in much the same manner as a timer except that there is a count of the number of times that an event occurs rather than a timed clock count. The counter therefore requires an input which is indicative of the event that is to be counted. In a similar manner to the timer, the counter must be reset from another input before it can be used again. This is illustrated in ladder format in Fig. 13.34 and the corresponding mnemonic codes in Mitsubishi notation are

$$
\begin{array}{ll}
\text{LD} & 400 \\
\text{RST} & 460 \\
\text{LD} & 403 \\
\text{OUT} & 460 \\
\text{K} & 10 \\
\end{array}
$$

Controlling Pneumatic Systems

Electro-pneumatic valves with actuators which incorporate a variety of mechanical attachments are commonly used for component handling in automation systems. Programmable logic controllers are now accepted as part of the automation scene as they can enhance the flexibility and intelligence in a variety of applications. The PLC accepts signals from sensors and switches

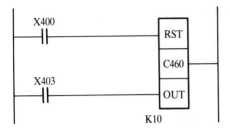

Figure 13.34 Operating a counter.

in the system and outputs power to the solenoid operated control valves in a sequence prescribed by the ladder logic diagram. The basic principles of electro-pneumatic systems are outlined in Chapter 6.

Directional control valves may be switched by either pure solenoid activation or solenoid-operated pilot-assisted. The type of control used will affect the form of the ladder logic adopted. This is due to the method that the PLC employs for executing the instructions supplied in the ladder format. As previously outlined the PLC operates by scanning all of the inputs and storing their states in a register. The outputs are then set according to the program logic and the cycle is continuously repeated at a fast rate. The order of the sequence of the ladder instructions is not really too important although it is natural to adopt a logical sequence which is relevant to the cycle of events.

Example Consider the continuous sequencing of a double acting pneumatic cylinder using a 4/2-way solenoid-operated pilot controlled valve as illustrated in Fig. 13.35. The end of stroke condition is indicated by means of sensors.

The ladder diagram is shown in Fig. 13.36.

If the directional control valve was solenoid operated with spring return then it would be necessary to latch the output Y431 ON and switch it OFF by means of the sensor X403. The corresponding ladder diagram for the continuous sequencing is shown in Fig. 13.37.

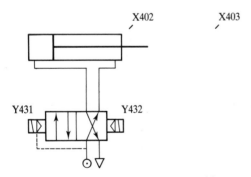

Figure 13.35 Sequencing with a solenoid operated pilot controlled valve.

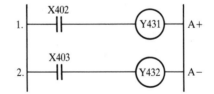

Figure 13.36 Ladder diagram for system with a solenoid operated pilot controlled valve.

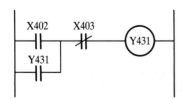

Figure 13.37 Ladder diagram for system with a solenoid operated, spring return controlled valve.

If the control valves have solenoid operation then it is necessary to latch the outputs ON since the ladder is continuously scanned. This means that once the piston has left the end of the stroke the corresponding output will be switched OFF unless latched. This does not apply for pilot assisted valves since the air is used to move the valve spool and once activated it is independent of the solenoid state.

Example A double-acting cylinder is to sequence as follows:

$$A+; \ 2s \ delay; \ A-$$

repeating 10 times.

A normally open start switch (X400) and a normally closed stop switch (X401) are used to switch a 3/2-way valve that controls the air supply into the system. The valve is solenoid/spring return controlled and the 4/2-way directional control valve is solenoid operated pilot assisted. The I/O arrangement is as follows:

Start switch (NO)	X400
Stop switch (NC)	X401
Position sensor (retracted)	X402
Position sensor (extended)	X403
Main air valve solenoid	Y430
Directional control valve solenoid (extend)	Y431
Directional control valve solenoid (retract)	Y432
Timer for 2 second delay	T450
Counter for 10 cycles	C460

The ladder diagram for the sequence is shown in Fig. 13.38.

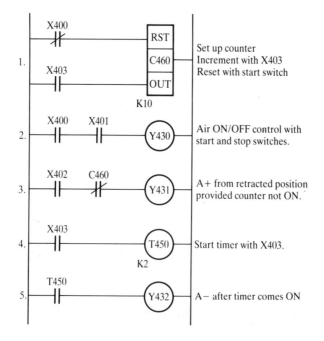

Figure 13.38 Sequencing with counter and timer.

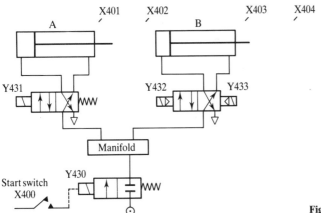

Figure 13.39 Sequencing of two cylinders.

Example During part of an automatic assembly operation two double acting pneumatic cylinders are to sequence for 10 consecutive cycles once a start switch has been activated. The cycle is

$$A+; 5\,s \text{ delay}; B+; A-; 3\,s \text{ delay}: B-$$

The end of stroke condition is detected by limit switches and details of the electro-pneumatic control valves are as follows:

Start switch valve	2/2-way with solenoid and spring return
Cylinder A valve	4/2-way with solenoid and spring return
Cylinder B valve	4/2-way with solenoid-operated pilot-controlled

The circuit is shown in Fig. 13.39.
The sequence requires five inputs, four outputs, two timers and one counter from the PLC. The appropriate numbers are indicated on the circuit diagram and the corresponding ladder control program is given in Fig. 13.40.

It is important that manufacturing industry adopts developments in microprocessor technology in order to enhance the intelligence and flexibility of production systems. Programmable logic controllers are within this category and can be integrated into a system to allow it to function easier and safer with an ensured quality, efficiency and ease of maintenance. A modern workforce should be technically literate and competent in the operation of such devices as PLCs. Although there are a large number of different types of programmable controllers on the market the majority adopt a ladder logic form of instruction. The concepts relating to input, output, timers and counters are however basically similar to those dealt with in this section.

13.6 THE PC AS A CONTROLLER

Since the first appearance of the IBM-PC in 1981, several other manufacturers have produced so-called compatibles which are based on the 16-bit 8086 microprocessor. The upwardly compatible 80286 was introduced in 1984 and further upgrades have since included the 80386 which features a 32-bit data bus and an addressable real memory of 16M bytes. These microprocessors allow the users to write programs that use more memory than is actually available in a given system by exchanging data between the main memory and secondary storage

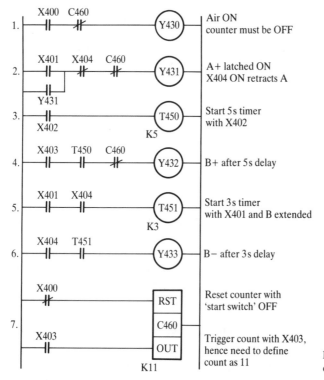

1. X400 C460 — (Y430) — Air ON / counter must be OFF

2. X401 X404 C460 — (Y431) — A+ latched ON / X404 ON retracts A
   Y431

3. X402 — (T450) K5 — Start 5s timer with X402

4. X403 T450 C460 — (Y432) — B+ after 5s delay

5. X401 X404 — (T451) K3 — Start 3s timer with X401 and B extended

6. X404 T451 — (Y433) — B− after 3s delay

7. X400 — RST C460 — Reset counter with 'start switch' OFF
   X403 — OUT K11 — Trigger count with X403, hence need to define count as 11

Figure 13.40 Ladder logic diagram for the sequencing of two cylinders.

devices. In the case of the 80386 microprocessor, this virtual memory address space is 4G bytes. It is this processing power and memory availability that has made such a dramatic impact on the general engineering acceptance of personal computers for data acquisition and control applications. In more recent times an 80486 microprocessor has been released. This device incorporates about one million transistors on the chip and is about five times faster than the 80386. In addition to an increase in the processing power, there are many other advantages in using a PC as the centrepiece in any control application. These advantages are:

1. There is a large choice of applications software which is not generally available for dedicated controllers.
2. There is a large choice of tools available to produce applications software efficiently.
3. The PC is available in a variety of forms ranging from a single card, a portable, a desk-top and a ruggedized industrial version for use on the factory floor.
4. Expansion plug-in slots to the PC bus structure are available and a large range of cards for digital or analogue I/O have been produced by a number of manufacturers.
5. The PC-based controller is more flexible than the dedicated, or minicomputer system, and can be easily configured indefinitely to suit different applications.

Data acquisition and control add-ons for the PC exist either as external rack-mounted systems, or as plug-in boards. The external box approach usually involves attaching a separate rack-type enclosure with power supply to the host PC. The connection is made either through the included serial, or the parallel data communications channels. Various modules based on a standard card format, such as the 'Eurocard', can be plugged into the enclosure housing as required.

There are basically two options available for capturing data using a PC. The first option is to use an A/D converter card connected directly to the host computer's backplane. The cards are generally 'port addressed' and may be driven by any program language which supports IN/ OUT commands. The base address is usually switch selectable on the card. This enables different cards, or more than one of the same card, to be connected and run from the same host computer. The second option uses instruments such as digital voltmeters, frequency meters, etc., which have an interface board that enables data transfers from or to the controlling PC. The most common standard is the IEEE-488 (GPIB) parallel communications link which is featured in Sec. 8.4. The quickest, easiest and least expensive way to get measured data into a PC however, or to get control signals out, is to use the first option of the port addressed I/O card. Versatile cards are readily available offering such features as:

1. Multichannel digital I/O, with opto-isolation and Darlington driver facilities.
2. Pulse counting and timing facilities.
3. Multiplexed analogue to digital conversion with programmable gain.
4. Digital to analogue conversion.
5. Thermocouple input.

Recent advances have included substantial developments in the software available for data capture and control. Software packages are now available, for example, which provide the user with a development system having a mouse-driven environment of windows and pull-down menus. The National Instruments 'Lab Windows', for use with PCs is an example which contains a library of function modules for programming specific instruments with the IEEE-488 interface. These modules are accessed in the development program, via function panels, to interactively set up and capture data from external instruments. In addition, a suite of programs are included for data presentation, analysis and formatting in an interactive environment using either QUICKBASIC, or C.

Digital and Analogue I/O Using a PC

Digital and analogue input/output boards for data acquisition and control are keeping pace with the new generations of PCs. These boards must permit the effective transfer of data and status signals through the software to utilise the full capabilities of the PC. External peripherals which readily adapt PCs to process control environments are now enabling users to employ desk-top systems in an area once fielded only by minicomputers and mainframes. High-speed data acquisition, real-time system monitoring and closed-loop control can all be readily implemented on a PC. In addition, the system can perform statistical operations on the acquired data, generate reports and store the results on disk for future evaluation.

The range of plug-in boards for PCs include digital and analogue I/O, relays with opto-isolation, solid-state relays, stepper motor drivers, serial and parallel communication interfaces and voice I/O technology.

Although the PC processor is usually of the 16-bit, or the 32-bit variety, the I/O boards are invariably based on 8-bit technology, namely the 8255 PPI. This interface chip, used with a dedicated I/O bus provides three ports A, B and C, which can be set by software through the associated control register (Sec. 10.4).

The digital operation is relatively straightforward as is the digital-to-analogue conversion. Analogue-to-digital conversion is based on writing to one of the ports, usually port C, a value which specifies the selected channel and possibly the gain. This may be sufficient to start the conversion, or sometimes a logic 0 followed by a logic 1 must be included in the data sent from the specified port. The end of conversion must then be sensed from a logic level change on a specified bit of the port. On some boards, this end of conversion bit is not available to the user and it may be unnecessary to make a check when operating in high-level BASIC due to the speed of execution of the code. If a compiled language, or machine level code is used to drive the A/D converter, then a short delay may be necessary in order to give the circuitry enough time to complete the conversion.

Once the analogue input voltage has been converted into a digital value then the corresponding number can be read at one, or more of the ports, usually A and B, depending upon the resolution. The majority of the A/D conversion boards are of 12-bit resolution and the corresponding value in the range 0–4095 is obtained by combining the low byte with the required 4 bits, or nibble, of the high byte. It is necessary to mask out the unwanted nibble of the high byte using a logical AND in the software routine.

The above input and output procedures are common to most applications in a general control context. A relevant illustrative example concerns a speed control application for a small DC motor.

Digital Control of a DC Motor

Details of each constituent part of the control loop with the necessary interfacing are as follows:

Process This is effectively a 12 V precision DC servomotor, RS 336-292, connected to a 5:1 ratio precision gearbox, RS 336-220, driving a high inertial load. The inertial load consists of an aluminium drum 40 mm diameter by 40 mm long which is mounted on a steel spindle that runs in brass bushes. These are held between two support plates with the drive from the gearbox made via a universal joint. The configuration is shown in Fig. 13.41 and the drum provides a means of supplying stepped loads in order to observe the controller action and the resulting motor response.

Measurement transducer A magnetic sensor is used in conjunction with a tachometer circuit to measure the drum rotational speed. The signal pulses are generated from four metal blocks attached to the side of the aluminium drum. The resulting output voltage from the tachometer is amplified to give a voltage of 10 V to correspond to a drum speed of 2000 rev/min. This value is then suitable for inputting directly to the chosen analogue-to-digital converter.

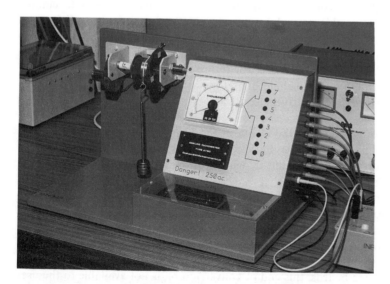

Figure 13.41 DC servomotor driving an inertial load.

Controller Use is made of an IBM compatible PC with an interface card which has the following specification:

1. A 16-channel multiplexed sample and hold 12-bit resolution A/D converter with an overall conversion time of 35 μs and an input voltage range of 0 V to +10 V.
2. Three 8-bit programmable input/output ports A, B and C.

The output speed is read on channel 1 of the multiplexer and the control effort value (0–255), generated by the control strategy algorithm, is output to port B.

The I/O address space used by the card to utilize two 8255 PPIs is as follows:

The base address (BA) is set as 700 hex.

PPI 1 – for use with the A/D converter

Address	Function
BA + 00	Port A, input 8 LSBs from ADC
BA + 01	Port B, input 4 MSBs (lower nibble) from ADC
BA + 02	Port C, lower nibble – start ADC conversion by toggling bit 0 low/high while keeping bit 1 high
	Upper nibble-select multiplexer channel
BA + 03	Control word for PPI 1 (=92 hex)

PPI 2 – providing the three digital I/O ports

Address	Function
BA + 08	Port A
BA + 09	Port B, set to output for 8-bit control effort value
BA + 10	Port C
BA + 11	Control word for PPI 2 (=90 hex)

Hence the A/D converter is enabled for channel 1 with:

$$\text{OUT \&H702,\&H12}$$
$$\text{OUT \&H702,\&H13}$$

There is no 'end of conversion' sensing facility and a small delay is included to ensure that the conversion is complete.

The 12-bit value representing the output speed is obtained by reading addresses &H700 and &H701, i.e.

$$I = 256*(\text{INP}(\&H701)\ \text{AND}\ 15) + \text{INP}(\&H700)$$

from which the corresponding speed in rev/min is

$$PV = 2000*(I/4095)$$

This gives an error, expressed as a percentage of the measuring span, at any particular time, of

$$E = 100*(SP - PV)/2000$$

The control effort interface The 8-bit number generated by the chosen digital control strategy to represent the control effort has to be converted into a voltage within the range 0 to 12 V. This should also have a suitable power driving capability to suit the motor. The DC servomotor control module, RS 591-663, is suitable for this purpose and requires an input voltage of 0–4 V to vary the motor speed over its full range. The voltage is generated by taking the 8-bit output from port B of PPI 2 into a ZN 428 D/A converter, RS 303-523, and amplifying the output to give a maximum of 4 V. The corresponding wiring diagram is shown in Fig. 13.42.

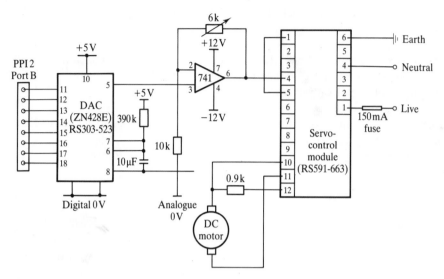

Figure 13.42 DC servomotor power driving circuit.

The digital control algorithm The normal PID control strategy (Sec. 11.6) is easily translated into a digital algorithm based on a chosen interval sampling time of dt. The integral term is then obtained from the summation of the error value and the derivative term from the finite change in the error over the time interval dt. The choice of step length is dependent upon the actual application but an empirical rule is to use at least one-tenth of the closed loop control settling time. For the application considered, the motor with inertial load takes two or three seconds to achieve a steady output speed of around 1200 rev/min with a step input from rest. A suitable increment of 0.2 s or less would therefore be appropriate. Since the TIMER function in BASIC is specified as having an accuracy of about one-tenth of a second, dt is taken as 0.1 s in the digital control algorithm. Program 13.3 in **IBM BASICA** inputs the required set point speed and controller settings and controls the motor speed over a specified time period.

Program 13.3 Digital control program for a DC servomotor.

```
10 REM set up both 8255PPI ports as required
20 OUT &H703, &H92
30 OUT &H70B, &H90
40 REM switch motor OFF
50 OUT &H709,0
60 CLS
70 LOCATE 3,10:PRINT"This program illustrates the characteristics of a servo"
80 LOCATE 5,10:PRINT"motor in response to a three term PID control action"
90 LOCATE 11,10:INPUT"Required speed in rev/min= ";SP
100 LOCATE 13,10:INPUT"Controller gain= ";K
110 LOCATE 15,10:INPUT"Controller integral time in seconds= ";TI
120 LOCATE 17,10:INPUT"Controller derivative time in seconds= ";TD
130 LOCATE 19,10:INPUT"Duration of required run time in seconds= ";D
140 REM*********************************************************************
150 DT=.1:SUM=0:EP=0 ·
160 IC=K*DT/TI:DC=K*TD/DT
```

```
170 REM zero timer for run duration
180 T1=TIMER
190 REM Start of control loop sequence
200 WHILE (TIMER-T1)<D
210 T2=TIMER
220 OUT &H702, &H12
230 OUT &H702, &H13
240 FOR J=1 TO 5:NEXT J
250 A=INP(&H701):B=INP(&H700)
260 I=256*(A AND 15)+B
270 PV=2000*I/4095
280 E=(SP-PV)/2000*100
290 SUM=SUM+E
300 VOUT%=INT((K*E)+(IC*SUM)+(DC*(E-EP)))
310 IF VOUT%<0 THEN VOUT%=0
320 IF VOUT%>100 THEN VOUT%=100
330 REM Output control effort to DAC
340 OUT &H709,INT(OUT%*2.55)
350 REM Check for control loop contained within DT seconds
360 IF (TIMER-T2)<DT THEN GOTO 360
370 WEND
380 OUT &H709, 0
390 END
```

Typical controller setting values to achieve a reasonable response are

$$K = 0.3, \quad T_i = 0.6\,\text{s}, \quad T_d = 0.15\,\text{s}$$

Adding a graphical output to the program greatly enhances its value in demonstrating the effect of various settings on the system response and a screen dump from the PC when running with the above values to achieve a set point of 1000 rev/min is shown in Fig. 13.43.

While the example given serves as an illustration, the principles employed are fundamental and are basically those that would be applied in an industrial context to implement PID control of virtually any plant or process.

13.7 THE PLC VERSUS THE MICROCOMPUTER

Although both the PLC and the microcomputer contain the same basic constituent components they are entirely different in operation and in physical appearance. It is understandable, although inaccurate, to assume that a PLC is equivalent to a 'dedicated microcomputer'. Its

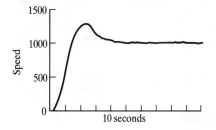

Figure 13.43 Graphics output for DC servomotor speed response.

CPU may be less intelligent than that in a microcomputer but it processes data very fast. It is tailor-made to carry out logical operations such as AND and OR in a program. A microcomputer requires several program steps to implement these functions irrespective of whether a high- or a low-level language is used. For the PLC the operation of the CPU and memory is basically a repetitive sequence which:

1. examines the state of all the inputs related to the process being controlled and puts the information into an image memory;
2. compares this information with the control program logic stored in memory;
3. decides whether any control action is needed;
4. executes the control action by transmitting signals to the in-built output interface as necessary;
5. once again examines the input states and repeats the sequence of events.

The output interface is used to convert the control actions into signals which are capable of driving output devices such as lamps, motors, solenoids, relays or contactors.

The main advantages of a small PLC for industrial sequence control applications are:

1. It is relatively cheap and is of a rugged compact construction which is suitable for shop floor applications.
2. It is highly reliable, virtually immune to electrical noise and its maintenance requirements are low.
3. Memory is economically used due to the method adopted for the processing of data and its resulting speed of program execution is very fast.
4. Input/output devices are easily connected through an in-built interface and the only requirement is an external power source which is usually either 24 V DC or 110 V AC.

The PLC is not as flexible as a microcomputer and the small variety are incapable of even simple arithmetic operations. The PC, on the other hand, is available in a variety of forms such as a desk-top, lap-top, or as an industrial standard rack-based system. A large range of plug-in cards are available from a number of suppliers and these provide the PC with a variety of digital and analogue I/O facilities. There are numerous applications packages on the market which include wordprocessors, spreadsheets, databases and dedicated data acquisition and control software. The system can be easily reconfigured through the operating system for any specific application. Customized control software can be developed by using a large choice of programming languages.

Large PLCs, capable of handling over 1000 I/O lines, are available in modular form. The basic essentials are a rack or mounting assembly with a power supply, a processor and memory module. Digital and analogue I/O modules along with communications and possibly graphics facilities are then selected as appropriate. These controllers have enhanced processing capabilities with full mathematical manipulation of data and built-in routines for such real-time requirements as digital filtering and PID control implementation.

Although the small single-purpose PLC is relatively secure in its role in the market, the larger machines face considerable competition from PCs with enhanced graphical user interfaces (GUIs) for data acquisition and control applications. Examples include the National Instruments packages such as LABWINDOWS and LABVIEW.

13.8 ADVANCED CONTROL SYSTEMS

Adaptive and Self-tuning Control

The concept of adaptive control is based on the ability to measure the system behaviour at any time and to alter the controller settings automatically to provide an optimum system response. Adaptive control has been a very active research topic over the last ten years but it is only recently that practical applications using adaptive controllers have appeared.

The simplest approach to adaptive control is the so-called 'gain scheduling' method, Fig. 13.44. The principle of gain scheduling is that some relevant external parameter is measured and an appropriate value of gain is then selected for the controller. Gain scheduling was first developed for aileron control in high altitude aircraft. The low air density at high altitude has a profound effect on the in-flight dynamics and the purpose of gain scheduling was to provide the pilot with a more consistent 'feel' to the aircraft's handling independently of altitude. Gain scheduling has the advantage that the system stability margins can be well established for any value of gain and the technique is generally fast acting. The method is limited however since the gain adjustment is a function of usually only one measured parameter. In most systems the process may be subject to any number of external influences and the more modern adaptive controllers use some mathematical model as a basis of comparison with the actual control system, Fig. 13.45.

The mathematical model in Fig. 13.45 receives the same input as the actual system and an error is created relating the difference between the actual and the model system output. The error may then be used as a basis for altering the controller settings. Obviously, the quality of the control depends on how well the model reflects the actual system. The usual implementation of model reference adaptive control is illustrated in Fig. 13.46.

It is worth noting that the original feedback loop is left intact such that failure of the adaptive loop will not render the system inoperative. External disturbances operating on the actual plant will change the actual/model error signal and provide the basis for re-tuning the controller settings via the adaptive loop. The adjustment of the controller settings implies that there must be some well-defined strategy to determine the level and nature of the adjustments made. Self-tuning control takes the adaptive concept one stage further in that the mathematical model of the system is also updated as more input and output data from the actual system is acquired. The schematic diagram of a self-tuning controller is shown in Fig. 13.47.

The computer-based self-tuning controller estimates the system dynamics and then uses this estimate to implement the optimum controller settings. The continuous updating of the system parameters at each sampling interval is called 'recursive parameter estimation'. Previously estimated parameters are also available and these can be used in perhaps a 'least-squares' method to provide some overall smoothing of the control function. With the latest system parameters available, the self-tuning controller then goes through some 'design' procedure to

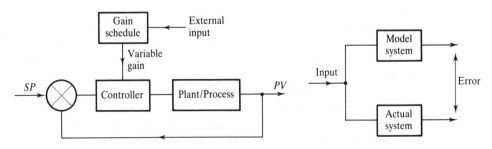

Figure 13.44 Adaptive control by gain scheduling.

Figure 13.45 Model/actual error generation.

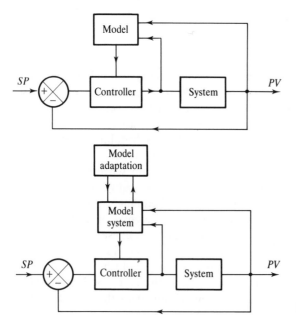

Figure 13.46 Model reference adaptive control.

Figure 13.47 Self-tuning controller.

optimize the controller settings. This 'design' is usually based on the desired output response of the system. One particular design procedure is based on the root locus method for stability analysis. By adjustment of gains and time constants in the control algorithm, the method seeks to tune the transfer function and thereby govern the output response. Other procedures are often based on the rules of Ziegler and Nichols (Sec. 11.6). The final process in the self-tuning control cycle is the physical imposition of the optimized controller settings on the actual system. Self-tuning control is generally applied to the more complex processes where transportation delays, nonlinearities and multiple control loops greatly add to the complexity. The stability of such systems is in most cases non-deterministic since there is no generalized theory available. Traditionally then, most self-tuning controllers are based on well-established three-term control principles, but with the added enhancement of adaptability. A number of proprietry self-tuning controllers are available commercially, for example, Kraus and Myron (see further reading), describe the Foxboro Company's 'EXACT' controller. The EXACT controller is based on PID principles and uses the Ziegler and Nichols rules in the self-tuning mode.

Hierarchical Control Systems

The ultimate aim in industrial optimization is the efficient control of complex interactive systems. Recent hardware developments and microprocessor-based controllers with extensive data handling power and enhanced communications have opened up the possibilities for the control of interlinked systems. What is required, but not yet realized, is a theoretical framework on which to base the analysis of such systems. Nonetheless, and in the absence of theory, hierarchical control systems do exist and are currently being used effectively in the control of various large-scale plant and processes.

The usual approach adopted is to subdivide the complex system into a number of more manageable parts. This is the concept of hierarchical control which might be thought of as a subdivision in decreasing order of importance. Hierarchical control exists in two basic forms, which are multilayer and multilevel. Multilayer control is that in which the control tasks are subdivided in order of complexity. Multilevel control, on the other hand, is that where local

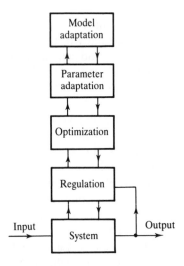

Figure 13.48 Multilayer control system.

control tasks are coordinated by an upper echelon of supervisory controllers. Multilayer control is illustrated concisely in an elaborate adaptive type controller. The hierarchy is depicted in Fig. 13.48.

The first level is that of regulation which is characterized by the classical single closed-loop control system. Moving up the hierarchy we have optimization of the controller parameters. Optimization is representative of the basic adaptive controller, using simple gain schedulling or some model reference criterion. The next highest level is that of parameter adaptation. Parameter adaptation is embodied in the self-tuning controller which might be thought of as the beginnings of an 'expert system' approach. The highest level is that of model adaptation which is based on long-term comparisons between the model and the actual performance. If the system is modelled accurately to begin with, the model adaptation level might only rarely be entered.

Multilevel control is characterized by local controllers whose actions are governed by higher levels of supervisory controllers. The local controllers operate independently to achieve local targets. The function of the supervisory controller is to reconcile the interaction of the local controllers to achieve the 'best' overall performance. The multilevel concept has some similarity with cascade control but is not so amenable to analysis. Multilevel control gives rise to a pyramid-like structure, typified by that in Fig. 13.49.

At the base of the pyramid are the local controllers, monitoring and adjusting individual parameters in the overall process. At the next highest level the supervisory controllers 'oversee' a more complete picture of the process. The intermediate supervisory controllers have more input data to contend with and they might perhaps relax the control of one of the process variables while tightening up on another. This, of course, would only be done to benefit the process overall.

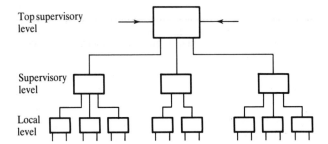

Figure 13.49 Multilevel control system.

The highest level of supervisory controller has the responsibility for the entire process. This controller may have access to additional input data which is not available to any of the lower level controllers. The main supervisory controller then is in overall 'command' and can influence any of the 'subordinate' controllers. The similarity between multilevel control and the organizational structure of an industrial company is not just coincidental. The latter is the structural model upon which the former is based.

A unified theory for complex control systems involving multilayer and multilevel concepts has yet to be formulated. However, at a more fundamental level, the digital control of complex plant and processes is already realizable. Adaptive and self-tuning controllers do exist and they are known to work well in practice. At this stage of development then, complex digital control systems are industrially functional and the users are already reaping the benefits associated with enhanced intelligence within the control system. While the application of these complex digital control systems are implemented by 'rule-of-thumb', rather than by mathematical fact, the success of the digital approach will ensure its continuance and ultimate progress.

Digital control principles, and their subsequent application to real mechanical systems, acts as an integrating factor for all of the previous topics covered in this book. It is only when a real industrial problem has to be faced that all of the previous knowledge is sifted, gathered together and finally fused into a working solution. The general design solution to an automation problem will involve the selection of measuring transducers, signal conditioning interfaces, A/D, D/A and other communication interfaces, power actuators and various controllers to suit a particular application. A suitable control strategy will then have to be implemented in some form of program language and the system performance will have to be evaluated and perhaps modified. System evaluation and modification are likely to involve modelling and simulation of the system in order to assess the response to variable system parameters. This multi-disciplinary approach to a problem is embodied within the general philosophy associated with mechatronics. In the final chapter which follows, we hope to be able to illustrate, to a limited extent, the multi-disciplinary nature of a mechatronic solution to a restricted range of particular problems.

FURTHER READING

Babb, M. (1989) 'Implementing distributed control in the 1990s', *Control Engineering*, August.

Bollinger, J. G. and N. A. Duffie (1988) *Computer Control of Machines and Processes*, Addison-Wesley, Reading, Mass.

Cahill, S. J. (1987) *The Single Chip Microcomputer*, Prentice-Hall, Englewood Cliffs, NJ.

Cassel, D. A. (1983) *Microcomputers and Modern Control Engineering*, Reston Publishing, Reston, Virginia.

Crispin, A. J. (1990) *Programmable Logic Controllers and their Engineering Applications*, McGraw-Hill, London.

Doebelin, E. O. (1985) *Control System Principles and Design*, Wiley, New York.

Franklin, G. F., J. D. Powell and M. L. Workman (1990) *Digital Control of Dynamic Systems*, 2nd edn, Addison-Wesley, Reading, Mass.

Kraus, T. and T. J. Myron (1984) 'Self-tuning PID controller uses pattern recognition approach', *Control Engineering*, June.

Kuo, B. C. (1990) *Digital Control Systems*, Holt-Rinehart & Winston, New York.

Leigh, J. R. (1985) *Applied Digital Control*, 2nd edn, Prentice-Hall, New York.

Pessen, D. W. (1989) *Industrial Automation—Circuit Design and Components*, Wiley, New York.

Swainston, F. A. (1991) *Systems Approach to Programmable Controllers*, Newnes-Butterworth Heinemann, Oxford.

Warnock, I. G. (1988) *Programmable Controllers: Operation and Application*, Prentice-Hall, London.

Webb, J. W. (1988) *Programmable Controllers—Principles and Applications*, Merrill Publishing Company, Columbus, Ohio.

EXERCISES

13.1 Using the technique of partial fractions, determine the corresponding z-transforms of the Laplace transforms given as:

$$(a) \quad G(s) = \frac{1}{(s+a)(s+b)} \qquad (b) \quad G(s) = \frac{ab}{s(s+a)(s+b)}$$

$$\left[\frac{1}{(a-b)} \frac{z[e^{-bT} - e^{-aT}]}{(z - e^{-bT})(z - e^{-aT})} ; \quad \frac{z}{z-1} + \frac{b}{(a-b)} \frac{z}{(z - e^{-aT})} - \frac{a}{(a-b)} \frac{z}{(z - e^{-bT})} \right]$$

13.2 Determine the corresponding z-transform of the Laplace transform given as:

$$G(s) = a^2 / [s(s+a)^2]$$

$$\left[\frac{z}{z-1} - \frac{z}{z - e^{-aT}} - \frac{zaTe^{-aT}}{(z - e^{-aT})^2} \right]$$

13.3 Write a BASIC program to solve Eq. (13.14) and develop a suitable graphics routine to display the computed process variable PV as a function of time. Figures 13.8 and 13.9 can be used as a basis for comparison.

13.4 Determine the pole locations of the closed-loop transfer function given as:

$$PV(z)/SP(z) = z/[z^2 + z + 0.4]$$

Hence comment on the system transient response.

$$[-0.5 +/- j0.775, \text{ stable oscillation}]$$

13.5 A process is modelled as a first-order system in which the process gain $k = 1$, and the process time constant $\tau = 1$ s. A digital proportional controller with variable gain K is used to output the control effort to the process and the sampling time is $T = 0.1$ s. The system uses unity feedback to close the control loop. Plot the pole locus for increasing gain and determine the maximum value of K corresponding to marginal stability.

$$[20.05]$$

13.6 In a digital temperature control system the process can be modelled as a first-order system with a time constant of 20 s, and a system gain of $k = 0.1$. A digital proportional controller with a gain $K = 5$ is used to control the temperature using a unity feedback loop. The sampling time is 1 s.
  (a) Determine the closed-loop transfer function and state the significance of the pole location.
  (b) If the controller gain is variable, determine the maximum value corresponding to marginal stability.

$$[PV(z)/SP(z) = 0.122/(z - 0.829), \ 80]$$

13.7 A process is modelled with a transfer function $G(s) = K/s^2$, where K is a variable. Show that this system is always unstable even if the sampling time approaches zero.

13.8 A process is modelled with an open-loop transfer function in the form $G(s) = 4/(s+3)$. A proportional digital controller, with a gain of 3 is used to output the control effort to the process and the loop is closed with a unity feedback line. Determine the maximum sampling time T for the system to remain stable.

$$[0.17 \text{ s}]$$

13.9 Compare and contrast the application of microcomputers (PCs) and programmable logic controllers (PLCs) for digital control applications.

13.10 Discuss the advantages and disadvantages of inputting ladder logic instructions into a PLC by using either a hand-held programmer or by using a PC with appropriate software.

13.11 Develop a ladder logic program which would output a square wave signal at a frequency of 5 Hz. The operation is to be started by a normally open spring return start switch, stopped at any time if required by a normally closed spring return stop switch, and 100 cycles are to be produced before a normal stop.

13.12 Consider the *time driven* sequence control example with the ladder logic program given in Fig. 13.30. The system is to be made *event driven* by adding two level sensors and a temperature switch. Draw the corresponding ladder logic diagram for the required sequence.

13.13 Part of an automatic bottle filling system with a motor (Y1) driven conveyor belt is shown in Fig. Q13.13. Sensor X1 at the side of the transport conveyor is used to detect the presence of a bottle and stop the belt. A measured quantity of liquid in a prefill tank is then discharged into the bottle by opening valve Y2. Sensors X2 and X3 are used to set the quantity discharged by controlling valve Y3 appropriately. Both valves are solenoid operated and the level sensors are ON when the liquid covers the sensor. An ON/OFF switch is used to start the system or stop it at any time if necessary.

(a) Specify clearly the sequence of operations for the system.
(b) Draw an explicit flow diagram for the operation of the system which could be translated into computer code.
(c) Draw a ladder relay logic diagram for the control of the system using a PLC.

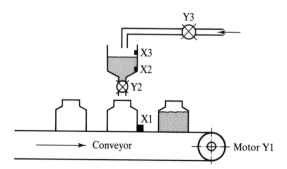

Figure Q13.13

13.14 A large vessel used in a food processing industry is shown diagrammatically in Fig. Q13.14 and is cleaned according to the following sequence:

The spring-loaded normally open start button switch operates a solenoid (Y0) which allows water to enter the vessel. The tank fills with water until the upper level switch (X2) operates and then the water is turned off. The stirrer is then operated by motor (Y1) for a period of 5 min.

After the 5 min cleaning period the stirrer stops and the outlet pump motor (Y2) is switched on. The water level is then allowed to drop until the lower level switch (X3) operates. At this stage the cleaning cycle is complete and the pump is switched off.

A spring loaded normally closed stop switch (X1) can be used at any time to stop the process. Draw a ladder logic diagram for the control of the described sequence.

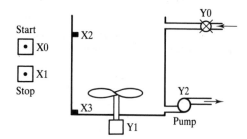

Figure Q13.14

13.15 Two double-acting pneumatic cylinders are to sequence, after a normally open start switch has been activated, as follows:

$$A+; B+; B-; A-$$

A normally closed stop switch can stop the operation at any time.
The electro-pneumatic control valves used are:

valve to switch air into supply manifold	2/2-way, solenoid with spring return
valve to control direction of cylinder A	4/2-way, solenoid operated
valve to control direction of cylinder B	4/2-way, solenoid operated

Develop a ladder logic diagram which would provide the sequence.

13.16 Repeat exercise 13.15 with directional control valves that are solenoid operated pilot controlled.

APPLICATIONS TO MECHATRONIC SYSTEMS

14.1 INTRODUCTION

In this final chapter it is our intention to provide detailed descriptions of some of the applications of the principles which have been covered in the preceding chapters of the book. We hope that the descriptions of the solutions devised for the problems considered will be useful to those readers who have been faced, or are likely to be faced, with similar problems. The applications also serve to illustrate the integration of subject material generally associated with a mechatronic solution to a particular problem.

14.2 SIMULATION OF A DC MOTOR DRIVE WITH A P + I CONTROLLER

The physical system to be simulated consists of a high inertial load with some inherent bearing friction. This load is driven by a DC motor through a 100/1 reduction gearbox. The basic system is illustrated in schematic form in Fig. 14.1. This system is to incorporate a P + I controller and the control loop is to be closed with a unity feedback line. The purpose of the simulation is to establish the optimum settings for the controller gain and the integral time constant for use in the actual system.

The following system parameters have been measured, or are otherwise known:

Motor armature inertia, $J_m = 0.1 \, \text{kg m}^2$
Armature resistance, $R = 0.5 \, \text{ohms}$
Armature inductance, $L = 0.1 \, \text{H}$
Motor bearing friction, $F_1 = 0.05 \, \text{Nm s/rad}$
Load bearing friction, $F_2 = 200 \, \text{Nm s/rad}$
Load inertia, $J_L = 800 \, \text{kg m}^2$
Gear ratio, $K_G = 100/1$
Transmission efficiency, $\eta = 0.9$

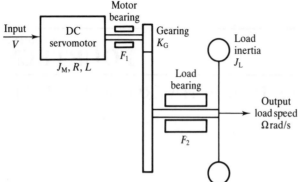

Figure 14.1 High inertial load with DC motor drive.

The armature equation takes the same form given as Eq. (12.14) (Sec. 12.2), i.e.

$$V = E + L\,di/dt + Ri \tag{14.1}$$

where V = armature voltage
E = back e.m.f. generated by the armature winding
L = inductance of the armature winding
R = resistance of the armature
i = armature current

The back e.m.f. is directly related to the motor speed:

$$E = K_e\omega \tag{14.2}$$

where K_e is the e.m.f. constant given as 0.2 V s/rad and ω is the motor speed in rad/sec. Expressing Eq. (14.2) in terms of the load speed gives

$$E = K_e K_G \Omega = 0.2 \times 100 \times \Omega = 20\Omega \tag{14.3}$$

The motor torque is proportional to the armature current

$$T_M = K_t i \tag{14.4}$$

For the motor in question, $K_t = 0.2\,\text{Nm A}^{-1}$.

If we denote the load speed as Ω rad/s, then the power required to drive the load is

$$P = T\Omega \tag{14.5}$$

where T is the torque which would be required to drive the load directly. Note that

$$T = J_L\alpha + F\Omega = J_L(d\Omega/dt) + F\Omega \tag{14.6}$$

where α is the angular acceleration of the load in rad/s^2.

From Eqs (14.5) and (14.6) we obtain

$$P = [J_L\,d\Omega/dt + F\Omega]\Omega \tag{14.7}$$

Equation (14.7) gives the power required to drive the load directly. The source of the driving torque, however, is supplied from the motor through the gearbox. The relationship between the power required by the load and that supplied from the motor is given as

$$P = (T_M\omega\eta) = [(J_L + J_M\eta K_G^2)d\Omega/\,dt]\Omega + [F_2 + (F_1\eta K_G^2)]\Omega^2 \tag{14.8}$$

Note that in scaling the motor inertia and friction terms to the load speed, through the square of the gearing ratio, the transmission efficiency η must also be taken into account.

Dividing Eq. (14.8) through by Ω, gives

$$T_M(\omega/\Omega)\eta = (J_L J_M \eta K_G^2)\mathrm{d}\Omega/\,\mathrm{d}t + [F_2 + (F_1 \eta K_G^2)]\Omega \tag{14.9}$$

The speed ratio (ω/Ω) is also defined as the gearing ratio K_G, thus

$$T_M K_G \eta = (J_L + J_M \eta K_G^2)\mathrm{d}\Omega/\,\mathrm{d}t + [F_2 + (F_1 \eta K_G^2)]\Omega \tag{14.10}$$

Substituting the quoted numerical values gives

$$T_M \times 100 \times 0.9 = (800 + 0.1 \times 0.9 \times 100^2)\,\mathrm{d}\Omega/\mathrm{d}t + [200 + (0.05 \times 0.9 \times 100^2)]\Omega$$
$$90 T_M = 1700(\mathrm{d}\Omega/\mathrm{d}t) + 650\Omega \tag{14.11}$$

Using these physical relationships, it is possible to model the system in terms of the load speed Ω, as a function of time. From Eq. (14.4), for the motor torque, we obtain

$$\mathrm{d}T_M/\mathrm{d}t = 0.2\,\mathrm{d}i/\mathrm{d}t \quad\text{or}\quad \mathrm{d}i/\mathrm{d}t = 5\,\mathrm{d}T_M/\mathrm{d}t \tag{14.12}$$

and

$$i = 5T_M \tag{14.13}$$

Differentiating Eq. (14.11) with respect to time

$$90\,\mathrm{d}T_M/\mathrm{d}t = 1700\,\mathrm{d}^2\Omega/\mathrm{d}t^2 + 650\,\mathrm{d}\Omega/\mathrm{d}t \tag{14.14}$$

and from Eq. (14.12)

$$\mathrm{d}T_M/\mathrm{d}t = 0.2\,\mathrm{d}i/\mathrm{d}t = [1700\,\mathrm{d}^2\Omega/\mathrm{d}t^2 + 650\,\mathrm{d}\Omega/\mathrm{d}t]/90$$

giving

$$\mathrm{d}i/\mathrm{d}t = (5/90)[1700\,\mathrm{d}^2\Omega/\mathrm{d}t^2 + 650\,\mathrm{d}\Omega/\mathrm{d}t] \tag{14.15}$$

Similarly, from Eqs (14.11) and (14.13):

$$i = (5/90)[1700\,\mathrm{d}\Omega/\mathrm{d}t + 650\Omega] \tag{14.16}$$

Substituting Eqs. (14.3), (14.15) and (14.16) into Eq. (14.1) gives

$$V = 20\Omega + (5L/90)[1700\,\mathrm{d}^2\Omega/\mathrm{d}t^2 + 650\,\mathrm{d}\Omega/\mathrm{d}t] + (5R/90)[1700\,\mathrm{d}\Omega/\mathrm{d}t + 650\Omega]$$

For $L = 0.1\,\mathrm{H}$ and $R = 0.5\,\mathrm{ohms}$, the voltage equation becomes

$$(90/5)V = (90 \times 20/5)\Omega + [170\,\mathrm{d}^2\Omega/\mathrm{d}t^2 + 65\,\mathrm{d}\Omega/\mathrm{d}t] + [850\,\mathrm{d}\Omega/\mathrm{d}t + 325\Omega]$$

or

$$170\,\mathrm{d}^2\Omega/\mathrm{d}t^2 + 915\,\mathrm{d}\Omega/\mathrm{d}t + 685\Omega = (90/5)V$$

hence

$$\mathrm{d}^2\Omega/\mathrm{d}t^2 + 5.382\,\mathrm{d}\Omega/\mathrm{d}t + 4.029\Omega = 0.1059V \tag{14.17}$$

Writing Eq. (14.17) in terms of the Laplace variable gives

$$\Omega(s)[s^2 + 5.382s + 4.029] = 0.1059V(s)$$

i.e.

$$\Omega(s)/V(s) = 0.1059/[s^2 + 5.382s + 4.029] \tag{14.18}$$

Equation (14.18) gives the open loop transfer function for the complete system in Laplace notation. It is clear that the system conforms to the standard second-order type. Comparison of Eq. (14.17) with the standard form, i.e. Eq. 4.6, shows that

$$\omega_n^2 = 4.029 \quad \text{or} \quad \omega_n = \sqrt{4.029} = 2.007\,\text{rad/s}$$

and

$$2\zeta\omega_n = 5.382 \quad \text{or} \quad \zeta = 5.382/(2 \times 2.007) = 1.34$$

Also

$$k_s\omega_n^2 = 0.1059 \quad \text{or} \quad k_s = 0.1059/4.029 = 0.02628$$

where k_s is the physical system gain.

The motor and its driven load is therefore represented mathematically as a second-order, overdamped system. The analytical solution for an overdamped second-order system is given as Eq. (4.9). For the system considered:

$$\Omega = G\,\exp[-\zeta\omega_n t - (\omega_n\sqrt{\zeta^2-1})t] + H\,\exp[-\zeta\omega_n t + (\omega_n\sqrt{\zeta^2-1})t] + A \qquad (14.19)$$

where A is the particular integral, or steady-state solution, and G and H are arbitrary constants. The particular integral is

$$A = k_s\omega_n^2[s^2 + 2\zeta\omega_n s + \omega_n^2]^{-1}V(s)$$

i.e.

$$A = k_s[1 + \{(s^2/\omega_n^2) + (2\zeta s/\omega_n)\}]^{-1}(10)$$

For the step input of 10 V, all derivatives are equal to zero. The solution of the particular integral therefore gives

$$A = k_s(10) = 0.02628 \times (10) = 0.2628$$

i.e. the final steady-state load speed output is 0.2628 rad/s.
Substituting the numerical values of ω_n and ζ into Eq. (14.19) gives

$$\Omega = G\,\exp(-4.48t) + H\,\exp(-0.9t) + A \qquad (14.20)$$

The constants G and H are determined by the initial conditions at time $t = 0$: thus at time $t = 0$, $\Omega = 0$. Equation (14.20) gives

$$G + H = -A = -0.2628 \qquad (14.21)$$

Also at time $t = 0$, $d\Omega/dt = 0$. Differentiation of Eq. (14.20) gives

$$d\Omega/dt = 0 = -4.48G\,\exp(-4.48t) - 0.9H\,\exp(-0.9t)$$

i.e.

$$-4.48G - 0.9H = 0 \qquad (14.22)$$

Solving Eqs. (14.21) and (14.22) simultaneously gives $G = 0.066$ and $H = -0.329$. The complete solution for the output load speed then becomes

$$\Omega = 0.066\,e^{-4.48t} - 0.329\,e^{-0.9t} + 0.2628\,\text{rad/s} \qquad (14.23)$$

A plot of the solution to Eq. (14.23) is shown in Fig. 14.2. The actual system response, for a step input of 10 V, compares favourably with Fig. 14.2 and provides confirmation of the validity of the system model developed.

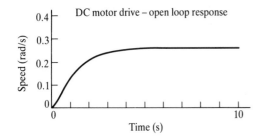

Figure 14.2 Output load speed response to a step input of 10 V.

The system is to be controlled by a P + I controller and it remains to determine the optimum values for the controller settings. The form of the open-loop response shown in Fig. 14.2 is similar to the reaction curve shown in Fig. 11.20. This might suggest that the system could be modelled as a first-order system with a transport delay. Using the empirical rules of Zeigler and Nichols (Sec. 11.6), an apparent dead time of $T_1 = 0.1$ s, and an apparent time constant of $T_2 = 1.9$ s can be measured from the response. Using Table 11.2, this gives optimum controller settings of

$$K = 0.9T_2/(k \times T_1) = 0.9 \times 1.9/(0.1059 \times 0.1) = 160$$

and

$$T_i = T_1/0.3 - 0.1/0.3 = 1/3 = 0.333 \text{ s}$$

Note however that if the inductance of the armature coil was 0.01 H, then the open-loop response curve is similar, but the dead time becomes too small to be measured accurately. This is the more usual case for a fast acting mechanism, and the open-loop reaction curve cannot then be used with any confidence in estimating the appropriate controller settings.

We already know however that the system is an overdamped second-order type and the above simplification can only give a first approximation for the controller settings. A more scientific approach is to complete the model of the closed-loop system and to experiment with various controller settings in a simulation of the closed-loop system response. The complete system is shown in block diagram form in Fig. 14.3.

The transfer function for the controller is

$$C(s) = K[1 + 1/(T_i s)] \tag{14.24}$$

Equation (14.18) gives the open-loop transfer function $G(s)$ for the controlled system. The closed-loop transfer function is given by Eq. (11.20). Thus

$$PV(s)/SP(s) = C(s)G(s)/[1 + C(s)G(s)] \tag{11.20}$$

Now

$$C(s)G(s) = K[1 + 1/(T_i s)] \times [k_s \omega_n^2/(s^2 + 2\zeta\omega_n s + \omega_n^2)]$$
$$= K[T_i s + 1] \times [k/\{T_i(s^3 + 2\zeta\omega_n s^2 + \omega_n^2 s)\}]$$

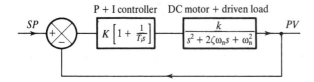

Figure 14.3 Closed loop DC motor drive system with P + I controller.

where $k = k_s\omega_n^2$. The closed-loop transfer function for the complete system then becomes

$$\frac{PV(s)}{SP(s)} = \frac{kK[T_i s + 1]}{T_i s^3 + 2\zeta\omega_n T_i s^2 + T_i\omega_n^2 s + kK[T_i s + 1]} \tag{14.25}$$

Defining the following variables

$$A = kK = k_s\omega_n^2 K = 0.02628 \times 4.029 \times K = 0.1059K$$
$$B = 2\zeta\omega_n = 2 \times 1.34 \times 2.007 = 5.378$$
$$C = \omega_n^2 = 4.029$$

then Eq. (14.25) can be rewritten as

$$\frac{PV(s)}{SP(s)} = \frac{A[s + (1/T_i)]}{s^3 + Bs^2 + Cs + A[s + (1/T_i)]} \tag{14.26}$$

In differential form, Eq. (14.26) becomes

$$\frac{d^3 PV}{dt^3} + B\frac{d^2 PV}{dt^2} + C\frac{dPV}{dt} + A\left[\frac{dPV}{dt} + \frac{PV}{T_i}\right] = A\left[\frac{dSP}{dt} + \frac{SP}{T_i}\right]$$

or

$$\dddot{PV} + B\ddot{PV} + (C + A)\dot{PV} + (A/T_i)PV = A\dot{SP} + (A/T_i)SP$$

The final form of the closed-loop transfer function shows that the closed-loop speed response of the system is governed by a third-order differential equation. Comparisons with standard system equations cannot be applied in this case and we must therefore resort to some other method for a solution. The state-variable technique presented in Sec. 11.11 provides a very effective and consistent method for handling higher-order equations.

Solving for the highest derivative in PV gives

$$\dddot{PV} = A\dot{SP} + (A/T_i)SP - B\ddot{PV} - (C + A)\dot{PV} - (A/T_i)PV \tag{14.27}$$

Equation (14.27) can be represented in the block diagram form depicted in Fig. 14.4. Choosing state variables $X1 = PV : X2 = \dot{PV} : X3 = \ddot{PV}$, allows the system to be defined as

$$\dot{X1} = X2 \tag{14.28}$$

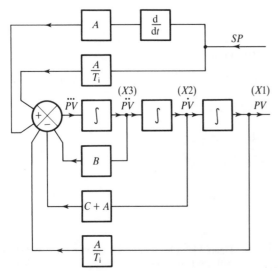

Figure 14.4 Block diagram representation of Eq. (14.27).

$$\dot{X}2 = X3 \qquad (14.29)$$

$$\dot{X}3 = P\ddot{V} = A[\dot{SP} + SP/T_{\mathrm{i}}] - BX3 - (C + A)X2 - X1/T_{\mathrm{i}} \qquad (14.30)$$

The starting values at time $t = 0$, are $X1 = X2 = X3 = 0$. A finite difference approximation of Eqs (14.28) to (14.30) can then be solved for a time increment of, say, $\mathrm{d}t = 0.01\,\mathrm{s}$ and a step input of $SP = 0.25\,\mathrm{rad/s}$. Program 14.1 takes a keyboard input of the controller gain K, the integral time constant T_{i}, and is also written generally to accept any keyboard input of the desired set point speed in rad/s. The state equations are then solved and a non-dimensional graphical display is shown of the output load speed response as a function of time.

Program 14.1 Simulation of the closed-loop speed response of a DC motor-driven load.

```
REM Closed loop system response
REM Initialisation and variable inputs
SCREEN 9:COLOR 4,7:KEY OFF:CLS
T=10
DT=.01
N=T/DT
DIM X1(N),X2(N),X3(N)
LOCATE 4,6:INPUT"Controller gain = ";KC
LOCATE 6,6:INPUT"Integral time constant = ";TI
LOCATE 8,6:INPUT"Required speed, rad/sec = ";SPEED
KS=.1059
WN=2.0075
ZETA=1.3406
CLS
REM F-D simulation
X1(1)=0:X2(1)=0:X3(1)=0
A=KS*KC
B=2*ZETA*WN
C=WN*WN
D=A/TI
REM Solution of system equations
FOR I=2 TO N
IF I=2 THEN DSP=SPEED ELSE DSP=0
IF I=2 THEN SP=0 ELSE SP=SPEED
DX3=DT*(A*(DSP/DT+SP/TI)-B*X3(I-1)-(C+A)*X2(I-1)-D*X1(I-1))
X3(I)=X3(I-1)+DX3
DX2=DT*X3(I)
X2(I)=X2(I-1)+DX2
DX1=DT*X2(I)
X1(I)=X1(I-1)+DX1
NEXT I
REM Graphical output
LOCATE 6,8:PRINT"DC motor drive - closed loop response with P+I controller"
LOCATE 8,18:PRINT"Controller gain, K = ";KC
LOCATE 9,18:PRINT"Integral time, Ti = ";TI
LOCATE 13,2:PRINT"SP"
LOCATE 23,34:PRINT"Time - sec"
```

```
LOCATE 23,68:PRINT"10"
LINE (40,300)-(40,100)
LINE (40,300)-(550,300)
FOR J=0 TO 24 STEP 3
LINE (40+J*20,180)-(40+(J+1)*20,180)
NEXT J
FOR J=1 TO 10
LINE (40+J*50,305)-(40+J*50,295)
NEXT J
REM Plot of system response
T=0-DT
FOR K=2 TO N
T=T+DT
LINE (40+T*50,300-X1(K-1)*120/SPEED)-(40+(T+DT)*50,300-X1(K)*120/SPEED),1
NEXT K
LOCATE 22,2
```

With controller settings $K = 160$ and $T_i = 0.333$, as suggested by the open-loop reaction curve, the output response would be regarded as too oscillatory for most practical purposes. A more acceptable speed response is shown in Fig. 14.5 for controller settings of $K = 120$ and $T_i = 0.6\,\text{s}$. With these controller settings, the steady-state speed is reached in about 3 s with an acceptable amount of overshoot. The actual system, with these controller settings, behaves much as predicted by the simulation.

To a practising control engineer, the numerical value of the controller gain K might at first seem to be exceptionally large. The high value of the controller gain is a consequence of the fact that we have elected to express the process variable, i.e. the load speed, in terms of rad/s. If we had decided to quote the load speed in terms of rev/s then Eq. (14.3), for example, would be written as

$$E = 20\Omega = (20/2\pi)N = 10N/\pi \tag{14.31}$$

where N is the load speed in rev/s. Using the substitution $N = \Omega/2\pi$ throughout the system of governing equations, the reader may show, as an exercise, that the resulting differential equation for the load speed becomes

$$\mathrm{d}^2 N/\mathrm{d}t^2 + 5.382\,\mathrm{d}N/\mathrm{d}t + 4.029N = 0.665V \tag{14.32}$$

The constants appearing on the left-hand side are exactly the same as those in Eq. (14.17). This should not be a surprise since these are physical constants which define the system dynamics. The system gain on the right-hand side, however, is different. The ratio of the system gain

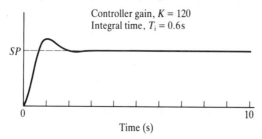

DC motor drive – closed loop response with P + I controller

Controller gain, $K = 120$
Integral time, $T_i = 0.6\,\text{s}$

SP

0
10

Time (s)

Figure 14.5 Closed-loop speed response for a step input.

values, in fact, is the numerical parameter (2π) which is the constant of proportionality between speed in rad/s and the corresponding speed in rev/s.

In addition the system response to the same step input would have the exact same form as shown in Fig. 14.2, except that the vertical axis would be scaled by the factor (2π). This, however, has implications on the appropriate value selected for the controller gain K. Using Table 11.2, the optimum value of the controller gain, according to the rules of Ziegler and Nichols, would be $0.9 \times 1.9/(0.665 \times 0.1) = 25.7$. When the process variable was defined in terms of rad/s, the optimum controller gain was 160. The important point to be aware of here is that if the system gain has physical units then this will influence the numerical value of the controller gain. The integral time constant T_i is unaltered, however, since it is simply related to the system apparent dead time and apparent time constant, both of which are independent of the units chosen.

The process control industry is well aware of this problem and current industrial practice is to define the process variable as a percentage of the maximum value, or span. The set point and error signal are also expressed in terms of a percentage of the span. This unified approach imparts a non-dimensional quality to the system variables and eliminates the problems associated with physical units.

For the system considered the maximum input voltage to the drive motor is 12 V. On open-loop test, a step input of 12 V results in a steady-state load speed of 0.315 rad/s. This is the maximum load speed which the system is capable of delivering and the span is therefore 0–0.315 rad/s. If the process variable is now defined as a percentage of the span then we can write

$$PV\% = 100\Omega/0.315 = 317.5\Omega \tag{14.33}$$

where Ω, as before, is the actual load speed in rad/s.

Making the substitution $\Omega = PV\%/317.5$, and working again through the governing equations, we arrive at the following relation for the process variable:

$$\mathrm{d}^2(PV\%)/\mathrm{d}t^2 + 5.382\,\mathrm{d}(PV\%)/\mathrm{d}t + 4.029PV\% = 33.62V \tag{14.34}$$

The system open-loop response is again the same, apart from the vertical axis scaling factor, but the optimum value of the controller gain, according to Ziegler and Nichols, is now about 0.51.

Although this application, as presented, does not involve any hardware as such, it is a good illustration of how a real system can be modelled, and the fine tuning of the industrial controller investigated by simulation.

 ## 14.3 CONTROL OF A PICK AND PLACE PNEUMATIC ROBOT

The operation which is most commonly encountered in any automated manufacturing process is the handling of components by movement from place to place. This is typical of automated assembly where, up until a few years ago, automation and adapting to changing market or customer needs were virtually incompatible. This is no longer the case as modern modular construction concepts can be implemented by virtue of the flexibility and intelligence level possible with microprocessor-based control. A large variety of standardized components and modules are available on the market to the designer of mechatronic systems. These devices provide economical solutions for mechanization and automation for a variety of assembly tasks.

Many automated assembly processes involving say 20 parts, as in the automotive industry, require the application of a high-level intelligent industrial robot such as a Unimate PUMA or a SCARA type robot. Basic pick and place activities can however be conducted with relatively simple mechanical mechanisms.

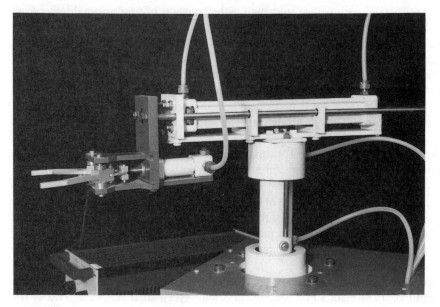

Figure 14.6 A pick and place pneumatic robot.

Pneumatically Operated Pick and Place Robot

The robot is shown in Fig. 14.6 and has three degrees of freedom as follows:

1. Rotation of 180° by means of a rotary pneumatic actuator.
2. Vertical lift movement by means of a double acting pneumatic cylinder.
3. Extension reach movement by means of a double acting pneumatic cylinder.

A gripping action is achieved by a single-acting/spring-return pneumatic cylinder with a mechanical wedge arrangement.

The directional control valves associated with the pneumatic actuators are solenoid operated with spring return and a typical pick and place repeating sequence is:

extend–grip–lift–retract–rotate forward–extend–down–release grip–retract–rotate backward

An air ON/OFF valve is also incorporated in the pneumatic circuit.

Controller

The low-level controller chosen for operating the pick and place device is based on Intel 8086/8088 technology—the uE188 microcontroller. This single-board controller is a high-density control module manufactured by GNC Electronics of Diss in Norfolk. It is based around the powerful 80188 microprocessor. The board measures 100 mm by 80 mm and features 48 digital I/O lines and up to 64K bytes of memory. A 20 MHz crystal clocks the CPU at 10 MHz. The uE188 is fully CMOS and requires very little power. The software is compatible with the 8086/8088 assembly language. An EPROM resident user program can be executed by applying a system reset. Alternatively the 80188 can condition its own reset pulse to execute codes directly on power up.

The board has 32K of RAM and either 8, 16 or 32K of EPROM, depending upon configuration. When operating with 8K of EPROM the memory map is basically:

```
00000–7FFFF  32K RAM
08000–FCFFF  No-man's land
FE000–FFFFF  8K EPROM
```

Memory decoding is performed through internal registers in the 80188 and is fully programmable by the user by means of an on-board chip-select unit. This simplifies the interfacing of memory because memory address decoders and I/O port decoders are built into the 80188. Hence in small systems such as the uE188 no additional decoding hardware is necessary. Information is supplied by the manufacturer for the setting up of the chip select registers for all memory and I/O peripheral devices.

There are two 8255PPIs on board and the port addresses in hex are as follows:

	PPI-1	PPI-2
portA	000	080
portB	001	081
portC	002	082
control register	003	083

Whenever an 80X86 family microprocessor is RESET it starts to execute instructions held from the memory location FFFF0. This location would normally contain a JUMP (JMP) instruction which directs execution of the codes held at the start address of the EPROM, which in this case is FE000.

The application program, written in 8086 assembly language, can then easily be accommodated within a set framework which sets up the decoding of memory and peripheral I/O in addition to defining the RESET condition.

Software Development System

The basic requirements are a PC-based editor and an assembler with a means of transferring the codes into the EPROM socket on the uE188 target system. An alternative to actually blowing the EPROM is to use an EPROM emulator during the software development stage. The one chosen for this application is the PROMulator supplied by SMART Communications of Barnet in Herts. This can be used to emulate EPROMs which include CMOS types from 8K (2716) to 128K (27010). It connects to the parallel printer port of an IBM PC compatible and the assembled codes are transmitted to the EPROM socket on the target system using the software utilities supplied. Emulation saves endless time developing software for embedded applications and once a working program has been obtained an EPROM can be blown to give a stand-alone cost effective controller. Figure 14.7 shows the general layout of the controller board and the PROMulator.

There are a number of 8086 assemblers available on the market and the one used in this case is A86 purchased through 'Shareware Marketing'. It accepts assembly language source files and transfers them into either .COM or .OBJ files. The .COM file is always produced with an offset of 100 from the code segment address—i.e. CS:0100. The OBJ format can be used for feeding to a linker program. The procedure for obtaining executable codes in the target system is therefore:

1. Prepare source code, say pprobot.asm, using an editor.
2. Assemble the source code with A86

  A86 pprobot.asm < CR >

  which produces the file pprobot.com.

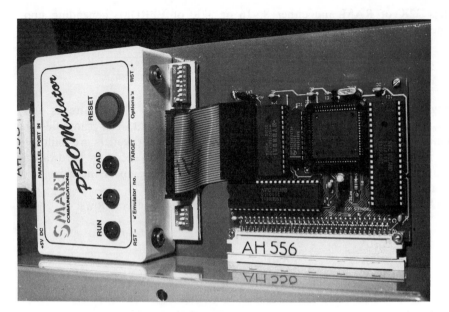

Figure 14.7 Single board microcontroller and PROMulator.

3. Transfer the COM file via the LPT1 port on the PC using the program LD.EXE supplied
   LD pprobot.com/8k < CR >
4. The resets on the PROMulator and the uE188 controller are then activated to run the program.

A debugging program D86 complements the A86 assembler and it is useful for the step-by-step execution of a program when running within the PC environment. It is useful for displaying memory and inserting break points. It will not operate, however, during execution within the target system.

Application Program to Control the Pick and Place Robot

Rather than develop a program in 8086 assembly language for the complete cycling operation, consider for illustrative purposes a routine which would give an operator, say, manual control of the robot movement. This is to take the form of an input switch pad connected to an input port such that an operator can switch on the air, extend the arm, lift the arm, rotate the arm and operate the gripper as required. The input switches are of the normally open type and the arrangement is such that a logic 0 corresponds to the activation of the switch. This input arrangement is shown in Fig. 14.8.

For example, the gripper can be closed and opened by keeping bit 0 ON and toggling bit 4 ON/OFF. The output port should therefore mimic the input port state in order to switch on the corresponding pneumatic actuator. The power switching interface consists of an inverter, an opto-isolator, a Darlington driver and a normally open electro-mechanical relay to switch in the 24 V DC power required by a valve solenoid. A logic 0 corresponds to the ON state.

A source code program listing is given in Program 14.2 and is illustrative of the configuring of the controller memory and peripheral I/O, the setting up of the segments, and the implementing of the system RESET to execute the codes.

Controller input port

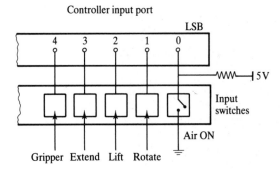

Figure 14.8 Input arrangement for a pick and place robot control.

Program 14.2 Configuration of the uE188 microcontroller and the control of the pick and place robot.

```
; Program pprobot.asm for the control of a pick and place pneumatic robot
; using the uE188 microcontroller with a 80188 microprocessor.

reseg    equ      0fe00h          ;start address of the 8K EPROM

porta    equ      000h            ;addresses for the ports on PPI-1
portb    equ      001h
portc    equ      002h
cntreg   equ      003h


rom      segment at reseg         ;set up code segment at bottom of EPROM
         assume  cs:rom
         org     0000

start:
rom      ends

code     segment                  ;set up other segments
         assume  cs:code

         mov     dx,0
         mov     es,dx
         mov     ss,dx
         mov     ds,dx            ;data segment starts at bottom of RAM
         mov     sp,08000h        ;set stack pointer at top of RAM

         mov     dx,0ffa2h        ;set up LMCS (Low Memory Chip Select)
         mov     ax,07fch         ;for 32K of RAM
         out     dx,ax

         mov     dx,0ffa4h ·      ;set up PACS (Peripheral Adapter Chip
         mov     ax,003eh         ;Select) to make 8255's start at 0000
         out     dx,ax

         mov     dx,0ffa8h        ;set MPCS (Memory Peripheral Chip Select)
```

```
        mov     ax,81b8h        ;for 8255's in I/O space
        out     dx,ax


;******************************************************************
; User application program goes in here

        mov     dx,cntreg       ;set up ports for PPI-1
                                ; A input and B/C output
        mov     al,90h
        out     dx,al

more:
        mov     dx,porta        ;read state of portA
        in      al,dx
        mov     dx,portb        ;output state to portB
        out     dx,al
        jmp     more            ;repeat continuously


;******************************************************************

;TAIL OF PROGRAM

        org     020f0h          ;transmitting a COM file with offset 100
                                ;code segment set for FE00, hence
                                ;absolute address is (20F0-100)+FE000
                                ;=FFFF0 which is the RESET vector address
        mov     dx,0ffa0h       ;set up UMCS ( Upper Memory Chip Select)
        mov     ax,0fe3ch       ;for 8K EPROM
        out     dx,ax
        jmp     far ptr start   ;jump instruction in RESET vector to
                                ;start of codes held at FE00:0000
;******************************************************************


code    ends

        end
```

14.4 CONTROL OF THE WATER LEVEL IN A TANK

The concept of closed-loop control is widely applied in industry particularly in the process sector. One such application is the control of the water level in a tank which supplies a process requirement. As this requirement changes then the inflow into the tank must be automatically adjusted to suit. The basic hardware needed for the control of the system is as below:

1. A level sensor
2. Input interface
3. A digital controller
4. Output interface
5. A flow control valve.

A program executed within the controller and implementing a P+I strategy will control the system to a specified set point level. The inputs to the program are the desired set point and the controller settings. The output from the controller is the control effort which is to be applied to the flow control valve in order to vary the flow from the pump into the tank when a change in set point, or discharge flow, occurs. The system is shown in Fig. 14.9. Figure 14.10 diagrammatically illustrates the interrelationship between the various hardware elements.

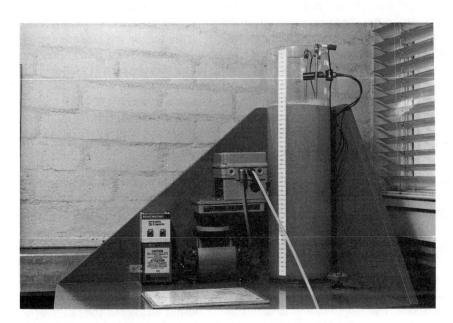

Figure 14.9 The level control system.

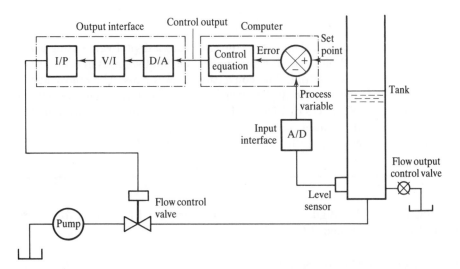

Figure 14.10 Hardware interconnection for level control loop.

Level Sensor

In order to utilize a computer-based control system it is necessary to be able to measure the level in the tank as a voltage, which in turn can be converted into a corresponding numerical value with an analogue-to-digital converter (ADC). Methods commonly employed for measuring level include:

1. *RF capacitance.* Operates on the principle that the amount of capacitance between a positively charged probe and the appropriate ground will increase as an empty tank is filled. The change in capacitance, which corresponds to the rise or fall of the level, is measurable using an invasive probe connected to capacitance based electronics. For a non-conductive fluid the ground is the tank wall. With conductive fluids an insulated probe is used and the capacitance through the probe insulation is used as a measure of the level.
2. *Ultrasonic.* Operates on the principle of sound navigation and ranging (SONAR). Non-contacting sensing can be used by mounting the transducer above the maximum fluid level in the tank. It transmits ultrasonic pulses down towards the surface. The pulses reflect and return to the transducer which then translates the time elapsed into a measure of distance.
3. *Float.* Operates with a float rising or falling with the fluid level. Various methods for translating this movement into a corresponding voltage level are available. These include the moving of a magnetic sleeve into or out of the field of a switch activating magnet or the turning of a potentiometer through a linkage.

However, for this application the level in the tank is measured simply by immersing two electrodes into the water (see Fig. 4.31). The electrical resistance between the electrodes varies according to the depth and this can be measured directly as a voltage. This principle of operation is basically to amplify the volt drop signal across a resistor which is placed in series with one of the electrodes. The amplification is such that an output voltage in the range of 0–2.55 V corresponds to the range of level in the tank. Although the relationship between voltage and level is slightly nonlinear, and not too satisfactory at small depths, the arrangement is inexpensive and suitable for illustrative purposes.

Input Interface

The voltage representative of the level in the tank is converted into a digital value using a ZN 439-8 ADC (RS 656-029). This has 8-bit resolution and can handle input voltages in the range of 0–2.55 V which suits the level sensor output. The conversion time is 5 ms. The conversion is started by a high to low pulse applied to the start conversion pin ($\overline{SC}$) on the integrated circuit package. The end of conversion (STATUS or EOC) is detected by a low to high transition. The 8 bits of data can then be read at an input port.

The circuit drawing for connecting up the ADC is given in Fig. 14.11.

Digital Controller

The controller is a PC fitted with a digital I/O card based on an 8255 PPI and set for a base address of 1B0 hex. The control system I/O involves:

- Reading the 8 bits from the ADC on port A.
- Writing 8 bits to a DAC using port B.
- Switching the supply pump ON (1) and OFF (0) using bit 7 of port C.

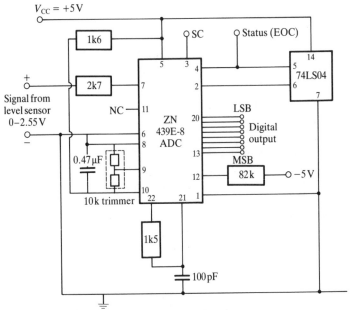

Figure 14.11 Electrical wiring diagram for the ADC.

- Starting the ADC process using bit 6 of port C.
- Checking the end-of-conversion status using bit 0 of port C.

The above requires port A to be input, port B to be output, the lower nibble of C to be input and the upper nibble of C to be output. The corresponding control word which is to be placed into the control register is 91 hex.

The pump which supplies water from a sump to the tank is driven by a single-phase 240 V AC motor and it can be switched on as required through a solid-state relay connected directly to PC7.

The calibration of the ADC output (I) read on port A for various set levels (h) yields a slightly nonlinear relationship which was curve-fitted using the least squares technique to give:

$$h\,\text{mm} = 0.0030\,I^2 + 0.79I + 30$$

The P + I control algorithm is coded in QUICKBASIC running on the PC.

Output Interface

The function of the output interface is to translate the output control effort evaluated within the range of 0–100 per cent into the physical movement of the flow control valve between the full-shut and the full-open position. Since it requires a torque to move the valve the final positioning element generally involves an electric, pneumatic or hydraulic actuator. This is usually mounted directly above the valve. A digital-to-analogue conversion normally starts the interfacing process in order to produce an analogue voltage range which is directly proportional to the control effort. A circuit diagram with a ZN 428E (RS 303-523) digital-to-analogue converter (DAC) is given in Fig. 14.12. The DAC is 8-bit resolution and generates a maximum voltage of 2.55 V which is then amplified using a 741 op amp to provide a voltage in the range 0–5 V to correspond with numerical values of 0–255. This is effectively the control effort as output from port B of the digital I/O card in the PC controller.

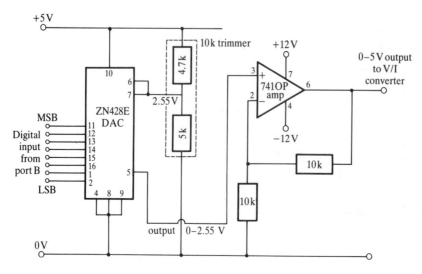

Figure 14.12 Electrical wiring diagram for the DAC.

The actuator, mounted above a Worcester Controls 44/45 15 mm diameter ball valve, is a Norbro 10 B40 R pneumatic actuator. This is based on a rack and pinion principle using opposed twin pistons which operate about a central drive shaft that rotates through 90°. The pistons are fixed on stainless steel guide rods running in bearings located in the end caps of the actuator housing. They are operated by an internal air distribution system which uses the hollow guide rods as air passages. The actuator is of the single-acting spring-return type with an anticlockwise movement, corresponding to the valve opening, which is proportional to the supply air pressure.

In order to achieve accurate positioning of the valve over the 0–90° travel a controlled pressure supply to the pneumatic actuator is required. This is achieved by an Eckardt Electro-Pneumatic Positioner, SRI 982, which is mounted directly on to the top of the actuator pinion spindle. The positioner generates a controlled pressure within the range of 3–15 lbf in^{-2} from an input of 4–20 mA. The 3 lbf in^{-2} (4 mA) corresponds to the valve shut position and the 15 lbf in^{-2} (20 mA) to the valve being fully open. A mechanical pointer clearly indicates the degree of opening. The positioner is designed for the direct operation of pneumatically controlled valves from analogue control signals.

Most process control hardware operates with 4–20 mA signals and since the DAC outputting the control effort produces a voltage it is necessary to incorporate a voltage-to-current signal converter to complete the output interface. The one used is a Moore Industries SCT signal converter. The standard unit consists of a single printed circuit board on which all electronic components are mounted. It converts input voltages in the range of 0–5 V into currents of 4–20 mA and additionally provides isolation between a floating input and a common ground output.

To summarize, the complete output interface for generating a flow control valve movement which is proportional to the control effort evaluated from a control strategy is:

1. Control effort (U) as a percentage 0–100 is evaluated within the control of algorithm.
2. U corresponds to a range of 0–255 for an 8-bit resolution DAC.
3. U is output to the DAC to produce voltages in the range 0–5 V.
4. This voltage is converted into a current (V/I) within the range 4–20 mA.

5. The current is converted into a pressure (I/P) within the range 3–15 lbf in^{-2}.
6. This pressure, applied to the positioner, physically moves a pneumatic actuator fitted directly above the actual 90° movement ball valve.

These elements are illustrated in Fig. 14.9.

Control Software

The requirements of the control software for implementing a P + I strategy are as follows:

1. Input the required set point level (*SP*) and controller settings for proportional band (*PB*) and integral time (T_i).
2. Read level in tank (*PV*).
3. Calculate error value as a percentage of the span of the level which is 400 mm, i.e.

$$E = 100^*(SP - PV)/400$$

4. Evaluate the control effort (*U*) as a percentage value within the range 0–100 from:

$$U = KE + K/T_i \int E \, dt$$

5. Output the control effort from a port.
6. Repeat from step 2.

For this to be conducted discretely it is necessary to work within a chosen sample time of 'd*t*' such that the control loop from step 2 to step 5 takes exactly a time of d*t* seconds. This can be implemented in the program through some time measuring function. The choice of a suitable d*t* value is obviously dependent upon the application and for the control of such variables as level or temperature then 0.5 or even 1 s is usually satisfactory. For servo-systems the loop time is generally much shorter and might only be a few milliseconds or even less.

A suitable listing of a control program for the level system in QUICKBASIC is given in Program 14.3. For the set-up described, suitable controller settings are a proportional band of 10 per cent and an integral time of 25 s. For illustrative purposes the system response for proportional control only, with *PB* = 10 per cent and $T_i = 10^9$, is shown in Fig. 14.13. This was obtained by adding appropriate graphics instructions to the program.

Program 14.3 Control program for the water level in a tank.

```
'program in QUICKBASIC to apply a P+I control strategy to a level system
'
    BA = &H1B0: porta = BA: portb = BA + 1: portc = BA + 2: cr = BA + 3
    OUT cr, &H91: 'set up ports as required
    OUT portb, 0: OUT portc, 0: 'switch off pump and close control valve
'
    CLS
    INPUT "setpoint level in mm                        = ", sp
    INPUT "controller proportional band as a %         = ", pb
    INPUT "controller integral time setting in seconds = ", Ti
'
    k = 100 / pb: sum = 0: span = 400
```

```
      dt = .5: 'discrete sample time for loop is 0.5 seconds
,
start:           'this is the control loop
    t = TIMER
    GOSUB adc
    e = 100 * (sp - pv) / span
    sum = sum + e
    u% = INT((k * e) + ((k * dt / Ti) * sum))
    IF u% < 0 THEN u% = 0
    IF u% > 100 THEN u% = 100
    OUT portb, u% * 2.55
    WHILE (TIMER - t) < dt: WEND
    GOTO start
,
adc:             'this is the A/D converter routine to measure level
    OUT portc, 192   'start the conversion
    OUT portc, 128
eoc:             'check for the end of conversion
    IF (INP(portc) AND 1) = 0 THEN GOTO eoc
    i = INP(porta)
    pv = .003 * i ^ 2 + .79 * i + 30 'this is the level in mm
    RETURN
```

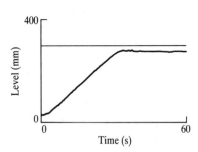

Figure 14.13 System response with a proportional control strategy.

The application described is fairly typical of a single-loop process control system irrespective of the nature of the process variable. The interfacing may vary somewhat, especially on the output from the controller where the evaluated control effort is translated into some physical power to set the position of a valve, apply heat to an environment or adjust the armature supply voltage to a motor. However, the basic principles applied are the same and industrial controllers which employ microprocessor technology adopt the same concepts with perhaps additional facilities such as alarm setting, integral wind-up, and even self-tuning.

14.5 ON/OFF CONTROL OF AN AIR-CONDITIONING PLANT

There are many instances in the industrial environment where the quality of the air is a critical parameter which requires to be controlled. Air quality could be taken to mean the concentration of airborne impurities, but for this application the air quality will refer only to the temperature and the moisture content. Moisture content is measured in terms of the mass of water vapour contained in a unit mass of dry air. The numerical values are quite small since at any particular temperature the air can only contain a finite amount of water vapour. When this limiting value is exceeded, then the water vapour will precipitate out leaving the air containing the maximum amount of water vapour that it is capable of holding at that temperature. The terms relative humidity and percentage saturation are also frequently encountered in air-conditioning applications. These two parameters are not equivalent, but for most practical cases they are numerically within a few per cent and they can be regarded as being equal. The theory of psychrometric mixtures can be found in almost any standard textbook on thermodynamics. This application however, is more concerned with the control of a psychrometric system and we will therefore limit the thermodynamic considerations to a brief discussion of the more common air conditioning processes. These are:

1. *Heating*. Heating causes the temperature of the air/water vapour mixture to rise. The moisture content is not affected however and the relative humidity decreases with heating.
2. *Cooling*. Cooling causes the temperature of the mixture to fall. Provided the temperature does not fall below the 'dew point' of the mixture, then there is no change in the moisture content and the relative humidity increases.
3. *Cooling below the dew point*. When the temperature of the mixture falls below the dew point, then the mixture can no longer hold the same mass of water vapour. The water vapour then condenses out of the mixture and appears on any cold surface which, in general, is the source of the cooling. This degree of cooling is often used in air-conditioning systems to remove water vapour from the mixture. Subsequent reheating of the mixture can result in the same original mixture temperature, but with a reduced relative humidity.
4. *Humidifying*. This process refers to the injection of water into the air to give an increased moisture content. Humidifying is usually associated with an attendant decrease in the mixture temperature. If the mixture is reheated, then it can be brought back to the same original temperature, but the relative humidity will be increased.

The above are the main processes carried out in an air-conditioning plant and they are used in any suitable combination to obtain the required air quality in terms of temperature and relative humidity. For human comfort for example, an air temperature of 20°C, with a relative humidity of 55 per cent is regarded as normal.

Figure 14.14 shows a schematic diagram of an experimental air conditioning plant. The plant incorporates all of the basic elements required to action any of the above thermodynamic processes. The air passing through the system can be heated, reheated, chilled or humidified. Humidification is carried out by injecting steam from a small boiler into the air stream. Air chilling, or de-humidification, is carried out by passing the air over a cooling coil which forms the evaporator of a self-contained vapour compression refrigeration plant. Air heating is carried out by energizing any one of the electrical heating elements in the system.

To bring the system under computer control we must first of all measure the two output variables. These are the air temperature and the relative humidity. The sensor used is the 'Vaisala' humidity and temperature probe. This sensor operates from a DC supply between 9 and 15 V and produces calibrated outputs:

> Temperature, 10 mV/°C giving a range of 0 to 1 V corresponding to 0–100°C
> Humidity, 0 to 1 V corresponding to 0 to 100 per cent relative humidity

In the original system the power actuators are switched in manually and all are operated from the AC mains. The switching interface used to power the actuators automatically is shown in Fig. 14.15.

Switching interfaces, as shown in Fig. 14.15, were connected in parallel with each of the manual switches shown in Fig. 14.14. This allows the system to be operated both manually or

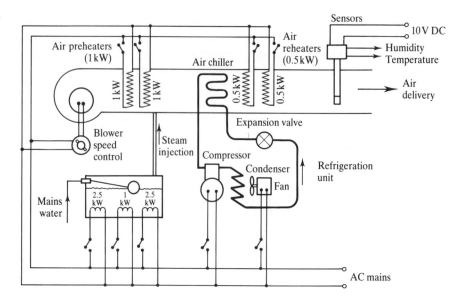

Figure 14.14 Schematic diagram of air-conditioning plant.

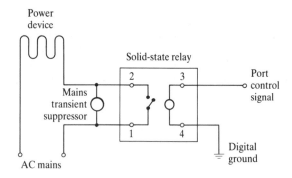

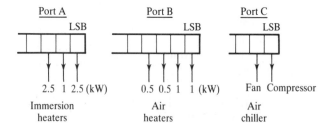

Figure 14.15 Power switching interface and port control signals.

under remote control using a logic level signal from an output port to activate any one of the system elements. The port arrangement is also shown in Fig. 14.15, where the main groups of switching functions are operated from the three available ports for programming clarity.

The computer interface card chosen for this application was the Blue Chip Technology, ACM-42, which was described in Sec. 10.4. This card has a base address of 300 hex, and provides 16 single-ended, or 8 differential, analogue input channels and 24 digital I/O lines. Ports A, B and C are designated as port + 8, port + 9 and port + 10, respectively, and the card was configured to have these three ports set for output, by writing the hex value 80 to the control register, i.e. port + 11. The temperature input signal was connected to channel 0 of the card and the humidity signal to channel 2. These channels are selected by writing the channel number to port + 12,. e.g.

to select the temperature channel, out (port + 12),0

Analogue-to-digital conversion is initiated by reading port + 2, i.e. reading the low byte of the digital representation of the analogue input channel. This data is subsequently disregarded. A small time delay is allowed for A/D conversion and the 12-bit number is then read and calibrated as follows:

```
at = inp(port + 1):REM low byte
bt = inp(port + 2): REM high nibble
t = (at*256) + bt: REM 12-bit representation
tem = (t-2048)*5/4095: REM conversion to actual voltage
temp = tem*100: REM conversion to actual temperature
```

The variable 'temp' in the above coding is the numerical value of the measured temperature in °C. In the example program, the anlogue input signals were averaged over 20 samples for better accuracy. The required air temperature and relative humidity are read in at the start of the program and a simplified control strategy is adopted. The control strategy is shown in flow chart form in Fig. 14.16. Implementation of this simplified control strategy is actioned in the QUICKBASIC Program 14.4.

The program constantly monitors the output air temperature and relative humidity and switches in the system elements as required to achieve the set points. If for example the air temperature is below the prescribed set point then all of the air heaters are switched ON. Likewise, if the humidity is below set point value then all of the immersion heaters are switched ON. This is quite a crude implementation of a control strategy, but it serves to illustrate the basic operation of the system. A more elaborate control strategy can make much better use of the system by switching in only those heaters required for the individual psychrometric processes. More efficient use of the boiler, for example, could easily be imagined. In addition, the measurement of the inlet air temperature and humidity can accommodate a more sophisticated control strategy for the unit. These considerations however are well beyond the intended scope of this section and we conclude by presenting some typical advanced graphical representations of the air-conditioning system. Figure 14.17 shows the unit as a graphics mimic where the current state of the system is depicted in easily recognizable symbols.

Actual power requirements are shown on the screen and the mimic incorporates animated displays of the system in real time with heaters and fan etc. shown ON, or OFF in direct relation to the state of the actual system. Such graphical displays are often used in the process control industries as a guide to the overall state of the systems being controlled. The thermodynamic processes undergone by the air in typical winter conditions, Fig. 14.18, are also included as a final illustration of the powerful use which can be made of the graphics facilities available in the microcomputer environment.

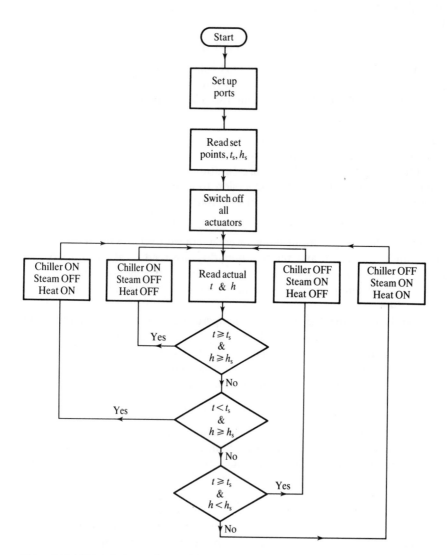

Figure 14.16 Control strategy for an air-conditioning unit.

Program 14.4 Control program for the air-conditioning unit

```
REM*****************************************
REM ON/OFF CONTROL OF AIR CONDITIONING PLANT
REM *****************************************
REM SETING PORTS - A, B and C as OUTPUTS
port=&H300:REM base address
out port+11,&h80
REM *****************
REM STATING SET POINTS
REM*****************
```

```
input"temperature set point =";sp
input"humidity set point=";sv
REM CLOSE DOWN
10
out port+8,&h00
out port+9,&h00
out port+10,&h00
REM*******************************
REM READING TEMPERATURE AND HUMIDITY
REM*******************************
15
stem=0:shum=0
for k=1 to 20
out (port+12),0
con=inp(port+2)
for del=1 to 10:next del
at=inp(port+1)
bt=inp(port+2)
t=(at*256)+bt
tem=(t-2048)*5/4095
stem=stem+tem*100
out (port+12),2
con=inp(port+2)
for del=1 to 10:next del
ah=inp(port+1)
bh=inp(port+2)
h=(ah*256)+bh
hum=(h-2048)*5/4095
shum=shum+hum*100
next k
print" temp = ";stem/20;" humidity = ";shum/20
atem=stem/20:ahum=shum/20
REM ****************
REM DECISION STRATEGY
REM*****************
if atem>=sp and ahum>=sv then 100
if atem<sp and ahum>=sv then 200
if atem>=sp and ahum<=sv then 300
goto 400
REM*****************************************
REM CONTROL ACTION
REM*****************************************
REM AIR CHILLER ON, AIR HEATERS OFF, STEAM OFF
REM*****************************************
100
out port+8,&h00
out port+9,&h00
out port+10,&h03
t5=timer
while(timer-t5)<5:wend
goto 15
```

```
REM******************************************
REM AIR HEATERS ON, AIR CHILLER OFF, STEAM OFF
REM******************************************
200
out port+8,&h00
out port+9,&h0F
out port+10,&h03
t1=timer
while(timer-t1)<5:wend
goto 15
REM******************************************
REM AIR HEATERS OFF, AIR CHILLER OFF, STEAM ON
REM******************************************
300
out port+8,&h07
out port+9,&h00
out port+10,&h00
t2 =timer
while(timer-t2)<5:wend
goto 15
REM ******************************************
REM AIR HEATERS ON, STEAM ON, AIR CHILLER OFF
REM******************************************
400
out port+8,&h07
out port+9,&h0F
out port+10,&h00
t3=timer
while(timer-t3)<5:wend
goto 15
```

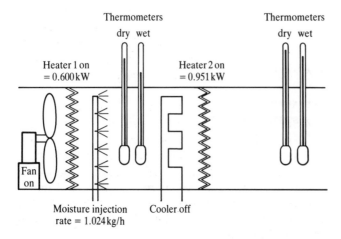

Figure 14.17 Graphics mimic of air-conditioning unit.

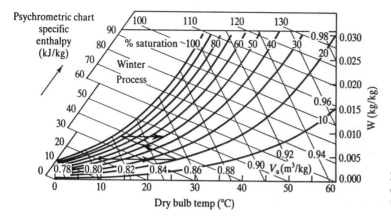

Figure 14.18 Psychrometric processes for typical winter conditions.

14.6 CONTROL OF AN AUTOTELLER MACHINE (ATM) MECHANISM

There are many, and varied, industrial applications of mechanical type mechanisms which are controlled by microprocessor based controllers. A typical example is a bank teller machine which offers bank and building society customers such services as cash withdrawal, account enquiry, cash deposit, credit card advances, account transferral and utility bill payment facilities.

One of the world leaders in automated banking technology is the NCR company which is now part of AT&T. NCR (Manufacturing) Ltd in Dundee was the first of a wave of manufacturing operations to be set up by large American organisations in Scotland in the late 1940s. Initially, manufacture centred on mechanical type products such as cash registers but due to the advances in microelectronic technology the nature of the business changed to meet market needs. Throughout the years the Dundee plant has matured in an environment of continuous challenge and change. It has established a market leadership position and Dundee now has directional business authority for the company's offerings in the world-wide self-service financial market. The machines are exported to over 70 countries world-wide and somewhere between one-third and one-half of all cash dispensing machines currently in use around the world have been designed and manufactured in Dundee. Their market dominance, complemented by a combination of strong management and dedicated staff, earned NCR Dundee the award of 'Best Factory in Britain' in 1990.

One other contributing factor to the company's success has been their approach to the product development process in order to remain competitive and stay ahead in the market. Research and Development Engineering at the Dundee plant has a strength of some 120 management, professional and support staff. Software, electronic and mechanical engineers integrate their knowledge, understanding and skills in product development activities to produce intelligent machines for the world-wide market place.

Since its inception, the ATM mechanism has become much more complex and it now requires a suite of computer programs to be resident in the machine to control its actions. This large software element has produced some challenges in the product development stage associated with parallel development of the mechanical and electronic hardware. One example is the need for a development engineer to control new mechanism designs prior to prototype electronic or software availability. This problem was addressed through a 'universal' power switching interface directly between the ATM sensors and actuators and a PC with digital I/O facilities. A graphical user interface (GUI) facilitates the production of the codes needed to sequence the mechanism through any prescribed routine.

Figure 14.19 An ATM mechanism.

Basic Operation of an ATM Mechanism

The ATM mechanism is shown in Fig. 14.19 and consists basically of a set of modules. Currency is loaded into cassettes and the 'pick module' is responsible for the first part of the cash dispensing cycle. The bank notes are picked from a cassette with suction pads through a vacuum applied using controlled solenoid action. The main mechanism motor also drives the vacuum pump and the pick arm. Once a note has been picked from the exit door on the cassette it is fed into the 'transport module' which is synchronized with the motion of the pick arm. This module consists basically of a set of transport rollers which carry the bank notes up the back of the machine and across its top towards the front. At this point the notes enter a toothed arrangement known as a stacker wheel from which the notes are stripped off to leave them in a neat bundle. A clamping mechanism is then applied to despatch the notes through the 'present module'. The present drive motor is used to convey the notes to the gate at the front of the machine where they can be taken by the customer. This gate is opened and closed by a solenoid that operates a mechanical linkage. The ATM mechanism therefore consists of a variety of electrically powered actuators such as solenoids, uni- and bi-directional AC and DC motors, and stepper motors.

The cycling of the ON/OFF states of the actuators is governed by the states of a number of sensors strategically located within the system. For example, the position of the exit gate is monitored by two optical sensors which check the position of the gate lift linkage. If the top sensor is covered then the gate is closed, and if the bottom sensor is covered the gate is open.

Sensors also monitor how far the notes are presented to the customer and an exit sensor checks if the notes have been removed. If the notes are not removed by the customer within a certain time interval then a purge cycle commences in order to withdraw them and put them into a purge bin. Once a purge cycle is initiated the present motor direction of rotation is reversed and when the notes are clear of the gate the exit sensor indicates that the gate can be closed. The passage of the notes into the purge bin is monitored by two optical sensors mounted on the purge guides. Once into the bin the machine is reset ready for the next transaction.

Control of the Mechanism during the Product Development Stage

Machines which are in service have all the necessary sensor and actuator interfacing incorporated into the system along with the controlling software. If alterations are made to any parts of the mechanism design, or any changes made to the input/output during a development stage of the product, then there is generally a requirement for appropriate interfacing hardware and controlling software.

A 'universal interface box' to handle the voltages and currents associated with the detecting sensors and power driving actuators provides a means of screw terminal connection directly from the devices within the mechanism. The voltage levels are basically 0–24 V DC and 110 V 50/60 Hz AC. The substance of the interface is a series of PCB-mounted opto-isolated I/O modules such as OPTO 22 (Sec. 10.1). A number of solid-state and electro-mechanical relays along with stepper motor driver boards are incorporated into the box. This hardware interface communicates with a PC through two digital I/O boards which each provide 48 lines configured as 6 ports from two 8255 PPIs. The I/O on the box provides for the following:

- 6 solenoids
- 4 AC motors (bi-directional)
- 4 DC motors (bi-directional)
- 4 stepper motors (bi-directional)
- 12 sensors (two different operating types)

The order of direct connection between the actual I/O device within the mechanism and the interface box is unimportant as long as a note is made of the connection number corresponding to a specific I/O function in the control of the system. For example, the gate solenoid can be made to correspond to solenoid say number 3 on the box.

A prescribed sequence can be ordered through a PC-based graphical user interface which operates in a 'windows' environment (Fig. 14.20). This software development for the control of the mechanism is written in C and can be used with little computing knowledge.

ON/OFF states for actuators with sensor input dependence and delay times, if required, can be selected by clicking a mouse on any I/O function icon displayed on the screen. The current state is shown and this can be altered if necessary. The GUI system creates a list of state transactions that a development engineer requires and stores them in a dynamic list structure. When the program is executed in the 'RUN' mode the GUI traverses the list and creates a series of control words which are dispatched through the interface cards to the hardware 'box'. The signals are decoded to appropriately handle all the input and output needs.

In this way sequencing programs are quickly built up of state changes in the mechanism and this allows parts of the ATM to be run for testing functionality, reliability, timing and other design criteria.

Complete sequencing files can be saved, loaded, edited, listed to screen, printed or executed. Having selected a 'RUN' of the prescribed sequence the user is allowed to specify a number of cycles and each successful cycle completed is logged onto a disk file. This is useful for reliability

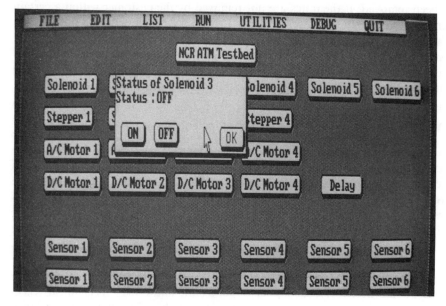

Figure 14.20 Screen display illustrating the GUI.

testing with a large number of cycles and any failure point, if occurring, is automatically recorded.

Expert System Technology Applied to the ATM Mechanism

An intelligent machine may be described as one which is capable of solving a class of problems set by its environment. It has a capacity for effective action which is dependent upon both knowledge and data. There are now a number of applications within products and systems which require a decision-making process that include 'rules of thumb' which have to be translated into knowledge-based algorithms. Such knowledge-based rules can be embedded into a computer program to attempt to implement the knowledge of a human expert. Such a technique is termed 'an expert system'.

A number of PID digital controllers are now available on the market which utilize expert system technology to provide a self-tuning facility that reduces the requirements for skilled personnel. These controllers can handle variable system dynamics, process non-linearities, deadtime, setpoint changes and variations in load. One such controller is the Foxborough 'EXACT Controller' which employs a direct performance feedback by monitoring the process variable and applying expert rules, or knowledge, in order to automatically calculate the 'best' PID settings. This is termed 'pattern recognition' and no reference is made to any mathematical model of the process. Such controllers are data based only. They deal with the virtual dynamics of the system in order to achieve a more dynamically stable system overall. Future controllers using knowledge-based technology, with fuzzy logic techniques and neural networks, will integrate virtual data with substantial intelligence and knowledge to enhance the overall intelligence level within products and systems.

The expert system, on the other hand, imitates the knowledge of the human expert on a computer so that it is capable of matching the expert's decisions over a limited field of application. The acquired knowledge is generally presented to an expert system shell, such as

CRYSTAL, and software, referred to as the 'inference engine', takes control of the decision-solving process. The package usually has to be resident in memory and with overheads such as a text input handler and a graphical front end, it is generally too slow for real-time applications such as the driving of an ATM mechanism.

An alternative approach is to write the inference engine specifically for the application, thus optimizing the expert system to produce the required speed for real-time monitoring and control. Object oriented programming (OOP) involves the decomposition of a problem into a set of objects. These objects can respond to actions carried out on them. An object can be a variable, a data structure, package or subprogram. The basic aim of decomposition is to reduce the size and complexity of the initial problem into a set of smaller problems. When solved, these smaller problems are the building blocks used to allow a solution to the main problem to be constructed. These building blocks can also be useful in helping to solve other problems, and may be added to a library of useful functions or packages. With this method of constructing programs, the concepts of coupling and cohesion are used to maintain the independence of objects. They also maintain the interfaces between the programs and ensure their reusability. 'Coupling' is the amount of knowledge of an object that is required in order to build another which interfaces with it. This should be minimized and objects should be as self-contained as possible. 'Cohesion' is the name given to how well all the code within a package connects together. Code with a similar function should be grouped into a general package to create one which is functionally cohesive and more likely to be useful for a wide range of problem solutions. This should be maximized, for example by keeping all file handling in the one package. Using these methods allows easier maintenance of the code and make it more reliable. It also makes it easier to upgrade and therefore prolongs its usefulness. C^{++} is just such an object oriented programming language.

This is basically the current approach taken to integrate knowledge based technology into an ATM mechanism and to enhance the intelligence level of the machine. The net result should increase the availability and reliability, provide an error reporting database, and allow additional knowledge to be added into the rule base to predict failures based on historical data.

This application gives some idea of the nature of industrially related development work which requires multi-disciplinary mechatronic skills which incorporate mechanical engineering with microelectronics and software to produce intelligent and flexible machines.

FURTHER READING

Forrest, S. J., J. S. Milne and N. G. Taylor (1992) 'Integrating intelligence into a mechatronic system', *Proceedings of the 1992 IEEE International Symposium on Intelligent Control*, IEEE Control Systems Society 92, CH3110-4, Glasgow, pp. 132–135.

Fraser, C. J., J. S. Milne and G. M. Logan (1992) 'From woven bags to expert systems and broken digits', *Conference Mechatronics—The Integration of Engineering Design*, University of Dundee, Mechanical Engineering Publications, Suffolk, UK.

Kraus, T. W. and T. J. Myron (1984) 'Self-tuning PID controller uses pattern recognition approach', *Control Engineering*, June.

Milne, R. (1986) 'Artificial intelligence applied to condition health monitoring', *Chartered Mechanical Engineer*, May, 45–46.

Narayanan, A. and J. Yuanping (1991) 'An object-oriented approach to expert diagnostic systems', *Journal of Object-Oriented Programming*, October, 19–29.

PRINTABLE ASCII CHARACTERS

Alphabetical						Numerical			Other		
Upper case			Lower case								
	decimal	hex		decimal	hex		decimal	hex		decimal	hex
A	65	41	a	97	61	0	48	30	space	32	20
B	66	42	b	98	62	1	49	31	!	33	21
C	67	43	c	99	63	2	50	32	"	34	22
D	68	44	d	100	64	3	51	33	#	35	23
E	69	45	e	101	65	4	52	34	$	36	24
F	70	46	f	102	66	5	53	35	%	37	25
G	71	47	g	103	67	6	54	36	&	38	26
H	72	48	h	104	68	7	55	37	'	39	27
I	73	49	i	105	69	8	56	38	(	40	28
J	74	4A	j	106	6A	9	57	39	)	41	29
K	75	4B	k	107	6B				*	42	2A
L	76	4C	l	108	6C				+	43	2B
M	77	4D	m	109	6D				,	44	2C
N	78	4E	n	110	6E				-	45	2D
O	79	4F	o	111	6F				.	46	2E
P	80	50	p	112	70				/	47	2F
Q	81	51	q	113	71				:	58	3A
R	82	52	r	114	72				;	59	3B
S	83	53	s	115	73				<	60	3C
T	84	54	t	116	74				=	61	3D
U	85	55	u	117	75				>	62	3E
V	86	56	v	118	76				?	63	3F
W	87	57	w	119	77				@	64	40
X	88	58	x	120	78				[	91	5B
Y	89	59	y	121	79				\	92	5C
Z	90	6A	z	122	7A				]	93	5D
									^	94	5E
									−	95	5F
									{	123	7B
									|	124	7C
									}	125	7D
									~	126	7E
									delete	127	7F
									£	156	9C
									CR	13	0D

GLOSSARY OF TERMS

alias	transmutation of a signal due to an insufficiently rapid sampling rate
bandwidth	frequency range over which a system gain is constant
baud	serial transmission rate
bit	discrete element of a logic level signal
buffer	high input impedance, low output impedance amplifier
byte	group of eight bits
dB	decibels
e.m.f.	electromotive force
hex	hexadecimal
kVA	kilovolt amps
kVAR	kilovolt amps reactive
kW	kilowatts
nibble	four bits, i.e. half a byte
op-amp	operational amplifier
r.m.s.	root mean square
port	8-bit parallel input/output channel
ADC	analogue-to-digital converter
AC	alternating current
ACR	auxiliary control register
ALU	arithmetic and logic unit
ANSI	American National Standards Institute
ASCII	American Standard Code for Information Interchange
ASIC	application specific integrated circuit
ATM	automatic teller machine
BCD	binary coded decimal
BIOS	basic input output system
BS	British Standard
CGA	colour graphics adaptor

CMMR	common mode rejection ratio
CMOS	complimentary metal oxide semiconductor
CONVERT	start conversion
CPU	central processor unit
CS	channel select
D/A	digital to analogue
DAC	digital-to-analogue converter
DC	direct current
DDR	data direction register
DIL	dual in-line
DMA	direct memory access
DOS	disk operating system
DR	data register
ECD	enhanced colour display
EEPROM	electrically erasable programmable read only memory
EGA	enhanced graphics adaptor
E²PROM	electrically erasable programmable read only memory
EIA	American Electrical Industries Association
EOC	end of conversion
EPLD	erasable programmable logic device
EPROM	erasable programmable read only memory
FPLA	field programmable logic array
GAL	generic array logic
GBW	product of gain and bandwidth
GND	ground, i.e. electrical earth
GPIB	general purpose interface bus
GUI	graphical user interface
IBM	International Business Machines
IBM PC	International Business Machines personal computer
IC	integrated circuit
IEC	International Electrotechnical Commission
IEEE	Institute of Electrical and Electronic Engineers
IEEE-488	parallel communication standard
I/O	input/output
I/P	current to pressure
ISO	International Organisation for Standardisation
I/V	current to voltage
LCD	liquid crystal display
LED	light-emitting diode
LSB	least significant bit
LSI	large scale integration
LVDT	linearly variable differential transformer
MDPA	monochrome display printer adaptor
MSB	most significant bit
MS-DOS	MicroSoft—disc operating system
MUX	multiplexor
NC	normally closed
NO	normally open
OOP	object-oriented programming
OS	operating system

PAL	programmable array logic
PB	proportional band
PC	personal computer, program counter
PC-DOS	personal computer—disk operating system
PCR	peripheral control register
PEEL	programmable electrically erasable logic
PID	proportional, integral, derivative
PLA	programmable logic array
PLC	programmable logic controller
PLD	programmable logic device
PO	percentage overshoot
PPI	programmable peripheral interface
PROM	programmable read only memory
PV	process variable
PWM	pulse width modulation
RAM	random access memory
RC	resistive capacitive
RL	resistive inductive
RLC	resistive inductive capacitive
ROM	read only memory
RFI	radio frequency interference
RS232	serial communication standard
RS232c	serial communication standard
RS422/RS423	serial communication standard
SC	start conversion
SCD	standard colour display
SCM	single chip (or card) microcomputer
SCR	silicon controlled rectifier
S/H	sample and hold
SP	set point
STATUS	end of conversion
TDC	top dead centre
TTL	transistor transistor logic
UART	universal asynchronous receiver transmitter
VDU	visual display unit
VGA	video graphics adaptor
VIA	versatile interface adaptor
V/I	voltage to current
VLSI	very large scale integration